Lab Safety

Safety symbol	What it means	What to do in the event of an accident
Eye protection	Wear safety goggles anytime there is the slightest chance that your eyes could be harmed.	If anything gets into your eyes, notify your teacher immediately and flush your eyes with running water for 15 minutes.
Hand safety	Wear appropriate protective gloves when working with an open flame, chemicals, or plants. Your teacher will provide the type of gloves necessary for a given activity.	If any chemical gets on your hands, rinse it off immediately with water for at least 5 minutes while calling to your teacher. Report any burn of the hands to your teacher no matter how minor it seems. Wash your hands with soap and hot water at the end of every lab.
Clothing protection	Wear your apron whenever you are working with chemicals or whenever you are instructed to do so.	If you spill a corrosive chemical onto your clothing, rinse it off immediately by using a faucet or the safety shower and remove the affected clothing while calling to your teacher.
Sharp/pointed object safety	Use knives and other sharp objects with extreme care. Place objects on a suitable work surface for cutting.	Notify your teacher immediately in the event of a cut or puncture no matter how minor it seems.
Heating safety	Wear safety goggles when using a heating device or flame. Wear heat-resistant gloves whenever instructed to do so. When heating materials in a test tube, angle the test tube away from yourself and others.	Notify your teacher immediately in the event of a burn or fire no matter how minor it seems.
Electrical safety	Do not place electrical cords where they could trip someone or cause equipment to fall. Do not use equipment with damaged cords. Do not use electrical equipment near water or when your clothing or hands are wet. Make sure that electrical equipment is in the "off" position before plugging it in. Turn off and unplug electrical equipment when you have finished using it.	Notify your teacher immediately if you notice any abnormal or potentially dangerous equipment. In the event of an electric shock, notify your teacher no matter how minor it seems.
Chemical safety	Wear safety goggles, an apron, and gloves whenever working with chemicals.	If a chemical spills onto your skin, rinse it off immediately by using the faucet or safety shower for at least 5 minutes while calling to your teacher.
Animal safety	Handle animals only as your teacher directs. Treat animals carefully and respectfully. Wash your hands thoroughly after handling any animal.	Notify your teacher immediately if you injure yourself or any live specimen no matter how minor the injury seems.
Plant safety	Do not eat any part of a plant or plant seed used in the laboratory. When in nature, do not pick any wild plants unless your teacher instructs you to do so. Wash your hands thoroughly after handling any part of a plant.	Notify your teacher immediately if any potentially dangerous plant material comes into contact with your skin or if any plant matter is inhaled or ingested no matter how minor the event seems.

Common Words with Multiple Meanings

Word	Common meaning	Scientific meaning
area	a region (for example, a rural area)	a measure of the size of a surface or a region
cell	a small, confining room	the smallest structural and functional unit of all living organisms
class	a group of students who are taught together at regular meetings	a taxonomic category below the phylum and above the order
condensation	the droplets of liquid on the outside of a glass or window	the change of state from a gas to a liquid
consumer	someone who purchases goods or services	an organism that eats other organisms or organic matter
date	an engagement to go out socially	to measure the age of an event or object
daughter	one's female child	the offspring of cell division; not dependent on gender
egg	a thin-shelled product from a bird used in cooking	a sex cell produced by a female
family	all of the members of a household	the taxonomic category below the order and above the genus
host	to serve as the entertainer or receiver of guests	an organism from which a parasite takes food or shelter
instrument	a device used for making music (for example, a trumpet)	a piece of equipment used during experimentation (for example, a scalpel)
kingdom	a region ruled by a king or queen	the taxonomic category below the domain and above the phylum
law	a rule of conduct established by the government	a descriptive statement or equation that reliably predicts events under certain conditions
legend	a romanticized story or myth	a list of map symbols and their meanings
mass	a quantity of material that has an unspecified shape	a measure of the amount of matter in an object
matter	a subject of concern or topic of discussion	anything that has mass and takes up space
medium	an intermediate measurement between small and large	a physical environment in which phenomena occur
model	a person who poses (for example, a fashion model)	a pattern, plan, representation, or description designed to show the structure or workings of an object, system, or concept
order	a command	the taxonomic category below the class and above the family
organ	a musical instrument similar to a piano	a collection of tissues that carry out a specialized function of the body
reaction	a response to a stimulus	the process by which one or more substances change to produce one or more different substances
resolution	an expression of intent (for example, a New Year's resolution)	in microscopes, the ability to form images in fine detail
theory	an assumption based on limited knowledge	a system of ideas that explains many related observations and is supported by a large body of evidence acquired through scientific investigation
tissue	a soft, absorbent piece of paper	a group of similar cells that perform a common function

Contents in Brief

Contents

UNIT 1 The Study of Living Things

CHAPTER 1

 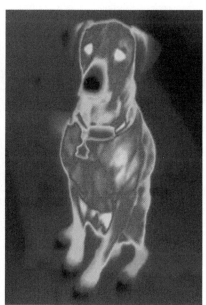
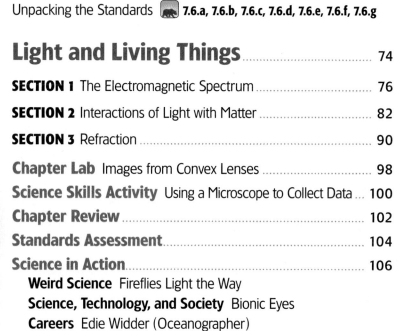

UNIT 2 Cells

CHAPTER 4

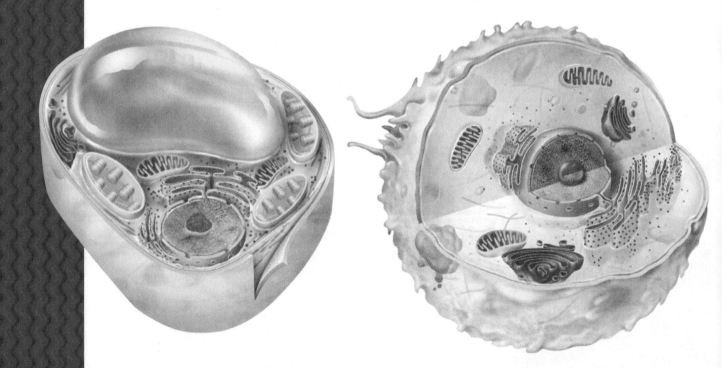

CHAPTER 5

 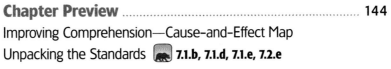

UNIT 3 Heredity and Genes

UNIT 4 Earth and Life History

CHAPTER 8

Studying Earth's Past 232

CHAPTER

11

UNIT 5 Structure and Function in Plants and Animals

Contents   **xiii**

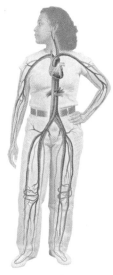

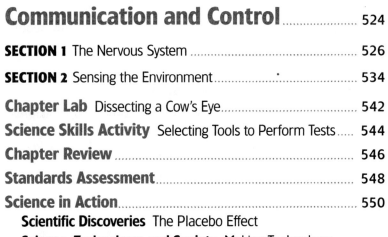

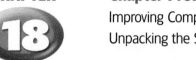
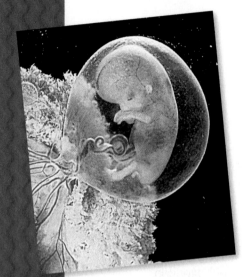
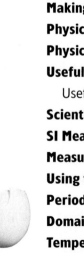

Chapter Previews

Improving Comprehension

> **Jump-start your learning!**
>
> Each chapter starts with a **Chapter Preview** that does two things. The Chapter Preview describes how to make a **Graphic Organizer** to improve your comprehension. And it helps you "unpack" the **California Science Standards,** which will help you better understand what the standards say and mean.

Unpacking the California Standards

Standard 🐻

Organize Activities

Reading Strategies

There are ways to make reading easier.

Reading Strategies at the beginning of each section will help you remember and organize information as you read the chapter.

Math Practice

Math Focus

Quick Labs

The more labs, the better!

Take a minute to browse the variety of exciting labs in this textbook. All **labs** are designed to help you experience science firsthand. But please don't forget to be safe. Read the Safety First! section before starting any of the labs.

Labs and Activities

Chapter Labs

Explore Activities

Start your engines with an activity!

Get motivated to learn by doing an activity at the beginning of each chapter. The **Explore Activity** helps you gain scientific understanding of the chapter material through hands-on experience.

Get caught in the Web!

Go to **go.hrw.com** for **Internet Activities** related to each chapter. To find the Internet Activity for a particular chapter, just type in the keyword.

Internet Activities

School-to-Home Activities

Science is not just for the classroom!

Bring science into your home by doing **School-to-Home Activities** with a family member or another adult in your household.

Science Skills Activities

Learn and practice the skills of a scientist!

The **Science Skills Activity** in each chapter helps you build investigation and experimentation skills. These skills are essential to learning science.

Science in Action

Science moves beyond the classroom!

Read **Science in Action** articles to learn more about science in the real world. These articles will give you an idea of how interesting, strange, helpful, and action-packed science is. And if your thirst is still not quenched, go to **go.hrw.com** for details about each article.

How to Use Your Textbook

Your textbook may seem confusing at first. But with a little introduction, you'll realize that your science textbook can be a big help. In the next few pages, you'll learn how this textbook can help you become a successful science student. You will also learn how interesting and exciting science can be.

Jump-Start Your Learning

The Chapter Preview helps you brush up on your learning skills and helps you focus on what is important.

Each chapter starts with instructions on how to make a **Graphic Organizer,** a tool for organizing the information that you read. A sample Graphic Organizer gives you a sneak preview of the major concepts in the chapter.

California has important **Science Standards** that guide your learning. Use this page to get to know the standards better. The chart contains **Academic Vocabulary** found in the standards. Also, **What It Means** describes each standard in basic terms.

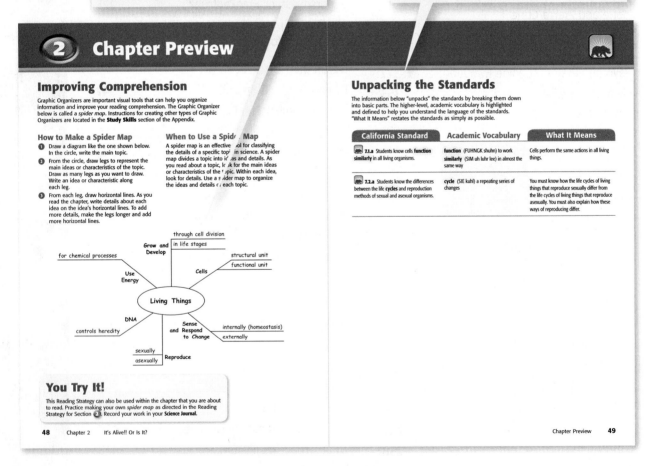

2 Chapter Preview

Improving Comprehension

Graphic Organizers are important visual tools that can help you organize information and improve your reading comprehension. The Graphic Organizer below is called a *spider map*. Instructions for creating other types of Graphic Organizers are located in the **Study Skills** section of the Appendix.

How to Make a Spider Map
1. Draw a diagram like the one shown below. In the circle, write the main topic.
2. From the circle, draw legs to represent the main ideas or characteristics of the topic. Draw as many legs as you want to draw. Write an idea or characteristic along each leg.
3. From each leg, draw horizontal lines. As you read the chapter, write details about each idea on the idea's horizontal lines. To add more details, make the legs longer and add more horizontal lines.

When to Use a Spider Map
A spider map is an effective tool for classifying the details of a specific topic in science. A spider map divides a topic into ideas and details. As you read about a topic, look for the main ideas or characteristics of the topic. Within each idea, look for details. Use a spider map to organize the ideas and details of each topic.

You Try It!
This Reading Strategy can also be used within the chapter that you are about to read. Practice making your own *spider map* as directed in the Reading Strategy for Section 3. Record your work in your **Science Journal.**

Unpacking the Standards

The information below "unpacks" the standards by breaking them down into basic parts. The higher-level, academic vocabulary is highlighted and defined to help you understand the language of the standards. "What It Means" restates the standards as simply as possible.

California Standard	Academic Vocabulary	What It Means
7.1.a Students know cells **function similarly** in all living organisms.	**function** (FUHNGK shuhn) to work **similarly** (SIM uh luhr lee) in almost the same way	Cells perform the same actions in all living things.
7.2.a Students know the differences between the life **cycles** and reproduction methods of sexual and asexual organisms.	**cycle** (SIE kuhl) a repeating series of changes	You must know how the life cycles of living things that reproduce sexually differ from the life cycles of living things that reproduce asexually. You must also explain how these ways of reproducing differ.

Step into Science

The beginning of each chapter is designed to get you involved with science. You will immediately see that science is cool!

Check out the **Big Idea** to see the focus of the chapter. The entire chapter supports this Big Idea.

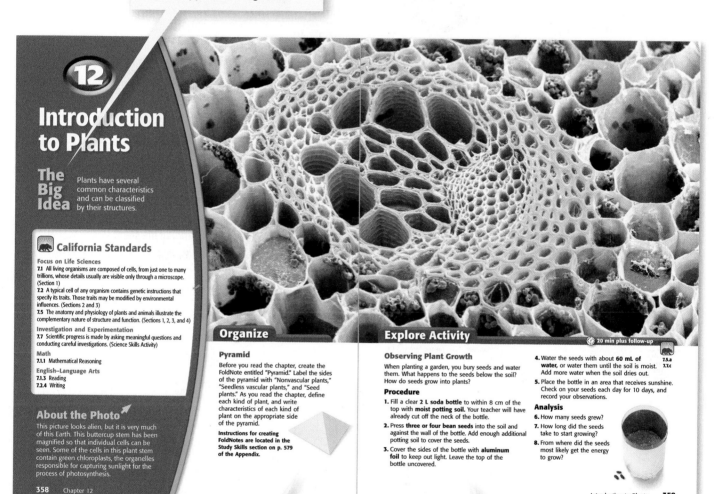

12

Introduction to Plants

The Big Idea

Plants have several common characteristics and can be classified by their structures.

California Standards

Focus on Life Sciences
7.1 All living organisms are composed of cells, from just one to many trillions, whose details usually are visible only through a microscope. (Section 1)
7.2 A typical cell of any organism contains genetic instructions that specify its traits. Those traits may be modified by environmental influences. (Sections 2 and 3)
7.5 The anatomy and physiology of plants and animals illustrate the complementary nature of structure and function. (Sections 1, 2, 3, and 4)

Investigation and Experimentation
7.7 Scientific progress is made by asking meaningful questions and conducting careful investigations. (Science Skills Activity)

Math
7.1.1 Mathematical Reasoning

English–Language Arts
7.1.3 Reading
7.2.4 Writing

About the Photo

This picture looks alien, but it is very much of this Earth. This buttercup stem has been magnified so that individual cells can be seen. Some of the cells in this plant stem contain green chloroplasts, the organelles responsible for capturing sunlight for the process of photosynthesis.

358 Chapter 12

Organize

Pyramid
Before you read the chapter, create the FoldNote entitled "Pyramid." Label the sides of the pyramid with "Nonvascular plants," "Seedless vascular plants," and "Seed plants." As you read the chapter, define each kind of plant, and write characteristics of each kind of plant on the appropriate side of the pyramid.

Instructions for creating FoldNotes are located in the Study Skills section on p. 579 of the Appendix.

Explore Activity

🏅 **20 min plus follow-up**

Observing Plant Growth
When planting a garden, you bury seeds and water them. What happens to the seeds below the soil? How do seeds grow into plants?

Procedure
1. Fill a clear **2 L soda bottle** to within 8 cm of the top with **moist potting soil.** Your teacher will have already cut off the neck of the bottle.
2. Press **three or four bean seeds** into the soil and against the wall of the bottle. Add enough additional potting soil to cover the seeds.
3. Cover the sides of the bottle with **aluminum foil** to keep out light. Leave the top of the bottle uncovered.
4. Water the seeds with about **60 mL of water,** or water them until the soil is moist. Add more water when the soil dries out.
5. Place the bottle in an area that receives sunshine. Check on your seeds each day for 10 days, and record your observations.

Analysis
6. How many seeds grew?
7. How long did the seeds take to start growing?
8. From where did the seeds most likely get the energy to grow?

Introduction to Plants **359**

You can't be organized enough when learning science. The **FoldNote** provided here gives you note-taking options. These FoldNotes are fun to make and help you understand and remember what you have learned.

It is never too early for exploration in science. The **Explore Activity** gives you a chance to get some hands-on experience right away. Each activity is a lot of fun and introduces you to one or more California Science Standards from the chapter.

Read for Meaning

You want to get the most out of your reading. One way to do so is to take a minute to learn how the sections are organized.

> Be sure to start each section by reading the information in the margin. This information tells you **What You Will Learn** and **Why It Matters**. Believe it or not, knowing these things will improve your learning.

> Don't skip the **Reading Strategy**. Each strategy provides tips on how to take better notes and how to read for better understanding.

> The **Key Concept** sets the stage for your understanding of the section. Read it carefully, and notice how it relates to the chapter's Big Idea. Together, the Big Idea and the Key Concepts give you an excellent overview of the chapter.

> Do you understand what you are reading? Don't wait until test time to find out. The **Standards Checks** help you see if you are understanding the standards.

> Notice how vocabulary is treated in the margins. All vocabulary terms are defined in the margins for quick reference. Also look for **Wordwise** items, which help you understand how prefixes and suffixes are used in scientific words.

SECTION 1

Cell Energy

Key Concept All cells need energy to carry out cell functions. However, cells may obtain and process energy in different ways.

What You Will Learn
- In plant cells, chloroplasts capture energy from the sun in order to make food during photosynthesis.
- Cells release energy from food through either cellular respiration or fermentation.

Why It Matters
Understanding the differences in how plants and animals obtain energy is an important part of cell biology.

Vocabulary
- photosynthesis
- cellular respiration
- fermentation

READING STRATEGY

Graphic Organizer In your **Science Journal**, create a Cause-and-Effect Map about fermentation.

photosynthesis
(FOHT oh SIN thuh sis) the process by which plants, algae, and some bacteria use sunlight, carbon dioxide, and water to make food
Wordwise The root *phot-* means "light."

Wordwise **chloroplast**
The root *chlor-* means "green." The root *plast-* means "to form."

► Why do you get hungry? Feeling hungry is your body's way of telling you that your cells need energy. All cells need energy to live, grow, and reproduce. Plant cells get their energy from the sun. Many animal cells get their energy from food.

From Sun to Cell

Nearly all of the energy that fuels life comes from the sun. Plants absorb energy from the sun and change the energy into food through a process [...]. that plants make gives them [...] a source of energy for the org[...].

Photosynthesis

Plant cells have molecule [...] molecules are called *pigme[...]* the main pigment used i[...] ph[...] green color. Chlorophyll [...] fo[...]

Plants cannot use er[...]rgy directly from the sun to perform life processes. Instead they use the sun's energy to change carbon dioxide and water into food. The food is in the form of the simple sugar glucose. Glucose can be stored and used by the plant's cells. Photosynthesis also produces oxygen. The chemical equation for photosynthesis is shown in **Figure 1.**

Standards Check What kind of cell has chloroplasts? 7.1.b

Figure 1 *Photosynthesis takes place in chloroplasts. Chloroplasts are found inside plant cells.*

Photosynthesis

$$6CO_2 + 6H_2O + \text{light energy} \longrightarrow C_6H_{12}O_6 + 6O_2$$

Carbon dioxide   Water   Glucose   Oxygen

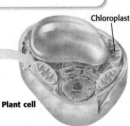

Chloroplast

Plant cell

7.1.b Students know the characteristics th[...] distinguish plant cells from animal cells, inc[...]ng chloroplasts and cell walls.
7.1.d Students know that mitochondria liberate energy for the work that cells do and that chloroplasts capture sunlight energy for photosynthesis.

148   Chapter 5   The Cell in A[...]n

Keep an Eye on the Headings

Notice how the headings in the textbook are different sizes and different colors. The headings help you organize your reading and form a simple outline, as shown below.

Blue: section title

Red: major subheads

Light blue: minor subheads

One good way to study is to write down the headings in outline form in your notes. Reviewing this outline will give you a good idea of the main concepts in the chapter and will show you how they are related.

Science Is Doing

You get many opportunities throughout the textbook to actually do science.

Each section has at least one **Quick Lab** to help you get real experience doing science. Also look for **School-to-Home Activities** for cool activities that you can do at home.

Quick Lab

Modeling Blood Pressure

In this activity, you will demonstrate systolic and diastolic blood pressure. You will use a pipet bulb to represent the heart.

1. Fill a **pipet bulb** with water. Stretch the mouth of a **long balloon** around the end of the pipet bulb. Secure with **tape**.
2. Carefully squeeze the pipet bulb in one hand. Describe the pressure in the balloon.
3. Release your squeeze on the pipet bulb. Describe the pressure in the balloon now.

7.6.j
7.7.d

4. If the pipet bulb represents the heart, what does the balloon represent?
5. Which state, bulb squeezed or not squeezed, is similar to systolic pressure? Explain.
6. What is your blood pressure if your diastolic pressure is 60 mm Hg and your systolic pressure is 95 mm Hg?

⏱ 10 min

The **Chapter Lab** at the end of each chapter helps you build your understanding of scientific methods. These labs reinforce the California Science Standards with a hands-on activity.

Science Skills Activity

Scientific Methods | Research | Data Analysis | Models, Maps & Diagrams

Investigation and Experimentation
7.7.a Select and use appropriate tools and technology (including calculators, computers, balances, spring scales, microscopes, and binoculars) to perform tests, collect data, and display data.

Using a Microscope to Collect Data

▶ **Tutorial**

A microscope is a tool often used by life scientists to collect data. Follow these instructions when you use a light microscope.

① Turn on the light source of your microscope, and select the low-power objective lens.
② Light from the light source passes through a small hole in the stage. Place a prepared slide over this hole. Secure the slide with the stage clips.
③ Look at the stage from eye level. Slowly turn the adjustment knob to lower the objective lens until the lens almost touches the slide.
④ Look through the ocular lens. Turn the adjustment knob to raise the objective lens until the image is in focus.
⑤ Make sure that the image is exactly in the center of your field of vision. Then, switch to the high-power objective. If necessary, use the adjustment knob to focus.

Ocular lens
Objective lens
Stage clip
Stage
Light
Adjustment knob

▶ **You Try It!**

Procedure

① Obtain a **light microscope**, and identify its parts. Learn how the various parts work. If you are not familiar with how the microscope works, ask your teacher for a **prepared slide**.
② Follow the steps described above to view a slide. Be sure to view the slide by using at least two different objective lenses.

Analysis

③ **Collecting Data** Draw a diagram of the image that you saw when you used each objective lens.
④ **Identifying Relationships** How do different objective lenses change what you see?

100   Chapter 3   Light and ...

Using Scientific Methods

Skills Practice Lab

Images from Convex Lenses

OBJECTIVES

Use a convex lens to form images.

Determine the characteristics of real images formed by convex lenses.

MATERIALS

- candle
- card, index, 4 × 6 in. or larger
- clay, modeling
- convex lens
- jar lid
- matches
- meterstick

SAFETY

A convex lens is thicker in the center than at the edges. Parallel light rays passing through a convex lens come together at a focal point. Under certain conditions, a convex lens will create a real image of an object. The characteristics of this image depend on the distance between the object and the lens. In this experiment, you will determine the characteristics of real images created by a convex lens—the kind of lens that is used as a magnifying lens.

Ask a Question

① What are the characteristics of real images created by a convex lens? For example, are the images upright or inverted (upside down)? Are the images larger or smaller than the object?

Form a Hypothesis

② Write a hypothesis that is a possible answer to the questions above. Explain your reasoning.

Test the Hypothesis

③ Copy the table below.

Data Collection

Image	Orientation (upright/inverted)	Size (larger/smaller)	Image distance (cm)	Object distance (cm)
1				
2				
3				

④ Use modeling clay to make a base for the lens. Place the lens and base in the middle of the table.
⑤ Stand the index card upright in some modeling clay on one side of the lens.
⑥ Place the candle in the jar lid, and anchor it with some modeling clay. Place the candle on the table so that the lens is halfway between the candle and the card. Light the candle. Caution: Use extreme care around an open flame.
⑦ In a darkened room, slowly move the card and the candle away from the lens while keeping the lens exactly halfway between the card and the candle. Continue until you see a clear image of the candle flame on the card. This image is image 1.
⑧ Measure and record the distance between the lens and the card (image distance) and the distance between the lens and the candle (object distance).
⑨ Is the image upright or inverted? Is it larger or smaller than the candle? Record this information in the table.
⑩ Move the lens toward the candle. The new object distance should be less than half the object distance measured in step 8. Move the card back-and-forth until you find a sharp image (image 2) of the candle on the card.
⑪ Repeat steps 8 and 9 for image 2.
⑫ Leave the card and candle in place, and move the lens toward the card to get the third image (image 3).
⑬ Repeat steps 8 and 9 for image 3.

Analyze the Results

⑭ **Recognizing Patterns** Describe the relationship between image distance and image size.
⑮ **Examining Data** What are the similarities between the real images that are formed by a convex lens?

Draw Conclusions

⑯ **Making Predictions** The lens of your eye is a convex lens. Use the information that you collected to describe the image projected onto the back of your eye when you look at an object.

Big Idea Question

⑰ **Making Predictions** Light can interact with matter in many different ways. Describe two different ways that light from the candle can have interacted with matter in the room.

Applying Your Data

Convex lenses are used in film projectors. Explain why your favorite movie stars appear truly "larger than life" on the screen in terms of image distance and object distance.

7.6.d Students know how simple lenses are used in a magnifying glass, the eye, a camera, a telescope, and a microscope.
7.6.f Students know light can be reflected, refracted, transmitted, and absorbed by matter.

98   Chapter 3   Light and Living Things

Each chapter has one **Science Skills Activity,** which gives you an opportunity to develop your science skills. Scientific methods, doing research, analyzing data, and making graphs are highlighted here. The step-by-step instructions make learning these skills easy.

Review What You Have Learned

You can't review too much when you are learning science. To help you review, a **Section Review** appears at the end of every section and a **Chapter Summary** and **Chapter Review** appear at the end of every chapter. These reviews not only help you study for tests but also help further your understanding of the content.

Just a few clicks away, each **Super Summary** gives you even more ways to review and study for tests.

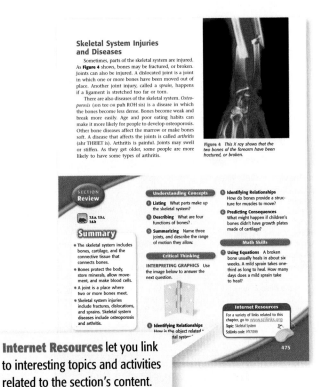

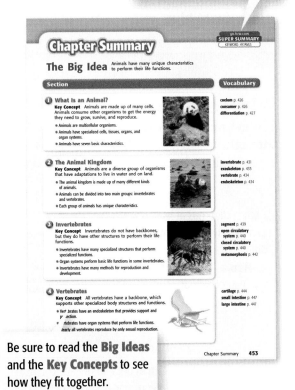

Internet Resources let you link to interesting topics and activities related to the section's content.

Be sure to read the **Big Ideas** and the **Key Concepts** to see how they fit together.

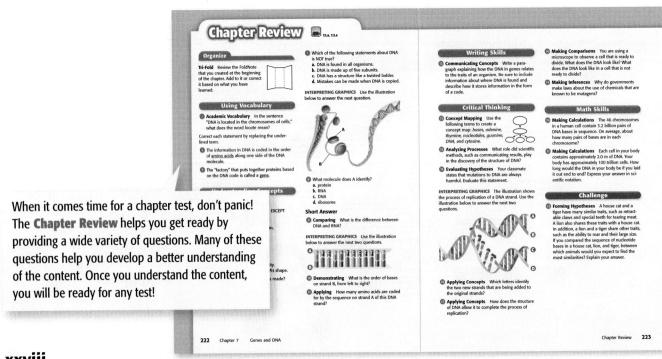

When it comes time for a chapter test, don't panic! The **Chapter Review** helps you get ready by providing a wide variety of questions. Many of these questions help you develop a better understanding of the content. Once you understand the content, you will be ready for any test!

Review the Standards

Mastering the California Science Standards takes practice and more practice! The **Standards Assessment** helps you review the California Science Standards covered in the chapter. The multiple-choice questions also give you some additional practice with standardized tests.

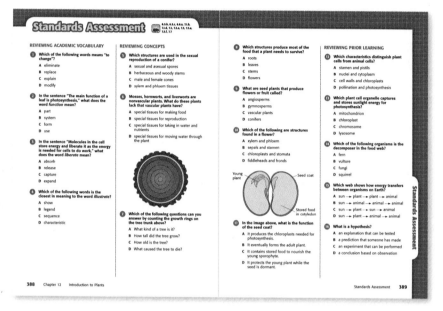

Test-Drive Your Understanding

How well can you use the book now? Use Chapter 1 to answer the questions below and to find out!

❶ Which type of Graphic Organizer is used in the Chapter Preview?

❷ Which California Science Standards are covered in Chapter 1?

❸ What is the Big Idea of this chapter?

❹ What will you be doing in the Explore Activity?

❺ What is the Key Concept of Section 2?

❻ What is the Reading Strategy for Section 1?

❼ What new vocabulary terms are introduced in Section 3?

❽ How many Standards Checks are in Section 1?

❾ What is the name of the Quick Lab in Section 4?

❿ On what page does the Chapter Summary appear?

⓫ How many Standards Assessment questions are there?

⓬ What is the Super Summary code for Chapter 1?

➚ Be Resourceful—Use the Web!

Internet Resources for Each Section

A box on the Section Review page for each section takes you to resources that you can use for science projects, reports, and research papers. To find information on a topic, go to **scilinks.org** and type in the code provided.

Current Events in Science

Check out the online magazine articles and other materials that go with your textbook at **go.hrw.com.** Click on the textbook icon and the Table of Contents to see all of the resources for each chapter.

Your Online Textbook

If your teacher gives you a special password to log onto the **Holt Online Learning** site, you'll find your complete textbook on the Web. In addition, you'll find some great learning tools and practice quizzes. You'll be able to see how well you know the material from your textbook.

SAFETY FIRST!

Exploring, inventing, and investigating are essential to the study of science. However, these activities can also be dangerous. To make sure that your experiments and explorations are safe, you must be aware of a variety of safety guidelines. You have probably heard of the saying "It is better to be safe than sorry." This is particularly true in a science classroom where experiments and explorations are being performed. Being uninformed and careless can result in serious injuries. Don't take chances with your own safety or with anyone else's.

The following pages describe important guidelines for staying safe in the science classroom. Your teacher may also have safety guidelines and tips that are specific to your classroom and laboratory. Take the time to be safe.

Safety Rules!

Start Out Right

Always get your teacher's permission before attempting any laboratory exploration. Read the procedures carefully, and pay particular attention to safety information and caution statements. If you are unsure about what a safety symbol means, look it up or ask your teacher. You cannot be too careful when it comes to safety. If an accident does occur, inform your teacher immediately no matter how minor the event seems.

If you are instructed to note the odor of a substance, wave the fumes toward your nose with your hand. Never put your nose close to the source.

Safety Symbols

All of the experiments and investigations in this book and their related worksheets include important safety symbols to alert you to particular safety concerns. Become familiar with these symbols so that when you see them, you will know what they mean and what to do. It is important that you read this entire safety section to learn about specific dangers in the laboratory.

Eye protection

Clothing protection

Hand safety

Heating safety

Electric safety

Chemical safety

Animal safety

Sharp object

Plant safety

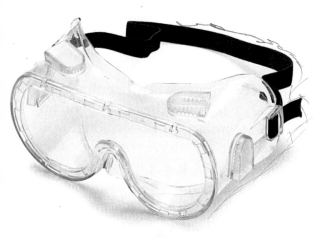

Eye Safety

Wear safety goggles when working around chemicals, acids, bases, or any type of flame or heating device. Wear safety goggles anytime there is the slightest chance that your eyes could be harmed. If anything gets into your eyes, notify your teacher immediately and flush your eyes with running water for at least 15 minutes. Treat any unknown chemical as if it were a dangerous chemical. Never look directly into the sun. Doing so could cause permanent blindness.

Avoid wearing contact lenses in a laboratory situation. Even if you are wearing safety goggles, chemicals can get between the contact lenses and your eyes. If your doctor requires that you wear contact lenses instead of glasses, wear eye-cup safety goggles in the lab.

Safety Equipment

Know the locations of the nearest fire alarms and any other safety equipment, such as fire blankets and eyewash fountains, as identified by your teacher. And know the procedures for using the equipment.

Neatness

Keep your work area free of all unnecessary books and papers. Tie back long hair, and secure loose sleeves or other loose articles of clothing, such as ties and bows. Remove dangling jewelry. Don't wear open-toed shoes or sandals in the laboratory. Never eat, drink, or apply cosmetics in a laboratory setting. Food, drink, and cosmetics can easily become contaminated with dangerous materials.

Certain hair products (such as aerosol hair spray) are flammable and should not be worn while working near an open flame. Avoid wearing hair spray or hair gel on lab days.

Sharp/Pointed Objects

Use knives and other sharp instruments with extreme care. Never cut objects while holding them in your hands. Place objects on a suitable work surface for cutting.

Be extra careful when using any glassware. When adding a heavy object to a graduated cylinder, tilt the cylinder so that the object slides slowly to the bottom.

Heat

Wear safety goggles when using a heating device or a flame. Whenever possible, use an electric hot plate as a heat source instead of using an open flame. When heating materials in a test tube, angle the test tube away from yourself and others. To avoid burns, wear heat-resistant gloves whenever instructed to do so.

Electricity

Be careful with electrical cords. When using a microscope with a lamp, do not place the cord where it could trip someone. Do not let cords hang over a table edge in a way that could cause equipment to fall if the cord is accidentally pulled. Do not use equipment with damaged cords. Do not use electrical equipment near water or when your clothing or hands are wet. Make sure that electrical equipment is in the "off" position before plugging it in. Turn off and unplug electrical equipment when you have finished using it.

Chemicals

Wear safety goggles when handling any potentially dangerous chemicals. Wear an apron and protective gloves when you work with chemicals or whenever you are told to do so. If a spill gets on your skin or clothing, rinse it off immediately with water for at least 5 minutes while calling to your teacher. If you spill a corrosive chemical onto your clothing, rinse it off immediately by using a faucet or the safety shower and remove the affected clothing while calling to your teacher.

Never mix chemicals unless your teacher tells you to do so. Never taste, touch, or smell chemicals unless you are specifically directed to do so. Before working with a flammable liquid or gas, check for the presence of any source of flame, spark, or heat.

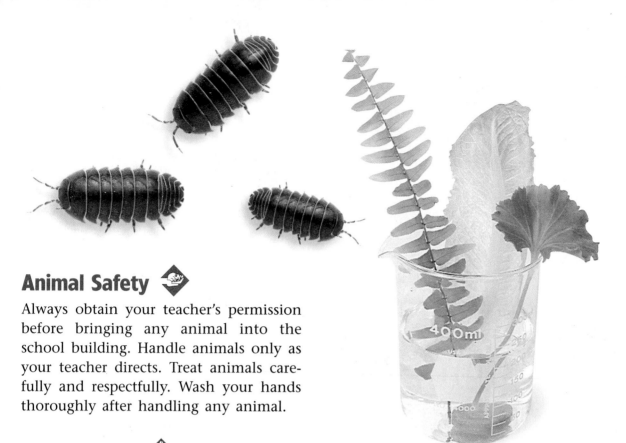

Animal Safety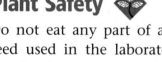

Always obtain your teacher's permission before bringing any animal into the school building. Handle animals only as your teacher directs. Treat animals carefully and respectfully. Wash your hands thoroughly after handling any animal.

Plant Safety

Do not eat any part of a plant or plant seed used in the laboratory. Wash your hands thoroughly after handling any part of a plant. When in nature, do not pick any wild plants unless your teacher instructs you to do so.

Glassware

Examine all glassware before use. Be sure that glassware is clean and free of chips and cracks. Report damaged glassware to your teacher. Glass containers used for heating should be made of heat-resistant glass.

TIMELINE

The Study of Living Things

Life science is the study of living things—from the tiniest bacterium to the largest tree! In this unit, you will discover the similarities of all living things. You will learn about the tools that life scientists use, and you'll learn to ask your own questions about the living world around you.

People have always searched for answers about life. This timeline includes a few of the many people who have studied living things and a few events that have shaped the history of life science. And there's always more to be learned, so keep your eyes open.

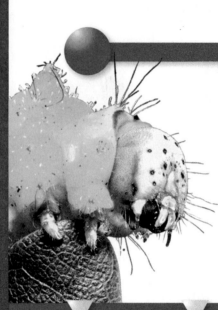

Around 2700 BCE

Si Ling-Chi, empress of China, observes silkworms in her garden and develops a process to cultivate them and make silk.

1931

The first electron microscope is developed.

1934

Dorothy Crowfoot Hodgkin uses X-ray techniques to determine the protein structure of insulin.

1970

Floppy disks for computer data storage are introduced.

1983

Dian Fossey writes *Gorillas in the Mist*, a book about her research on mountain gorillas in Africa and her efforts to save them from poachers.

Around 1000

Arab mathematician and physicist Ibn al Haytham discovers that vision is caused by the reflection of light from objects into the eye.

1684

Improvements to microscopes allow the first observation of red blood cells.

1914

His studies on agriculture and soil conservation lead George Washington Carver to perform research on peanuts.

1944

Oswald T. Avery demonstrates that **DNA** is the material that carries genetic properties in living organisms.

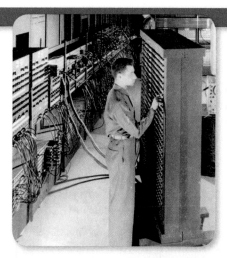

1946

ENIAC, the first entirely electronic computer, is built. It weighs 30 tons.

1967

Dr. Christiaan Barnard performs the first successful human heart transplant.

1984

A process known as **DNA** fingerprinting is developed by Alec Jeffreys.

1998

In China, scientists discover a fossil of a dinosaur that had feathers.

2001

A team of scientists led by Philippa Uwins announces that tiny nanobes that are 20 to 150 nanometers wide have been found in Australia. Scientists debate whether these particles are living.

Improving Comprehension

Graphic Organizers are important visual tools that can help you organize information and improve your reading comprehension. The Graphic Organizer below is called an *idea wheel*. Instructions for creating other types of Graphic Organizers are located in the **Study Skills** section of the Appendix.

How to Make an Idea Wheel

❶ Draw a circle. Draw a larger circle around the first circle. Divide the ring between the circles into sections by drawing lines from one circle to the other across the ring. Divide the ring into as many sections as you want.

❷ Write a main idea or topic in the smaller circle. Label each section in the ring with a category or characteristic of the main idea.

❸ In each section of the ring, include details that are unique to the topic.

When to Use an Idea Wheel

An idea wheel is an effective type of visual organization in which ideas in science can be divided into categories or parts. It is also a useful way to illustrate characteristics of a main idea or topic. As you read, look for topics that are divided into ideas or categories, that can be organized around an idea wheel.

Questioning
• ask a question
• make observations
• form a hypothesis
• test the hypothesis
• analyze the results
• draw conclusions
• communicate results

Scientific Methods
• Asking a question is the first step in scientific investigation.
• Answers to questions in life science affect you and your community.

The Nature of Life Science

Tools and Models
• Scientists choose and use tools of measurement to test hypotheses, and to collect, store, and analyze data.
• Scientific models are tools that help explain how something works or is structured.

Safety
• Following directions is the most important safety rule.
• Safety symbols can help identify potential dangers.
• Using safety equipment can protect you from injury.

You Try It!

This Reading Strategy can also be used within the chapter that you are about to read. Practice making your own *idea wheel* as directed in the Reading Strategies for Section ❹ and Section ❺. Record your work in your **Science Journal.**

Unpacking the Standards

The information below "unpacks" the standards by breaking them down into basic parts. The higher-level, academic vocabulary is highlighted and defined to help you understand the language of the standards. "What It Means" restates the standards as simply as possible.

California Standard	Academic Vocabulary	What It Means
7.7.a Select and use **appropriate** tools and **technology** (including calculators, **computers,** balances, spring scales, microscopes, and binoculars) to perform tests, collect data, and **display** data.	**select** (suh LEKT) to choose, to pick up **appropriate** (uh PROH pree it) correct for the use; proper **technology** (tek NAHL uh jee) tools, including electronic products **computer** (kuhm PYOOT uhr) an electronic device that stores, retrieves, and calculates data **display** (di SPLAY) to show	Choose the correct tools and technology (including calculators, computers, balances, spring scales, microscopes, and binoculars) to perform an experiment. Use these tools and technology to collect facts and figures, and show your research findings.
7.7.b Use a variety of print and electronic **resources** (including the World Wide Web) to collect information and evidence as part of a **research project.**	**resource** (REE sawrs) anything that can be used to take care of a need **research** (REE suhrch) a careful search for and study of information **project** (PRAH jekt) a special task done to use, explain, or add information to classroom lessons	Do research by using both print sources (such as newspapers and books) and electronic sources (such as websites and databases) to collect information, facts, and figures as part of a research project.
7.7.c Communicate the **logical** connection among hypotheses, science **concepts,** tests **conducted,** data collected, and conclusions drawn from the scientific evidence.	**communicate** (kuh MYOO ni kayt) to make known, to tell **logical** (LAHJ i kuhl) reasoned, well thought out **concept** (KAHN sept) an idea or thought **conduct** (kuhn DUHKT) to carry out; to do	Tell others how possible explanations for observations, ideas, experiments, facts and figures, and results and conclusions are related.
7.7.d Construct scale models, maps, and **appropriately labeled** diagrams to communicate scientific knowledge (e.g., motion of Earth's plates and cell structure).	**construct** (kuhn STRUHKT) to build; to make from parts **appropriately** (uh PROH pree it lee) in a correct or proper way **labeled** (LAY buhld) marked with a name or description	Build models, maps, and diagrams that are proportional to what they represent in the real world and that have correct and useful labels to explain scientific information. For example, build a model or make a diagram that shows the motion of Earth's plates or the structure of a cell.
7.7.e Communicate the steps and results from an **investigation** in written reports and oral presentations.	**investigation** (in ves tuh GAY shuhn) a detailed search for answers	Clearly explain the steps and the results of an experiment by using written reports and oral presentations.

1

The Nature of Life Science

The Big Idea

Scientists use scientific processes to study the patterns of natural events and to solve problems.

California Standards

Investigation and Experimentation
7.7 Scientific progress is made by asking meaningful questions and conducting careful investigations. (Sections 1, 2, 3, 4, and 5 and Science Skills Activity)

Math
7.1.2 Number Sense

English–Language Arts
7.1.3 Reading
7.2.5 Writing

About the Photo

What happened to the legs of these frogs? Life science can help answer this question. Deformed frogs, such as the ones in this photo, have been found in the northern United States and southern Canada. Sometimes, frogs are injured by predators. But other frogs develop deformities while they are growing. Scientists and students like you have been using life science to investigate why frogs develop deformities.

Organize

Layered Book

Before you read this chapter, create the FoldNote entitled "Layered Book." Label each tab of the layered book with "Scientific methods," "Tools and measurement," "Scientific models," and "Safety." As you read the chapter, write information that you learn about each category on the appropriate tab.

Instructions for creating FoldNotes are located in the Study Skills section on p. 580 of the Appendix.

Explore Activity

🕐 15 min

7.7.c

Identifying Unknown Objects

In this activity, you will find out that you can learn about the unknown without having to see it.

Procedure

1. Your teacher will give you a **coffee can** to which a **sock** has been attached. Do not look into the can.

2. Reach through the opening in the sock. You will feel **several objects** inside the can.

3. Record observations you make about the objects by feeling the objects, shaking the can, and so on.

4. What do you think is in the can? List your guesses. State some reasons for your guesses.

5. Pour the contents of the can onto your desk. Compare your list with what was in the can.

Analysis

6. Did you guess the contents of the can correctly? What might have caused you to guess wrongly?

7. What observations did you make about each of the objects while the objects were in the can? Which of your senses did you use?

Asking About Life

Key Concept Asking questions is the first step in a scientific investigation.

What You Will Learn

- Questions lead to learning about science.
- Print or electronic resources can be used to find information.
- Your everyday life is affected by life scientists in many ways.

Why It Matters

Asking questions and performing scientific investigations help you learn about the world around you.

Vocabulary

- life science

READING STRATEGY

Prediction Guide Before reading this section, write each heading from this section in your **Science Journal.** Below each heading, write what you think you will learn.

▶ Imagine that it's summer. You are lying in the grass at the park, casually looking around. Three dogs are playing on your left. A few bumblebees are visiting nearby flowers. And an ant is carrying a crumb away from your sandwich.

Suddenly, a question pops into your head: How do ants find food? Then, you think of another question: Why do the bees visit the yellow flowers but not the red ones? Congratulations! You have just taken the first steps toward becoming a life scientist. How did you do it? You observed the living world around you. You were curious, and you asked questions about your observations. Once you have a question, you can start thinking about ways to find answers. Those steps are what science is all about. **Life science** is the study of living things.

Starting with a Question

The world around you is full of an amazing diversity of life. Single-celled algae, giant redwood trees, and 40-ton whales are living things. For every living thing, or organism, you could ask questions such as: (1) How does the organism get its food? (2) Where does it live? and (3) Why does it behave in a particular way?

In Your Own Backyard

Questions are easy to think of. Take a look around your room, your home, and your neighborhood. What questions about life science come to mind? The student in **Figure 1** has questions about some very familiar organisms. Do you know the answer to any of her questions?

Touring the World

The questions you can ask about your neighborhood are examples of the questions you could ask about the world. The world is made up of many different types of places, such as deserts, forests, coral reefs, and tide pools. Just about anywhere you go, you will find some kind of living organism. If you observe this organism, you can easily think of questions to ask about it.

Figure 1 Part of science is asking questions about the world around you.

Why do leaves change color in the fall?

How are a frog and a lizard different?

How do birds know where to go when they migrate?

Investigation: The Search for Answers

Once you ask a question, it's time to look for an answer. But how do you start your investigation? There are several methods that you can use.

Research

You can find answers to some of your questions by doing research, as **Figure 2** shows. You can ask someone who knows a lot about the subject of your questions. You can look up information in print resources, such as textbooks, encyclopedias, and magazines. You can also use electronic resources, such as the World Wide Web. The World Wide Web is a computer network that allows people all over the world to share information. You may learn more about your subject if you find the report of an experiment that someone has done. But be sure to think about the source of the information that you find. Scientists use information only from reliable sources.

Standards Check What is an example of an electronic resource that you can use to do research? **7.7.b**

Observation

You can also find answers to questions by making careful observations. For example, if you want to know which birds live around you, you can go for a walk and look for them. Or you can hang a bird feeder outside your window and observe the birds that use it.

Experimentation

You can even answer some of your questions by doing an experiment, as **Figure 3** shows. An experiment should be carefully designed to answer a specific question. Making good observations and analyzing data are some of the other important parts of doing experiments.

life science (LIEF SIE uhns) the study of living things

Figure 2 *At a library, you will find many print and electronic resources.*

Quick Lab

Asking Questions **7.7.b**

1. With your group, pick a living thing. Print the name of the living thing in the middle of a large piece of **paper.**

2. Use **markers** to write questions about the living thing on the paper.

3. Choose one of the questions. On the back of the paper, list all of the possible ways that you could find an answer to that question.

🕐 **15 min**

Investigation and Experimentation
7.7.b Use a variety of print and electronic resources (including the World Wide Web) to collect information and evidence as part of a research project.

Figure 3 *This student is doing an experiment to find the hardness of a mineral.*

Why Ask Questions?

What is the point of asking all of these questions? Life scientists may find some interesting answers, but do any of the answers matter? Will the answers affect *your* life? Absolutely! As you study life science, you will see how the investigations of life science affect you and all living things around you.

Fighting Diseases

Polio is a disease that causes paralysis by affecting the brain and nerves. Do you know anyone who has had polio? Probably not. The polio virus has been eliminated from most of the world. But at one time, it was much more common. In 1952, before life scientists discovered ways to prevent the spread of the polio virus, it infected 58,000 Americans.

Today, life scientists continue to search for ways to fight diseases. Acquired immune deficiency syndrome (AIDS) is a disease that kills millions of people every year. The scientist in **Figure 4** is trying to learn more about AIDS. Life scientists have discovered how the virus that causes AIDS is carried from one person to another. Scientists have also learned about how the virus affects the body. By learning more about the virus, scientists may find a cure for this deadly disease.

Researching Food Sources

How can enough food be produced to feed everyone? How can we make sure that food is safe to eat? Many scientists do research to find answers to these types of questions. The scientist in **Figure 5** is studying a plant that was grown in a lab. Some scientists do experiments to see if they can make plants grow faster or larger. Other scientists research ways to preserve food so that it lasts longer.

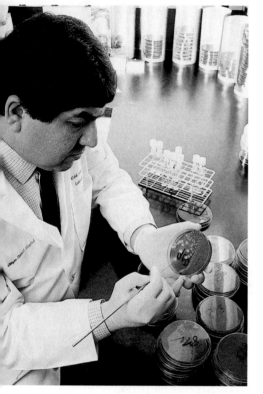

Figure 4 *Scientists hope to find a cure for AIDS by studying the virus that causes the disease.*

Figure 5 *Scientists study plants to find better ways to produce food.*

Protecting the Environment

Life scientists also study environmental problems on Earth. Many environmental problems are caused by the misuse of natural resources. Understanding how we affect the world around us is the first step in finding solutions to problems such as pollution and the extinction of wildlife.

Why should we try to decrease pollution? Pollution can harm our health and the health of other organisms. Water pollution may be a cause of frog deformities seen in parts of the world. Pollution in oceans kills marine mammals, birds, and fish. The scientists in **Figure 6** are monitoring water quality to determine if the water is polluted.

The actions of humans affect many living things. When we cut down trees to clear land for crops or to get lumber, we change and sometimes destroy habitats. Hunting and loss of habitat have caused many animals, including Siberian tigers, California condors, and some species of fish, to become endangered. By learning about the food and habitat needs of endangered animals, scientists hope to develop a plan that will ensure the survival of these animals.

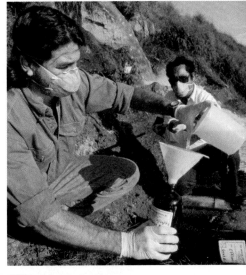

Figure 6 *These environmental scientists are testing water quality.*

SECTION Review

7.7.b

Summary

- Science is a process of gathering knowledge about the natural world. Science includes making observations and asking questions. Life science is the study of living things.

- To find answers to your questions, you can make observations, do experiments, or use print and electronic resources to do research.

- Life science can help find cures for diseases, can research food sources, can monitor pollution, and can help living things survive.

Using Vocabulary

1. Write an original definition for *life science.*

Understanding Concepts

2. **Describing** Why are questions important in life science?

3. **Listing** Give three examples of resources that you can use to do research.

INTERPRETING GRAPHICS Use the picture below to answer the next item.

4. **Listing** Propose five questions about the animal in this picture.

Critical Thinking

5. **Expressing Opinions** You can find a wide variety of information on the World Wide Web. What do you think makes a source reliable?

6. **Applying Concepts** When would a life scientist study a nonliving thing, such as a lake or a rock?

7. **Making Comparisons** A volcanologist is a scientist who studies volcanoes. How is the work of a volcanologist similar to the work of a life scientist? How do the two jobs differ?

Scientific Methods

Key Concept Scientific methods are used to investigate questions and to solve problems.

What You Will Learn

- Scientists ask questions, make observations, form hypotheses, test hypotheses, analyze results, and draw conclusions.
- Scientists communicate their steps and results from investigations in written reports and oral presentations.

Why It Matters

You can use scientific methods to investigate your questions about the natural world.

Vocabulary

- scientific methods
- hypothesis
- controlled experiment
- variable

READING STRATEGY

Outlining In your **Science Journal,** create an outline of the section. Use the headings from the section in your outline.

Investigation and Experimentation
7.7.c Communicate the logical connection among hypotheses, science concepts, tests conducted, data collected, and conclusions drawn from the scientific evidence.
7.7.e Communicate the steps and results from an investigation in written reports and oral presentations.

Imagine that your class is on a field trip to a wildlife refuge. You discover several deformed frogs. You wonder what is causing the deformities.

A group of students from Le Sueur, Minnesota, actually made this discovery! By making observations and asking questions about the observations, the students used scientific methods.

What Are Scientific Methods?

When scientists observe the natural world, they often think of questions or problems. But scientists don't guess the answers. They use scientific methods. **Scientific methods** are the ways in which scientists follow steps to answer questions and solve problems. The steps used for all investigations are the same. But the order in which the steps are followed may vary, as **Figure 1** shows. Scientists may use all of the steps or just some of the steps during an investigation. They may even repeat some of the steps. The order depends on what will work best to answer their questions. No matter where they work or what questions they try to answer, all life scientists have two things in common. They are curious about the natural world, and they use similar methods to investigate it.

Standards Check What are scientific methods? 7.7.c

Figure 1 *Scientific methods often include the same steps, but the steps are not always used in the same order.*

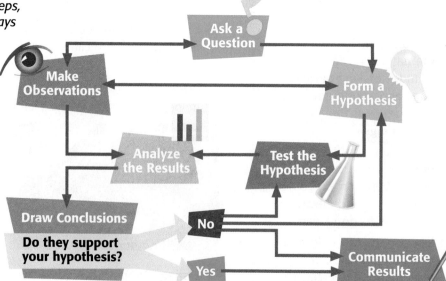

Ask a Question

Have you ever observed something that was out of the ordinary or difficult to explain? Such an observation usually raises questions. For example, you might ask, "Could something in the water be causing the frogs' deformities?" Looking for answers may include making more observations.

Make Observations

After the students from Minnesota realized something was wrong with the frogs, they decided to make additional, careful observations. They counted the number of deformed frogs and the number of normal frogs that they caught. The students also photographed the frogs, took measurements, and wrote a detailed description of each frog.

In addition, the students collected data on other organisms living in the pond. They also conducted many tests on the pond water, measuring things such as the level of acidity. The students carefully recorded their data and observations. Observations are only useful if they are accurately made and recorded.

Types of Observations

Any information gathered through the senses is an observation. Observations can take many forms. They may be measurements of length, volume, time, speed, or loudness. They may describe the color or shape of an organism. Or they may describe the behavior of organisms. Scientists use many standard tools and methods to make and record observations. Examples of these tools are shown in **Figure 2.**

INTERNET ACTIVITY

Careers in Life Science
Would you like to be a life scientist? Write an essay on your investigation of an interesting career. Go to **go.hrw.com** and type in the keyword HY7LIVW.

scientific methods
(SIE uhn TIF ik METH uhds) a series of steps followed to solve problems

Figure 2 *Microscopes, rulers, and thermometers are some of the tools that scientists use to collect information. Scientists record their observations carefully.*

Form a Hypothesis

hypothesis (hi poth es is) a testable idea or explanation that leads to scientific investigation

Wordwise The prefix *hypo-* means "under." The root *thesis* means "proposition." Other examples are *hypodermic* and *hypoallergenic.*

After asking questions and making observations, scientists may form a hypothesis. A **hypothesis** (hie PAHTH uh sis) is a possible explanation or answer to a question. A good hypothesis is based on observations and can be tested. When scientists form hypotheses, they think logically and creatively and consider what they already know.

Scientists thought about the different things that could be affecting the frogs. Some chemicals can be dangerous to living things. Maybe chemicals used in agriculture and industry had been washed into ponds. Some parasites can cause diseases that produce deformities. Maybe small parasites in the water were attacking the frogs. Large amounts of ultraviolet (UV) light can cause damage in living things. Maybe human activity had damaged the ozone layer, which was letting in more UV light from the sun. Chemical pollutants, parasites, or UV light were possible explanations for the deformities seen in frogs.

Scientists used their observations and reasoning to form the hypotheses in **Figure 3.** Were any of these explanations correct? To find out, scientists had to test each hypothesis.

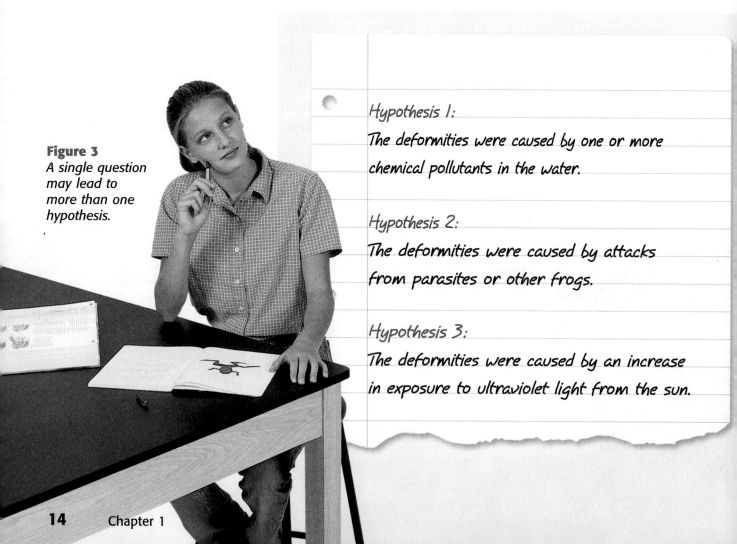

Figure 3
A single question may lead to more than one hypothesis.

Hypothesis 1:
The deformities were caused by one or more chemical pollutants in the water.

Hypothesis 2:
The deformities were caused by attacks from parasites or other frogs.

Hypothesis 3:
The deformities were caused by an increase in exposure to ultraviolet light from the sun.

Predictions

Before scientists can test a hypothesis, they must first make predictions. A prediction is a statement of cause and effect that can be used to set up a test for a hypothesis. Predictions are usually stated in an if-then format, as shown in **Figure 4.**

More than one prediction may be made for each hypothesis. For the hypotheses on the previous page, the predictions in **Figure 4** were made. A prediction for hypothesis 3 is as follows: If an increase in exposure to UV light is causing the deformities, then frog eggs exposed to more ultraviolet light in a laboratory will be more likely to develop into deformed frogs than frog eggs that are exposed to less UV light will.

Scientists can conduct experiments to see whether the results match the predictions of the hypothesis. Sometimes, the results clearly match the predictions of one hypothesis. At other times, the results may not have been predicted by any of the hypotheses. In these cases, new hypotheses and new tests are needed.

Figure 4 *A single hypothesis may lead to more than one prediction.*

Standards Check What is the connection between hypotheses and the tests that are conducted in an investigation? 🐻 **7.7.c**

Hypothesis 1:
Prediction: If a substance in the pond water is causing the deformities, then the water from ponds that have deformed frogs will be different from the water from ponds in which no abnormal frogs have been found.
Prediction: If a substance in the pond water is causing the deformities, then some tadpoles will develop deformities when they are raised in pond water collected from ponds that have deformed frogs.

Hypothesis 2:
Prediction: If a parasite is causing the deformities, then this parasite will be found more often in frogs that have deformities than in frogs that do not have deformities.

Hypothesis 3:
Prediction: If an increase in exposure to ultraviolet light is causing the deformities, then frog eggs exposed to more ultraviolet light in a laboratory will be more likely to develop into deformed frogs than frog eggs that are exposed to less UV light will.

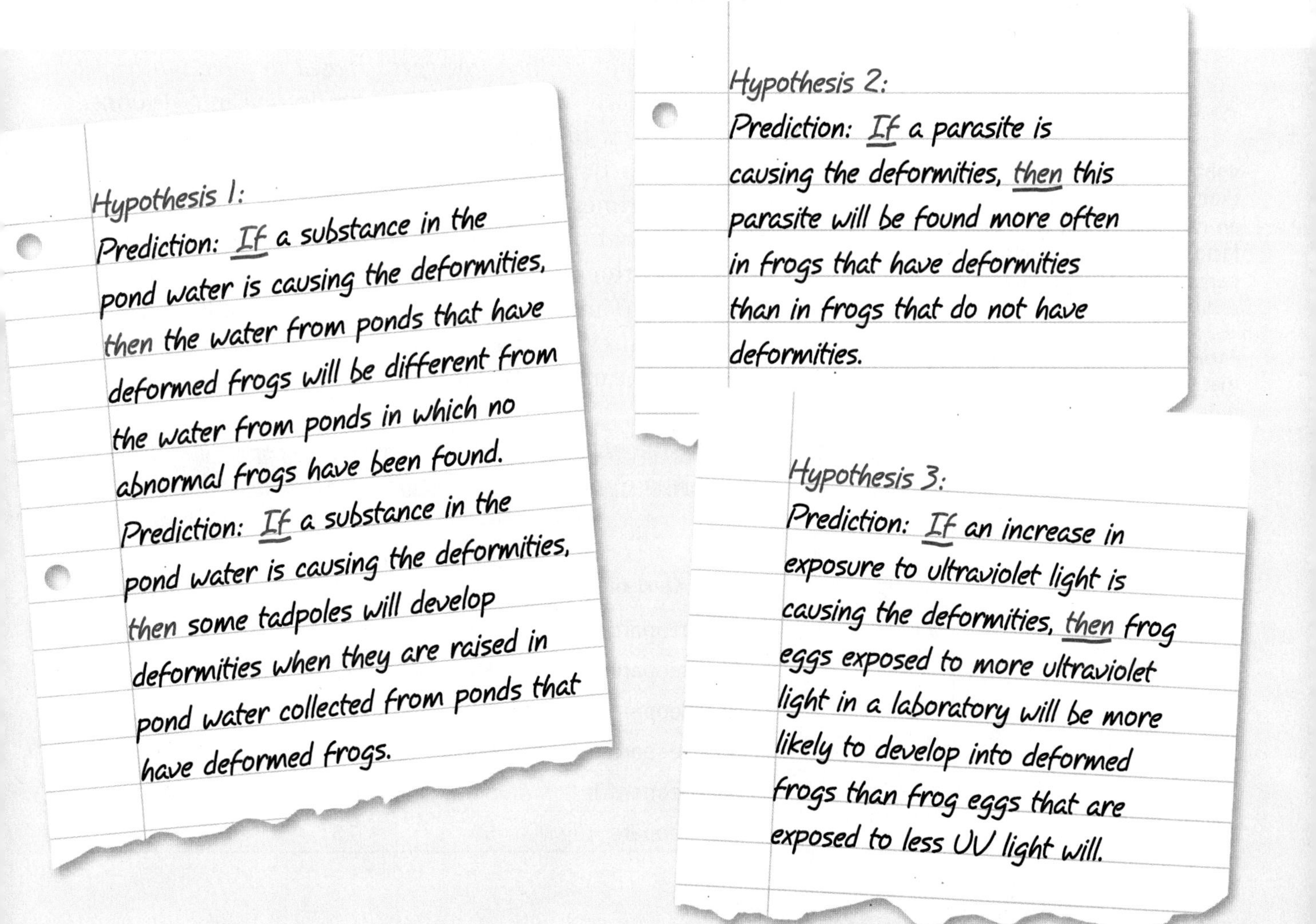

Test the Hypothesis

Scientists try to design experiments that will show whether a particular factor caused an observed outcome. A *factor* is anything in an experiment that can influence the experiment's outcome. Factors can be anything from temperature to the type of organism being studied. Many factors affect the development of frogs in the wild, as **Figure 5** shows.

To study the effect of each factor, scientists perform controlled experiments. A **controlled experiment** tests only one factor at a time and consists of a control group and one or more experimental groups. All of the factors for the control group and the experimental groups are the same except for one. The one factor that differs is called the **variable.** Because the only difference between the control group and the experimental groups is the variable, any differences observed in the outcome of the experiment are probably caused by the variable.

Designing an Experiment

Every factor must be considered when designing an experiment. Scientists must also use ethics guidelines when designing and conducting an experiment. Examine the prediction for Hypothesis 3: *If an increase in exposure to ultraviolet light is causing the deformities, then frog eggs exposed to more ultraviolet light in a laboratory will be more likely to develop into deformed frogs than frog eggs that are exposed to less UV will.* An experiment to test this hypothesis is summarized in **Table 1.**

In the experiment shown in **Table 1,** the variable is the length of time that the eggs are exposed to UV light. All other factors, such as the temperature of the water, are the same in the control group and in the experimental groups. Because the experiment requires the use of animals, scientists use compassion when they care for the frogs in the experiment.

Figure 5 *Many factors affect this tadpole in the wild. These factors include chemicals, light, temperature, and parasites.*

controlled experiment
(kuhn TROLD ek SPER uh muhnt) an experiment that tests only one factor at a time by using a comparison of a control group with an experimental group

variable (VER ee uh buhl) a factor that changes in an experiment in order to test a hypothesis

Table 1	Experiment to Test Effect of UV Light on Frogs				
		Control Factors			**Variable**
Group	**Tank**	**Kind of frog**	**Number of eggs**	**Temperature of water (°C)**	**UV light exposure (days)**
#1 (control)	A	leopard frog	50	25	0
	B	leopard frog	50	25	0
#2 (experimental)	C	leopard frog	50	25	15
	D	leopard frog	50	25	15
#3 (experimental)	E	leopard frog	50	25	24
	F	leopard frog	50	25	24

Figure 6 UV Light Experiment

Control Group	Experimental Groups	

Group #1
No UV light exposure

Tank A: 0 deformed frogs

Tank B: 0 deformed frogs

Group #2
UV light exposure for 15 days

Tank C: 0 deformed frogs

Tank D: 0 deformed frogs

Group #3
UV light exposure for 24 days

Tank E: 23 deformed frogs

Tank F: 24 deformed frogs

Collecting Data

As **Table 1** shows, each group in the experiment contains 100 eggs. Scientists always try to test many individuals. The greater the number of organisms that they test, the more certain they can be of the data. They want to be certain that differences between control and experimental groups are caused by differences in the variable, not by differences between individuals. To support their conclusions, scientists repeat their experiments. If an experiment produces the same results again and again, they can be more certain about the effect of the variable on the outcome of the experiment. The experimental setup to test Hypothesis 3 and the results are shown in **Figure 6.**

Analyze the Results

A scientist's work does not end when an experiment is finished. After scientists finish their tests, they must analyze the results. They organize the data so that the data can be analyzed. For example, scientists may organize the data in a table or a graph. The data collected from the UV light experiment are shown in the bar graph in **Figure 7.** Analyzing results helps scientists explain and focus on the effect of the variable. For example, the bar graph shows that the length of UV exposure has an effect on the development of deformities in frogs.

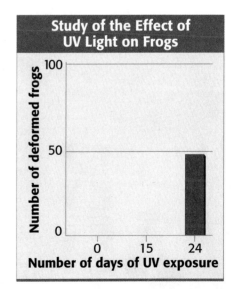

Figure 7 *This graph shows that 24 days of UV exposure had an effect on deformities in frogs. Shorter exposure had no effect.*

Quick Lab

Investigating and Experimenting with Yeast

7.7.c

1. Mix **1/2 tsp of yeast** with **warm water** and **sugar.**

2. Make observations. Compose a list of questions about the factors that influence yeast to activate.

3. Use scientific methods to investigate yeast activation. For this investigation, you will need to form a hypothesis, design and conduct an experiment to test the hypothesis, analyze and collect data, and state the conclusions.

4. Did your results support your hypothesis?

⏱ **30 min**

Figure 8 *This student scientist is communicating the results of his investigation at a science fair.*

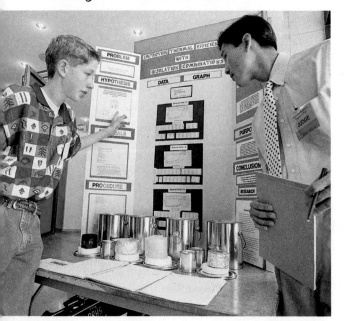

Draw Conclusions

After scientists have analyzed the data from several experiments, they can draw conclusions. They decide whether the results of the experiments support a hypothesis. When scientists find that a hypothesis is not supported by the tests, they must try to find another explanation for what they have observed. Proving that a hypothesis is wrong is just as helpful as supporting it. Why? The scientist have learned something, which is the purpose of using scientific methods.

What Is the Answer?

The UV light experiment supports the hypothesis that the deformities in frog can be caused by exposure to UV light. Does the experiment prove that UV light caused the frogs living in the Minnesota wetland to be deformed? No, the only thing this experiment shows is that UV light may cause deformities in frog. Results of tests performed in a laboratory may differ from results of tests performed in the wild. In addition, the experiment did not investigate the effects of parasites or other substances on the frogs. In fact, more than one factor could be causing the deformities.

Puzzles as complex as the deformed-frog mystery are rarely solved with a single experiment. The quest for a solution may continue for years. Finding an answer doesn't always end an investigation. Often, that answer begins another investigation. In this way, scientists continue to build knowledge.

Communicate Results

After they complete an investigation, scientists communicate their steps and results. Written reports and oral presentations are two ways in which scientists share information. **Figure 8** shows a student explaining a science project.

There are several reasons that scientists regularly share their results. First, other scientists may repeat the experiments to see if they get the same results. Second, the information can be considered by other scientists with similar interests. The scientists can then compare hypotheses and form consistent explanations. New data may strengthen existing hypotheses or show that the hypotheses need to be altered. After learning about an experiment, a scientist might have questions and decide to perform his or her own investigation.

Standards Check Why do scientists communicate the results of their investigations? 🐻 **7.7.e**

Summary

- Scientific methods are the ways in which scientists follow steps to answer questions and solve problems.

- Any information gathered through the senses is an observation. Observations often lead to the formation of questions and hypotheses.

- A hypothesis is a possible explanation or answer to a question. A well-formed hypothesis may be tested by experiments.

- A controlled experiment tests only one factor at a time and consists of a control group and one or more experimental groups.

- After testing a hypothesis, scientists analyze the results and draw conclusions about whether the hypothesis is supported.

- Communicating results allows others to check the results, add to their knowledge, and design new experiments.

Using Vocabulary

1 Use *hypothesis, controlled experiment,* and *variable* in the same sentence.

Understanding Concepts

2 **Describing** The steps of scientific methods are not always used in the same order in every investigation. Support or argue this statement.

3 **Describing** What are the essential parts of a controlled experiment?

4 **Listing** What are two ways in which scientists share results?

5 **Classifying** A team of scientists wants to study the size of Anaconda snakes in the wild. After capturing a snake, the team measures and records the length of each snake. After the snakes are released, the team finds the average length of the captured snakes. Which scientific methods have the scientists used?

Critical Thinking

6 **Analyzing Methods** Why was UV light chosen to be the variable in the frog experiment?

7 **Analyzing Processes** Why do scientists repeat the examples of other scientists?

8 **Making Inferences** Why might two scientists working on the same problem draw different conclusions?

INTERPRETING GRAPHICS The table below shows how long one bacterium takes to divide and become two bacteria. Use the table below to answer the next question.

Temperature (°C)	Time to double (min)
10	130
20	60
25	40
30	29
37	17
40	19
45	32
50	no growth

9 **Evaluating Data** Plot this information on a graph. Put temperature on the x-axis and the time to double on the y-axis. Do not graph values for which there is no growth. What temperature allows the bacteria to multiply most quickly?

Challenge

10 **Predicting Consequences** You are doing an experiment and get surprising results. However, you realize that two factors were changed at the same time. How does this fact affect your ability to draw conclusions?

Tools and Measurement

Key Concept Scientists select and use tools and technology to perform tests and collect data.

What You Will Learn

- Scientists use technology, such as computers and microscopes, to perform tests and collect information.
- The International System of Units enables scientists to compare information and to convert between units.
- Measurements such as length, area, volume, temperature, and mass can be obtained with the right tools.

Why It Matters

Selecting and using the right tools and technology will help you conduct your own scientific investigations.

Vocabulary

- technology
- compound light microscope
- electron microscope
- area
- volume
- mass
- weight
- temperature

READING STRATEGY

Clarifying Concepts Take turns reading this section out loud with a partner. Stop to discuss ideas that seem confusing.

technology (tek NAHL uh jee) the application of science for practical purposes; the use of tools, machines, materials, and processes to meet human needs

▶ Would you use a knife to mix cake batter? You probably would not. To be successful in many tasks, you need the correct tools.

Life scientists use various tools to make observations and to collect, store, and analyze information. Selecting and using tools properly are important parts of scientific work.

Technology in Science

The application of science for practical purposes is called **technology.** By using technology, life scientists are able to find information and solve problems in new ways. New technology allows scientists to get information that was not available previously.

Calculators and Computers

Calculators and computers are two types of technology that are frequently used in science. Scientists frequently collect large amounts of data. Calculators and computers can be used to quickly and accurately make calculations of data. Some calculators and computers can be programmed to create graphs and to solve complex equations. Computers also help scientists share data and ideas with each other and publish reports about their research.

Binoculars

Imagine that you are studying eagles that nest in tall trees. You need to make observations. But it is not always easy or safe to get close to what you are studying. Binoculars can help you make observations from a distance. **Figure 1** shows a scientist using binoculars to make observations.

Figure 1 *Binoculars help scientists make observations when they cannot get close to their subject.*

Figure 2 Types of Microscopes

Compound Light Microscope
Light passes through the specimen and produces a flat image.

Transmission Electron Microscope Electrons pass through the specimen and produce a flat image.

Scanning Electron Microscope Electrons bounce off the surface of the specimen and produce a three-dimensional (3-D) image.

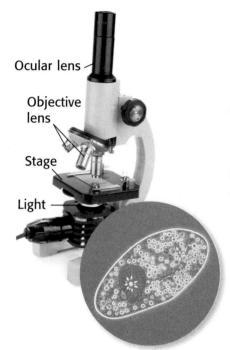

Ocular lens

Objective lens

Stage

Light

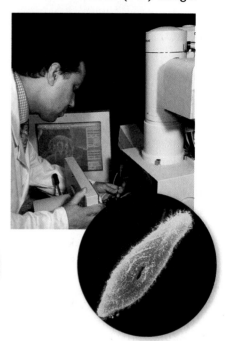

Compound Light Microscope

The compound light microscope is a common tool in a life science laboratory. A **compound light microscope** is an instrument that magnifies small objects so that they can be seen easily. It has three main parts—a tube with two or more lenses, a stage, and a light. Items may be colored with special dyes to make them more visible. Items are placed on the stage so that the light passes through them. The lenses at each end of the tube magnify the image.

Electron Microscopes

Not all microscopes use light. In **electron microscopes,** tiny particles called *electrons* are used to produce magnified images. The images produced are clearer and more detailed than those made by light microscopes. However, living things cannot be viewed with electron microscopes because the preparation process kills them. The two kinds of electron microscopes used in life science are the transmission electron microscope (TEM) and the scanning electron microscope (SEM). **Figure 2** shows three kinds of microscopes and an example of the images that each kind can produce.

Standards Check Which type of technology would you use to observe the movement of a small living thing? **7.7.a**

compound light microscope
(kahm POWND LIET MIE kruh SKOHP) an instrument that magnifies small objects so that they can be seen easily by using two or more lenses
Wordwise The root *micro-* means "small." The root *-scope* means "an instrument for seeing or observing."

electron microscope
(ee LEK trahn MIE kruh SKOHP) a microscope that focuses a beam of electrons to magnify objects

Investigation and Experimentation
7.7.a Select and use appropriate tools and technology (including calculators, computers, balances, spring scales, microscopes, and binoculars) to perform tests, collect data, and display data.

Table 1	Common SI Units and Conversions	
Length 	**meter (m)**	
	kilometer (km)	1 km = 1,000 m
	decimeter (dm)	1 dm = 0.1 m
	centimeter (cm)	1 cm = 0.01 m
	millimeter (mm)	1 mm = 0.001 m
	micrometer (μm)	1 μm = 0.000001 m
	nanometer (nm)	1 nm = 0.000000001 m
Volume	**cubic meter (m³)**	
	cubic centimeter (cm³)	$1\ cm^3 = 0.000001\ m^3$
	liter (L)	$1\ L = 1\ dm^3 = 0.001\ m^3$
	milliliter (mL)	$1\ mL = 0.001\ L = 1\ cm^3$
Mass	**kilogram (kg)**	
	gram (g)	1 g = 0.001 kg
	milligram (mg)	1 mg = 0.000001 kg
Temperature	**kelvin (K)**	
		0°C = 273 K
		100°C = 373 K

*The Celcius (°C) scale is a commonly used non-SI temperature scale.

SCHOOL to HOME

How You Measure Matters

Measure the length and width of a desk or table, but do not use a ruler. Pick a common object as your unit of measurement. It could be a pencil, your hand, or anything else. Use that unit to determine the area of the desk or table.

To calculate the area of a rectangle, first measure the length and width. Then, use the following equation:

area = length × width

Ask your parent or guardian to do this activity on his or her own. When he or she is finished, compare your area calculations.

area (ER ee uh) a measure of the size of a surface or a region

volume (VAHL yoom) a measure of the size of a body or region in three-dimensional space

Measurement

The ability to make reliable measurements is an important skill in science. But different standards of measurement have developed throughout the world. Ancient measurement units were based on parts of the body, such as the foot, or on objects, such as grains of wheat. Such systems were not very reliable. Even as better standards were developed, they varied from country to country.

The International System of Units

In the late 1700s, the French Academy of Sciences began to form a global measurement system now known as the *International System of Units*. (The system is also called *SI*, or *Système International d'Unités*). Today, most scientists and almost all countries use this system. One advantage of using SI measurements is that scientists can share and compare their observations and results.

Another advantage is that almost all SI units are based on the number 10, which makes conversions from one unit to another easy. **Table 1** contains SI units for length, volume, mass, and temperature. Notice how the prefix of each SI unit relates to a base unit.

Length

How long is an ant? A life scientist would probably use millimeters (mm) to describe an ant's length. If you divide 1 m into 1,000 parts, each part equals 1 mm. Although millimeters seem like a small unit, some living things and structures are so tiny that even smaller units—micrometers (µm) or nanometers (nm)—must be used.

Area

How much paper would you need to cover the top of your desk? To answer this question, you must find the area of the desk. **Area** is a measure of how much surface an object has. Area can be calculated from measurements such as length and width. Area is stated in square units, such as square meters (m^2), square centimeters (cm^2), and square kilometers (km^2).

Volume

How many books will fit into a bag? The answer depends on the volume of the bag and the volume of each book. **Volume** is a measure of the size of something in three-dimensional space.

The volume of a liquid is most often described in liters (L). Liters are based on the meter. A cubic meter (1 m^3) is equal to 1,000 L. So, 1,000 L will fit into a box measuring 1 m on each side. A milliliter (mL) will fit into a box that is 1 cm on each side. So, 1 mL = 1 cm^3. Graduated cylinders are used to measure the volume of liquids, as **Figure 3** shows.

The volume of a solid object is given in cubic units, such as cubic meters (m^3), cubic centimeters (cm^3), or cubic millimeters (mm^3). To find the volume of a box-shaped object, multiply the object's length by its width and height. As **Figure 3** shows, the volume of an irregularly shaped object can be found by measuring the amount of liquid that the object displaces.

Standards Check What tool would you select to measure the volume of a liquid? 🐻 **7.7.a**

Averages

Finding the average, or mean, of a group of numbers is a common way to analyze data.

Let us look at an example. Three seeds were kept at 25°C and sprouted in 8, 8, and 5 days. To find the average number of days the seeds took to sprout, add 8, 8, and 5 and divide the sum by 3, the number of subjects (seeds). These seeds took an average of 7 days to sprout.

Suppose three seeds were kept at 30°C and sprouted in 6, 5, and 4 days. What is the average number of days that these seeds took to sprout? Record your work in your **Science Journal.**

Figure 3 *Adding a rock to a graduated cylinder raised the level of water from the 70 mL mark to the 80 mL mark. Because the rock displaced 10 mL of water and 1 mL = 1 cm^3, the volume of the rock is 10 cm^3.*

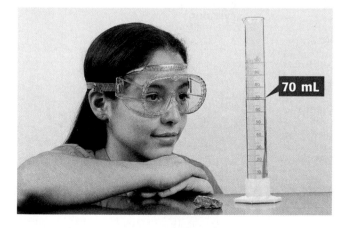

Figure 4 Tools Used to Measure Mass and Weight

You can use a **spring scale** to measure weight. ▶

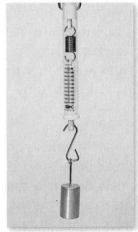

You can use a **balance** to measure mass. ▶

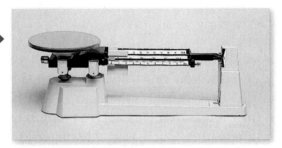

Mass and Weight

mass (MAS) a measure of the amount of matter in an object

weight (WAYT) a measure of the gravitational force exerted on an object; its value can change with the location of the object in the universe

temperature (TEM puhr uh chuhr) a measure of how hot (or cold) something is; specifically, a measure of the average kinetic energy of the particles in an object

A measure of the amount of matter in an object is called **mass.** The mass of an object is constant anywhere in the universe because the amount of matter stays the same. The kilogram (kg) is the base unit for mass. The mass of a small object may be described in grams (g). Mass can be measured by using a balance, as **Figure 4** shows. Weight and mass are sometimes confused, but they are different. **Weight** is a measure of the force of gravity on an object and is expressed in newtons (N). The force of gravity changes depending on where the object is in the universe. So, the weight of an object on Earth differs from the weight of the object on the moon. Weight is measured by using a spring scale, as **Figure 4** shows.

Quick Lab

Measure Up!

1. Your teacher will provide you with a variety of tools, such as a **graduated cylinder, balance, spring scale, thermometer,** and **meterstick**.

2. Make a table similar to the table at right.

3. Select a tool to take the measurement of each object listed in the table. Record each tool in your table.

4. Take each measurement and record it in your table.

Measuring Objects				7.7.a
Object	Measurement needed	Tools needed	Measurement (with units)	
Water in a cup	volume	graduated cylinder	350 mL	
Classroom	area			
Bolt	volume			
Chalk board	length			
Shoe	weight			
Outside air	temperature			
Pencil	mass			

DO NOT WRITE IN BOOK

🕐 **25 min**

Temperature

How much should food be heated to kill any bacteria in the food? To answer this question, a life scientist would measure the temperature at which bacteria die. **Temperature** is a measure of how hot or cold something is. Temperature is actually an indication of the amount of energy within matter. You are probably used to describing temperature in degrees Fahrenheit (°F). Although the kelvin (K) is the official SI base unit for temperature, scientists commonly use degrees Celsius (°C). You will use degrees Celsius in this book. The thermometer in **Figure 5** shows how the Fahrenheit and Celsius scales compare.

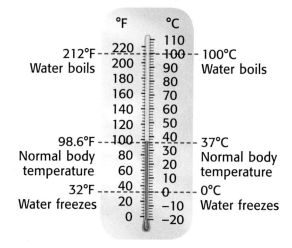

Figure 5 *This thermometer shows the relationship between degrees Fahrenheit and degrees Celsius.*

SECTION Review

7.7.a

Summary

- Life scientists use tools to collect, store, organize, analyze, and share data.

- Scientists use technology such as calculators, computers, binoculars, and microscopes.

- The International System of Units (SI) is a simple and reliable system of measurement that is used by most scientists.

- Graduated cylinders measure the volume of liquids, rulers measure length, thermometers measure temperature, and balances measure mass.

- You can calculate the area and volume of box-shaped solids by using measurements taken with a ruler.

Using Vocabulary

Use a term from the section to complete each sentence below.

1 The measure of the surface of an object is called ___.

2 Life scientists use kilograms when measuring an object's ___.

3 The ___ of a liquid is usually described in liters.

Understanding Concepts

4 **Describing** Why do scientists use SI units when making measurements?

5 **Describing** How are computers used in scientific investigations?

6 **Identifying** Which tool would you select to measure the mass of an object?

Math Skills

7 **Making Calculations** Convert 3.0 L into cubic centimeters.

8 **Making Calculations** Calculate the volume of a textbook that is 28.5 cm long, 22 cm wide, and 3.5 cm thick.

Critical Thinking

9 **Predicting Consequences** What problems could occur if some scientists measured objects by using SI units and other scientists measured objects by using other units, such as inches?

INTERPRETING GRAPHICS Use the picture of a mite below to answer the next question.

10 **Making Inferences** The mite shown above is about 500 μm long in real life. What tool was probably used to produce this image? How can you tell?

Internet Resources

For a variety of links related to this chapter, go to www.scilinks.org

Topic: Tools of Life Science; SI Units
SciLinks code: HY71535; HY71390

Scientific Models and Knowledge

Key Concept   Models are used to study living things, test hypotheses, explain observations, and communicate knowledge.

What You Will Learn

- Physical models, mathematical models, and conceptual models are all representations of ways to study objects or systems.
- Scientific theories are conceptual models that organize scientific thinking and explain why things happen.
- Scientific laws tell you what will happen in a specific situation.

Why It Matters

Learning about models and theories will give you a better understanding of how science works.

Vocabulary

- model
- scale
- theory
- law

READING STRATEGY

Graphic Organizer   In your **Science Journal,** create an Idea Wheel about the types of scientific models.

model (MAHD' l) a pattern, plan, representation, or description designed to show the structure or workings of an object, system, or concept

Your body is made up of trillions of cells. You need a microscope to see inside most cells. But how do you learn about the parts of a cell if you don't have a microscope? Models are useful tools for sharing information, such as the structure of cells.

Types of Scientific Models

A **model** is a representation of an object or a system. Models are used in science to help explain how something works or is structured. Models can also be used to make predictions or to explain observations. However, models have limitations. A model is never exactly like the real thing. If it were, it would not be a model. There are many kinds of scientific models. Some examples are physical models, mathematical models, and conceptual models.

Physical Models

A toy rocket and a plastic skeleton are examples of physical models. Many physical models, such as the model of a human body in **Figure 1,** look like the thing that they model. A limitation of the model of a body is that the model is not alive and doesn't act exactly like a human body. Yet the model is useful for understanding how the body works. Other physical models may look and act more like or less like what they represent than the model in **Figure 1** does. Scientists often use the model that is simplest to use but that is still helpful.

Figure 1   *This physical model looks a lot like a real human body. But it is easier to see inside this model than to see inside a real human body.*

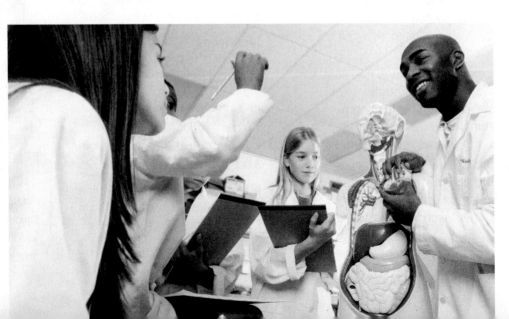

Mathematical Models

A mathematical model may be made up of numbers, equations, or other forms of data. Some mathematical models are simple and can be used easily. The graph in **Figure 2** is a model of life expectancy—a measure of how long, on average, people live. This model was created by collecting information in different areas of the world over many years. Then, the information was used to predict life expectancy in the future. For example, if the life expectancy in an area increased by 5 years in the last 10 years, one might hypothesize that the life expectancy will continue to increase at a similar rate.

Computers are very useful for creating and manipulating mathematical models. They make fewer mistakes than humans do and can keep track of more variables than humans can. But a computer model can be incorrect in many ways. The more complex a model is, the more carefully scientists must build the model.

Conceptual Models

Conceptual models are diagrams, drawings, or verbal descriptions of how something works or is put together. The conceptual model in **Figure 3** describes how mercury released from burning coal could travel through the environment and affect humans. Scientists create such diagrams to show how the parts of a system affect one another.

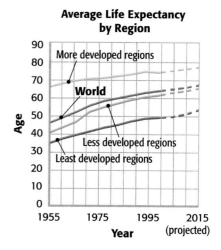

Average Life Expectancy by Region

Figure 2 *This mathematical model shows average life expectancy in the past. This information is used to predict what the life expectancy will be in the future.*

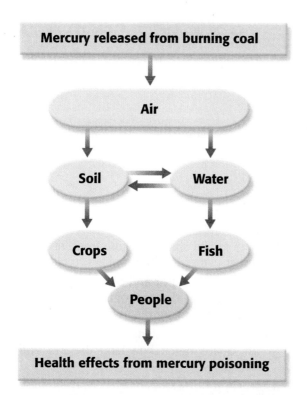

Mercury released from burning coal → Air → Soil ⇄ Water → Crops, Fish → People → Health effects from mercury poisoning

Figure 3 *This conceptual model shows how mercury released from burning coal could end up affecting humans.*

Investigation and Experimentation
7.7.c Communicate the logical connection among hypotheses, science concepts, tests conducted, data collected, and conclusions drawn from the scientific evidence.
7.7.d Construct scale models, maps, and appropriately labeled diagrams to communicate scientific knowledge (e.g., motion of Earth's plates and cell structure).

27

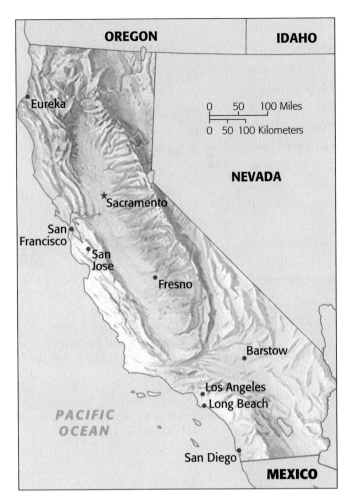

Figure 4 *This map of California is drawn to a scale of 1 cm:100 km.* **How far is San Francisco from Los Angeles?**

Using Scale in Models

Imagine that you see a model of your school with a new addition for a swimming pool. In the model, the new addition is the size of the cafeteria. You expect that a large pool will be built. But when the addition is finished, the pool is only as large as the principal's office. What happened?

The model that you saw was not drawn to scale. **Scale** is the relationship between the measurement of a model and the actual measurement of the real object. Measurements in a scale model are proportionally smaller or larger than the real object. In a scale model of your school, the new pool would be the size of the principal's office, not as big as the cafeteria.

Maps and diagrams can also be drawn to scale. For example, **Figure 4** shows a map of California. The scale of the map is 1 cm: 100 km. This ratio means that 1 cm on the map represents 100 km in California. Because the proportions of a map, model, or diagram match the proportions of the real object, scale models, maps, and diagrams can accurately communicate scientific knowledge.

Standards Check What is scale? 7.7.d

Quick Lab

Constructing Scale Diagrams

You have been hired to design a monkey exhibit for a zoo. You are required to submit a scale diagram of the exhibit. The zoo has given you the following requirements for the new monkey exhibit.

1. The exhibit will house five adult monkeys. Each animal needs at least 50 m² of space.

2. The exhibit should include a pond. The pond should cover 10 m².

3. The exhibit should include a shelter for each animal. Each shelter should enclose an area of 1 m².

7.7.d

4. The exhibit should include trees, tires, and other places for the monkeys to play.

5. Use **graph paper** and **colored pencils** to draw a scale diagram of the exhibit. Indicate the scale on your diagram.

6. Label the dimensions of the exhibit. Indicate in square meters how large the area of the exhibit is.

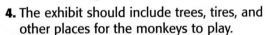

🕐 20 min

Benefits of Models

Models are often used to represent things that are very small or very large. Models may also represent things that are very complicated or things that no longer exist. For example, **Figure 5** is a computer model of a dinosaur. Such computer models have been used for many things, including to make movies about prehistoric life on Earth. Models are used, of course, because filming a real dinosaur in action is impossible. But in building models, scientists may discover things that they hadn't thought of before.

A model can be a kind of hypothesis and can be tested. To build a model of an organism, scientists must gather information collected from fossils and other observations. Then, they can test whether their model fits with their ideas about how an organism moved or what the organism ate.

Figure 5 *This computer-generated model doesn't just look like a dinosaur. This model includes the movement of bones and muscles.*

Building Scientific Knowledge

Sometimes, scientists may draw different conclusions from the same data. Other times, new results show that old conclusions are wrong. Sometimes, more information is needed. Life scientists are always asking new questions or looking at old questions from a new angle. As they find new answers, scientific knowledge continues to grow and change.

Scientific Theories

For every hypothesis, more than one prediction can be made. Each time the results of an investigation match a prediction, the hypothesis gains more support. Over time, scientists try to tie together all that they have learned. An explanation that ties together many related facts, observations, and tested hypotheses is called a **theory.** Theories are conceptual models that help organize scientific thinking. Theories are used to explain observations and to predict what might happen in the future.

Scientific Laws

The one kind of scientific idea that rarely changes is called a *scientific law*. In science, a **law** is a summary of many experimental results and observations. Unlike traffic laws, scientific laws are not based on what people may want to happen. Instead, scientific laws are statements of what *will* happen in a specific situation. And unlike theories, scientific laws tell you what happens, not why it happens.

scale (SKAYL) the relationship between the measurements on a model, map, or diagram and the actual measurement or distance

theory (THEE uh ree) a system of ideas that explains many related observations and is supported by a large body of evidence acquired through scientific investigation

law (LAW) a descriptive statement or equation that reliably predicts events under certain conditions

Combining Scientific Ideas

Scientific laws are at work around you every day. For example, the law of gravity is at work when you see a leaf fall to the ground. The law of gravity tells us that objects fall toward the center of Earth. Many laws of chemistry are at work inside your cells. However, living organisms are very complex. So, there are very few laws within life science. But some theories are very important in life science and are widely accepted. An example is the theory that all living things are made up of cells.

Scientific Change

Scientific ideas can change. For example, scientists used to think that the dinosaur *Apatosaurus* (uh PA tuh SAWR uhs) used its long neck to reach leaves high in trees, as **Figure 6** shows. To test this idea, scientists took measurements of the vertebrae, or neck bones, of fossils from the dinosaur. Then, they entered this information into computer models to study how the bones fit together. The models showed that an *Apatosaurus* could not have held its head up straight. Now, many scientists think that an *Apatosaurus* held its head horizontally, as **Figure 6** shows. The models show that the neck muscles and bones would have worked better in a horizontal position.

Figure 6   **An Example of Scientific Change**

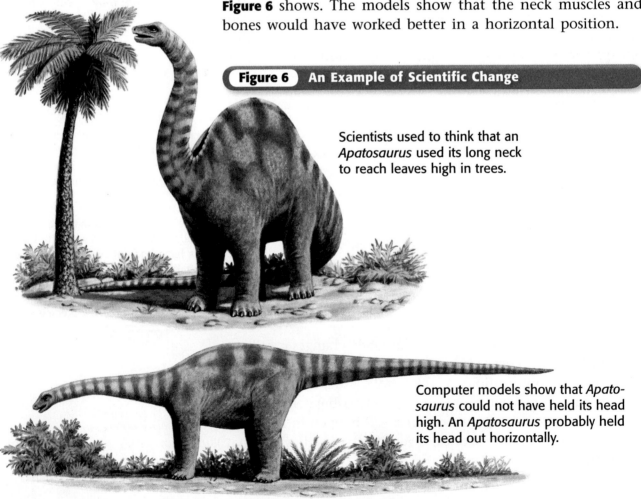

Scientists used to think that an *Apatosaurus* used its long neck to reach leaves high in trees.

Computer models show that *Apatosaurus* could not have held its head high. An *Apatosaurus* probably held its head out horizontally.

Evaluating Scientific Ideas

When a scientist proposes a theory, other scientists examine the evidence and decide if the evidence supports the theory. Scientists use scientific methods to test the new theory. If the theory and evidence are contradictory, scientists revise the theory or propose alternative theories. The theory that provides the best explanation and has the most evidence supporting it becomes the theory that most scientists accept.

Scientists should be open to new ideas, but they should always test those ideas with scientific methods. The process of building scientific knowledge never ends.

Standards Check How can new evidence change scientific theories?
7.7.c

SECTION Review

 7.7.c, 7.7.d

Summary

- A model is a representation of an object or system. Models often use familiar things to represent unfamiliar things. Three main types of models are physical, mathematical, and conceptual models.

- Scale models, maps, or diagrams match the proportions of the objects they represent.

- Scientific knowledge is built as scientists form and revise scientific hypotheses, models, theories, and laws.

Using Vocabulary

Use a term from the section to complete each sentence below.

1 A ___ is an explanation that matches many hypotheses but that may change.

2 A ___ tells you exactly what to expect in certain situations.

Understanding Concepts

3 **Describing** What is a limitation of a model?

4 **Listing** What are three types of models? Give an example of each type.

5 **Comparing** Compare how scientists use theories with how they use laws.

Critical Thinking

6 **Applying Concepts** You are making a three-dimensional model of an extinct plant. Describe some of the potential uses for your model. What are some limitations of your model?

7 **Analyzing Processes** How do scientists evaluate theories?

Math Skills

8 **Making Calculations** If Jerry is 2.1 m tall, how tall is a scale model of Jerry that has a scale of 10 cm:1 m?

Challenge

9 **Analyzing Processes** Most doctors give advice to their patients about their diet. Imagine that an organization announces that it has discovered that a high-fat diet is the healthiest diet. What should happen before doctors start to recommend that their patients eat a high-fat diet?

Internet Resources

For a variety of links related to this chapter, go to www.scilinks.org
Topic: Using Models
SciLinks code: HY71588

31

Safety in Science

Key Concept Following safety rules during scientific investigations will help prevent accidents and injury.

▶ While walking by a construction site, you notice a sign on the fence: "Hard Hat Area." When you look through the fence, you see that all of the construction workers are wearing heavy plastic helmets.

Construction workers wear hard hats to prevent injury if an accident happens. Likewise, you take precautions to be safe at home and in school. You also take special care when you learn science, as **Figure 1** shows.

The Importance of Safety Rules

Safety is the state of being free of danger or injury. To be safe while doing science, you must learn some safety rules. Perhaps the most important safety rule is to follow the directions given by your teacher. Following directions will make your work easier, and will help you get better results. And, you will be safer!

Standards Check What is safety?

Preventing Accidents

Following rules may not seem like fun. But following rules is better than getting hurt! The most important reason for obeying safety rules is to prevent accidents. Your teacher will remind you of safety rules, but it's your job to follow them. Accidents are less likely to happen when safety rules are followed.

Preventing Injury

Unfortunately, accidents can happen even when all safety rules are obeyed. When an accident does happen, you or someone nearby could get hurt. Following safety rules can help you avoid or reduce injury. For example, wearing gloves will help protect your skin if you accidentally spill a chemical on your hands.

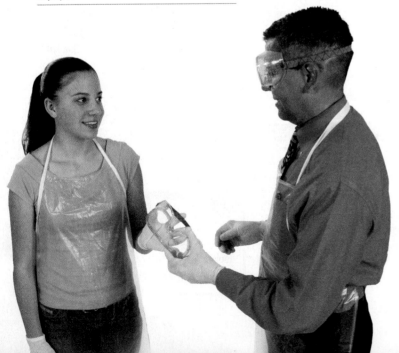

Figure 1 *Wearing safety equipment and following your teacher's directions will keep you safe in the science lab.*

Figure 2 Safety Symbols

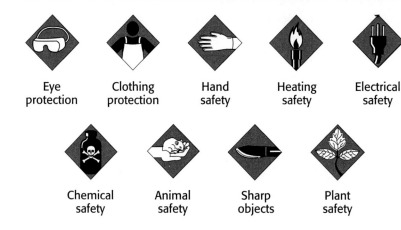

Eye protection	Clothing protection	Hand safety	Heating safety	Electrical safety
Chemical safety	Animal safety	Sharp objects	Plant safety	

For more safety tips, read the Safety First! section at the front of your book.

Elements of Safety

There are many parts to safety. Recognizing safety symbols can alert you to potential dangers. Reading directions and being neat can prevent accidents. Safety equipment keeps you safe during experiments, and proper cleanup procedures keep your classroom safe after an experiment is over.

Safety Symbols

Most road signs have specific meanings. For example, a stop sign means that cars must stop moving. A one-way sign means that cars must travel only in a certain direction. Signs and symbols that have specific meanings are also used in science. **Figure 2** shows the safety symbols that are used in this book. For example, if you see the symbol for goggles listed on an activity, you should wear eye protection during that activity. Learning the meaning of and obeying these symbols can help prevent injury or an accident.

In some experiments, such as the one shown in **Figure 3,** you must work with live animals. When you do an experiment with animals, you will see the symbol for animal safety. This symbol tells you to be careful when handling animals. For example, you should never squeeze or frighten animals. You should follow your teacher's directions on how to pick up animals and how to dispose of animal waste. You should handle only the animals provided by your teacher and should never bring wild animals into the classroom. And after working with animals, you should wash your hands thoroughly with soap and water.

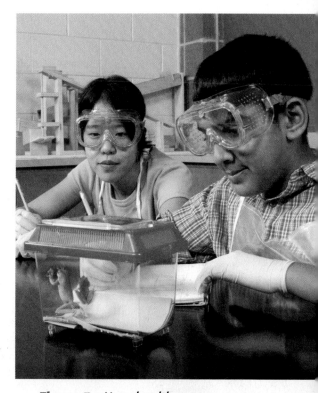

Figure 3 *You should wear protective gloves when handling animals during an experiment.*

Reading and Following Directions

If you want to bake a cake successfully, you will probably use a recipe. The recipe tells you the ingredients to use and the proper procedure to follow. When scientists work in the laboratory, they also follow directions. Likewise, when you work in the laboratory, you must follow directions given by your teacher and the lab procedure.

Before starting a science experiment, you should read all of the instructions. Reading the directions before you start will help you get better results and will reduce the chance of having an accident. If you don't understand the instructions in a lab procedure, you should ask your teacher to explain the directions in a different way.

When you do an experiment, you should leave your book open to the page that shows the instructions. You will be able to find the instructions quickly if you need to reread them.

Neatness Counts!

Before starting any science activity, you should clear your work area of books, backpacks, and any other unneeded objects. These objects can get in the way and may cause you to trip or spill your materials. Also, you should prepare data tables and gather necessary safety equipment, as **Figure 4** shows.

Neatness also counts when you are doing an experiment. You should arrange the lab materials on the desk or table so that you can find them easily. And you should label all chemicals so that they won't be mixed up. And you should record your findings carefully in a notebook or data table so that you and others can read them.

Figure 4 *Proper preparation before an experiment will help keep you safe in the laboratory.*

Figure 5 *These students are wearing protective gloves when they work with chemicals. But they put on heat-resistant gloves before lifting the beakers off the hot plates.*

Using Proper Safety Equipment

Safety equipment can protect you from injury. Safety goggles, gloves, and aprons are some examples of lab safety equipment. The safety symbols shown next to laboratory instructions indicate what kind of safety equipment to use. For example, when you see the eye protection symbol, you must put on your safety goggles. Goggles should fit comfortably but snugly.

If you see the symbol for hand protection, you need to wear gloves. If you are using chemicals or animals, you must wear protective gloves. But if you are handling warm objects, using a hot plate, or using an open flame, you must wear heat-resistant gloves. Both kinds of gloves are shown in **Figure 5.**

Standards Check Why is it important to select the appropriate safety equipment when you perform a scientific investigation? **7.7.a**

Proper Cleanup Procedures

After finishing a science experiment, you should clean up your work area. You should place caps on bottles, and return everything to its proper place. If you have used burners, you must be sure to turn off the gas. Wash all of your glassware, and check for chips and cracks. You must give any damaged glassware to your teacher. You should dispose of any extra or waste chemicals as your teacher directs. Once your desk or table is clear, you should wipe it with a wet paper towel. Finally, you should wash your hands thoroughly with soap and water.

Quick Lab

Preparing for an Experiment   **7.7.a**

1. Select an animal. Think of a question about that animal's behavior.

2. Design an experiment to investigate the behavior of the animal.

3. Compile a list of all of the tools and technology needed for the experiment.

4. Create a second list of all of the safety materials and safety procedures that you would need to follow during the experiment.

 20 min

Figure 6 Emergency Equipment

▼ A **first-aid kit** contains many things for treating injury, including things to clean and cover wounds.

A **fire extinguisher** ▶ is a safe and effective tool for putting out fires.

An **eyewash** is ▶ used to remove chemicals or small particles from the eye.

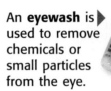

Proper Accident Procedures

Sometimes, accidents do happen. After any accident, you should the follow the four steps below in order.

- Remain calm, and assess the situation. Look around, and do your best to determine what happened.
- Secure the area around the accident. Make sure that you are safe and that no one else is in danger.
- Tell your teacher, or call for help. Always tell your teacher if an accident happens, even if the accident seems minor.
- Assist your teacher with cleaning up or giving aid. Do exactly what your teacher tells you to do.

After an accident, your teacher may need you to get emergency equipment. The emergency equipment shown in **Figure 6** is often found in labs. You should learn how to use the emergency equipment and you should know where it is kept in your classroom.

Table 1	Simple First-Aid Procedures
Injury	**First-aid procedure**
Minor heat-related burn	Hold affected area under cold, running water for at least 15 min.
Small cuts	Clean the area, cover it with a clean cloth or gauze pad, and apply pressure.
Chemicals on skin	Rinse area with running water.
Chemical in eye	Rinse eye with running water or in an eyewash.

Proper First-Aid Procedures

If an accident results in an injury, it is important that you know what to do. Fortunately, almost all laboratory injuries are minor and are treated easily. When treating an injury in the lab, your teacher will use first aid. **First aid** is emergency medical care for someone who has been hurt.

You should not perform first aid unless you are properly trained. If first aid is not done properly, a victim can be more seriously injured. However, you may do a few simple first-aid procedures that you can do without training. These procedures are listed in **Table 1.** Because first aid is only temporary care, an injured person should see a doctor for more treatment.

first aid (FUHRST AYD) emergency medical care for someone who has been hurt or who is sick

SECTION Review

 7.7.a

Summary

- Following safety rules helps prevent accidents and helps reduce injury.
- Five elements of safety are recognizing safety symbols, following directions, being neat, using proper safety equipment, and using proper cleanup procedures.
- Animals used in scientific research require special care.
- When an accident happens, you should assess the situation, secure the area, tell your teacher, and help your teacher with cleanup or first aid.
- First aid is emergency medical care. Some first-aid procedures can be done without training.

Using Vocabulary

1. Write an original definition for *first aid*.

Understanding Concepts

2. **Describing** Why are safety rules important?

3. **Describing** What are five elements of safety?

4. **Listing** List the four steps that you should take after an accident happens.

5. **Applying** What should you do if you spill a chemical on your skin?

Critical Thinking

6. **Making Inferences** Suppose that you are doing research to determine how quickly a mouse can learn to run a maze. Explain how you would care for and handle the mouse.

7. **Applying Concepts** Imagine that your lab partner dropped a glass beaker and cut his finger on the broken glass. Describe what you should do next.

8. **Applying Concepts** Rabies is a viral disease that is often transmitted through the bite of an animal that is infected by the rabies virus. People who get the rabies virus suffer from a variety of symptoms and will die if not treated in time. Many types of animals including bats, dogs, and raccoons can carry rabies. What precautions should scientists who are studying bats take?

INTERPRETING GRAPHICS Use the symbols below to answer the next question.

9. **Applying Concepts** The symbols above appear on an activity. What precautions should you take before you begin this activity?

Internet Resources

For a variety of links related to this chapter, go to www.scilinks.org
Topic: Safety
SciLinks code: HY71339

37

Skills Practice Lab

Collecting and Displaying Data

When performing an experiment, you usually need to collect data. To understand the data, you can often organize the data into a graph. Graphs can show trends and patterns that you may not notice in a table or list. In this exercise, you will practice collecting data and organizing the data into a graph.

OBJECTIVES

Collect data during an experiment.

Create a graph to display the data.

MATERIALS

- beaker, 500 mL
- clock (or watch) with a second hand
- gloves, heat-resistant
- hot plate
- ice
- paper, graph
- thermometer, Celsius, with a thermometer holder
- water (200 mL)

SAFETY

Procedure

1. Make a table like the one below. Leave space to continue recording for more than 20 min.

| Water Temperature ||
Time (min)	Temperature (°C)
0	
1	
2	
3	

DO NOT WRITE IN BOOK

2. Pour 200 mL of water into a 500 mL beaker. Add ice to the beaker until the waterline is at the 400 mL mark.

3. Place a Celsius thermometer into the beaker. Use a thermometer holder to prevent the thermometer from touching the bottom of the beaker.

4. Place the beaker and thermometer on a hot plate. Record the temperature of the ice water. The initial temperature is recorded as "0 min" because the water has been heated for 0 minutes.

Investigation and Experimentation
7.7.a Select and use appropriate tools and technology (including calculators, computers, balances, spring scales, microscopes, and binoculars) to perform tests, collect data, and display data.

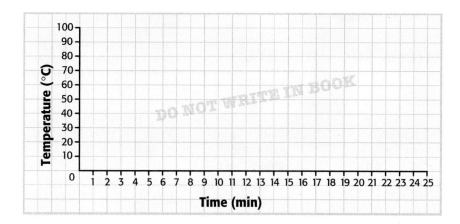

5. Turn the hot plate on medium heat. After 1 min Record the temperature every minute until the water temperature reaches 100°C.

6. Using heat-resistant gloves, remove the beaker from the hot plate. Continue to record the temperature of the water each minute for 10 more min. **Caution:** Don't forget to turn off the hot plate.

7. On a piece of graph paper, create a graph similar to the one above Label the horizontal axis (the *x*-axis) "Time (min)," and mark the axis in increments of 1 min. Label the vertical axis (the *y*-axis) "Temperature (°C)," and mark the axis in increments of 10°.

8. Find the 0 min mark on the *x*-axis, and move up the graph to the temperature that you recorded at 0 min. Place a dot on the graph at that point. Plot each temperature in the same way. When you have plotted all of your data, connect the dots with a smooth line.

Analyze the Results

9. **Examining Data** Examine your graph. Do you think that the water heated faster than it cooled? Explain.

10. **Analyzing Results** Estimate what the temperature of the water was 2.5 min after you placed the beaker on the hot plate. Explain how you can make a good estimate of temperature.

Draw Conclusions

11. **Evaluating Methods** Explain how a graph may give more information than the same data in a table does.

Big Idea Question

12. **Evaluating Methods** Why is it important to collect and display data from a scientific investigation?

Science Skills Activity

Investigation and Experimentation

7.7.b Use a variety of print and electronic resources (including the World Wide Web) to collect information and evidence as part of a research project.

Using Internet Resources for Research

▶ Tutorial

Because the Internet contains a great deal of information, it can be a useful tool for doing research. But you may find that the Internet contains too much information or that most of the information is not *reliable*. Reliable information is information that is likely to be correct because it is based on observations or research. In this tutorial, you will learn tips for using the Internet to do research.

Procedure

1 Use Keywords Choose keywords for the topic that you are researching.
- Use multiple keywords to narrow your search.
- Use quotation marks around keywords to find exact matches. For example, if you are researching a person, put quotation marks around the person's full name to exclude other people who share part of the person's full name.
- Enter the keywords into a search engine.

2 Find Reliable Information A search may return many sites that contain information about the topic. You need to determine which sites contain reliable information. Only use reliable information in your investigation.

- Reliable information usually comes from reliable sources. Look for information from government agencies, museums, and newspapers.
- Be careful when reviewing personal Web sites. They may contain more opinions than facts.
- Watch for biased sources. A *biased source* contains incomplete or misleading information. If you suspect that a source is biased, find other sources to check the information.

3 Cite Sources If you use information from the Internet in a report, you must cite that source in a bibliography. Your teacher will tell you the information that you should include and the format in which the information should be listed. The following information is often included:
- author of the material
- specific page of the site
- name of the Web site
- date the page was created
- address of the Web site
- date the Web site was viewed

▶ You Try It!

In this activity, you will practice finding and using sources on the Internet. The question that you are researching is the following: How many Siberian tigers are left in the wild?

Procedure

1 Use Keywords Determine the keywords that you will use for your search. Enter different combinations of keywords into a search engine and record the number of Web sites that each combination returns. Which keyword search returned the most Web sites that contain information on your topic?

2 Find Reliable Information Find at least three sources that contain reliable information. What makes this information reliable? Read the sources, and write a paragraph describing what you learned.

3 Cite Sources Create a bibliography that shows the sources that you used. When you cite a source, be sure to include all the important information for that source.

Chapter Summary

The Big Idea
Scientists use scientific processes to study the patterns of natural events and to solve problems.

Section

Vocabulary

1 Asking About Life

Key Concept Asking questions is the first step in a scientific investigation.

- Questions lead to learning about science.
- Print or electronic resources can be used to find information.
- Your everyday life is affected by life scientists in many ways.

life science p. 8

2 Scientific Methods

Test the Hypothesis

Key Concept Scientific methods are used to investigate questions and to solve problems.

- Scientists ask questions, make observations, form hypotheses, test hypotheses, analyze results, and draw conclusions.
- Scientists communicate their steps and results from investigations in written reports and oral presentations.

scientific methods p. 12

hypothesis p. 14

controlled experiment p. 16

variable p. 16

3 Tools and Measurement

Key Concept Scientists select and use tools and technology to perform tests and collect data.

- Scientists use technology, such as computers and microscopes, to perform tests and collect information.
- The International System of Units enables scientists to compare information and to convert between units.
- Measurements such as length, area, volume, temperature, and mass can be obtained with the right tools.

technology p. 20

compound light microscope p. 21

electron microscope p. 21

area p. 23

volume p. 23

mass p. 24

weight p. 24

temperature p. 25

4 Scientific Models and Knowledge

Key Concept Models are used to study living things, test hypotheses, explain observations, and communicate knowledge.

- Physical models, mathematical models, and conceptual models are representations of ways to study objects or systems.
- Scientific theories are conceptual models that organize scientific thinking and explain why things happen.
- Scientific laws tell you what will happen in a specific situation.

model p. 26

scale p. 28

theory p. 29

law p. 29

5 Safety in Science

Key Concept Following safety rules during scientific investigations will help prevent accidents and injuries.

- The elements of safety include following safety symbols, following directions, being neat, using proper safety equipment, and using proper cleanup procedures.
- Following the proper procedure for accidents can help reduce the effects of an accident.

first aid p. 37

   7.7.a, 7.7.b, 7.7.c, 7.7.d, 7.7.e

Organize

Layered Book Review the Fold-Note that you created at the beginning of the chapter. Add to or correct the FoldNote based on what you have learned.

Using Vocabulary

1 **Academic Vocabulary** In the sentence "They used a variety of print resources in their research project," what does the word *resources* mean?
a. materials used to make products
b. materials containing information
c. materials used to gather information
d. materials about science

2 Use *controlled experiment* and *variable* in the same sentence.

For each pair of terms, explain how the meanings of the terms differ.

3 *theory* and *hypothesis*

4 *compound light microscope* and *electron microscope*

5 *area* and *volume*

Understanding Concepts

Multiple Choice

6 The steps of scientific methods
a. must all be used in every scientific investigation.
b. must always be used in the same order.
c. often start with a question.
d. always result in the development of a theory.

7 Which of the following tools is best for measuring 100 mL of water?
a. 10 mL graduated cylinder
b. 150 mL graduated cylinder
c. 250 mL graduated cylinder
d. 500 mL graduated cylinder

INTERPRETING GRAPHICS Use the symbols below to answer the next question.

8 The directions for a lab include the safety icons shown above. These icons mean that
a. you should be careful.
b. you are going into the laboratory.
c. you should wash your hands first.
d. you should wear safety goggles, a lab apron, and gloves during the lab.

INTERPRETING GRAPHICS The pictures below show how an egg can be measured by using a beaker and water. Use the pictures below to answer the next two questions.

Before: 125 mL  After: 200 mL

9 What kind of measurement is being taken?
a. area
b. length
c. mass
d. volume

10 Which of the following is an accurate measurement of the egg in the picture?
a. 75 cm^3
b. 125 cm^3
c. 125 mL
d. 200 mL

Short Answer

11 **Listing** What are three examples of resources scientists might use to collect information as part of a research project?

12 **Listing** List two ways that scientists communicate the steps and results of investigations.

13 **Describing** What are some advantages and limitations of models?

14 **Identifying** Which SI units can be used to describe an object's volume?

Writing Skills

15 **Communicating Concepts** Write a paragraph explaining how scientific explanations change. Include information about why scientists propose new theories. Also, describe how scientists evaluate new theories.

Critical Thinking

16 **Concept Mapping** Use the following terms to create a concept map: *observations, predictions, questions, controlled experiments, variable,* and *hypothesis.*

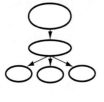

17 **Expressing Opinions** Your classmate says that all information on the Internet is reliable. Do you agree with this statement? Explain your answer.

18 **Analyzing Methods** Why is it important for scientists to write reports about the scientific investigations that they perform?

INTERPRETING GRAPHICS Use the table below to answer the next question.

Number of Frogs		
Year	Normal	Deformed
1999	25	0
2000	21	0
2001	19	1
2002	20	2
2003	17	3
2004	20	5

19 **Expressing Opinions** A group of citizens wants the local government to ban the use of a new chemical pesticide. The group proposes that since 1999, when the pesticide was first used, the number of deformed frogs has increased. To support the proposal, the group submits the table above. Do you think that the pesticide should be banned, or is more information needed? Explain your answer.

20 **Forming Hypotheses** A scientist who studies mice observes that on the day the mice are fed vitamins with their meals, they perform better in mazes. What hypothesis would you form to explain this phenomenon? Write a testable prediction based on your hypothesis.

Math Skills

INTERPRETING GRAPHICS Use the scale map below to answer the next question.

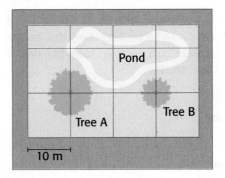

21 **Making Calculations** If the scale of this map is 1 square:10 m, what is the distance between the center of Tree A and the center of Tree B?

Challenge

22 **Analyzing Methods** Madison wants to test the following hypothesis: "Plants grow better with plant fertilizer than without it." So, she plants seeds in pots and places the plants in a window so that all the plants get the same amount of sunlight. Then, she divides the plants into two groups: Group A and Group B. Group A plants get 50 mL of water each day, and Group B plants get 100 mL of water each day. Once a week, she mixes fertilizer into the water. After three weeks, Madison measures the plants and finds that all of the plants are the same height. She concludes that fertilizer does not make plants grow better. Did Madison's experiment test her hypothesis? Explain your answer.

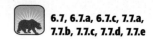
REVIEWING ACADEMIC VOCABULARY

1 In the sentence "After conducting the science experiment, we recorded and analyzed the results," what does the word *conducting* mean?

A directing

B doing

C researching

D constructing

2 In the sentence "A two-year-old child is too young to understand the concept of cooperation," what does the word *concept* mean?

A act

B idea

C reward

D process

3 Choose the appropriate form of the word *construct* for the following sentence: I have _____ a model of Earth's layers.

A construct

B will construct

C are constructing

D constructed

4 Which of the following words is the closest in meaning to the word *appropriate*?

A regular

B formal

C proper

D common

REVIEWING CONCEPTS

5 Which of the following is a print resource that is useful for researching a topic?

A television

B computer

C newspaper

D typewriter

6 What is the name of the computer network that allows scientists from all over the world to share information?

A The Punnett Square

B World Wide Web

C International System of Units

D Public Broadcasting System

7 Which of the following is a tool for measuring the volume of a liquid?

A graduated cylinder

B cubic centimeter

C spring balance

D meterstick

8 It is important to know proper first-aid procedures when conducting laboratory experiments. What is the proper treatment for a minor burn?

A to apply firm pressure to the burn

B to apply first-aid cream to the burn

C to cover the burn with a clean cloth

D to rinse the burn under cold water

9 The steps in a scientific investigation must

A include laboratory experiments.

B begin with a good hypothesis.

C include the development of a theory.

D be performed in a logical sequence.

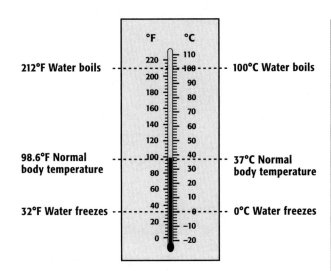

°F
212°F Water boils
98.6°F Normal body temperature
32°F Water freezes

°C
100°C Water boils
37°C Normal body temperature
0°C Water freezes

10 The conversion table above shows Fahrenheit and Celsius temperature scales. According to the conversion chart, which of the following sentences is true?

A You can swim in water that is 100°C.

B You can boil eggs in water that is 150°F.

C You can skate on water that is 10°C.

D Your body temperature is about 37°C.

11 In which type of model are the measurements of the model proportional to the measurements of the real object?

A a conceptual model

B a scale model

C a simple model

D a mathematical model

12 Written reports and oral presentations are part of which step of scientific methods?

A communicating results

B asking questions

C performing tests

D analyzing results

REVIEWING PRIOR LEARNING

Experiment to Test Effect of UV Light on Frogs				
	Control factors			Variable
Group	Kind of frog	Number of eggs	Temperature of water (°C)	UV light exposure (days)
#1 (control)	leopard frog	100	25	0
#2 (experimental)	leopard frog	100	25	15
#3 (experimental)	leopard frog	100	25	24

13 The data in the table above were collected during an experiment to test the effects of UV light on frogs. What is the variable in the experiment?

A water temperature

B length of exposure to UV light

C number of eggs

D kind of frog

14 What is a hypothesis?

A an accurate prediction

B a possible explanation that can be tested

C a sentence that states statistical data

D a factor that may cause a certain result

15 What is the purpose of scientific investigation?

A to demonstrate how scientific methods work

B to learn about discoveries

C to perform experiments

D to answer questions about the natural world

Science in Action

Scientific Debate

Should We Stop All Forest Fires?

Each year in California, forest fires endanger lives and damage homes and timber. Since 1972, the policy of the National Park Service has been to manage the national parks as naturally as possible. Most fires caused by lightning are allowed to burn. The only lightning-caused fires that are put out are those that threaten lives, property, uniquely scenic areas, or endangered species. All human-caused fires are put out. However, this policy has caused some controversy. Some people want this policy followed in all public forests and even grasslands. Others think that all fires should be put out.

Social Studies ACTiViTY

Research a location where there is a debate about controlling forest fires. You might look into national forests or parks. Record your research in your **Science Journal.** Write a newspaper article about the issue. Be sure to present all sides of the debate.

Science Fiction

"The Homesick Chicken"
by Edward D. Hoch

Why did the chicken cross the road? You think you know the answer to this old riddle, don't you? But "The Homesick Chicken," by Edward D. Hoch, may surprise you. That old chicken may not be exactly what it seems.

One of the chickens at the high-tech Tangaway Research Farms has escaped. Then, it was found in a vacant lot across the highway from Tangaway, pecking away contentedly. Why did it bother to escape? Barnabus Rex, a specialist in solving scientific riddles, is called in to work on this mystery. As he investigates, he finds clues and forms a hypothesis. Read the story, and see if you can explain the mystery before Mr. Rex does.

Language Arts ACTiViTY

In your **Science Journal,** write your own short story about a chicken crossing a road for a mysterious reason. Give the reader clues (evidence) about the mysterious reason but do not reveal the truth until the end of the story. Be sure that the story makes sense scientifically.

Yvonne Cagle

Flight Surgeon and Astronaut Most doctors practice medicine with both feet on the ground. But Dr. Yvonne Cagle found a way to fly with her medical career. Cagle became a flight surgeon for the U. S. Air Force and an astronaut for the National Aeronautics and Space Administration (NASA).

Cagle's interest in both medicine and space flight began early. As a little girl, Cagle spent hours staring at X rays in her father's medical library. Those images sparked an early interest in science. Cagle also remembers watching Neil Armstrong walk on the moon when she was five years old. As she tried to imagine the view of Earth from space, Cagle decided that she wanted to see it for herself.

Becoming a flight surgeon in the U. S. Air Force was a good first step toward becoming an astronaut. As a flight surgeon, Cagle learned about the special medical challenges that humans face when they are launched high above Earth. Being a flight surgeon also allowed Cagle to work with some of the best pilots and to fly in the latest jets.

It wasn't long before Cagle worked as an occupational physician for NASA at the Johnson Space Center. Two years later, she was chosen to begin astronaut training. Cagle completed two years of training and is now qualified for flight assignment as a mission specialist. Through hard work and dedication, Cagle has achieved many of her childhood goals.

Math ACTIVITY

In spaceflight, astronauts experience changes in gravity that affect their bodies in several ways. Because of gravity, a person who has a mass of 50 kg weighs 110 lb on Earth. But on the moon, the same person weighs about 17% of his or her weight on Earth. How much does the person weigh on the moon? Show your work in your **Science Journal**.

Internet Resources

- To learn more about careers in science, visit **www.scilinks.org** and enter the SciLinks code HY70225.

- To learn more about these Science in Action topics, visit **go.hrw.com** and type in the keyword HY7LIVF.

- Check out articles related to this chapter by visiting **go.hrw.com**. Just type in the keyword HY7LIVC.

Improving Comprehension

Graphic Organizers are important visual tools that can help you organize information and improve your reading comprehension. The Graphic Organizer below is called a *spider map*. Instructions for creating other types of Graphic Organizers are located in the **Study Skills** section of the Appendix.

How to Make a Spider Map

1 Draw a diagram like the one shown below. In the circle, write the main topic.

2 From the circle, draw legs to represent the main ideas or characteristics of the topic. Draw as many legs as you want to draw. Write an idea or characteristic along each leg.

3 From each leg, draw horizontal lines. As you read the chapter, write details about each idea on the idea's horizontal lines. To add more details, make the legs longer and add more horizontal lines.

When to Use a Spider Map

A spider map is an effective tool for classifying the details of a specific topic in science. A spider map divides a topic into ideas and details. As you read about a topic, look for the main ideas or characteristics of the topic. Within each idea, look for details. Use a spider map to organize the ideas and details of each topic.

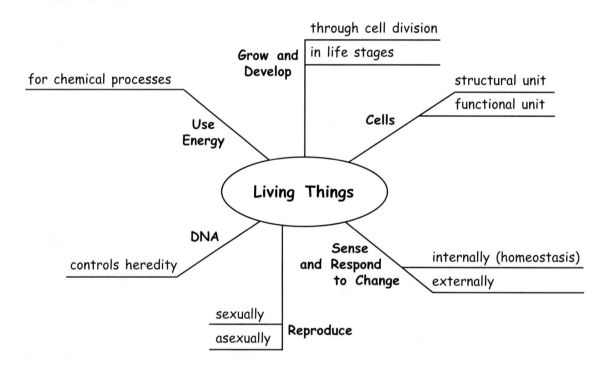

You Try It!

This Reading Strategy can also be used within the chapter that you are about to read. Practice making your own *spider map* as directed in the Reading Strategy for Section **2**. Record your work in your **Science Journal.**

Unpacking the Standards

The information below "unpacks" the standards by breaking them down into basic parts. The higher-level, academic vocabulary is highlighted and defined to help you understand the language of the standards. "What It Means" restates the standards as simply as possible.

California Standard	Academic Vocabulary	What It Means
7.1.a Students know cells **function similarly** in all living organisms.	**function** (FUHNGK shuhn) to work **similarly** (SIM uh luhr lee) in almost the same way	Cells perform the same actions in all living things.
7.2.a Students know the differences between the life **cycles** and reproduction methods of sexual and asexual organisms.	**cycle** (SIE kuhl) a repeating series of changes	You must know how the life cycles of living things that reproduce sexually differ from the life cycles of living things that reproduce asexually. You must also explain how these ways of reproducing differ.

2

It's Alive!! Or Is It?

The Big Idea

All living things share characteristics and needs.

 California Standards

Focus on Life Sciences

7.1 All living organisms are composed of cells, from just one to many trillions, whose details usually are visible only through a microscope. (Sections 1 and 2)

7.2 A typical cell of any organism contains genetic instructions that specify its traits. Those traits may be modified by environmental influences. (Section 1)

Investigation and Experimentation

7.7 Scientific progress is made by asking meaningful questions and conducting careful investigations. (Science Skills Activity)

Math

7.1.1 Mathematical Reasoning
7.1.1 Algebra and Functions

English–Language Arts

7.1.3 Reading
7.2.1 Writing

About the Photo

What does it mean to say that something is alive? To be alive, an organism must have all of the characteristics of living things. Machines have some but not all of the characteristics of living things. This amazing robotic insect can respond to changes in its environment. It can walk over obstacles. It can perform some tasks. But it is not alive. How is it like and unlike a living insect?

 **Organize**

Double Door

Before you read this chapter, create the FoldNote entitled "Double Door." Write "Characteristics" on one flap of the double door and "Needs" on the other flap. As you read the chapter, compare the two topics, and write characteristics of each topic on the inside of the appropriate flap.

Instructions for creating FoldNotes are located in the Study Skills section on p. 579 of the Appendix.

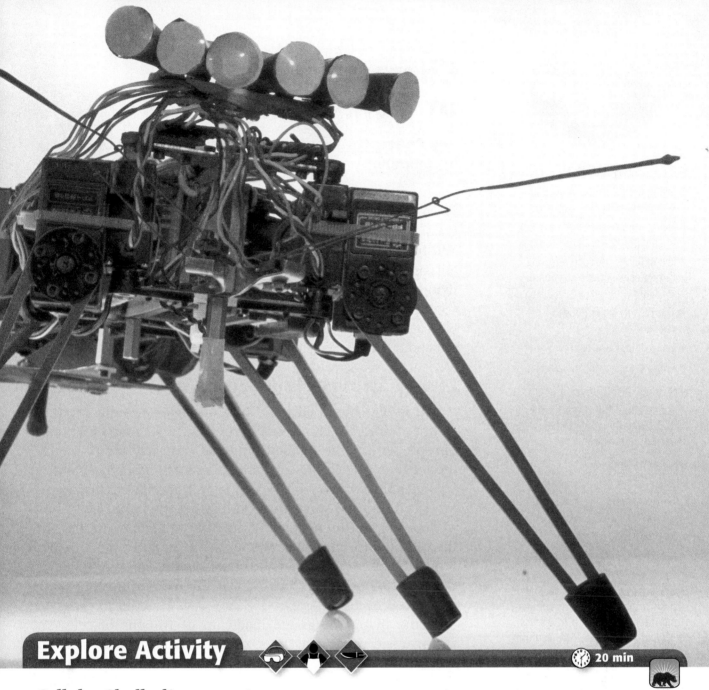

Explore Activity

20 min

Cellular Similarity

One characteristic shared by all living things is being composed of cells. Nonliving things, such as robots, are not made of cells. In this activity, you will observe a reaction produced by an enzyme found in both liver cells and potato cells.

Procedure

1. On a **plate**, use a **knife** to cut a few slices of **potato.** Place the potato pieces in a **beaker.**

2. Pour in enough **hydrogen peroxide** to cover the potatoes. Observe any changes in their appearance in the next few minutes.

3. Use the knife to cut up a small piece of **chicken liver.** Use **forceps** to place the liver pieces in a **beaker.**

4. Pour in enough hydrogen peroxide to cover the liver. Observe any changes in the liver's appearance in the next few minutes.

7.1.a
7.7.c

Analysis

5. What happened when the hydrogen peroxide was poured over the potato?

6. What happened when the hydrogen peroxide was poured over the liver?

7. How can your observations be used to support the idea that living things are similar?

51

Characteristics of Living Things

Key Concept   Living things have six characteristics in common.

▶ While outside one day, you notice something strange in the grass. It is slimy and bright yellow and is about the size of a dime. You have no idea what it is. Is it alive? How can you tell? An amazing variety of *organisms,* or living things, exist on Earth. All living things are alike in several ways. What does a dog have in common with a bacterium? And what do *you* have in common with a slimy, yellow blob known as a *slime mold?* Read on to find out about the six characteristics that all organisms share.

Living Things Have Cells

All living things, such as those in **Figure 1,** are composed of one or more cells. A **cell** is the structural and functional unit of life. It is the smallest unit that can carry out the activities of life. All cells are surrounded by a *cell membrane,* which separates the contents of the cell from the cell's environment. Most cells are too small to be seen with the naked eye.

In an organism made up of only one cell, different parts of the cell perform different functions. For example, a one-celled protist needs to eat. So, some parts of the cell take in food. Other parts of the cell break down the food. Still other parts of the cell excrete wastes.

Some living things are made up of trillions of cells. In an organism with many cells, different kinds of cells perform specialized functions. For example, your nerve cells transport signals, and your muscle cells are specialized for movement.

Standards Check   What are all living things made of? ⬛ **7.1.a**

Figure 1   *Some organisms, such as the California quail on the left, are made up of trillions of cells. The protists on the right are made up of one cell or a few cells. They are so small that they can be seen only with a microscope.*

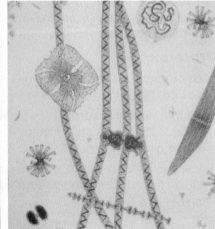

Living Things Sense and Respond to Change

All living things are able to sense change in their environment and to respond to that change. When your pupils are exposed to light, they respond by becoming smaller. A change that affects the activity of an organism is called a *stimulus* (plural, *stimuli*).

Stimuli can be chemicals, gravity, light, sounds, hunger, or anything that causes organisms to respond in some way. A gentle touch causes a response in the plant shown in **Figure 2.**

Homeostasis

Even though an organism's outside environment may change, conditions inside its body must stay the same. Many chemical reactions keep an organism alive. These reactions can take place only when conditions are exactly right. An organism must maintain stable internal conditions to survive. The maintenance of a stable internal environment is called **homeostasis.**

Responding to External Changes

Your body maintains a temperature of about 37°C. When you get hot, your body responds by sweating. When you get cold, your muscles twitch in an attempt to warm you up. This twitching is called *shivering.* Whether you are sweating or shivering, your body is trying to return itself to normal.

Other organisms also need to have stable internal conditions. But many cannot respond the way you do. Some living things control their body temperature by moving from one environment to another. If they get warm, they move to the shade. If they get cool, they move into the sunlight. For example, turtles often can be seen sunning themselves on rocks. When they get too warm, the turtles slide into the water.

cell (SEL) the smallest functional and structural unit of all living organisms

homeostasis (HOH mee OH STAY sis) the maintenance of a constant internal state in a changing environment

Quick Lab

The Role of Cells   7.1.a

1. Gather **20 to 30 small marshmallows.**

2. Use **toothpicks** to connect your marshmallows into any shape that you like.

3. Compare your marshmallow arrangements with your classmates'. What do they have in common?

4. If your arrangement represents an organism, describe how the marshmallows represent cells.

 10 min

Figure 3 *Like most animals, bears produce offspring by sexual reproduction.*

Figure 4 *The hydra can reproduce asexually by forming buds that break off and grow into new individuals.* **How will the new buds compare to the original organism?**

sexual reproduction (SEK shoo uhl REE pruh DUHK shuhn) reproduction in which the sex cells from two parents unite to produce offspring that share traits from both parents

asexual reproduction (ay SEK shoo uhl REE pruh DUHK shuhn) reproduction that does not involve the union of sex cells and in which one parent produces offspring that are genetically identical to the parent

metabolism (muh TAB uh LIZ uhm) the sum of all chemical processes that occur in an organism

Living Things Reproduce

Living things make offspring like themselves by either sexual reproduction or asexual reproduction. In **sexual reproduction,** two parents produce offspring that share characteristics of both parents. Most plants and animals, such as the bears in **Figure 3,** reproduce sexually. In **asexual reproduction,** a single parent produces offspring that are identical to the parent. Most single-celled organisms and many multicellular organisms reproduce asexually. **Figure 4** shows a hydra, a multicellular animal that reproduces asexually.

Standards Check Describe asexual reproduction. 🐻 **7.2.a**

Living Things Have DNA

The cells of all living things contain the molecule **d**eoxyribo**n**ucleic **a**cid (dee AHK see RIE boh noo KLEE ik AS id), or DNA. DNA carries instructions for the organism's traits. When organisms reproduce, they pass copies of their DNA to their offspring. Passing DNA ensures that the traits of parents are passed to the offspring. This passing of traits is called *heredity.*

Living Things Use Energy

Living things use energy to carry out the chemical activities of life. Some of these activities are changing energy into food, breaking down food, moving materials into and out of cells, growing, and building cells. An organism's **metabolism** is the sum of all of the activities that the organism performs.

Living Things Grow and Develop

All living things grow during parts of their lives. In a single-celled organism, the cell gets larger and divides, which makes other organisms. In a multicellular organism, the number of cells increases, and the organism gets bigger. As living things grow, they also may develop and change. Like the organisms in **Figure 5**, you will pass through different stages in your life as you develop into an adult.

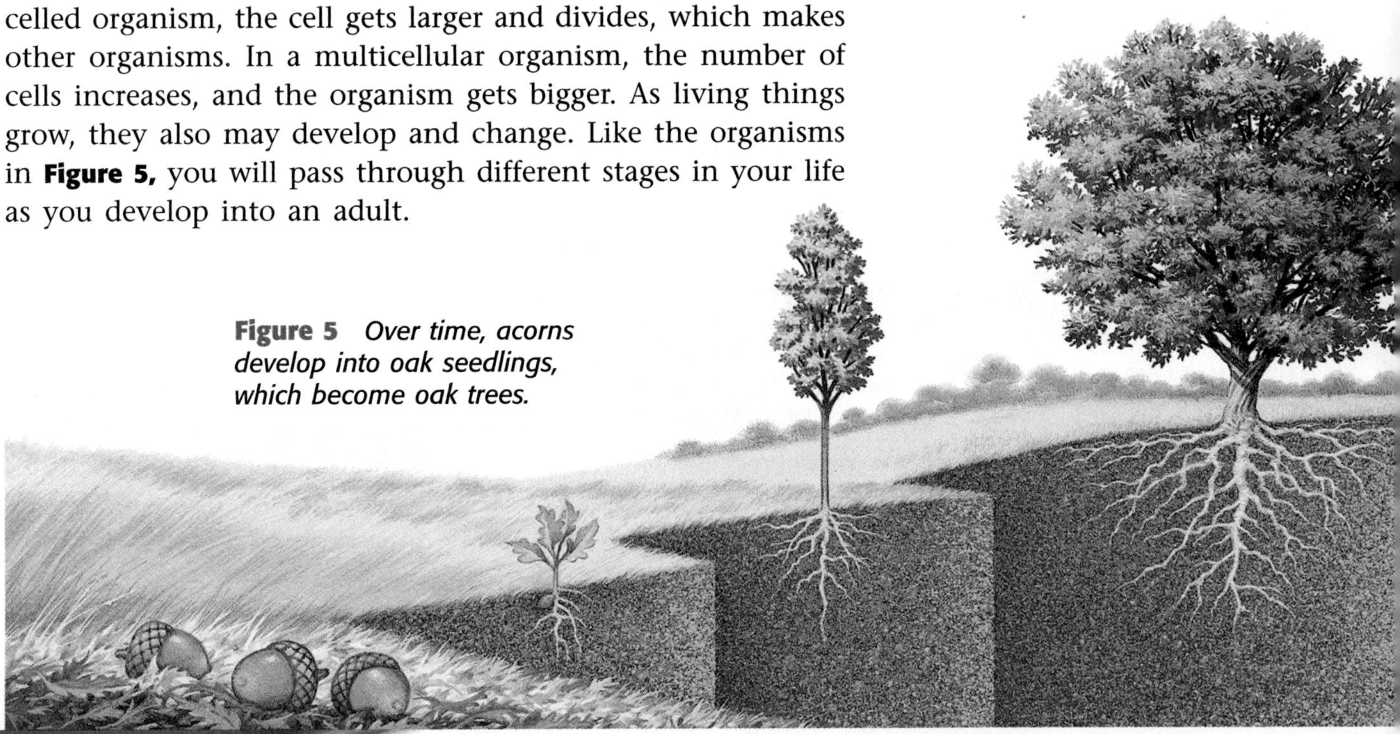

Figure 5 *Over time, acorns develop into oak seedlings, which become oak trees.*

SECTION Review

7.1.a, 7.2.a

Summary

- Organisms are made up of one or more cells.
- Organisms detect and respond to stimuli.
- Organisms reproduce through sexual or asexual reproduction.
- Organisms have DNA.
- Organisms use energy to carry out their activities.
- Organisms grow and develop.

Using Vocabulary

Complete each of the following sentences by choosing the correct term from the word bank.

cells — stimulus
homeostasis — metabolism

1. Sunlight can be a ___.
2. Living things are made of ___.

Understanding Concepts

3. **Describing** Describe the six characteristics of living things.
4. **Comparing** Explain the two types of reproduction.

Critical Thinking

5. **Applying Concepts** How are traits of parents passed to offspring? What traits might be passed to offspring if both parents are California quails?
6. **Identifying Relationships** How is the fur coat of a bear related to homeostasis?

Math Skills

7. **Using Equations** Bacteria double every generation. If one bacterium is in the first generation, how many bacteria will be in the sixth generation?

Challenge

8. **Making Inferences** Sexual reproduction produces offspring that share characteristics from two parents. What is an advantage of sexual reproduction?

Internet Resources

For a variety of links related to this chapter, go to www.scilinks.org
Topic: Characteristics of Living Things
SciLinks code: HY70258

The Necessities of Life

Key Concept Every living thing needs water, a place to live, and food in order to survive.

7.1.a Students know cells function similarly in all living organisms.

▶ Would it surprise you to learn that you have the same basic needs as a tree, a frog, and a fly? Almost every organism has the same basic needs: water, air, a place to live, and food.

Water

You may know that your body is made mostly of water. In fact, water makes up approximately 70% of your cells and the cells of almost all living things. Most of the chemical reactions involved in metabolism require water. But organisms differ greatly in terms of how much water they need and how they get it. You could survive for only about three days without water. You get water from the fluids you drink and the food you eat. The desert-dwelling kangaroo rat never drinks. It gets all of its water from food.

Standards Check Why do cells require water? 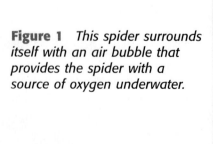 **7.1.a**

Air

Air is a mixture of several gases, including oxygen, nitrogen, and carbon dioxide. Most living things use oxygen in the chemical process that releases energy from food. Oxygen may come from the air or may be dissolved in water. The European diving spider in **Figure 1** goes to great lengths to get oxygen. Green plants, algae, and some bacteria need carbon dioxide as well as oxygen. They use oxygen and carbon dioxide to produce food and oxygen through the process of photosynthesis (FOHT oh SIN thuh sis).

Although most living things need air, some do not. Organisms that can live without air are *anaerobic*. A kind of bacterium that causes sickness in humans, *Clostridium botulinum,* is anaerobic. It will not grow in the presence of air.

Figure 1 *This spider surrounds itself with an air bubble that provides the spider with a source of oxygen underwater.*

A Place to Live

All living things need a place to live that has all of the things that they need to survive. Some organisms, such as elephants, must have a large amount of space. Other organisms may live their entire life in one small area.

Space on Earth is limited. Often, organisms must compete with each other for food, water, and other necessities. Many animals, including the warbler in **Figure 2,** will claim a particular space. After claiming a space, they try to keep other animals away.

Food

All living things need food. Food gives organisms energy and the raw materials needed to carry out life processes. Organisms use nutrients from food to make cells and build body parts. But not all organisms get food in the same way. In fact, every kind of organism can be placed into one of three groups based on how it gets food.

Making Food

Some organisms, such as plants, are producers. **Producers** make their own food through photosynthesis. Like most producers, plants use the sun's energy to make food from water and carbon dioxide. Some producers get energy and food from the chemicals in their environment.

Taking Food

Other organisms are consumers. **Consumers** must eat (consume) other organisms, such as plants or animals, to get food. The frog in **Figure 3** is a consumer. It gets the energy that it needs by eating insects and other organisms.

Some consumers get their food by breaking down the nutrients in dead organisms or in animal wastes. These organisms are **decomposers.** Decomposers are consumers because they must eat their food. The mushroom in **Figure 3** is a decomposer.

Figure 2 *A warbler's song is more than just a pretty tune. The warbler is protecting its home by telling other warblers to stay out of its territory.*

producer (proh DOOS uhr) an organism that can make its own food by using energy from its surroundings

consumer (kuhn SOOM uhr) an organism that eats other organisms or organic matter

decomposer (DEE kuhm POHZ uhr) an organism that gets energy by breaking down the remains of dead organisms or animal wastes and consuming or absorbing the nutrients

Figure 3 *The frog is a consumer. The mushroom is a decomposer. The green plants are producers.*

protein (PROH TEEN) a molecule that is made up of amino acids and that is needed to build and repair body structures and to regulate processes in the body

carbohydrate (CAHR boh HIE drayt) a class of molecules that includes sugars, starches, and fiber

Putting It All Together

Some living things make their own food. Some get food from eating other organisms. But all organisms need to break down their food in order to use the nutrients in it.

Nutrients are made up of molecules. A *molecule* is a substance made when two or more atoms join together. Molecules made of different kinds of atoms are *compounds*. Molecules found in living things are most often combinations of six elements: carbon, hydrogen, nitrogen, oxygen, phosphorus, and sulfur. These elements join together to form proteins, carbohydrates, lipids, ATP, and nucleic acids.

Proteins

Almost all life processes of a cell involve proteins. **Proteins** are large molecules that are made up of smaller molecules called *amino acids*. Living things break down proteins in food to supply their cells with amino acids. These amino acids then join together to form new proteins. Some proteins are made up of only a few amino acids. Others have more than 10,000 amino acids.

Proteins in Action

Proteins have many functions. Some proteins form structures that are easy to see, such as the examples in **Figure 4.** Other proteins are very small and help cells do their jobs. Inside red blood cells, the protein hemoglobin (HEE moh GLOH bin) binds oxygen and delivers it throughout the body. Some proteins protect cells. Other proteins, called *enzymes* (EN ziemz), start or speed up chemical reactions in cells.

Standards Check What function do enzymes in cells serve?
7.1.a

Figure 4 *Spider webs, hair, horns, and feathers are made from proteins.*

Quick Lab

Observing Enzymes in Pineapples

The enzymes in pineapple break down other proteins, such as the proteins in gelatin. In this activity, you will observe how altering an enzyme affects its function.

7.1.a
7.7.c

▶ Try It!

1. Gather **two small cups of gelatin,** a **piece of prepared pineapple,** and a **piece of fresh pineapple.** The pieces of pineapple should be similar in size.

2. Use a **marker** to label one cup "Prepared" and the other cup "Fresh."

3. Place the piece of prepared pineapple on top of the gelatin in the cup labeled "Prepared." Place the piece of fresh pineapple on top of the gelatin in the cup labeled "Fresh."

4. After 20 min, record your observations.

▶ Think About It!

5. Did the enzymes in the fresh pineapple break down the proteins in the gelatin? Explain your answer.

6. Did the enzymes in the prepared pineapple break down the proteins in the gelatin? Explain your answer.

7. The prepared pineapple was heated to denature its enzymes. To *denature* something is to remove the natural qualities of an object, such as its shape. Denaturing an enzyme makes it unable to perform its function. What might happen to a cell if all of its enzymes were denatured?

🕐 30 min

Carbohydrates

Molecules made of sugars are called **carbohydrates.** Carbohydrates provide and store energy for cells. A living thing's cells break down carbohydrates to free the energy that carbohydrates store. There are two kinds of carbohydrates: simple carbohydrates and complex carbohydrates.

Simple Carbohydrates

Simple carbohydrates are made up of one sugar molecule or a few sugar molecules. Table sugar and the sugar in fruits are examples of simple carbohydrates. The simple carbohydrate *glucose* is the most common source of energy for cells.

Complex Carbohydrates

When an organism has more sugar than it needs, its extra sugar may be stored as complex carbohydrates. *Complex carbohydrates* are made up of hundreds of sugar molecules linked together. Plants, such as the potato plant in **Figure 5,** store extra sugar as starch. When you eat mashed potatoes, you are eating the stored starch of the potato plant. Your body then breaks down this complex carbohydrate to free the energy stored in the potato.

Figure 5 *The extra sugar in a potato plant is stored in the potato as starch, a complex carbohydrate.*

Figure 6 Phospholipid Membranes

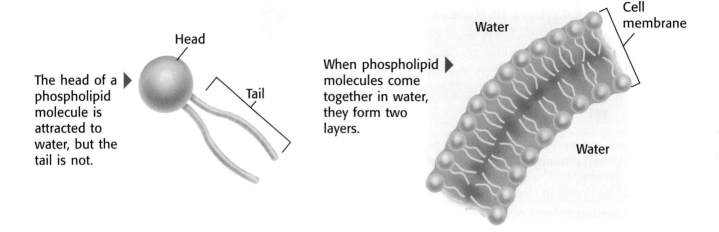

Head

Tail

The head of a phospholipid molecule is attracted to water, but the tail is not.

Water

Cell membrane

When phospholipid molecules come together in water, they form two layers.

Water

lipid (LIP id) a fat molecule or a molecule that has similar properties

phospholipid (FAHS foh LIP id) a lipid that contains phosphorus and that is a structural component in cell membranes
 Wordwise The root *phospho-* means "containing phosphorus." The root *lip-* means "fat."

ATP (AY TEE PEE) adenosine triphosphate, a molecule that acts as the main energy source for cell processes

nucleic acid (noo KLEE ik AS id) a molecule made up of subunits called *nucleotides*

Lipids

Lipids are molecules that cannot mix with water. Lipids have many jobs in the cell. Like carbohydrates, some lipids store energy. Other lipids form the membranes of cells.

Phospholipids

All cells are surrounded by a *cell membrane*. The cell membrane helps protect the cell and maintain homeostasis. **Phospholipids** are molecules that form much of the cell membrane. The head of a phospholipid molecule is attracted to water. The tail is not. When phospholipids are in water, the tails come together and the heads face out into the water. As **Figure 6** shows, the phospholipids form a two–layer membrane. This membrane protects the cell by making it difficult for materials to move into or out of the cell.

Standards Check List two functions of cell membranes. 🐻 **7.1.a**

Fats and Oils

Fats and oils are lipids that store energy. When an organism has used up most of its carbohydrates, it can get energy from these lipids. Fats and oils are almost the same in structure, but at room temperature, most fats are solid, and most oils are liquid. Most of the lipids stored in plants are oils. Most of the lipids stored in animals are fats.

ATP

Adenosine **tri**phosphate (uh DEN uh SEEN trie FAHS FAYT), or ATP, is another important molecule. **ATP** is the major energy-carrying molecule of cells. The energy in carbohydrates and lipids is transferred to ATP to provide fuel for cellular activities.

Pen a Menu

With an adult, write a menu for a favorite meal. Using Nutrition Facts labels, find out which items on your menu include proteins, carbohydrates, and fats.

Nucleic Acids

Nucleic acids are molecules that carry the directions for how to make proteins. Nucleic acids are made up of smaller molecules called *nucleotides* (NOO klee oh TIEDZ). A nucleic acid may have thousands of nucleotides. The nucleotide sequence stores information.

DNA is a nucleic acid. A DNA molecule is like a cookbook called *How to Make Proteins*. When a cell needs to make a certain protein, the cell gets directions from the sequence of the nucleotides in DNA. The sequence of nucleotides tells the cell the order in which the amino acids must be linked together to make the protein.

INTERNET ACTIVITY

Newfound Pet

What kind of information would help you properly care for a new pet? Write a short story about living with an unusual pet. Go to **go.hrw.com,** and type in the keyword HY7ALVW.

SECTION Review

7.1.a

Summary

- The cells of living things need water to function.
- The cells of some living things need gases, such as oxygen, to release the energy contained in food.
- Living things must have a place to live.
- Cells store energy in carbohydrates, which are made up of sugars.
- Proteins are made up of amino acids. Some proteins are enzymes.
- Lipids store energy and make up cell membranes.
- Cells use molecules of ATP to fuel their activities.
- Nucleic acids, such as DNA, are made up of nucleotides.

Understanding Concepts

1. **Summarizing** Summarize the way plants store extra sugar.

2. **Listing** List four things that all organisms need to survive.

3. **Describing** Describe the chemical building blocks of cells.

4. **Analyzing** How is water related to how a cell functions?

5. **Applying** What are the functions of the cell membrane?

Critical Thinking

6. **Making Inferences** Could life as we know it exist on Earth if air contained only oxygen? Explain.

7. **Predicting Consequences** What would happen to the supply of ATP in your cells if you ate too few carbohydrates? How would your cells be affected?

8. **Applying Concepts** Which resource do you think is most important to your survival: water, air, a place to live, or food? Explain your answer.

INTERPRETING GRAPHICS Use the figure below to answer the next question.

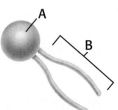

9. **Forming Hypotheses** Which end of the phospholipid is not attracted to water? How might this fact affect the arrangement of phospholipids in a cell membrane?

Math Skills

10. **Using Equations** Protein A is a chain of 660 amino acids. Protein B is a chain of 11 amino acids. How many times as many amino acids does protein A have than protein B?

Internet Resources

For a variety of links related to this chapter, go to www.scilinks.org

Topic: The Necessities of Life

SciLinks code: HY71018

Skills Practice Lab

Comparing Methods of Reproduction

Simulate methods of plant reproduction.

Compare sexual and asexual reproduction in plants.

- *Coleus* (whole plant)
- flower, complete
- flower seeds
- magnifying lens
- Petri dishes (2)
- pipe cleaner
- potting soil (1 cup)
- scissors

SAFETY

All types of organisms reproduce. Living things reproduce either by sexual reproduction or by asexual reproduction. In sexual reproduction, offspring are produced by two parents. As a result of this process, the offspring share traits from both parents. During asexual reproduction, a new individual is produced from one parent. This individual is an exact copy of the parent.

Plants can reproduce sexually or asexually. Some plants can use both methods to reproduce. During sexual reproduction, seeds are produced in the flower. Seed formation requires *pollination,* the transfer of pollen from the anther to the stigma. Although some plants can self-pollinate, pollination typically requires help from the wind, birds, and insects. Asexual methods of reproduction include planting runners, cuttings, and specialized plant parts from grown plants.

Part A: Sexual Reproduction

Procedure

1 Use the image of the flower below to identify the anthers and stigma of your flower. Observe them with your magnifying lens.

2 Gently brush the anthers with the pipe cleaner. Anthers are part of the male reproductive structure of a flower. Observe the pipe cleaner through the magnifying lens. You should see grains of pollen. Pollen contains male genetic information.

7.2.a Students know the differences between the life cycles and reproduction methods of sexual and asexual organisms.

Investigation and Experimentation
7.7.c Communicate the logical connection among hypotheses, science concepts, tests conducted, data collected, and conclusions drawn from the scientific evidence.

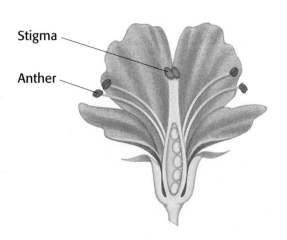

Stigma

Anther

③ Trade flowers with another group of students. Identify the stigma. The stigma is part of the female reproductive structure of a flower. The female reproductive structure contains the female genetic information.

④ Gently brush the same pipe cleaner on the stigma. You have now pollinated the flower.

⑤ Use your magnifying lens to study the flower seeds. These seeds are similar to those that your flower might have produced. The genetic information stored in seeds is a combination of the male and female genetic information.

⑥ Place one or two flower seeds in a Petri dish filled with moist potting soil.

Part B: Asexual Reproduction

Procedure

⑦ Snip off a tip from an actively growing *Coleus* stem. The cutting should be about 6 cm in length. Remove leaves from the bottom third of the cutting.

⑧ Place the cutting in a dish filled with moist potting soil.

Analyze the Results

⑨ **Explaining Events** How did you simulate asexual plant reproduction in this lab? How did you simulate sexual plant reproduction?

⑩ **Recognizing Patterns** Predict what the offspring will look like from each method of reproduction. Explain your predictions.

Draw Conclusions

⑪ **Interpreting Information** Examine the image above that shows an assortment of *Coleus* plants. Do you think that these plants were cuttings from the same parent plant? Explain.

⑫ **Drawing Conclusions** Can all organisms reproduce both sexually and asexually?

⑬ **Evaluating Methods** Compare sexual and asexual reproduction.

Big Idea Question

⑭ **Applying Conclusions** What is an advantage of sexual reproduction? What is an advantage of asexual reproduction?

Science Skills Activity

Investigation and Experimentation

7.7.a Select and use appropriate tools and technology (including calculators, computers, balances, spring scales, microscopes, and binoculars) to perform tests, collect data, and display data.

Selecting Tools to Collect Data

▶ Tutorial

Scientists ask many questions about the natural world, so they conduct experiments to find answers. To perform an experiment and communicate the results, scientists must choose the correct equipment and tools. It is very important to select these tools before beginning the experiment so that data are not lost.

Procedure

1 Write a question on a subject that you want to investigate. Then, write a hypothesis to explain your question. The hypothesis must be testable. If the hypothesis is not testable, revise it.

2 List all of the different things, or factors, that could influence the experiment's outcome. Choose one factor that you will test.

3 Write a list of all of the materials needed to perform your experiment. This list should include safety equipment.

4 Determine the scientific equipment and tools that you will need for observing, measuring, recording, analyzing, and communicating data.

1 *Question: Does ice exist at room temperature?*
Hypothesis: Ice melts at room temperature.

2 *Factors:*
– temperature
– purity of water
– time

3 *Materials:*
– water
– ice cubes
– cups

4 *Scientific Equipment Tools:*
– calculator   – thermometers
– binoculars   – graph paper

▶ You Try It!

Procedure

You are a scientist on the *Intergalactic Beagle Starship Explorer*. When your starship discovers a new planet, your job is to determine if there are any lifeforms on the planet. On one mission, you find many small, yellow blobs. Use the steps above to plan the experiment(s) and to select the appropriate equipment and tools to determine if the blobs are alive.

Analysis

1 **Forming a Hypothesis** What question are you asking? How does your hypothesis offer an explanation to your question?

2 **Analyzing Ideas** List the factors that you will be testing. How will you experiment for each factor?

3 **Analyzing Methods** What equipment and tools will you need for each experiment?

4 **Making Comparisons** Which of the following tools is best for determining whether your blob is made up of cells: a balance, a microscope, or binoculars? Explain your answer.

5 **Predicting Consequences** What might happen if you select inappropriate tools for your experiment? What might happen if you do not have the correct safety equipment?

Chapter Summary

The Big Idea All living things share characteristics and needs.

| **Section** | **Vocabulary** |

1 Characteristics of Living Things

Key Concept Living things have six characteristics in common.

- Living things are composed of one or more cells.
- Living things sense and respond to changes in their environment.
- Living things produce offspring through sexual reproduction or asexual reproduction.
- The cells of living things contain DNA.
- Living things use energy.
- Living things grow and develop.

An acorn develops into an oak tree.

cell p. 52
homeostasis p. 53
sexual reproduction p. 54
asexual reproduction p. 54
metabolism p. 54

2 The Necessities of Life

Key Concept Every living thing needs water, a place to live, and food in order to survive.

- The cells of every living thing need water and food in order to function properly.
- Proteins, carbohydrates, lipids, ATP, and nucleic acids are molecules that support the functions of cells.

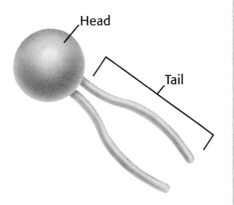

Head

Tail

A phospholipid is the type of lipid found in cell membranes.

producer p. 57
consumer p. 57
decomposer p. 57
protein p. 58
carbohydrate p. 59
lipid p. 60
phospholipid p. 60
ATP p. 60
nucleic acid p. 61

Chapter Review

Organize

Double Door Review the FoldNote that you created at the beginning of the chapter. Add to or correct the FoldNote based on what you have learned.

Using Vocabulary

1 **Academic Vocabulary** Choose the appropriate form of the word *similar* for the following sentence: "Cells function ___ in all organisms."
a. similarity
b. similar
c. similarly
d. dissimilar

Complete each of the following sentences by choosing the correct terms from the word bank.

lipid	carbohydrate
consumer	metabolism
homeostasis	producer

2 All of the chemical activities of an organism are the organism's ___.

3 A ___ obtains food by eating other organisms.

4 Starch is a ___ and is made up of sugars.

5 Fat is a ___ that stores energy for an organism.

Understanding Concepts

Multiple Choice

6 Which of the following statements about cells is true?
a. Cells are the smallest structural unit of life.
b. All organisms are made up of cells.
c. Sometimes, cells are specialized for particular functions.
d. All of the above

7 Which of the following statements about all living things is true?
a. All living things reproduce sexually.
b. All living things have one or more cells.
c. All living things must make their own food.
d. All living things reproduce asexually.

8 Organisms must have food because
a. food is a source of energy.
b. food supplies cells with oxygen.
c. organisms never make their own food.
d. All of the above

9 Organisms store energy in
a. nucleic acids.
b. phospholipids.
c. lipids.
d. water.

10 The molecule that contains the information about how to make proteins is
a. ATP.
b. a carbohydrate.
c. DNA.
d. a phospholipid.

11 The subunits of nucleic acids are
a. nucleotides.
b. oils.
c. sugars.
d. amino acids.

Short Answer

12 **Comparing** What is the difference between asexual reproduction and sexual reproduction?

13 **Summarizing** In one or two sentences, explain why living things must have water.

14 **Identifying** What is ATP, and why is it important to a cell?

INTERPRETING GRAPHICS Use the table below to answer the next two questions.

Characteristics of Three Living Organisms			
Organism	A	B	C
Comparison to parent(s)	slightly different	similar	identical

15 **Applying** Juan is studying three different organisms so that he can classify them according to how much each organism is like its parent. The table shows the characteristics of the three different organisms. Which of the organisms that Juan studied could have been produced from a single parent?

16 **Comparing** Juan adds organism D to the table. The organism has been produced through sexual reproduction. How will organism D compare to its parent(s)?

Writing Skills

17 Creative Writing You find a strange creature while walking on the beach one day. In a short story, describe the creature, including how it displays the six characteristics of living things.

Critical Thinking

18 Concept Mapping Use the following terms to create a concept map: *cell, carbohydrates, protein, enzymes, DNA, sugars, lipids, nucleotides, amino acids,* and *nucleic acid.*

19 Applying Concepts Using what you know about carbohydrates, lipids, and proteins, explain why a balanced diet is important?

20 Evaluating Hypotheses Your friend tells you that the stimulus of music makes his goldfish swim faster. How would you design a controlled experiment to test your friend's claim?

21 Analyzing Ideas A flame can move, grow larger, and give off heat. Is a flame alive? Explain.

INTERPRETING GRAPHICS Use the diagram below to answer the next two questions.

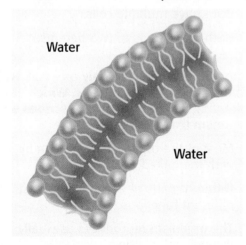

22 Evaluating Data What part of the cell does this image show?

23 Analyzing Relationships What is the function of this part of the cell?

INTERPRETING GRAPHICS The pictures below show the same plant over a period of three days. Use the pictures below to answer the next two questions.

24 Evaluating Data What is the plant doing?

25 Applying Concepts What characteristic(s) of living things is the plant exhibiting?

Math Skills

26 Using Equations A young tree grows 6 cm per year. Use the equation *height* = 6 cm × *number of years* to find how many years the tree would take to grow 1 m.

Challenge

27 Making Comparisons Some reptiles are able to grow a new tail if their original tail has been damaged or lost. Does this ability fit the description of asexual reproduction? Why or why not?

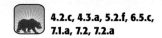
REVIEWING ACADEMIC VOCABULARY

1 Which of the following words is closest in meaning to the word *function*?

A control

B standard

C use

D rate

2 In the sentence "The cell membranes of all cells work similarly," what does the word *similarly* mean?

A from the start

B by cell division

C without interest

D in almost the same way

3 Which of the following words means "to define or describe in detail"?

A specify

B stimulate

C personalize

D associate

4 Which of the following words best completes the following sentence: The cell membrane of a one-celled animal protects the animal from ___ dangers.

A pivotal

B insignificant

C harmful

D environmental

REVIEWING CONCEPTS

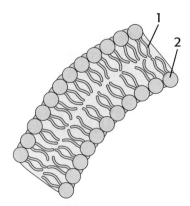

5 Which part of the phospholipid membrane is found at point 1 in the diagram above?

A water–loving tail

B water–loving head

C water–hating tail

D water–hating head

6 New organisms are created either by sexual or asexual reproduction. How are offspring produced sexually and offspring produced asexually similar?

A Both are identical to one parent.

B Both have DNA.

C Both have multiple cells.

D Both share traits of two parents.

7 Some organisms have only one cell, while others have trillions of cells. Which of the following statements best describes an organism that has many cells?

A Most of the organism's cells can be seen with the naked eye.

B Different parts of each cell perform different functions.

C The organism reproduces asexually through cell division.

D Different kinds of cells perform specialized functions.

8 You may think that humans do not have anything in common with a bacterium, but they do! Which of the following sentences best describes what bacteria and humans have in common?

A Both are multicellular organisms.

B Both reproduce sexually.

C Both are warmblooded.

D Both have DNA.

9 Proteins play a role in most cell processes. What do cells make proteins from?

A amino acids

B lipids

C nucleic acids

D carbohydrates

10 Which of the following sentences best describes how DNA affects heredity?

A DNA ensures that traits of the parent are passed to the offspring.

B The order of DNA nucleotides tells a cell how to make proteins.

C DNA controls the structure and function of cells in all organisms.

D Nucleic acids such as DNA are sometimes called the "blueprints of life."

11 Which of the following functions can be performed by a hydra but cannot be performed by a California quail?

A A hydra can reproduce without a partner.

B A hydra can divide cells through mitosis.

C A hydra can maintain homeostasis in cells.

D A hydra can pass traits to offspring.

REVIEWING PRIOR LEARNING

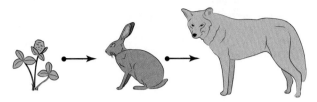

12 Which term best describes the rabbit in the food chain pictured above?

A omnivore

B top-level predator

C carnivore

D primary consumer

13 Plants make food through photosynthesis. What waste product do plants excrete as a result of this chemical process?

A carbon dioxide

B nitrogen

C oxygen

D sugar

14 Which group of organisms completes the food chain by returning nutrients to the soil?

A primary consumers

B secondary consumers

C decomposers

D producers

15 The nonliving components of an ecosystem are called

A abiotic components.

B rock cycles.

C natural disasters.

D organisms.

Standards Assessment

Science in Action

Weird Science

Breathing Arsenic

Searles Lake in the Mojave Desert of California isn't like most lakes. It's mostly salt-crusted ooze that smells like a combination of rotten eggs, dead fish, and old cheese. To top things off, Searles Lake contains extreme levels of deadly arsenic.

Scientists never expected to find organisms living in Searles Lake. Incredibly, one organism thrives in the poisonous lake. This organism, a bacterium named *SLAS-1,* is an extremophile. Extremophiles can exist in extreme environments where most other living things cannot. For example, most organisms need oxygen, but there is no oxygen in the ooze at Searles Lake. Instead, SLAS-1 uses arsenic for its cellular activities.

Math ACTIVITY

Searles Lake contains levels of arsenic that are 29,000 times as high as the levels in drinking water! If there are 0.01 mg of arsenic in 1 L of drinking water, how many grams of arsenic are in half of that volume at Searles Lake? Record your work in your **Science Journal.**

Science Fiction

"They're Made Out of Meat" by Terry Bisson

Two space explorers millions of light-years from home are visiting an uncharted sector of the universe to find signs of life. Their mission is to contact, welcome, and log any and all beings in this part of the universe.

During their mission, the explorers encounter a life-form quite unlike anything that they have ever seen before. It looks strange and disgusting. The explorers have very strong doubts about adding this new organism to the log. But their official duty is to contact and welcome all life-forms no matter how ugly they are. Can the explorers bring themselves to perform their duty?

You'll find out by reading "They're Made Out of Meat," a short story by Terry Bisson. This story is in the *Holt Anthology of Science Fiction.*

Language Arts ACTIVITY

Write a story about what happens when the explorers meet new creatures on a distant planet. Record your work in your **Science Journal.**

Janis Davis-Street

NASA Nutritionist Do astronauts eat shrimp cocktail in space? Yes, they do! Shrimp cocktail is nutritious and tastes so good that it is one of the most popular foods in the space program. And having a proper diet helps astronauts stay healthy while they are in space.

But who figures out what astronauts need to eat? Janis Davis-Street is a nutritionist and laboratory supervisor for the Nutritional Biochemistry Laboratory at the Johnson Space Center in Houston, Texas. She was born in Georgetown, Guyana, on the northeastern coast of South America. She was educated in Canada.

Davis-Street is part of a team whose members use their knowledge of nutrition, biology, and chemistry to figure out the nutritional requirements for spaceflight. For example, they determine how many Calories and other nutrients each astronaut needs per day during spaceflight.

The Nutritional Biochemistry Laboratory's work on the space shuttle missions and *Mir* space station developed into tests that allow NASA to help ensure the health of astronauts before, during, and after flight. These tests are important for understanding how the human body adapts to long space missions. They also help determine whether treatments for preventing bone and muscle loss during spaceflight are working.

Social Studies ACTiViTY

Scientists from more than 30 countries have been on space missions. Research which countries have provided astronauts or cosmonauts for space missions. On a map, place self-stick notes on countries that have provided scientists for space missions. Write the names of the appropriate scientists on the self-stick notes.

Internet Resources

- To learn more about careers in science, visit **www.scilinks.org** and enter the SciLinks code HY70225.

- To learn more about these Science in Action topics, visit **go.hrw.com** and type in the keyword HY7ALVF.

- Check out articles related to this chapter by visiting **go.hrw.com**. Just type in the keyword HY7ALVC.

Improving Comprehension

Graphic Organizers are important visual tools that can help you organize information and improve your reading comprehension. The Graphic Organizer below is called a *cause-and-effect map*. Instructions for creating other types of Graphic Organizers are located in the **Study Skills** section of the Appendix.

How to Make a Cause-and-Effect Map

1 Draw a box, and write a cause in the box. You can have as many cause boxes as you want. The diagram shown here is one example of a cause-and-effect map.

2 Draw another box to the right of the cause box to represent an effect. You can have as many effect boxes as you want. Draw arrows from each cause box to the appropriate effect boxes.

3 In the cause boxes, explain the process that makes up the cause. In the effect boxes, write a description of the effect or details about the effect.

When to Use a Cause-and-Effect Map

A cause-and-effect map is a useful tool for illustrating a specific type of scientific process. Use a cause-and-effect map when you want to describe how, when, or why one event causes another event. As you read, look for events that are either causes or results of other events, and draw a cause-and-effect map that shows the relationships between the events.

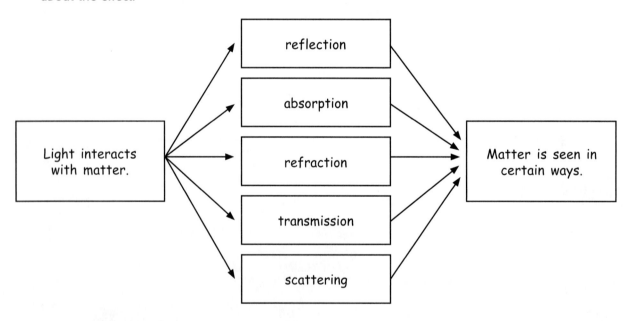

You Try It!

This Reading Strategy can also be used within the chapter that you are about to read. Practice making your own *cause-and-effect map* as directed in the Reading Strategy for Section **1**. Record your work in your **Science Journal.**

Unpacking the Standards

The information below "unpacks" the standards by breaking them down into basic parts. The higher-level, academic vocabulary is highlighted and defined to help you understand the language of the standards. "What It Means" restates the standards as simply as possible.

California Standard	Academic Vocabulary	What It Means
7.6.a Students know **visible** light is a small band within a very broad electromagnetic spectrum.	**visible** (VIZ uh buhl) that can be seen	The light you are able to see is just a small part of the range of radiation that surrounds you.
7.6.b Students know that for an object to be seen, light emitted by or scattered from it must be **detected** by the eye.	**detect** (dee TEKT) to notice	For you to see an object, the light that is given off by an object or that bounces off an object must enter your eye.
7.6.c Students know light travels in straight lines if the **medium** it travels through does not change.	**medium** (MEE dee uhm) a substance through which something else is sent or carried	Light moves in a straight line if the light passes through only one kind of material.
7.6.d Students know how simple lenses are used in a magnifying glass, the eye, a camera, a telescope, and a microscope.		You must know how simple lenses are used in a magnifying glass, the eye, a camera, a telescope, and a microscope.
7.6.e Students know that white light is a mixture of many wavelengths (colors) and that retinal cells **react** differently to different wavelengths.	**react** (ree AKT) to act in return; to respond	White light consists of many wavelengths of radiation, or colors. Cells in the back of human eyes respond to these different wavelengths in different ways.
7.6.f Students know light can be reflected, refracted, **transmitted,** and absorbed by matter.	**transmit** (trans MIT) to send or cause to go from one thing to another	Light can be reflected, bent (refracted), transmitted, and absorbed by matter.
7.6.g Students know the angle of reflection of a light beam is equal to the angle of **incidence.**	**incidence** (IN suh duhns) the point at which a line or something moving in a straight line, such as a ray of light, meets a surface	The angle at which light will bounce off of a mirror is the same angle at which the light hits the mirror's surface.

3

Light and Living Things

The Big Idea

Light is an electromagnetic wave that interacts with matter in many different ways.

 California Standards

Focus on Life Sciences
7.6 Physical principles underlie biological structures and functions. (Sections 1, 2, and 3)

Investigation and Experimentation
7.7 Scientific progress is made by asking meaningful questions and conducting careful investigations. (Science Skills Activity)

Math
6.2.1 Algebra and Functions

English–Language Arts
7.1.3, 7.2.3 Reading
7.2.5 Writing

About the Photo

What kind of alien life is this? Actually, these glowing blobs are animals that live off the coast of California. These jellyfish are bioluminescent, which means that they produce their own light. Many bioluminescent animals live in the oceans, but others, such as fireflies, live on land.

Organize

Key-Term Fold

Before you read the chapter, create the FoldNote entitled "Key-Term Fold." Write a key term from the chapter on each tab of the key-term fold. As you read the chapter, write the definition of each key term under the appropriate tab.

Instructions for creating FoldNotes are located in the Study Skills section on p. 581 of the Appendix.

Seeing Colors of Light

Is white light really white? In this activity, you will use a spectroscope to answer that question. A spectroscope is a device that separates light into different colors.

Procedure

1. Your teacher will give you a **spectroscope** or instructions for making one.

2. Turn on an **incandescent light bulb.** Look at the light bulb through your spectroscope. Write a description of what you see.

3. Repeat step 2 by using a **fluorescent light.** Again, describe what you see.

Analysis

4. Compare what you saw by using the incandescent light bulb with what you saw by using the fluorescent light bulb.

5. Both kinds of bulbs produce white light. What did you learn about white light by using the spectroscope?

6. Light from a flame is yellowish but is similar to white light. What do you think you would see if you used a spectroscope to look at light from a flame?

The Electromagnetic Spectrum

Key Concept Visible light, infrared waves, and ultraviolet light are small parts of a large electromagnetic spectrum.

When you look around, you can see things that reflect light to your eyes. But a bee might see the same things differently, as **Figure 1** shows. Bees can see a kind of light—called *ultraviolet light*—that you can't see!

It might seem odd to label something that you can't see with the term *light*. The light that you are most familiar with is called *visible light*. Ultraviolet light is similar to visible light. Both are forms of energy that travel as a certain kind of wave.

Light: An Electromagnetic Wave

Some kinds of waves, such as water waves, must travel through *matter,* which is anything that has mass and takes up space. All light waves can also travel through matter. But light does not need matter through which to travel. Light is an electromagnetic wave (EM wave). An **electromagnetic wave** is a wave that consists of changing electric and magnetic fields. EM waves can travel through empty space or matter.

Fields exist around certain objects and can exert a force on another object without touching that object. The electric field in an EM wave is similar to the electric fields around charged particles. And the magnetic field in an EM wave is similar to the magnetic fields around magnets. But keep in mind that these fields, like all fields, are not made of matter.

Figure 1 *The petals of the flower on the right look solid yellow to you. But a bee looking at the same flower can see the ultraviolet markings, which are shown in the flower on the left. These markings direct the bee to the center of the flower.*

Figure 2 The Electromagnetic Spectrum

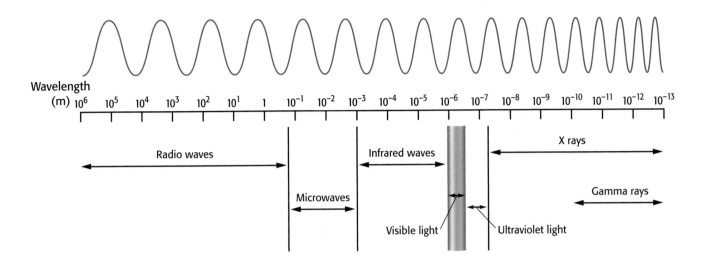

Wavelength
(m) 10^6 10^5 10^4 10^3 10^2 10^1 1 10^{-1} 10^{-2} 10^{-3} 10^{-4} 10^{-5} 10^{-6} 10^{-7} 10^{-8} 10^{-9} 10^{-10} 10^{-11} 10^{-12} 10^{-13}

Radio waves

Microwaves

Infrared waves

Visible light

Ultraviolet light

X rays

Gamma rays

A Spectrum of Waves

Visible light waves and ultraviolet light waves are both kinds of electromagnetic waves. Other kinds of EM waves include radio waves, infrared waves, and X rays. Visible light, ultraviolet light, and infrared waves are important to living things.

The entire range of electromagnetic waves is called the **electromagnetic spectrum.** The electromagnetic spectrum is shown in **Figure 2.** As you can see, visible light is only a small band within the broad electromagnetic spectrum. There is no sharp division between one kind of wave and the next. Some kinds even have overlapping ranges.

Standards Check What is the electromagnetic spectrum? 🐻 **7.6.a**

Wavelength and the EM Spectrum

You probably know how different kinds of EM waves are used. For example, microwaves are used to cook food in microwave ovens. Radio waves are used to send TV and radio signals. And X rays are used in X-ray machines to make images of tissues and bones. How is one kind of EM wave different from other kinds of EM waves? An important difference between kinds of EM waves is their wavelength.

A *wavelength* is the distance from any point on a wave to an identical point on the next wave. **Figure 3** shows how wavelength can be measured on a wave. Notice that the wavelength of the wave is the same no matter where it is measured. You can see the range of wavelengths for the different kinds of EM waves in **Figure 2.**

electromagnetic wave
(ee LEK troh mag NET ik WAYV) a wave that consists of electric and magnetic fields that vibrate at right angles to each other

electromagnetic spectrum
(ee LEK troh mag NET ik SPEK truhm) all of the frequencies or wavelengths of electromagnetic radiation

Figure 3 *Wavelength can be measured between any two corresponding points on adjacent waves.*

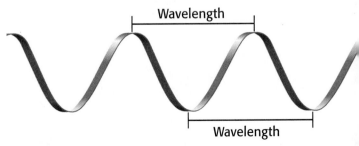

Wavelength

Wavelength

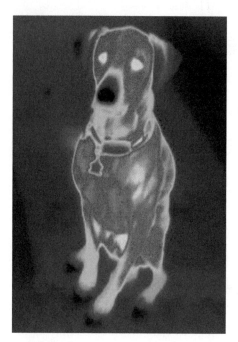

Figure 4 *In this photograph, brighter colors indicate higher temperatures. The dark color of the nose shows that this dog has a cold nose!*

Infrared Waves

Infrared waves are EM waves that have wavelengths between 700 nanometers and 1 mm. A nanometer (nm) is equal to 0.000000001 m. The size of an atom is about 0.1 nm.

Infrared waves are important to living things. On a sunny day, you may be warmed by infrared waves from the sun. The sun also warms other things on Earth and even warms Earth itself! In fact, infrared waves from the sun keep the temperatures on Earth suitable for life.

All things, including buildings, trees, animals, and you, give off infrared waves. The amount of infrared waves an object gives off depends on the object's temperature and the properties of the object's surface. Warmer objects give off more infrared waves than cooler objects do. You can see the temperature differences on the surface of a dog in **Figure 4.** This photo was taken with film that is sensitive to infrared waves.

Visible Light

Visible light is the very narrow range of wavelengths in the electromagnetic spectrum that humans can see. Visible light waves have wavelengths between 400 nm and 700 nm.

Visible light energy is changed into chemical energy by green plants during photosynthesis, as shown in **Figure 5.** The chemical energy can be stored in food that you can eat.

Standards Check What range of wavelengths can humans see?
7.6.a

Figure 5 **From Light Energy to Chemical Energy**

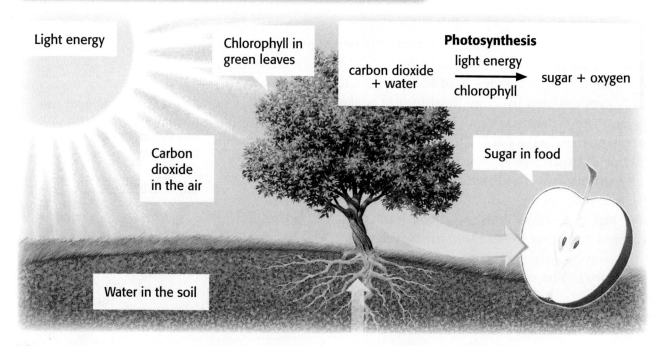

Light energy

Chlorophyll in green leaves

Photosynthesis

$$\text{carbon dioxide} + \text{water} \xrightarrow[\text{chlorophyll}]{\text{light energy}} \text{sugar} + \text{oxygen}$$

Carbon dioxide in the air

Sugar in food

Water in the soil

Figure 6 *Water droplets can separate white light into visible light of different wavelengths. As a result, you see the colors of visible light in a rainbow.*

Visible Light from the Sun

Some of the energy that reaches Earth from the sun is visible light. The visible light from the sun is white light. *White light* is visible light of all wavelengths combined. Light from lamps in your home as well as from the fluorescent bulbs in your school is also white light.

Standards Check What is white light?  **7.6.e**

Colors of Light

Cells in the human eye react differently to different wavelengths of light. As a result, humans see the different wavelengths of visible light as different colors, as shown in **Figure 6.** The longest wavelengths are seen as red light. The shortest wavelengths are seen as violet light.

The range of colors is called the *visible spectrum,* which is shown in **Figure 7.** To help you remember the colors, you can use the name *ROY G. BiV.* The capital letters in Roy's name represent the first letter of each color of visible light: **r**ed, **o**range, **y**ellow, **g**reen, **b**lue, and **v**iolet. You can think of *i* in Roy's last name as standing for the color indigo. Indigo is a dark blue color. Though the colors are given separate names, the visible spectrum is a continuous band of colors.

SCHOOL to HOME

Making a Rainbow
On a sunny day, ask an adult to use a hose or a spray bottle to make a mist of water outside. Move around until you see a rainbow in the water mist. In your **Science Journal,** draw a diagram that shows the positions of the water mist, the sun, the rainbow, and yourself.

ACTIVITY

Figure 7 *The visible spectrum contains all colors of light.*

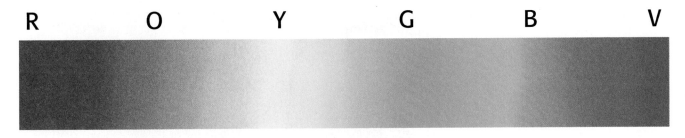

R   O   Y   G   B   V

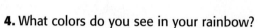

Quick Lab

Refraction Rainbow

1. **Tape** a **piece of construction paper** over the end of a **flashlight**. Use **scissors** to cut a slit in the paper.
2. Turn on the flashlight, and lay it on a table. Place a **prism** on end in the beam of light.
3. Slowly rotate the prism until you can see a rainbow on the surface of the table.

7.6.e

4. What colors do you see in your rainbow?
5. Compare the colors of the rainbow with the color of the light produced by the flashlight.

⏱ **15 min**

What's Your Frequency?

Create a brochure helping soon-to-propagate waves decide on a frequency that will meet their personal goals. Go to **go.hrw.com,** and type in the keyword **HY7LGTW.**

Ultraviolet Light

Ultraviolet light (UV light) is another kind of electromagnetic wave that affects living things. Ultraviolet waves have shorter wavelengths than visible light waves do. The wavelengths of ultraviolet light waves vary between 60 nm and 400 nm. Ultraviolet light affects your body in both bad and good ways.

Standards Check Compare ultraviolet light waves with visible light waves. 🐻 **7.6.a**

Bad Effects

On the bad side, too much ultraviolet light can cause sunburn, as you can see in **Figure 8.** Too much ultraviolet light can also cause skin cancer, wrinkles, and damage to the eyes. Luckily, much of the ultraviolet light from the sun does not reach Earth's surface. But you should still protect yourself against the ultraviolet light that does reach you. To do so, you should use sunscreen that has a high SPF (**s**un **p**rotection **f**actor). You should also wear sunglasses that block out UV light to protect your eyes. Clothes, such as hats, long-sleeved shirts, and long pants, can protect you, too. You need this protection even on overcast days because UV light can travel through clouds.

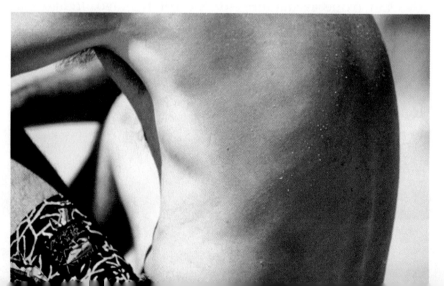

Figure 8 *Too much exposure to ultraviolet light can lead to a painful sunburn. Using sunscreen will help protect your skin.*

Good Effects

On the good side, ultraviolet light that is produced by ultraviolet lamps is used to kill bacteria on food and surgical tools. In addition, small amounts of ultraviolet light are good for your body. When exposed to ultraviolet light, skin cells produce vitamin D. This vitamin allows the intestines to absorb calcium. Without calcium, your teeth and bones would be very weak. **Figure 9** shows a good effect of ultraviolet light.

Figure 9 *Healthy teeth need calcium. Vitamin D that is produced when your skin is exposed to ultraviolet light helps your body absorb calcium.*

SECTION Review

 7.6.a, 7.6.e

Summary

- Light is an electromagnetic wave (EM wave). An EM wave can travel through matter or space.
- The entire range of EM waves is called the *electromagnetic spectrum*.
- Infrared waves from the sun warm Earth and everything on Earth.
- Visible light is the narrow range of wavelengths in the electromagnetic spectrum that humans can see.
- Humans see different wavelengths of visible light as different colors.
- Ultraviolet light is both harmful and helpful to living things.

Using Vocabulary

1. In your own words, write a definition for the term *electromagnetic spectrum*.

Understanding Concepts

2. **Comparing** Compare the size of the visible light spectrum with the size of the electromagnetic spectrum.

3. **Describing** How do the various kinds of EM waves differ from each other?

4. **Applying** Explain why ultraviolet light can be both helpful and harmful.

5. **Listing** What colors of light make up white light?

6. **Identifying** What is the visible spectrum?

Critical Thinking

7. **Applying Concepts** Describe three ways that electromagnetic waves have affected you today.

8. **Making Comparisons** Compare the wavelengths of infrared waves, ultraviolet light, and visible light.

INTERPRETING GRAPHICS Use the diagram of two EM waves below to answer the next two questions.

9. **Applying Concepts** Which wave has the longest wavelength?

10. **Analyzing Relationships** Suppose that one of the waves represents an infrared wave and that one of the waves represents a visible light wave. Which wave represents the visible light wave?

Internet Resources

For a variety of links related to this chapter, go to www.scilinks.org

Topic: Electromagnetic Spectrum
SciLinks code: HY70482

81

Interactions of Light with Matter

Key Concept Light interacts with matter during reflection, absorption, scattering, and transmission.

reflection (ri FLEK shuhn) the bouncing back of a ray of light, sound, or heat when the ray hits a surface that it does not go through

Wordwise The prefix *re-* means "again" or "back." The root *flect-* means "to bend."

▶ Have you ever seen a cat's eyes glow in the dark when light shines on them? Cats have a special layer of cells in the back of their eyes that reflects light. This layer helps the cat see better by giving the eyes a second chance to detect the light. Reflection is one interaction of light waves with matter.

Reflection

Light travels in straight lines as long as the material that the light travels through doesn't change. So, a ray of light shining through air is usually straight. One way to change the direction of a light beam is by reflection. **Reflection** is the bouncing back of light rays when they hit an object. But light doesn't change directions randomly. Instead, it follows the law of reflection.

The Law of Reflection

Light is reflected by surfaces the same way that a ball bounces off the ground. If you throw the ball straight down, it will bounce straight up. If you throw the ball at an angle, it will bounce away at an angle. The *law of reflection* states that the angle of incidence is equal to the angle of reflection. *Incidence* is the arrival of a beam of light at a surface. **Figure 1** shows this law.

Standards Check When does a ray of light travel in a straight line? What is the law of reflection? 🐻 **7.6.c, 7.6.g**

Figure 1 **The Law of Reflection**

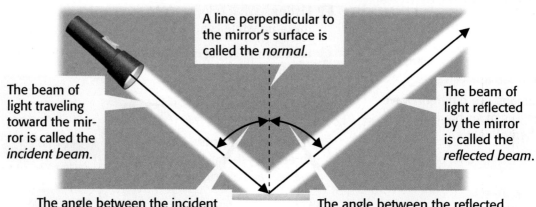

A line perpendicular to the mirror's surface is called the *normal*.

The beam of light traveling toward the mirror is called the *incident beam*.

The beam of light reflected by the mirror is called the *reflected beam*.

The angle between the incident beam and the normal is called the *angle of incidence*.

The angle between the reflected beam and the normal is called the *angle of reflection*.

Quick Lab

Reflecting Mirrors

In this activity, you will use the law of reflection to direct a beam of light.

1. Spread a sheet of **butcher paper** on a table or on the floor.

2. Lay a **flashlight** on its side on the edge of the butcher paper so that the beam of light will shine on the paper.

3. Place a **paper cup** on the edge of the paper. You can put the cup on any edge as long as the cup is not directly across from the flashlight.

4. Turn the flashlight on, and use **three small mirrors** to direct the beam of light so that the beam of light shines on the cup. Use pieces of **modeling clay** to hold each mirror in place.

7.6.c
7.6.g

5. Carefully trace the path of the beam of light on the paper. Also, trace the locations of the flashlight, the mirrors, and the cup.

6. Describe the path of the beam of light before and after the light hits a mirror.

7. Use a **protractor** to measure the angle of incidence and the angle of reflection for one mirror. Compare the angles.

🕐 **30 min**

Types of Reflection

Why can you see your image in a mirror but not in a wall? The answer has to do with the differences between the two surfaces. A mirror's surface is very smooth. Thus, light beams are reflected by all points of the mirror at the same angle. This kind of reflection is called *regular reflection*. A wall's surface is slightly rough. Light beams will hit the wall's surface and reflect at many different angles. So, the light scatters as it is reflected. This kind of reflection is called *diffuse reflection*. **Figure 2** shows the difference between the two kinds of reflection.

7.6.b Students know that for an object to be seen, light emitted by or scattered from it must be detected by the eye.
7.6.c Students know light travels in straight lines if the medium it travels through does not change.
7.6.e Students know that white light is a mixture of many wavelengths (colors) and that retinal cells react differently to different wavelengths.
7.6.f Students know light can be reflected, refracted, transmitted, and absorbed by matter.
7.6.g Students know the angle of reflection of a light beam is equal to the angle of incidence.

Figure 2 Regular Reflection Vs. Diffuse Reflection

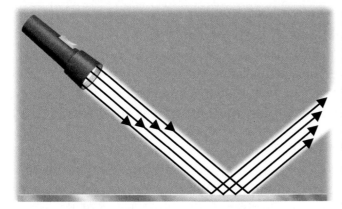

Regular reflection occurs when light beams are reflected at the same angle. When your eye detects the reflected beams, you can see a reflection on the surface.

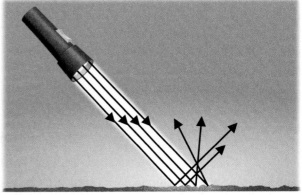

Diffuse reflection occurs when light beams reflect at many different angles. You can't see a reflection because not all of the reflected light is directed toward your eyes.

Figure 3 *You can see the tail of this firefly because it is luminous. But you see its body because it is illuminated.*

Light Source or Reflection?

If you look at a TV set in a bright room, you see the cabinet around the TV and the image on the screen. But if you look at the same TV in the dark, you see only the image on the screen. The difference is that the screen is a light source, but the cabinet around the TV is not.

You can see a light source even in the dark because light emitted by it is detected by your eyes. The tail of the firefly in **Figure 3** is a light source. Flames, light bulbs, and the sun are also light sources. Objects that emit visible light are called *luminous* (LOO muh nuhs).

Most things around you are not light sources. But you can still see them because light from light sources is reflected by the objects and then is detected by your eyes. A visible object that is not a light source is *illuminated.*

Standards Check Explain how you see luminous and illuminated objects. 🐻 **7.6.b**

Absorption and Scattering

Have you noticed that when you use a flashlight, the light is dimmer the farther it travels from the flashlight? Partly because the beam spreads out and partly because of absorption and scattering, the light is weaker the farther it is from the source.

Absorption of Light

The transfer of energy carried by light waves to particles of matter is called **absorption.** When a beam of light shines through the air, particles in the air absorb some of the energy from the light. As a result, the beam of light becomes dim. The farther the light travels from its source, the more the light is absorbed by particles, and the dimmer it becomes.

absorption (ab SAWRP shuhn) in optics, the transfer of light energy to particles of matter

Scattering of Light

Scattering is an interaction of light with matter that causes light to change direction. Light scatters in all directions after colliding with particles of matter or undergoing diffuse reflection. Light from the ship shown in **Figure 4** is scattered out of the beam by particles in the fog. This scattered light allows you to see things that are outside the beam. But because light is scattered out of the beam, the beam becomes dimmer.

Scattering makes the clear sky blue. Light that has shorter wavelengths is scattered more by particles of gas in the air than light that has longer wavelengths is. Sunlight is made up of many colors of light, but blue light (which has a very short wavelength) scatters more than any other color. So, when you look at the sky, you see a background of blue light.

Figure 4 *Partly because of scattering, a beam of light becomes dimmer the farther it is from its source.*

Light and Matter

When light hits any form of matter, the light can interact with the matter in different ways. The light can be reflected, absorbed, or transmitted.

You know that reflection happens when light bounces off an object. Reflected light allows you to see things. And you know that absorption is the transfer of light energy to matter. Absorbed light can make things feel warmer. **Transmission** is the passing of light through matter. In fact, without the transmission of light, you couldn't see! All of the light that reaches your eyes is transmitted through air and several parts of your eyes. Light can interact with matter in several ways at the same time, as **Figure 5** shows.

scattering (SKAT uhr ing) an interaction of light with matter that causes light to change its energy, direction of motion, or both

transmission (trans MISH uhn) the passing of light or other form of energy through matter

Standards Check What are three ways that light can interact with matter? 🐻 **7.6.f**

You can see objects outside because light is transmitted through the glass.

You can see the glass and your reflection in it because light is reflected off the glass.

The glass feels warm when you touch it because some light is absorbed by the glass.

Figure 5 *Light is transmitted, reflected, and absorbed when it strikes the glass in a window.* **Describe at least two ways that light interacts with the person in this photo.**

85

Figure 6 Transparent, Translucent, and Opaque

Transparent plastic makes it easy to see what you are having for lunch.

Translucent wax paper makes it a little harder to see exactly what's for lunch.

Opaque aluminum foil makes it impossible to see your lunch without unwrapping it.

Types of Matter

Matter through which visible light is easily transmitted is said to be *transparent*. Air, glass, and water are examples of transparent matter. You can see objects clearly when you view them through transparent matter.

Sometimes, windows in bathrooms are made of frosted glass. If you look through one of these windows, you will see only blurry shapes. You can't see clearly through a frosted window because it is translucent (trans LOO suhnt). *Translucent* matter transmits light but also scatters the light as it passes through the matter. Wax paper is an example of translucent matter.

Matter that does not transmit any light is said to be *opaque* (oh PAYK). You cannot see through opaque objects. Metal, wood, and this book are opaque. You can compare transparent, translucent, and opaque matter in **Figure 6.**

Standards Check Why can't you see clearly through translucent objects? 7.6.f

Colors of Objects

How is an object's color determined? Humans see different wavelengths of light as different colors. For example, humans see long wavelengths as red and short wavelengths as violet. And, some colors, such as pink and brown, are seen when certain combinations of wavelengths are present.

The color that something appears to be is determined by the wavelengths of light that reach your eyes. Light can reach your eyes after being reflected by an object, transmitted through an object, or emitted by an object. When your eyes receive the light, they send signals to your brain. Your brain interprets the signals as colors.

Figure 7 Opaque Objects and Color

When white light shines on a strawberry, only red light is reflected. Other colors of light are absorbed. Therefore, the strawberry looks red to you.

This cow's white hair reflects all of the colors of light, but the black hair absorbs all of the colors.

Colors of Opaque Objects

When white light strikes a colored opaque object, some colors of light are absorbed, and some are reflected. Only the light that is reflected reaches your eyes and is detected. So, the colors of light that are reflected by an opaque object determine the color you see. For example, if a sweater reflects blue light and absorbs all other colors, you will see that the sweater is blue. Another example is shown on the left in **Figure 7.**

What colors of light are reflected by the cow shown on the right in **Figure 7**? Remember that white light includes all colors of light. So, white objects—such as the cow's white hair—appear white because all of the colors of light are reflected. On the other hand, black is the absence of color. When light strikes a black object, all of the colors are absorbed.

Standards Check Describe what happens to the colors in white light when the light strikes a green, opaque object? 📖 **7.6.e, 7.6.f**

Colors of Transparent and Translucent Objects

The colors of transparent and translucent objects are determined differently than the colors of opaque objects. Ordinary window glass is colorless in white light because it transmits all of the colors that strike it. But some transparent or translucent objects are colored, such as the window in **Figure 8.** When you look through colored transparent or translucent objects, you see the color of light that was reflected by or transmitted through the material. The other colors were absorbed.

Figure 8 *Stained glass has different colors because different colors are reflected and transmitted.*

Figure 9 *Some leaves contain orange and yellow pigments. But you can't see these pigments if chlorophyll is present. In the fall, chlorophyll breaks down and other pigments in the leaves can be seen.*

Pigments and Color

A *pigment* is a material that gives a substance its color by absorbing some colors of light and reflecting others. Almost everything contains pigments. For example, *melanin* (MEL uh nin) is a pigment that gives your skin its color. *Chlorophyll* (KLAWR uh FIL) is the pigment that gives plants a green color. The light energy absorbed by chlorophyll is converted into chemical energy during photosynthesis. Some tree leaves have pigments other than chlorophyll, as **Figure 9** shows.

Standards Check What is a pigment? 🐾 **7.6.f**

Color Subtraction

Each pigment absorbs at least one color of light. When you mix pigments together, more colors of light are absorbed or taken away. So, mixing pigments is called *color subtraction.*

The *primary pigments* are yellow, cyan, and magenta. They can be combined to make any other color. In fact, every color in this book was made by using just the primary pigments and black ink. The black ink was used to provide contrast to the images. **Figure 10** shows how the four pigments combine to produce many different colors.

Figure 10 *The picture of the balloon on the left was made by overlapping yellow ink, cyan ink, magenta ink, and black ink.*

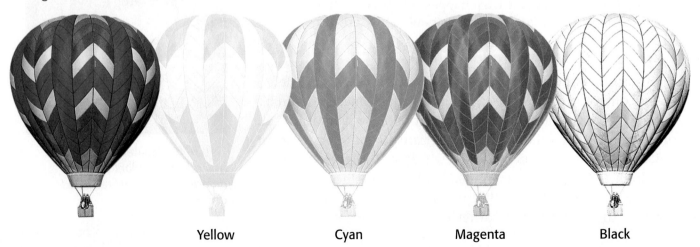

Yellow   Cyan   Magenta   Black

Summary

- Light travels in straight lines if the material that the light is traveling through does not change.
- The law of reflection states that the angle of incidence is equal to the angle of reflection.
- Things that are luminous can be seen because they emit light. Things that are illuminated can be seen because they reflect light.
- Absorption is the transfer of light energy to particles of matter. Scattering is an interaction of light with matter that causes light to change direction.
- Light can be reflected, transmitted, and absorbed by matter.
- Colors of opaque objects are determined by the colors of light that they reflect.
- Colors of translucent and transparent objects are determined by the colors of light they transmit and reflect.
- Pigments give objects color. The primary pigments are magenta, cyan, and yellow.

Using Vocabulary

1 Use the following terms in the same sentence: *absorption* and *scattering*.

2 Write an original definition for *reflection* and *transmission*.

Understanding Concepts

3 **Comparing** How is the angle of incidence related to the angle of reflection?

4 **Concluding** Why can you see through a car window?

5 **Describing** Name and describe at least three different ways light interacts with matter.

6 **Comparing** Explain why you can see both a light bulb and a lamp base.

7 **Summarizing** Describe how absorption and scattering can affect a beam of light.

8 **Concluding** Why do you see objects as different colors when white light is shining on them?

9 **Applying** Why is the beam of light from a flashlight that is shining in fog straight?

10 **Listing** What four colors of ink were used to print this book?

Critical Thinking

11 **Applying Concepts** What happens to the different colors of light when white light shines on an opaque, violet object?

12 **Analyzing Relationships** Explain why you can see your reflection in a spoon but not in a piece of cloth.

13 **Applying Concepts** How can you use a mirror to see around a corner? (Hint: You can draw a diagram to help explain your answer.)

INTERPRETING GRAPHICS Use the image below to answer the next question.

14 **Applying Concepts** The red rose was photographed in red light. Explain why the leaves appear black and the petals appear red.

Challenge

15 **Making Inferences** The planet Mars does not produce light. But if you look at Mars at night, it shines like a star with a reddish light. Explain why Mars shines and why you see reddish light.

Internet Resources

For a variety of links related to this chapter, go to www.scilinks.org
Topic: *Colors*
SciLinks code: HY70314

Refraction

Key Concept   Light can be bent, or refracted, by matter. Lenses refract light to form images.

Imagine that you and a friend are at a lake. Your friend wades into the water. You look at her, and her feet appear to have separated from her legs! You know her feet did not fall off, so how can you explain what you see? The answer has to do with refraction.

Refraction and Media

Light often travels through a medium, such as air, glass, or water. A *medium* is a substance through which a wave can travel. The plural of *medium* is *media*. If the medium through which light is travelling does not change, the light travels in a straight line. But if the medium changes, refraction can happen. **Refraction** is the bending of a wave as it passes at an angle from one medium to another. Refraction, shown in **Figure 1,** is one way that light interacts with matter.

Refraction can also happen when the density of a medium varies. For example, on sunny days, the air above a paved road has a higher temperature than the air around it has. So, the air above the road has a lower density than the surrounding air has. If you look over the pavement, the objects in the distance may seem to shimmer or wobble because of refraction.

Standards Check   When does light undergo refraction? **7.6.c, 7.6.f**

Figure 1   *Light travels more slowly through glass than it does through air. So, light refracts as it passes at an angle from air to glass or from glass to air.*

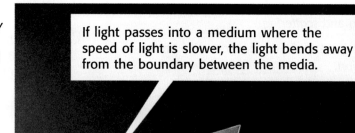

If light passes into a medium where the speed of light is slower, the light bends away from the boundary between the media.

Light in

If light passes into a medium where the speed of light is faster, the light bends toward the boundary.

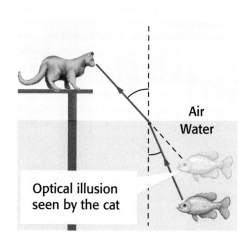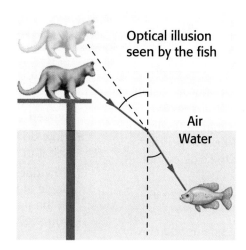

Optical illusion
seen by the fish

Optical illusion
seen by the cat

Air
Water

Air
Water

Figure 2 *Because of refraction, the cat and the fish see optical illusions. To the cat, the fish appears closer than it really is. To the fish, the cat appears farther away than it actually is.*

Refraction and Optical Illusions

Usually, when you look at an object, the light reflected by the object travels in a straight line from the object to your eye. Your brain always interprets light as traveling in straight lines. But when you look at something that is underwater, the light reflected by it does not travel in a straight line. Instead, it refracts. **Figure 2** shows how refraction creates an optical illusion. A similar kind of illusion causes a person's feet to appear separated from his or her legs when the person is wading.

refraction (ri FRAK shuhn) the bending of a wavefront as the wavefront passes between two substances in which the speed of the wave differs

Refraction and Color Separation

White light is made up of all of the wavelengths, or colors, of visible light. When white light is refracted, the amount that the light bends depends on its wavelength. Waves that have short wavelengths bend more than waves that have long wavelengths do. As **Figure 3** shows, white light can be separated into different colors during refraction. Color separation by refraction is responsible for rainbows. Rainbows form when sunlight is refracted by water drops.

Standards Check How do rainbows form? 🐻 **7.6.e, 7.6.f**

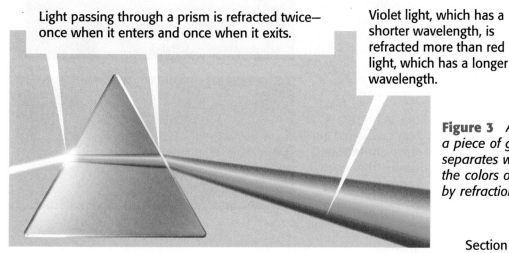

Light passing through a prism is refracted twice—once when it enters and once when it exits.

Violet light, which has a shorter wavelength, is refracted more than red light, which has a longer wavelength.

Figure 3 *A prism is a piece of glass that separates white light into the colors of visible light by refraction.*

Refracting Water

In this activity, you will see an optical illusion created by the refraction of light by water.

1. Place a **pencil** in a **clear, empty plastic cup** or an empty **250 mL beaker.** The pencil should be leaning against the side of the container.

2. Study the pencil from all angles. Write a description of what you see.

3. Watch the pencil from the side as you slowly pour **water** into the container. Fill the container half full with water.

4. Study the pencil from all angles again.

5. The pencil should look different when viewed from different angles. Describe how to look at the pencil to make it appear to be broken.

6. How do you have to look at the pencil to see it in one piece?

7. Why does changing the angle at which you look at the pencil change what you see?

7.6.c
7.6.f

⏱ **10 min**

Lenses and Refraction of Light

What do cameras, telescopes, and the human eye have in common? They all use lenses to form images. A **lens** is a transparent object that forms an image by refracting, or bending, light. Two kinds of lenses, convex and concave, are shown in **Figure 4.** The yellow beams in **Figure 4** show that light rays that pass through the center of any lens are not refracted. The point at which beams of light cross after going through a lens is called the *focal point*. The distance between the lens and the focal point is called a *focal length*.

lens (LENZ) a transparent object that refracts light waves such that they converge or diverge to create an image

Figure 4   How Lenses Refract Light

When light rays pass through a convex lens, the rays are refracted toward each other.

When light rays pass through a concave lens, the rays are refracted away from each other.

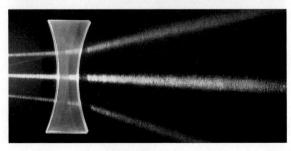

Figure 5   How Convex Lenses Form Images

If an object is less than 1 focal length away from a convex lens, a virtual image is formed. The image is larger than the object.

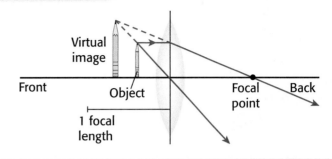

If an object is more than 2 focal lengths away from the lens, a real image is formed. The image is inverted and is smaller than the object.

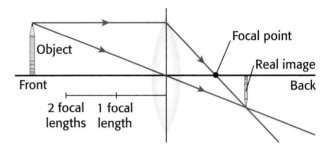

Convex Lenses

A lens that is thicker in the middle than at the edges is a **convex lens.** Convex lenses can form real images and virtual images. A *real image* can be projected onto a screen because light passes through the image. A *virtual image* cannot be projected because light doesn't travel through the image.

A magnifying glass has a convex lens. A magnifying glass can form images of an object that are larger or smaller than the object is. **Figure 5** shows how a convex lens, such as the lens in a magnifying glass, forms two kinds of images.

The lens of the human eye is also a convex lens. This lens refracts light and focuses the light on the back surface, or retina, of the eye, as shown in **Figure 6.** The muscles that hold the lens of the eye can change the shape of the lens to help it focus images. The cornea of the eye also refracts light.

convex lens (kahn VEKS LENZ) a lens that is thicker in the middle than at the edges

Standards Check   How are lenses used in a magnifying glass and in the eye? 🐻 **7.6.d**

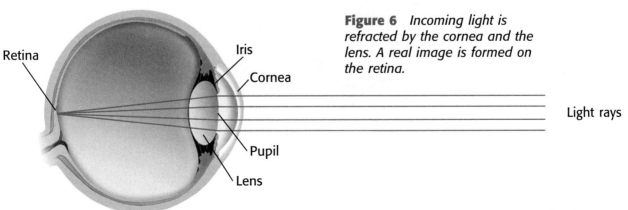

Figure 6 *Incoming light is refracted by the cornea and the lens. A real image is formed on the retina.*

Animal Eyes

Many animal eyes also contain convex lenses. The lenses of animal eyes focus light in a way similar to the way that the lenses of human eyes focus light. However, some animal eyes are very different from human eyes.

For example, dragonflies have compound eyes. Compound eyes are made of thousands of lens-like facets that each form a separate image. The dragonfly's brain uses these images to form a composite image.

Another animal that has interesting eyes is a fish called the *four-eyed fish*. This fish, shown in **Figure 7,** does not actually have four eyes. Each of the fish's two eyes are divided into two regions. The upper and lower regions of the eyes are shaped differently and have separate retinas. When the fish swims on the surface of the water, part of each eye is above water and part is below. The differences in the two regions allow the fish to see above water and below water at the same time.

Figure 7 *The four-eyed fish has eyes specially adapted to see above and below water at the same time.*

concave lens (kahn CAYV LENZ) a lens that is thinner in the middle than at the edges

Concave Lenses

A **concave lens** is a lens that is thinner in the middle than at the edges. Light rays entering a concave lens are refracted and bend away from each other. For a distant object, the refracted rays appear to come from a focal point in front of the lens. But the rays never actually meet. So, concave lenses do not form a real image. Instead, they form virtual images, as shown in **Figure 8.**

Standards Check What happens to light when it travels through a concave lens? 🐻 **7.6.f**

Figure 8 **How a Concave Lens Forms an Image**

Concave lenses can form only virtual images. The image formed is always smaller than the object.

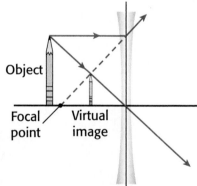

Object

Focal point

Virtual image

Optical Instruments and Refraction

Optical instruments are things that help people make observations. Many optical instruments contain convex and concave lenses that refract light to form images.

Some optical instruments help you see things that are very far away. Others help you see things that are very small. Some optical instruments record images. The optical instrument that you are probably most familiar with is the camera.

Cameras

Cameras are used to record images as photos. The way a camera works is similar to the way your eye works. Like your eye, a camera has a lens that focuses light to form an image. But unlike your eye, the lens of a camera is moved back-and-forth to focus light. The image formed by a camera lens is focused on the film. The image is then recorded on the film. **Figure 9** shows the parts of a 35 mm camera and explains how a camera works.

A digital camera has a lens, a shutter, and an aperture (AP uhr chuhr) like a 35 mm camera has. But instead of using film, a digital camera uses light sensors to record images. The sensors send an electrical signal to a computer in the camera. This signal carries data about the image that are stored in the computer and then on a memory stick, card, or disk.

Standards Check What does the lens of a camera do? **7.6.d**

Figure 9 **How a Camera Works**

The shutter opens and closes behind the lens to control how much light enters the camera. The longer the shutter is open, the more light enters the camera.

The lens of a camera is a convex lens that focuses light on the film. Moving the lens focuses light from objects at different distances.

The film is coated with chemicals that react when they are exposed to light. The result is an image stored on the film.

The aperture is an opening that lets light into the camera. The larger the aperture is, the more light enters the camera.

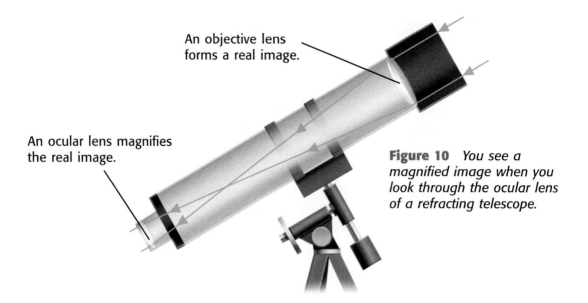

An objective lens forms a real image.

An ocular lens magnifies the real image.

Figure 10 *You see a magnified image when you look through the ocular lens of a refracting telescope.*

Telescopes

Telescopes are used to see images of large, distant objects. Astronomers use telescopes to study things in space, such as planets and stars. Telescopes that use lenses to focus light are called *refracting telescopes*. A simple refracting telescope has two convex lenses. An objective lens points toward the object being studied. An ocular lens is the lens that you look through. **Figure 10** shows how these lenses are used in a telescope.

Light Microscopes

Simple light microscopes are similar to refracting telescopes. These microscopes also have two convex lenses. Biologists use microscopes to see magnified images of tiny, nearby objects, such as cells and microscopic organisms. **Figure 11** explains how a microscope works.

Standards Check How are lenses used in telescopes and in microscopes? 7.6.d

Microscope Magnification

Some microscopes use more than one lens to magnify objects. The power of each lens indicates the amount of magnification the lens gives. For example, a 10× lens magnifies objects 10 times. To find the amount of magnification given by two or more lenses used together, multiply the powers of the lenses. What is the magnification given by a 5× lens used with a 20× lens?

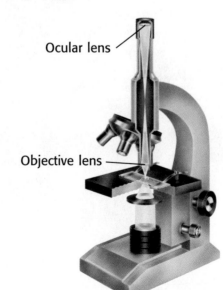

Ocular lens

Objective lens

Figure 11 *The objective lens of a microscope forms a real image. The ocular lens then produces a larger virtual image that you see when you look through the microscope.*

Summary

- Light travels in straight lines if the medium through which the light travels does not change.
- Refraction is the bending of a wave, such as light, as it passes at an angle from one medium to another.
- Refraction of light can create optical illusions and can separate white light into different colors.
- Lenses form images by refracting light.
- Convex lenses produce both real images and virtual images.
- A magnifying glass and the lens of the human eye are convex lenses.
- Concave lenses produce only virtual images.
- Cameras, telescopes, and microscopes are optical instruments that use lenses to form images.

Using Vocabulary

1. Use *refraction* and *lens* in the same sentence.

2. Explain how the meanings of *convex lens* and *concave lens* differ.

Understanding Concepts

3. **Applying** Why do you not normally see refraction when you look across a room?

4. **Describing** Explain the role of lenses in a magnifying glass, a camera, a telescope, a microscope, and the human eye.

5. **Summarizing** What happens to white light when it passes at an angle through a prism?

6. **Describing** What happens when light is refracted by matter?

7. **Comparing** How are telescopes and microscopes similar? How are they different?

8. **Analyzing** What are the similarities and differences between a camera and the human eye?

Critical Thinking

9. **Forming Hypotheses** Imagine that you are toasting a piece of bread in a toaster. As you wait for your toast, you notice that the air above the toaster appears to be wiggling or shimmering. Form a hypothesis that explains what you see.

10. **Making Inferences** Teachers sometimes use overhead projectors to show transparencies on a screen. What type of lens does an overhead projector use? Explain your reasoning.

INTERPRETING GRAPHICS Use the image below to answer the next two questions.

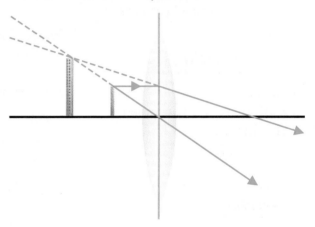

11. **Applying Concepts** What kind of lens is shown in the diagram?

12. **Making Inferences** Is the lens forming a real image or a virtual image?

Challenge

13. **Predicting Consequences** Some animals have simple eyes called *ocelli*. Ocelli have receptors that can detect light, but do not have lenses. What do you think an animal that has ocelli sees?

Internet Resources

For a variety of links related to this chapter, go to www.scilinks.org

Topic: Lenses
SciLinks code: HY70868

Skills Practice Lab

OBJECTIVES

Use a convex lens to form images.

Determine the characteristics of real images formed by convex lenses.

MATERIALS

- candle
- card, index, 4 × 6 in. or larger
- clay, modeling
- convex lens
- jar lid
- matches
- meterstick

SAFETY

Images from Convex Lenses

A convex lens is thicker in the center than at the edges. Parallel light rays passing through a convex lens come together at a focal point. Under certain conditions, a convex lens will create a real image of an object. The characteristics of this image depend on the distance between the object and the lens. In this experiment, you will determine the characteristics of real images created by a convex lens—the kind of lens that is used as a magnifying lens.

Ask a Question

1 What are the characteristics of real images created by a convex lens? For example, are the images upright or inverted (upside down)? Are the images larger or smaller than the object?

Form a Hypothesis

2 Write a hypothesis that is a possible answer to the questions above. Explain your reasoning.

Test the Hypothesis

3 Copy the table below.

	Data Collection			
Image	**Orientation (upright/ inverted)**	**Size (larger/ smaller)**	**Image distance (cm)**	**Object distance (cm)**
1				
2		*DO NOT WRITE IN BOOK*		
3				

7.6.d Students know how simple lenses are used in a magnifying glass, the eye, a camera, a telescope, and a microscope.

7.6.f Students know light can be reflected, refracted, transmitted, and absorbed by matter.

4 Use modeling clay to make a base for the lens. Place the lens and base in the middle of the table.

5 Stand the index card upright in some modeling clay on one side of the lens.

6 Place the candle in the jar lid, and anchor it with some modeling clay. Place the candle on the table so that the lens is halfway between the candle and the card. Light the candle. **Caution:** Use extreme care around an open flame.

7 In a darkened room, slowly move the card and the candle away from the lens while keeping the lens exactly halfway between the card and the candle. Continue until you see a clear image of the candle flame on the card. This image is image 1.

8 Measure and record the distance between the lens and the card (image distance) and the distance between the lens and the candle (object distance).

9 Is the image upright or inverted? Is it larger or smaller than the candle? Record this information in the table.

10 Move the lens toward the candle. The new object distance should be less than half the object distance measured in step 8. Move the card back-and-forth until you find a sharp image (image 2) of the candle on the card.

11 Repeat steps 8 and 9 for image 2.

12 Leave the card and candle in place, and move the lens toward the card to get the third image (image 3).

13 Repeat steps 8 and 9 for image 3.

Analyze the Results

14 **Recognizing Patterns** Describe the pattern between image distance and image size.

15 **Examining Data** What are the similarities between the real images that are formed by a convex lens?

Draw Conclusions

16 **Making Predictions** The lens of your eye is a convex lens. Use the information that you collected to describe the image projected on the back of your eye when you look at an object.

Big Idea Question

17 **Making Predictions** Light can interact with matter in many different ways. Describe four different ways that light from the candle may have interacted with matter in the room.

Applying Your Data

Convex lenses are used in film projectors. Explain why your favorite movie stars are truly "larger than life" on the screen in terms of image distance and object distance.

Science Skills Activity

Using a Microscope to Collect Data

Investigation and Experimentation
7.7.a Select and use appropriate tools and technology (including calculators, computers, balances, spring scales, microscopes, and binoculars) to perform tests, collect data, and display data.

▶ Tutorial

A microscope is a tool often used by life scientists to collect data. Follow these instructions when you use a light microscope.

1. Turn on the light source of your microscope, and select the low-power objective lens.

2. Light from the light source passes through a small hole in the stage. Place a prepared slide over this hole. Secure the slide with the stage clips.

3. Look at the stage from eye level. Slowly turn the adjustment knob to lower the objective lens until the lens almost touches the slide.

4. Look through the ocular lens. Turn the adjustment knob to raise the objective lens until the image is in focus.

5. Make sure that the image is exactly in the center of your field of vision. Then, switch to the high-power objective. If necessary, use the adjustment knob to focus.

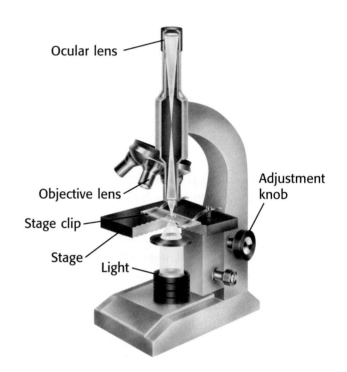

Ocular lens

Objective lens

Stage clip

Stage

Light

Adjustment knob

▶ You Try It!

Procedure

1. Obtain a **light microscope,** and identify its parts. Learn how the various parts work. When you are familiar with how the microscope works, ask your teacher for a **prepared slide.**

2. Follow the steps described above to view the slide. Be sure to view the slide by using at least two different objective lenses.

Analysis

3. **Collecting Data** Draw a diagram of the image that you saw when you used each objective lens.

4. **Identifying Relationships** How did the different objective lenses change what you saw?

5. **Making Inferences** Biologists often use microscopes to collect data about microscopic organisms. How could a biologist adapt a microscope to display data? (Hint: Think about other kinds of optical instruments.)

Chapter Summary

The Big Idea Light is an electromagnetic wave that interacts with matter in many different ways.

| Section | Vocabulary |

1 The Electromagnetic Spectrum

Key Concept Visible light, infrared waves, and ultraviolet light are small parts of a large electromagnetic spectrum.

- Light is an electromagnetic wave.
- Visible light is a small part of a very broad electromagnetic spectrum.
- White light is a mixture of many wavelengths of visible light.
- Infrared waves and ultraviolet light affect living things.

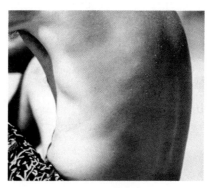

Exposure to ultraviolet light can cause sunburn.

electromagnetic wave p. 76
electromagnetic spectrum p. 77

2 Interactions of Light with Matter

Key Concept Light interacts with matter during reflection, absorption, scattering, and transmission.

- Light travels in straight lines if the material that the light travels through does not change.
- The angle of reflection of a light beam is equal to the angle of incidence.
- An object can be seen if light emitted by or reflected by it is detected by the eye.
- Light can be reflected, absorbed, scattered, or transmitted by matter.

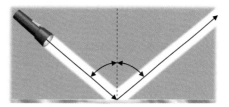

The angle of reflection is equal to the angle of incidence.

reflection p. 82
absorption p. 84
scattering p. 85
transmission p. 85

3 Refraction

Key Concept Light can be bent, or refracted, by matter. Lenses refract light to form images.

- Light is refracted when the medium it travels in changes.
- Convex and concave lenses refract light to form images.
- Human eyes, magnifying glasses, cameras, telescopes, and microscopes have lenses that form images.

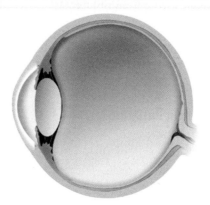

The lens of the eye refracts light and focuses the light on the retina.

refraction p. 90
lens p. 92
convex lens p. 93
concave lens p. 94

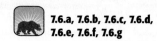
Organize

Key-Term Fold Review the FoldNote that you created at the beginning of the chapter. Add to or correct the FoldNote based on what you have learned.

Using Vocabulary

1 **Academic Vocabulary** Which of the following is the plural form of the word *medium*?
a. mediums
b. medians
c. media
d. medias

Complete each of the following sentences by choosing the correct term from the word bank.

refraction	reflection
scattering	transmission
electromagnetic wave	electromagnetic spectrum

2 ___ happens when light waves bounce off matter.

3 Visible light is a small part of the ___.

4 ___ happens when light waves enter a new medium at an angle.

5 Light is a kind of ___ and therefore can travel through matter and space.

6 During ___, light travels through an object.

Understanding Concepts

Multiple Choice

7 Objects that transmit light easily are
a. opaque.
b. translucent.
c. transparent.
d. colored.

8 You can see yourself in a mirror because of
a. absorption.   **c.** regular reflection.
b. scattering.   **d.** diffuse reflection.

9 Prisms produce the colors of the rainbow through
a. reflection.   **c.** scattering.
b. refraction.   **d.** absorption.

Short Answer

10 **Describing** What has to happen to light for you to see an object?

11 **Identifying** What kind of lenses are found in magnifying glasses and in the human eye? What do these lenses do?

12 **Summarizing** Describe how the lenses in telescopes and microscopes help people make observations.

13 **Concluding** Why can sunlight form a rainbow?

14 **Listing** Explain what happens to light when it is reflected, refracted, transmitted, and absorbed by matter.

15 **Comparing** What are the angle of reflection and the angle of incidence? How are they related?

INTERPRETING GRAPHICS Use the image below to answer the next two questions.

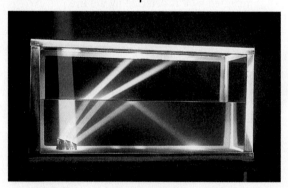

16 **Analyzing** Why doesn't the large beam of light bend like the two beams in the middle of the tank?

17 **Identifying** Which interaction of light explains what is happening to the bottom light beam?

Writing Skills

18 **Communicating Key Concepts**   Analyze the information in one section of this chapter. Then, write a one-page paper that identifies and explains the main concepts in your own words. Be sure to use vocabulary words from the section in your paper.

Critical Thinking

19 **Concept Mapping**   Use the following terms to create a concept map: *light, matter, reflection, absorption, refraction,* and *transmission.*

20 **Applying Concepts**   A tern is a type of bird that dives underwater to catch fish. When a young tern begins learning to catch fish, the bird is rarely successful. The tern has to learn that when a fish appears to be in a certain place underwater, the fish is actually in a slightly different place. Why does the tern see the fish in the wrong place?

21 **Evaluating Conclusions**   Imagine that you are teaching your brother about light. You tell him that white light is light of all of the colors of the rainbow combined. But your brother says that you are wrong because mixing different colors of paint produces black and not white. Why is your brother's conclusion wrong?

22 **Making Inferences**   If you look around a parking lot during the summer, you might see sunshades set up in the windshields of cars. How do sunshades help keep the insides of cars cool?

23 **Identifying Relationships**   What is the electromagnetic spectrum? How is the visible spectrum related to the electromagnetic spectrum?

24 **Applying Concepts**   Imagine that you are at a concert. While the music is playing, beams of laser light flash through the air. The light beams travel in straight lines. What can you conclude about the medium through which the light is travelling?

INTERPRETING GRAPHICS   Use the images below to answer the next question.

A

B

C

25 **Analyzing Processes**   Each photo shows at least one interaction of light with matter. Identify the interactions shown.

Math Skills

26 **Making Conversions**   One nanometer (1 nm) is equal to 0.000000001 m. Visible light has wavelengths between 400 nm and 750 nm. Convert this range of wavelengths to meters.

Challenge

27 **Predicting Consequences**   The phrase "looking at the world through rose-colored glasses," is an adage that means that a person has an overly positive view of things. What would you expect to see if you actually looked at the world through rose-colored glasses?

REVIEWING ACADEMIC VOCABULARY

1 **Which of the following words means "that can be seen"?**

A visible

B audible

C palpable

D sensible

2 **Which of the following sets of words best completes the following sentence: Light is _____ the eye.**

A detects with

B detected for

C detected by

D detecting in

3 **Which of the following sets of words best completes the following sentence: Light can be _____ matter.**

A transmitted with

B transmits in

C transmits by

D transmitted through

4 **Which of the following words is closest in meaning to the word *react*?**

A repeat

B renovate

C respond

D remove

REVIEWING CONCEPTS

5 **Which of the following best describes the relationship between infrared waves, ultraviolet light, and visible light?**

A Infrared waves are found on the electromagnetic spectrum, while ultraviolet and visible light are not.

B Infrared waves have the longest wavelength, followed by visible light and then ultraviolet light.

C Infrared waves and visible light are visible to the human eye, while ultraviolet light is not.

D Infrared waves consist of changing electric and magnetic fields, while ultraviolet light and visible light do not.

6 **Your eyes detect a burning candle in a candleholder. Your eyes see the candle flame because it emits light. Why do your eyes see the opaque candleholder?**

A It is luminous.

B It is illuminated.

C It absorbs light.

D It transmits light.

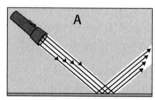 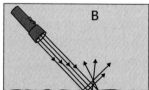

7 **The diagrams above show how light interacts with two different surfaces. Which of the following statements is true?**

A Diagram A illustrates the process of diffuse reflection.

B You will be able to see your reflection in surface B but not in surface A.

C Diagram B illustrates the process of regular reflection.

D You will be able to see your reflection in surface A but not in surface B.

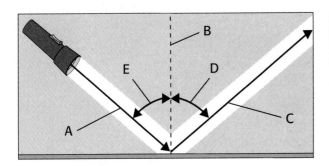

8 The diagram above illustrates the law of reflection. What is found at point E in the diagram?

A the angle of incidence

B the angle of reflection

C the incident beam

D the reflected beam

9 What happens to white light during refraction?

A It appears to be closer than it actually is.

B It absorbs the pigment of the medium it passes through.

C It separates into different wavelengths or colors.

D It is refracted at the same angle as the angle of incidence.

10 What part of a camera is most like the retina in the human eye?

A the lens   C the shutter

B the film   D the aperture

11 What happens when white light shines through a translucent, red, glass window?

A All colors of light except red are transmitted through the glass.

B Red light is transmitted through and reflected by the glass.

C Red light is absorbed by the glass.

D All colors of light except red are reflected by the glass.

REVIEWING PRIOR LEARNING

12 While you are conducting an experiment, your lab partner burns himself on a candle flame. After such an accident, you should

A take your partner to the bathroom and wash the burn with soap.

B perform first aid by rinsing the burned area with warm water.

C tell your teacher, even if the burn seems like a minor injury.

D continue with your lab and tell no one about what has happened.

13 Corals and producers live in the neritic zones of an ocean. Whales and squid live in the oceanic zone. Bacteria and worms live in the benthic zone. Which of the following factors most determines the types of organisms that live at each level?

A the strength of underwater currents and daily tides

B the amount of fresh water that falls as precipitation

C the number of predators living in the oceanic zone

D the depth to which sunlight can penetrate the water

14 If sunlight could not reach Earth's surface, which of the following would happen first?

A Producers would die.

B Consumers would die.

C Scavengers would die.

D Decomposers would die.

Standards Assessment

Science in Action

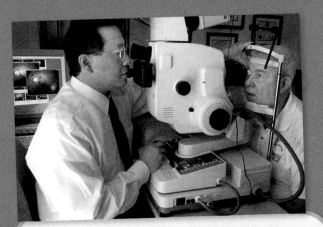

Weird Science

Fireflies Light the Way

Just as beams of light from lighthouses warn boats of approaching danger, the light of an unlikely source—fireflies—is being used by scientists to warn food inspectors of bacterial contamination.

Fireflies use an enzyme called *luciferase* to make light. Scientists have taken the gene from fireflies that tells cells how to make luciferase. They put this gene into a virus that preys on bacteria. The virus is not harmful to humans and can be mixed into meat. When the virus infects bacteria in the meat, the virus transfers the gene into the genes of the bacteria. The bacteria then produce luciferase and glow! So, if a food inspector sees glowing meat, the inspector knows that the meat is contaminated with bacteria.

Science, Technology, and Society

Bionic Eyes

Imagine bionic eyes that allow a person who is blind to see. Researchers working on artificial vision think that the technology will be available soon. Many companies are working on different ways to restore sight to people who are blind. Some companies are developing artificial corneas, while other companies are building artificial retinas. One item that has already been tested on people is a pair of glasses that provides limited vision. The glasses have a camera that sends a signal to an electrode implanted in the person's brain. The images are black and white and are not detailed, but the person who is wearing the glasses can see obstacles in his or her path.

Language Arts

Write a one-page story in your **Science Journal** about a teen who has his or her eyesight restored by a bionic eye. What would the teen want to see first? What would the teen do that he or she couldn't do before?

Social Studies ACTiViTY

Many cultures have myths to explain certain natural phenomena. Read some of these myths. Then, write your own myth titled "How Fireflies Got Their Fire."

Edie Widder

Oceanographer When Dr. Edie Widder studies the waters of the world's oceans, she's always searching for the light. She is not searching for light from a lighthouse or a nearby coastal town. She is searching for the light given off by marine animals.

Widder received a Ph.D. in neurobiology from the University of California, Santa Barbara in 1982. She is now one of the world's leading researchers on bioluminescence. *Bioluminescence* is the production and emission of light by a living organism. Many marine animals emit light when chemical energy is converted into light energy. Thousands of deep-sea creatures, including various species of shrimp, squid, and jellyfish, are bioluminescent. Widder also studies animals that give off light through a process called *fluorescence*. In fact, Widder was part of a team that discovered the only known fluorescent shark!

To help her research, Widder designed a special camera system called *Eye-in-the-Sea*. Eye-in-the-Sea sits on the sea floor and automatically films bioluminescent organisms. Widder recently used this device to explore the depths of California's Monterey Bay.

Math ACTiViTY

The fluorescent shark filmed by Widder's team is about 36 in. long. If 1 in. is equal to 2.54 cm, how long is the shark in centimeters? Show your work in your **Science Journal**.

Internet Resources

- To learn more about careers in science, visit **www.scilinks.org** and enter the SciLinks code HY70225.

- To learn more about these Science in Action topics, visit **go.hrw.com** and type in the keyword HY7LOWF.

- Check out articles related to this chapter by visiting **go.hrw.com**. Just type in the keyword HY7LOWC.

TIMELINE

Cells

Cells are everywhere. Even though most cells can't be seen with the naked eye, they make up every living thing. Living things may be made up of one cell or many cells. Your body alone contains trillions of cells!

In this unit, you will learn about different kinds of cells. You will also learn about what happens in a cell. This timeline shows some of the discoveries that scientists have made about cells. Each discovery has helped people understand more about these tiny, amazing structures.

1492

Christopher Columbus reaches North America after sailing from Europe.

Around 1595

Zacharias and Hans Janssen build the first compound microscope.

1838

Johannes Muller proves that cancerous tumors are made up of cells.

1869

Friedrich Miescher discovers a special material in the nucleus of a white blood cell. Later research on this material leads to the discovery of DNA.

White blood cell

1999

Elizabeth Gould and Charles Gross discover that cells in the brain can be repaired and regrown. This discovery contradicts previous scientific understanding.

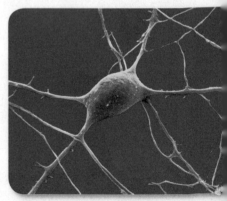

A neuron

1665

Robert Hooke looks at cork under a microscope and uses the name *cells* to describe the small structures that he sees.

1683

Anton van Leeuwenhoek uses a microscope to observe bacteria living on his teeth. He calls these bacteria *animalcules*.

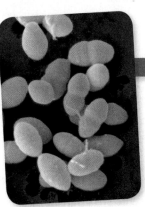

Streptococcus sanguis found on teeth

1809

Abraham Lincoln, the 16th president of the United States, is born.

1873

Camillo Golgi develops a stain that allows scientists to view the structure of entire nerve cells.

1937

Sir Hans Adolf Krebs discovers how cells produce energy from nutrients through the citric acid cycle.

1967

Ragnar Granit, Haldan Hartline, and George Wald are awarded a Nobel Prize for describing how cells in the eye are sensitive to light.

Rods and cones in the eye

1999

The largest known bacterial species, *Thiomargarita namibiensis,* is discovered near Namibia. The cell of one bacterium is 0.3 mm long!

2001

Two separate groups publish the decoded human genome.

2003

Peter Agre receives a Nobel Prize for discovering water channels in human cells.

Improving Comprehension

Graphic Organizers are important visual tools that can help you organize information and improve your reading comprehension. The Graphic Organizer below is called a *comparison table*. Instructions for creating other types of Graphic Organizers are located in the **Study Skills** section of the Appendix.

How to Make a Comparison Table

1. Draw a table like the one shown below. Draw as many columns and rows as you want to draw.

2. In the top row, write the topics that you want to compare.

3. In the left column, write the general characteristics that you want to compare. As you read the chapter, fill in the characteristics for each topic in the appropriate boxes.

When to Use a Comparison Table

A comparison table is useful when you want to compare the characteristics of two or more topics in science. Organizing information in a table helps you compare several topics at one time. In a table, all topics are described in terms of the same list of characteristics, which helps you make a thorough comparison. As you read, look for topics whose characteristics you may want to compare in a table.

	Prokaryotic cells	Eukaryotic cells
Nucleus	no	yes
DNA	yes	yes
Membrane-bound organelles	no	yes
Cell wall	yes	some
Cell membrane	yes	yes
Cytoplasm	yes	yes
Ribosomes	yes	yes

You Try It!

This Reading Strategy can also be used within the chapter that you are about to read. Practice making your own *comparison table* as directed in the Reading Strategies for Section **2** and Section **3**. Record your work in your **Science Journal.**

Unpacking the Standards

The information below "unpacks" the standards by breaking them down into basic parts. The higher-level, academic vocabulary is highlighted and defined to help you understand the language of the standards. "What It Means" restates the standards as simply as possible.

California Standard	Academic Vocabulary	What It Means
7.1.a Students know cells **function similarly** in all living organisms.	**function** (FUHNGK shuhn) to work **similarly** (SIM uh luhr lee) in almost the same way	Cells perform the same actions in all living things.
7.1.b Students know the characteristics that distinguish plant cells from animal cells, including chloroplasts and cell walls.		Plant cells have some unique structures that make plant cells different from animal cells. These structures include chloroplasts and a cell wall.
7.1.c Students know the nucleus is the repository for genetic information in plant and animal cells.		The nucleus of a plant cell or an animal cell contains information that the cell uses as blueprints for building new cells.
7.1.d Students know that mitochondria **liberate** energy for the work that cells do and that chloroplasts capture sunlight **energy** for photosynthesis.	**liberate** (LIB uhr AYT) to release; to set free **energy** (EN uhr jee) the capacity to do work	Mitochondria release energy from sugar to power the cell's life processes. Chloroplasts use energy from the sun to produce sugars and oxygen.
7.1.f Students know that as multicellular organisms develop, their cells **differentiate.**	**differentiate** (DIF uhr EN shee AYT) to become specialized in structure and function	As a living thing that is made of more than one cell grows, the structure of its cells change so that the cells perform specific jobs.
7.5.a Students know plants and animals have levels of organization for **structure** and **function,** including cells, tissues, organs, organ systems, and the whole organism.	**structure** (STRUHK chuhr) the arrangement of the parts of a whole **function** (FUHNGK shuhn) use or purpose	Plants and animals are made of smaller parts which are organized by shape and purpose. These layers of organization include cells, tissues, organs, organ systems, and the whole organism.

4

Cells: The Basic Units of Life

The Big Idea

All organisms are composed of one or more cells.

 California Standards

Focus on Life Sciences
7.1 All living organisms are composed of cells, from just one to many trillions, whose details usually are visible only through a microscope. (Sections 1, 2, and 3)
7.5 The anatomy and physiology of plants and animals illustrate the complementary nature of structure and function. (Section 3)

Investigation and Experimentation
7.7 Scientific progress is made by asking meaningful questions and conducting careful investigations. (Science Skills Activity)

Math
7.1.1 Algebra and Functions
7.2.3 Measurement and Geometry

English–Language Arts
7.1.3 Reading
7.2.1 Writing

About the Photo

Harmful bacteria may invade your body and make you sick. But wait—your white blood cells come to the rescue! In this image, a white blood cell (shown in yellow) reaches out to destroy bacteria (shown in purple). The red disks are red blood cells.

Organize

Layered Book

Before you read this chapter, create the FoldNote entitled "Layered Book." Label the tabs of the layered book with "Characteristics of all cells," "Prokaryotic cells," "Eukaryotic cells," and "Organization of living things." As you read the chapter, write information that you learn about each category under the appropriate tab.

Instructions for creating FoldNotes are located in the Study Skills section on p. 580 of the Appendix.

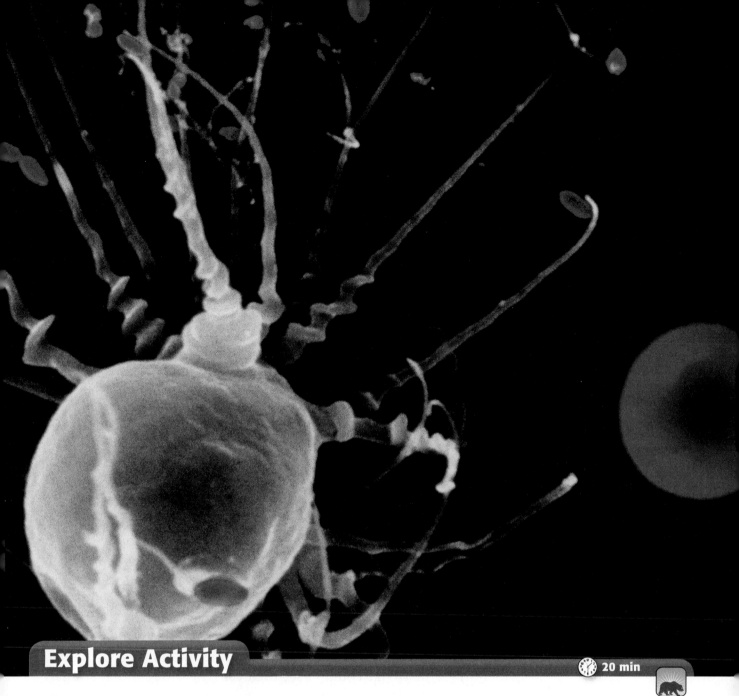

Explore Activity

🕐 20 min

7.1.a
7.7.a

What Are Plants Made Of?

All living things, including plants, are made of cells. What do plant cells look like? Do this activity to find out.

Procedure

1. Follow your teacher's directions on how to set up and operate a **microscope.**

2. Tear off a **small leaf** from near the tip of an *Elodea* sprig. Using **forceps,** place the whole leaf in a **drop of water** on a **microscope slide.**

3. Place a **coverslip** on top of the water drop by putting one edge of the coverslip on the slide near the water drop. Next, lower the coverslip slowly so that the coverslip does not trap air bubbles.

4. Place the slide on your microscope.

5. Using the lowest-powered lens first, find the plant cells. When you can see the cells under the lowest-powered lens, switch to a higher-powered lens.

6. Draw a picture of what you see.

Analysis

7. Describe the shape of the *Elodea* cells. Are all of the cells the same?

8. Do you think that human cells look like *Elodea* cells? How do you think they are different? How might they be similar?

Cells: The Basic Units of Life   **113**

The Characteristics of Cells

Key Concept Cells function similarly in all living organisms.

What You Will Learn

- The cell theory explains why cells are important for living things.
- All cells have a cell membrane, cytoplasm, and DNA.
- Prokaryotic cells and eukaryotic cells differ in how their genetic information is contained.

Why It Matters

Understanding how cells function makes it easier to learn how organisms function.

Vocabulary

- cell
- cell membrane
- organelle
- nucleus
- prokaryote
- eukaryote

READING STRATEGY

Asking Questions Read this section silently. In your **Science Journal**, write down questions that you have about this section. Discuss your questions in a small group.

cell (SEL) the smallest functional and structural unit of all living organisms; usually consists of a nucleus, cytoplasm, and a membrane

▶ Most cells are so small that they can't be seen with the naked eye. So, how did scientists find cells? They found cells by accident! The first person to see cells wasn't looking for them.

All living things are made of cells. A **cell** is the smallest structural and functional unit of living things. Because of their size, cells weren't discovered until microscopes were invented in the mid-1600s.

Cells and the Cell Theory

Robert Hooke was the first person to describe cells. In 1665, he built a microscope to look at tiny objects. One day, he looked at a thin slice of cork. Cork is found in the bark of cork trees. The cork looked as if it were made of little boxes. Hooke named these boxes *cells,* which means "little rooms" in Latin. Hooke's cells were really the outer layers of dead cork cells. His microscope and his drawing of the cork cells are shown in **Figure 1.**

Hooke also looked at thin slices of living plants. He saw that they too were made of cells. Some cells were even filled with "juice." The "juicy" cells were living cells.

Hooke also looked at feathers, fish scales, and the eyes of houseflies. But he spent most of his time looking at plants and fungi. The cells of plants and fungi have cell walls. Thus, they are easy to see. Animal cells do not have cell walls. The lack of cell walls makes seeing the outline of animal cells harder. Because Hooke couldn't see their cells, he thought that animals weren't made of cells.

Figure 1 *Hooke discovered cells by using this microscope. His drawing of cork cells is shown to the right of his microscope.*

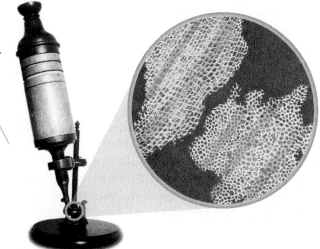

7.1.a Students know cells function similarly in all living organisms.
7.1.c Students know the nucleus is the repository for genetic information in plant and animal cells.

Euglena

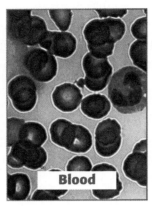

Blood

Yeast

Bacteria

Figure 2 *Leeuwenhoek examined many types of cells, including protists of the genus* Euglena *and the other types of cells shown above. The bacteria in the photo have been enlarged more than the other cells. Bacterial cells are much smaller than most other types of cells.*

Finding Cells in Other Organisms

In 1673, Anton van Leeuwenhoek (LAY vuhn HOOK), a Dutch merchant, made his own microscopes. He used one of his microscopes to look at pond scum. Leeuwenhoek saw small organisms in the water. He named these organisms *animalcules,* which means "little animals." Today, we call these single-celled organisms *protists* (PROH tists).

Leeuwenhoek also looked at animal blood. He saw differences in blood cells from different kinds of animals. For example, blood cells in fish, birds, and frogs are oval. Blood cells in humans and dogs are round and flat. Leeuwenhoek was also the first person to see bacteria. And he discovered that yeasts that make bread dough rise are single-celled organisms. Examples of the types of cells that Leeuwenhoek examined are shown in **Figure 2.**

The Cell Theory

Almost 200 years passed before scientists concluded that cells are present in all living things. Matthias Schleiden (muh THIE uhs SHLIE duhn) studied plants. In 1838, he concluded that all plant parts were made of cells. Theodor Schwann (THEE oh DAWR SHVAHN) studied animals. In 1839, Schwann concluded that all animal tissues were made of cells. Shortly thereafter, he wrote the first two parts of what is now known as the *cell theory:*

- All organisms are made up of one or more cells.
- The cell is the basic unit of all living things.

In his book published in 1858, doctor Rudolf Virchow (ROO DAWLF FIR koh), stated that all cells could form only from other cells. He then added the third part of the cell theory:

- All cells come from existing cells.

Standards Check What are the three parts of the cell theory?

🐻 **7.1.a**

Quick Lab

Observing Cells   7.1.a
                            7.7.d

1. Follow your teacher's directions on how to set up and operate a **microscope.**

2. Examine **prepared microscope slides** from a variety of living things.

3. Record your observations of the samples on the slides. Draw pictures of what you see, and label your drawings.

4. What similarities between the samples do you observe?

5. How do the samples differ?

⏱ **20 min**

Cell Size

Most cells are too small to be seen without a microscope. It would take 50 human cells to cover the dot on this letter *i*.

Figure 3 *The white and yolk of this chicken egg provide nutrients for the development of a chick.*

A Few Large Cells

Most cells are small. A few, however, are big. The yolk of a chicken egg, shown in **Figure 3,** is one big cell. The size of most cells is controlled by the relationship between the surface area and the volume of the cell.

Many Small Cells

There is a reason why most cells are so small. Cells take in food and get rid of wastes through their outer surface. As a cell gets larger, it needs more food and produces more waste. Therefore, more materials pass through its outer surface.

As the cell's volume increases, its surface area grows, too. But the cell's volume grows faster than its surface area. If a cell gets too large, the cell's surface area will not be large enough to take in enough nutrients or pump out enough wastes. So, the surface area of a cell—relative to the volume of the cell—limits the cell's size. The ratio of the cell's surface area to the cell's volume is called the *surface area–to–volume ratio*. It can be calculated by using the following equation:

$$surface\ area\text{–}to\text{–}volume\ ratio = \frac{surface\ area}{volume}$$

Surface Area–to–Volume Ratio Calculate the surface area–to–volume ratio of a cube whose sides measure 2 cm.

Step 1: Calculate the surface area.

surface area of cube =
number of sides × area of side

surface area of cube = 6 × (2 cm × 2 cm)

surface area of cube = 24 cm^2

Step 2: Calculate the volume.

volume of cube = side × side × side

volume of cube = 2 cm × 2 cm × 2 cm

volume of cube = 8 cm^3

Step 3: Calculate the surface area–to–volume ratio.

$$surface\ area\text{–}to\text{–}volume\ ratio = \frac{surface\ area}{volume} = \frac{24}{8} = \frac{3}{1}$$

Now It's Your Turn

1. Calculate the surface area–to–volume ratio of a cube whose sides are 3 cm long.
2. Calculate the surface area–to–volume ratio of a cube whose sides are 4 cm long.
3. Of the cubes from questions 1 and 2, which has the greater surface area–to–volume ratio?
4. What is the relationship between the length of a side and the surface area–to–volume ratio of a cell?

Parts of a Cell

Cells have many different functions and come in many shapes and sizes. But all cells have some parts in common.

The Cell Membrane and Cytoplasm

All cells are surrounded by a cell membrane. The **cell membrane** is a protective layer that covers the cell's surface and acts as a barrier. It separates the cell's contents from its environment. The cell membrane also controls materials going into and out of the cell. Inside the cell is a fluid. This fluid and almost all of its contents are called the *cytoplasm* (SIET oh PLAZ uhm).

Organelles

Cells have organelles that carry out many life processes. **Organelles** are structures that have specific jobs inside the cell. Different kinds of cells have different organelles. Most organelles are surrounded by membranes. For example, the algal cell in **Figure 4** has membrane-bound organelles. Some organelles float in the cytoplasm. Other organelles are attached to membranes or other organelles.

Genetic Material

All cells have DNA (**d**eoxyribo**n**ucleic **a**cid) at some point in their lives. DNA is genetic material. It carries information needed to make new cells and new organisms. DNA is passed on from parent cells to new cells and directs the activities of a cell. **Figure 5** shows the DNA of a bacterium.

In cells such as plant and animal cells, DNA does not float around the cell. The *repository,* or storage area, for DNA is an organelle called the **nucleus.** Other cells, such as bacterial cells, do not have a nucleus.

Some cells can live without DNA. When human red blood cells are first made, they have a nucleus with DNA. But as red blood cells mature, they lose their nucleus and DNA. Most cells, however, always need to have DNA. DNA gives these cells instructions on how to make proteins.

Standards Check   Where is DNA located in plant and animal cells?

![7.1.c icon] **7.1.c**

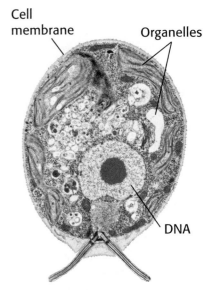

Figure 4   *The green alga in this photomicrograph has organelles. The organelles and the fluid surrounding them make up the cytoplasm.*

cell membrane (SEL MEM BRAYN) a phospholipid layer that covers a cell's surface and acts as a barrier between the inside of a cell and the cell's environment

organelle (AWR guh NEL) one of the small bodies in a cell's cytoplasm that are specialized to perform a specific function

nucleus (NOO klee uhs) in a eukaryotic cell, a membrane-bound organelle that contains the cell's DNA and that has a role in processes such as growth, metabolism, and reproduction

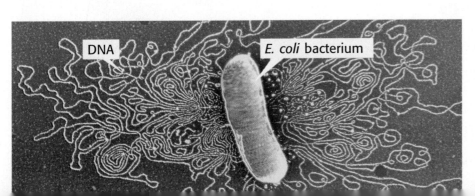

Figure 5   *This photomicrograph shows an Escherichia coli bacterium. The bacterium's cell membrane has been treated so that the cell's DNA is released.*

117

Two Kinds of Cells

All cells have cell membranes, organelles, cytoplasm, and DNA. But there are two basic types of cells. Cells without a nucleus are *prokaryotic* (proh KAR ee AHT ik) *cells*. Cells that have a nucleus are *eukaryotic* (yoo KAR ee AHT ik) *cells*. Prokaryotic cells are further classified into two groups: *bacteria* (bak TIR ee uh) and *archaea* (ahr KEE uh). **Figure 6** shows a prokaryotic cell and eukaryotic cell. Other prokaryotic and eukaryotic cells may look different from the cells in the diagrams below.

Standards Check How do prokaryotic cells differ from eukaryotic cells? 🐻 **7.1.a**

Prokaryotes

Bacteria and archaea are prokaryotes. **Prokaryotes** are single-celled organisms that do not have a nucleus. Even though prokaryotes do not have a nucleus, they do have DNA. The DNA of a prokaryote is a long, circular molecule. It is shaped like a twisted rubber band. Prokaryotes also do not have membrane-bound organelles. But they do have ribosomes. *Ribosomes* are tiny, round organelles made of protein and other material. Prokaryotic cells also have strong, weblike cell walls.

SCHOOL to HOME

Magnifying Glasses

You can make your own magnifying glasses by using items from around your home. Ask an adult to help you find clear drinking glasses. Look at a piece of newspaper through the glasses. Try holding the glasses at different heights and angles. Try putting small amounts of water in the glasses. Experiment until you find the best magnification.

ACTIVITY

prokaryote (proh KAR ee OHT) a single-celled organism that does not have a nucleus or membrane-bound organelles; examples are archaea and bacteria

Wordwise The prefix *pro-* means "before." The root *karyon* means "nut" or "kernel."

Figure 6 Two Kinds of Cells

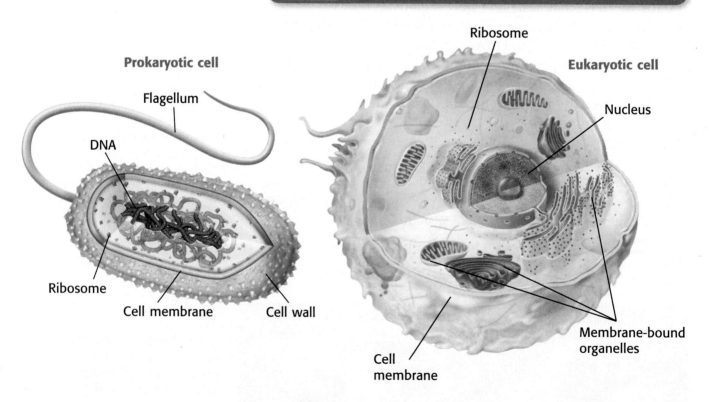

Prokaryotic cell
- Flagellum
- DNA
- Ribosome
- Cell membrane
- Cell wall

Eukaryotic cell
- Ribosome
- Nucleus
- Membrane-bound organelles
- Cell membrane

Eukaryotes

Eukaryotic cells are the largest cells. Most eukaryotic cells are still microscopic, but they are about 10 times as large as most prokaryotic cells.

Unlike bacteria and archaea, eukaryotic cells have a nucleus. The nucleus holds the cell's DNA. Eukaryotic cells have other membrane-bound organelles, too. Each kind of organelle has a specific job in the cell.

All living things that are not bacteria or archaea are made up of one or more eukaryotic cells. Organisms made up of eukaryotic cells are called **eukaryotes.** Yeasts and amoebas are single-celled eukaryotes. Plants and animals are eukaryotes that are made up of many cells.

eukaryote (yoo KAR ee OHT) an organism made up of cells that have a nucleus enclosed by a membrane; eukaryotes include protists, animals, plants, and fungi but not archaea or bacteria

---

SECTION Review

7.1.a, 7.1.c

Summary

- The cell theory states that all organisms are made of cells, the cell is the basic unit of all living things, and all cells come from other cells.

- All cells have a cell membrane, cytoplasm, and DNA.

- Most cells are too small to be seen with the naked eye. The surface area–to–volume ratio of a cell limits the size of the cell.

- The two basic kinds of cells are prokaryotic cells and eukaryotic cells. Eukaryotic cells have a nucleus and membrane-bound organelles. Prokaryotic cells do not.

- Prokaryotes are single-celled.

- Eukaryotes can be single-celled or multicellular.

Understanding Concepts

1. **Summarizing** What does the cell theory tell us about cells?

2. **Listing** Name three structures that every cell has.

3. **Describing** Why are most cells small?

INTERPRETING GRAPHICS The picture below shows an organism that has one cell. Use the picture to answer the next two questions.

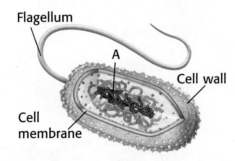

Flagellum

A

Cell wall

Cell membrane

4. **Identifying** Is this cell a prokaryotic cell or a eukaryotic cell? How can you tell?

5. **Identifying** What part of the organism is labeled "A"?

Critical Thinking

6. **Making Comparisons** Compare the ways in which eukaryotic cells and prokaryotic cells store their DNA.

7. **Applying Concepts** You have discovered a new single-celled organism. It has ribosomes and long, circular DNA. Is it a eukaryote or a prokaryote? Explain.

8. **Identifying Relationships** You are looking at a cell under a microscope. What characteristics would this cell have if the organism is a eukaryote? What characteristics would this cell have if the organism is a prokaryote? What would you look for first?

Math Skills

9. **Analyzing Shapes** Calculate the surface area–to–volume ratio of a cube whose sides are 3 cm long.

Internet Resources

For a variety of links related to this chapter, go to www.scilinks.org

Topic: Prokaryotic Cells
SciLinks code: HY71225

Eukaryotic Cells

Key Concept Eukaryotic cells have organelles that perform important functions.

What You Will Learn

- Eukaryotic cells have many parts—such as cell membranes, a nucleus, and ribosomes—in common.
- Plant cells and animal cells have some cell parts that are different.

Why It Matters

Learning how organelles function helps you know how cells stay alive.

Vocabulary

- cell wall
- cytoskeleton
- ribosome
- endoplasmic reticulum
- mitochondrion
- chloroplast
- Golgi complex
- vesicle
- lysosome

READING STRATEGY

Graphic Organizer In your **Science Journal,** make a Comparison Table that compares the structure, function, location in the cell, and presence in animal and plant cells of all the organelles discussed in this section.

cell wall (SEL WAWL) a rigid structure that surrounds the cell membrane and provides support to the cell

Even though most cells are small, cells are complex. A eukaryotic cell has many parts that help the cell stay alive. Some eukaryotic cells can be classified as plant cells or animal cells. Compare the plant cell in **Figure 1** with the animal cell in **Figure 2** to see the differences between these two types of cells.

Cell Wall

Plant cells have an outermost structure called a **cell wall.** A cell wall is a rigid structure that gives support to a cell. The cell walls of plants, fungi, archaea, and bacteria can be made of different materials. For example, plants and algae have cell walls made of a complex sugar called *cellulose.* **Figure 1** shows the cellulose fibers in the cell wall of a plant cell. Animal cells do not have cell walls.

Standards Check What is one characteristic that distinguishes plant cells from animal cells? 7.1.b

Figure 1 A Plant Cell

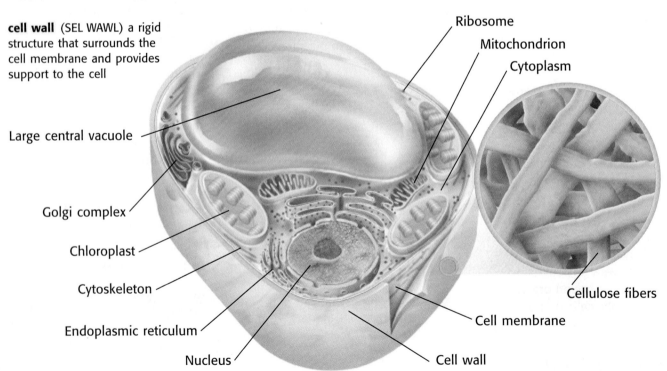

Ribosome
Mitochondrion
Cytoplasm
Large central vacuole
Golgi complex
Chloroplast
Cytoskeleton
Endoplasmic reticulum
Nucleus
Cell membrane
Cell wall
Cellulose fibers

Cell Membrane

All cells have a cell membrane made up of proteins and lipids. The *cell membrane* is a protective barrier that encloses a cell. It separates the cell's contents from the cell's environment. The cell membrane is the outermost structure in cells that lack a cell wall. In cells that have a cell wall, the cell membrane lies just inside the cell wall.

The cell membrane has two layers of phospholipids, shown in **Figure 2**. A *phospholipid* is a type of lipid. Each phospholipid has a *hydrophobic,* or "water fearing," end and a *hydrophilic,* or "water loving," end. The "water fearing" ends are on the inside of the cell membrane. The "water loving" ends form the outer part of the membrane. This structure makes it difficult for materials to pass through the membrane. Not allowing materials to pass through is one way the cell membrane protects the cell.

Some materials, such as nutrients and wastes, must pass through the cell membrane. These materials are able to pass through passageways made of proteins. Nutrients move into the cell—and wastes move out of the cell—through these protein passageways.

Standards Check How does the cell membrane protect the cell?
🐾 **7.1.a**

Figure 2 An Animal Cell

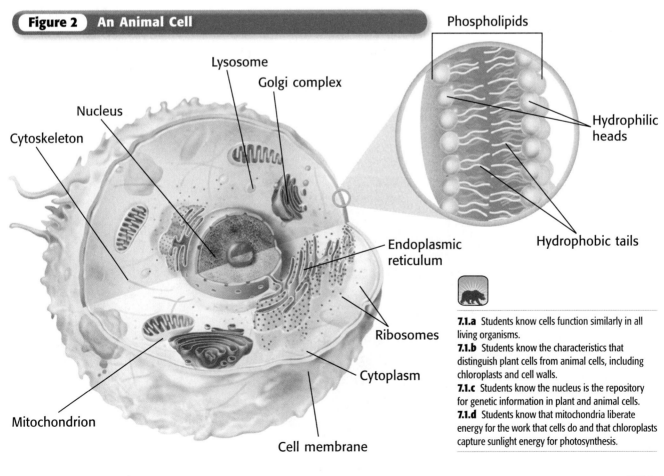

Phospholipids

Lysosome

Golgi complex

Nucleus

Cytoskeleton

Hydrophilic heads

Hydrophobic tails

Endoplasmic reticulum

Ribosomes

Cytoplasm

Mitochondrion

Cell membrane

7.1.a Students know cells function similarly in all living organisms.
7.1.b Students know the characteristics that distinguish plant cells from animal cells, including chloroplasts and cell walls.
7.1.c Students know the nucleus is the repository for genetic information in plant and animal cells.
7.1.d Students know that mitochondria liberate energy for the work that cells do and that chloroplasts capture sunlight energy for photosynthesis.

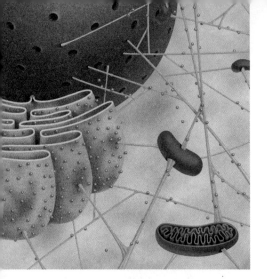

Cytoskeleton

The **cytoskeleton** is a web of proteins in the cytoplasm of some cells. Both plant cells and animal cells have a cytoskeleton. Many of the organelles in cells are attached to the cytoskeleton, as **Figure 3** shows. In an animal cell, the cytoskeleton defines the shape of the cell because the cell does not have a cell wall. Different cells in your body have different shapes because of how their cytoskeleton is arranged.

The cytoskeleton is also used for movement. The cytoskeleton can help objects move around within the cell. Some organisms use their cytoskeleton to form structures that help the organisms move.

Nucleus

All eukaryotic cells have a membrane-bound nucleus. The *nucleus* is a large organelle in a eukaryotic cell. It contains the cell's DNA. DNA is the genetic material that contains the information on how to make a cell's proteins. Proteins control the chemical reactions in a cell. They also provide structural support for cells and tissues. But proteins are not made in the nucleus. Messages for how to make proteins are given by the DNA. These messages are then sent out of the nucleus through the membranes that surround it.

The nucleus is covered by two membranes. Materials cross this double membrane by passing through pores. **Figure 4** shows a nucleus and nuclear pores. In many cells, the nucleus has a dark area called the *nucleolus* (noo KLEE uh luhs). A cell begins to make its ribosomes in the nucleolus.

Standards Check What is the function of the nucleus? **7.1.c**

Figure 3 *The cytoskeleton is a network of protein fibers that anchors the cell's organelles and other components of its cytoplasm.*

cytoskeleton (SIET oh SKEL uh tuhn) the cytoplasmic network of protein filaments that plays an essential role in cell movement, shape, and division

Figure 4 *The nucleus contains the cell's DNA.* **Does every cell have a nucleus?**

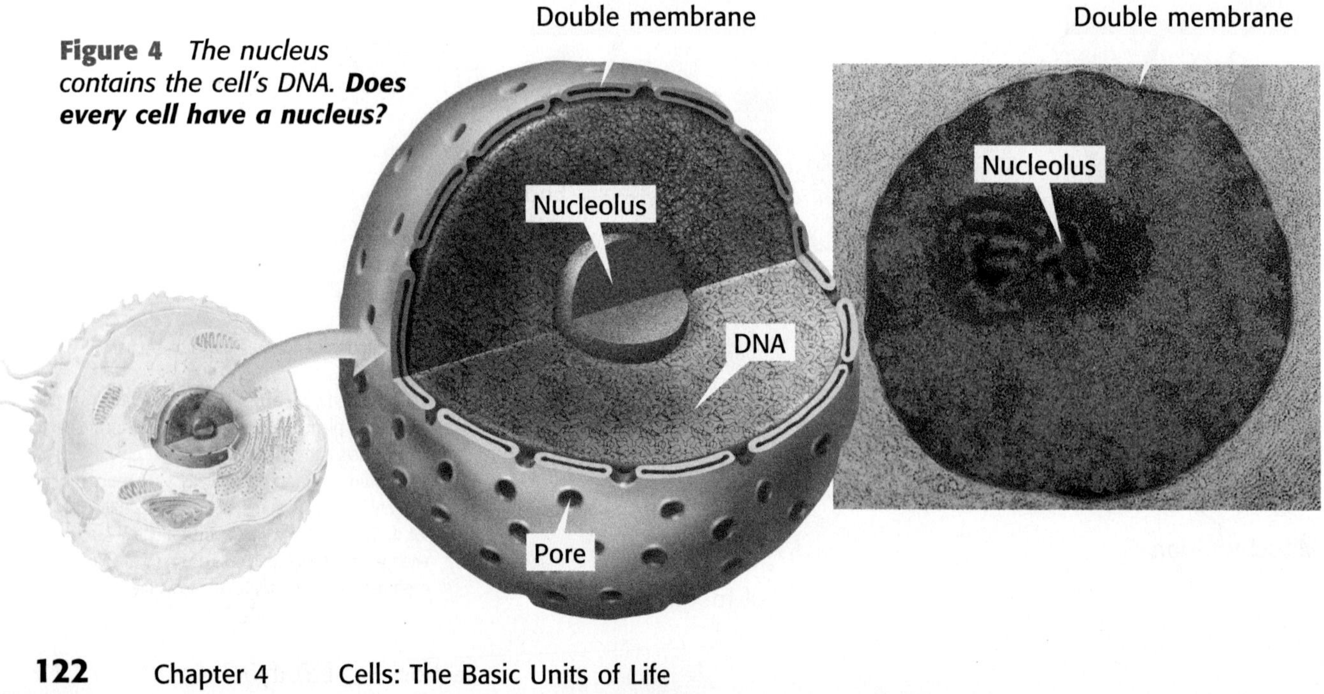

Double membrane

Double membrane

Nucleolus

Nucleolus

DNA

Pore

Ribosomes

Organelles that make proteins are called **ribosomes.** Ribosomes are the smallest organelles. And there are more ribosomes than there are any other organelles in a cell. Some ribosomes float freely in the cytoplasm. Others are attached to membranes or the cytoskeleton. Unlike most organelles, ribosomes are not covered by a membrane.

Ribosomes make proteins by assembling chains of amino acids. An *amino acid* is any of about 20 different organic molecules that are used to make proteins. All cells need proteins to live. Thus, all cells have ribosomes.

Endoplasmic Reticulum

Many chemical reactions take place in a cell. Many of these reactions happen on or in the endoplasmic reticulum. The **endoplasmic reticulum,** or ER, is a system of folded membranes in which proteins, lipids, and other materials are made. The ER is shown in **Figure 5.**

The ER is part of the internal delivery system of the cell. Its folded membrane contains many tubes and passageways. Substances move through the ER to different places in the cell.

The endoplasmic reticulum is either rough or smooth. The part of the ER covered in ribosomes is rough ER. Rough ER is usually found near the nucleus. Ribosomes on rough ER make many of the cell's proteins. The ER then delivers these proteins throughout the cell. The ER that lacks ribosomes is smooth ER. The functions of smooth ER include making lipids and breaking down toxic materials that could damage the cell.

ribosome (RIE buh sOHM) a cell organelle composed of RNA and protein; the site of protein synthesis

endoplasmic reticulum (EN doh PLAZ mik ri TIK yuh luhm) a system of membranes that is found in a cell's cytoplasm and that assists in the production, processing, and transport of proteins and in the production of lipids

Figure 5 *The endoplasmic reticulum (ER) is a system of membranes. Rough ER is covered with ribosomes. Smooth ER does not have ribosomes.*

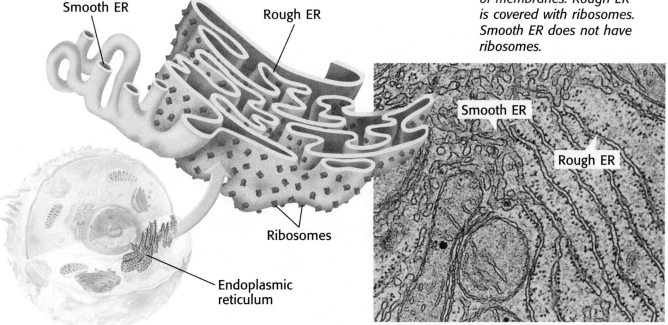

Smooth ER

Rough ER

Ribosomes

Endoplasmic reticulum

Smooth ER

Rough ER

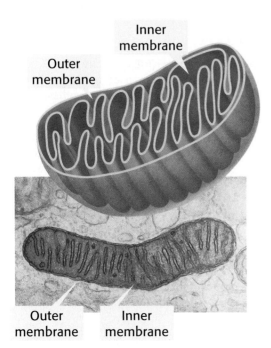

Inner membrane

Outer membrane

Outer membrane   Inner membrane

Figure 6 *Mitochondria break down sugar and make ATP. ATP is produced on the inner membrane.*

mitochondrion
(MIET oh KAHN dree uhn) in eukaryotic cells, the cell organelle that is surrounded by two membranes and that is the site of cellular respiration

chloroplast (KLAWR uh PLAST) an organelle found in plant and algae cells where photosynthesis occurs

Figure 7 *Chloroplasts harness and use the energy of the sun to make sugar. A green pigment—chlorophyll—captures the sun's energy.*

Mitochondria

A **mitochondrion** is the main power source of a cell. A mitochondrion is the organelle in which sugar is broken down to release energy. Mitochondria are covered by two membranes, as shown in **Figure 6.** Energy released by mitochondria is stored in a substance called *ATP* (**a**denosine **tri**phosphate). The cell then uses ATP to do work. ATP can be made at several places in a cell. But most of a cell's ATP is made on the inner membrane of the cell's mitochondria.

Most eukaryotic cells have mitochondria. Mitochondria are the size of some bacteria. Like bacteria, mitochondria have their own DNA, and mitochondria can divide within a cell.

Standards Check   Why are mitochondria important for cells?
🐻 **7.1.d**

Chloroplasts

Animal cells cannot make their own food. Plant cells are different. Some of them have chloroplasts. **Chloroplasts** are organelles in which photosynthesis takes place. They are found in plant, algae, and some prokaryotic cells. Like mitochondria, chloroplasts have two membranes and their own DNA. A chloroplast is shown in **Figure 7.** *Photosynthesis* is the process by which cells, such as plant cells, use sunlight, carbon dioxide, and water to make sugar and oxygen.

Chloroplasts are green because they contain *chlorophyll,* a green pigment. Chlorophyll is found in an internal membrane system within a chloroplast. Chlorophyll traps the energy of sunlight. This energy is used to make sugar. The sugar produced by photosynthesis is then used by mitochondria to make ATP.

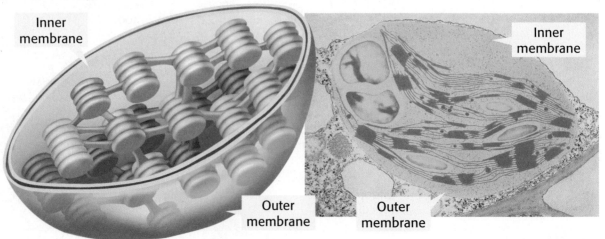

Inner membrane

Inner membrane

Outer membrane   Outer membrane

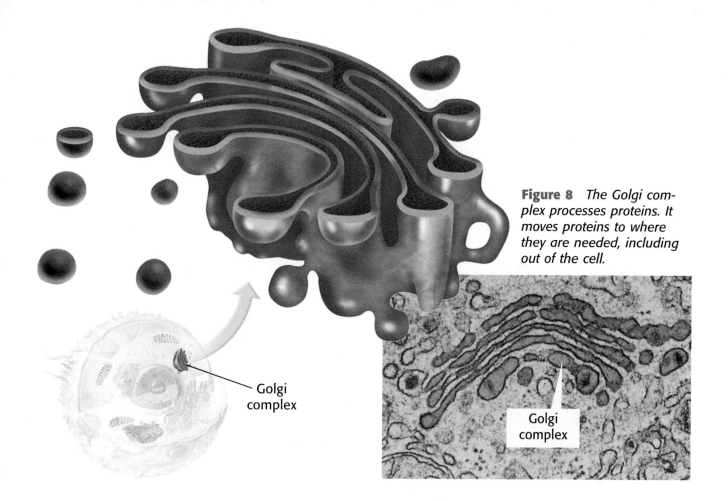

Figure 8 *The Golgi complex processes proteins. It moves proteins to where they are needed, including out of the cell.*

Golgi complex

Golgi complex

Golgi Complex

The organelle that packages and distributes proteins is called the **Golgi complex.** It is named after Camillo Golgi, the Italian scientist who first identified the organelle.

The Golgi complex, shown in **Figure 8,** looks like smooth ER. Lipids and proteins from the ER are delivered to the Golgi complex. There, the lipids and proteins may be modified to do different jobs. The final products are enclosed in a piece of the Golgi complex's membrane. This membrane pinches off to form a small bubble. The bubble transports its contents to other parts of the cell or out of the cell.

Cell Compartments

The bubble that forms from the Golgi complex's membrane is one example of a vesicle. A **vesicle** is a small sac that surrounds material to be moved into or out of a cell. All eukaryotic cells have vesicles. Vesicles also move material within a cell. For example, vesicles carry new proteins from the ER to the Golgi complex. Other vesicles carry material from the Golgi complex to other parts of the cell. Some vesicles form when part of the cell membrane surrounds an object that is outside the cell.

Golgi complex (GOHL jee KAHM PLEKS) a cell organelle that helps make and package materials to be transported out of the cell

vesicle (VES i kuhl) a small cavity or sac that contains materials in a eukaryotic cell

INTERNET ACTIVITY

Cell World

What would a cell look like from the inside? Create a brochure inviting tourists to visit various parts of the cell. Go to **go.hrw.com,** and type in the keyword HY7CELW.

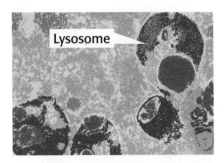

Lysosome

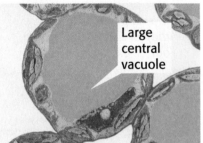

Large central vacuole

Figure 9 *Lysosomes digest materials inside a cell. In plant cells, the large central vacuole stores water.*

lysosome (LIE suh SOHM) a cell organelle that contains digestive enzymes

Lysosomes

Lysosomes are vesicles found mainly in animal cells. Lysosomes contain digestive enzymes. They are responsible for digestion inside a cell. Lysosomes destroy worn-out or damaged organelles, get rid of waste materials, and engulf foreign invaders. The foreign invaders are digested, and most of them are no longer harmful to the cell.

When eukaryotic cells engulf particles, they enclose the particles in vesicles. Lysosomes, shown in blue in **Figure 9,** bump into the vesicles, shown in purple, and pour enzymes into them. These enzymes digest the particles in the vesicles.

Standards Check Why are lysosomes important? 7.1.a

Vacuoles

A *vacuole* (VAK yoo OHL) is another type of vesicle found in cells. In plant and fungal cells, some vacuoles act like lysosomes. They store digestive enzymes and aid in digestion within the cell. The large central vacuole in a plant cell stores water and other liquids. Large central vacuoles that are full of water, such as the one in **Figure 9,** help support the cell. Some plants wilt when their large central vacuoles lose water. Some organelles and their functions are shown in **Table 1.**

Table 1	Organelles and Their Functions
Nucleus the organelle that contains the cell's DNA	**Chloroplast** the organelle that uses sunlight, carbon dioxide, and water to make food
Ribosome the organelle upon which amino acids are hooked together to make proteins	**Golgi complex** the organelle that processes and transports materials within and out of the cell
Endoplasmic reticulum the organelle that makes lipids, breaks down toxic substances, and packages proteins for the Golgi complex	**Large central vacuole** the organelle that stores water and other materials
Mitochondrion the organelle that breaks down food molecules to make ATP	**Lysosome** the organelle that digests wastes, cell parts, and foreign invaders

Summary

- Eukaryotic cells have organelles that perform functions that help cells remain alive.
- All cells have a cell membrane. Some cells have a cell wall. Some cells have a cytoskeleton.
- The nucleus of a eukaryotic cell contains the cell's genetic material, DNA.
- Ribosomes are the organelles that make proteins. Ribosomes are not covered by a membrane.
- The endoplasmic reticulum (ER) and the Golgi complex make and process proteins before the proteins are transported to other parts of the cell or out of the cell.
- Mitochondria and chloroplasts are organelles that provide chemical energy for the cell.
- Lysosomes are organelles responsible for digestion within a cell. In plant cells, the large central vacuole stores cell materials and sometimes acts like a large lysosome.
- Plant cells have cell parts that are not found in animal cells. Plant cells have cell walls, chloroplasts, and a large central vacuole.

Using Vocabulary

1. Write an original definition for *mitochondria, nucleus,* and *cell wall.*

Understanding Concepts

2. **Listing**   What are two functions of the cytoskeleton in animal cells?

3. **Describing**   What is the function of the Golgi complex? What is the function of the endoplasmic reticulum?

4. **Comparing**   Describe three ways in which plant cells differ from animal cells.

5. **Applying**   Every cell needs ribosomes. Explain why.

INTERPRETING GRAPHICS   Use the diagram below to answer the next two questions.

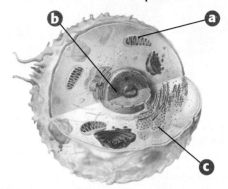

6. **Identifying**   Is this a diagram of a plant cell or an animal cell? Explain how you know.

7. **Describing**   What is the function of the organelle labeled "b"?

Critical Thinking

8. **Predicting Consequences**   A certain virus attacks the mitochondria in cells. What would happen to a cell if all of its mitochondria were destroyed?

9. **Expressing Opinions**   Do you think that having chloroplasts gives plant cells an advantage over animal cells? Support your opinion.

Math Skills

10. **Making Calculations**   There are 11 foreign invaders and 4 lysosomes in Cell A. If it takes each lysosome 1 h to digest 1 foreign invader, how long will it take to digest all of the foreign invaders?

Challenge

11. **Making Inferences**   Amoebas are single-celled eukaryotes. An amoeba moves by creating an extension of the cell. The cytoplasm from the rest of the cell flows into the extension. Given what you know about cell parts, determine which cell part inside of an amoeba is most likely used to make the extension.

Internet Resources

For a variety of links related to this chapter, go to www.scilinks.org
Topic: Eukaryotic Cells
SciLinks code: HY70541

The Organization of Living Things

Key Concept As multicellular organisms develop, their cells differentiate and form levels of organization.

▶ In some ways, organisms are like machines. Some machines have just one part. But most machines have many parts. Some organisms exist as a single cell. Other organisms have many cells—trillions in some cases.

Anything that can perform life processes by itself is an **organism.** There are two types of organisms: unicellular organisms and multicellular organisms.

Unicellular Organisms

Organisms that are made up of one cell are called *unicellular.* Prokaryotes, such as bacteria and archaea, are unicellular organisms. Eukaryotes such as yeasts, some algae, and some protists are also unicellular. A unicellular organism performs all of the necessary functions to stay alive. Unicellular organisms need fewer resources and can live in harsher conditions than organisms that have many cells.

Multicellular Organisms

Organisms that are made up of many cells are called *multicellular.* Plants, animals, some protists, and many fungi are multicellular organisms. A multicellular organism starts as a single cell, such as the fertilized egg shown in **Figure 1.** As the single cell develops into many cells, the cells become *differentiated,* or fixed, into different types of cells.

Figure 1 *Multicellular organisms that have differentiated cells, such as humans, can be traced back to a single fertilized egg.*

24 hours

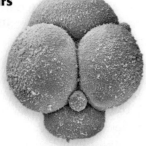

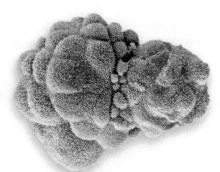

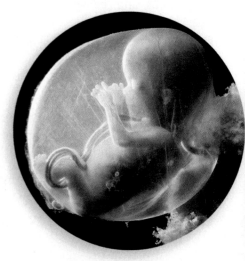

40 hours   **6 days**   **4 months**

The Characteristics of Being Multicellular

Multicellular organisms differ from unicellular organisms in many ways. Characteristics of multicellular organisms include the following:

- **Larger Size** Many multicellular organisms are small. But usually they are larger than unicellular organisms. Multicellular organisms grow by making more small cells, not by making their cells larger. Being large can be an advantage. Large organisms are prey for fewer predators. Large predators can eat a wider variety of prey.

- **Longer Life** A unicellular organism dies if its cell dies. But if a single cell in a multicellular organism dies, the organism continues to live.

- **Specialization** Each type of cell has a particular job. Specialization makes the organism more efficient than a unicellular organism. In some ways, having specialized cells is similar to having an assembly line at a factory. The assembly line allows the factory to produce more products in less time than a single individual could.

7.1.f Students know that as multicellular organisms develop, their cells differentiate.
7.5.a Students know plants and animals have levels of organization for structure and function, including cells, tissues, organs, organ systems, and the whole organism.

organism (AWR guh NIZ uhm) a living thing; anything that can carry out life processes independently

Standards Check How are multicellular organisms more efficient than unicellular organisms? 🐻 **7.1.f**

Quick Lab

A Division of Labor

In this activity, your teacher will ask you to model a unicellular organism or a multicellular organism. You will make paper chains according to the steps at right. The steps represent how organisms do work, such as making cell parts.

1. If you are a unicellular organism, you must complete all of the steps before you start over.

2. If you are a cell in a multicellular organism, you will be a member of a team. Each team will work together in an assembly line. Each team member represents a cell that completes only one step. Each team member will receive the product from the previous team member, complete the step, and pass the product to the next team member.

3. Listen for your teacher's directions about when to start and stop.

4. Who made longer chains: the multicellular organisms or the unicellular organisms?

5. How does this activity relate to cell specialization?

How to Make a Paper Chain

1. Use **scissors** to cut one 8 in. strip of paper.

2. Use a **marker** to draw a line down the middle of the length of one strip of paper.

3. Use a **marker of a different color** to draw three circles on the line.

4. Walk to a desk in the front of the classroom. For the first strip, tape the two ends together to form a loop. For the rest of the strips, thread one end of the strip through the previous loop, and tape the ends of the strip to form another loop.

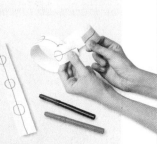

 15 min

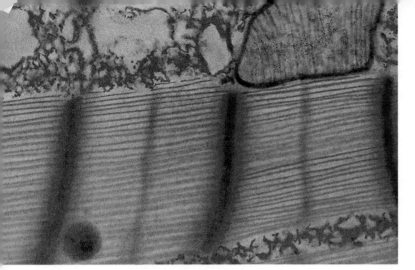

From Cells to Organisms

In a multicellular organism, such as a human, different kinds of cells perform different functions. These cells rely on each other and work together to do all of the activities needed for the organism to live. Such cells must be well organized in an organism. A multicellular organism can have four levels of organization: cells, tissues, organs, and organ systems.

Figure 2 *This photomicrograph shows a small part of one heart muscle cell. The green line surrounds one of many mitochondria, the powerhouses of the cell. The pink areas are muscle filaments.*

Cells: The First Level of Organization

Cells in a multicellular organism can be specialized. A *specialized* cell performs a specific function. The **function** of a cell is the activity that the cell performs. The function of a specialized cell relates to the cell's structure. **Structure** is the arrangement of parts in an organism. It includes the shape of a part and the material of which the part is made. For example, the cardiac muscle cell in **Figure 2** is a specialized muscle cell. Heart muscle cells have internal structures that contract and that make the heart pump blood.

Plants also have cells that perform specific functions. For example, a special type of cell is found in the layer between the inside of a plant and the outside of the plant. These cells are shaped like sausages, as **Figure 3** shows. Pairs of these sausage-shaped cells, which are called *guard cells,* control the size of openings called *stoma.* The stoma allow gases, such as carbon dioxide and oxygen, to move into and out of a leaf.

function (FUHNGK shuhn) the special, normal, or proper activity of an organ or part

structure (STRUHK shuhr) the arrangement of parts in an organism

Figure 3 *Some plant cells have structures that allow the cells to perform specialized functions.*

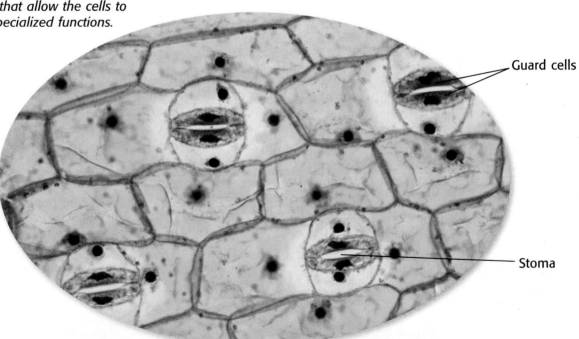

Guard cells

Stoma

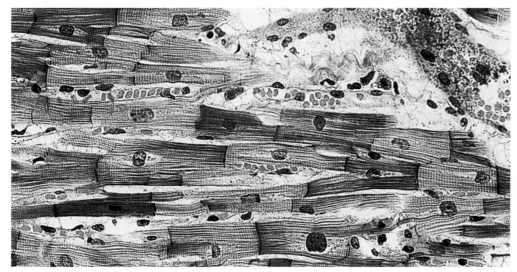

Figure 4 *This photomicrograph shows cardiac muscle tissue. Cardiac muscle tissue is made up of many cardiac cells.*

Tissues: The Second Level of Organization

A **tissue** is a group of cells that work together to perform a specific job. The material around and between the cells is also part of the tissue. The cardiac muscle tissue, shown in **Figure 4,** is made of many cardiac muscle cells. Cardiac muscle tissue is just one type of tissue in a heart.

Animals have four basic types of tissues: nerve tissue, muscle tissue, connective tissue, and protective tissue. In contrast, plants have three types of tissues: transport tissue, protective tissue, and ground tissue. Transport tissue moves water and nutrients through a plant. Protective tissue covers the plant. It helps the plant retain water and protects the plant from damage. Photosynthesis takes place in ground tissue.

Organs: The Third Level of Organization

A structure that is made up of two or more tissues working together to perform a specific function is called an **organ.** For example, your heart is an organ. It is made mostly of cardiac muscle tissue. But your heart also has nerve tissue and tissues of the blood vessels that work together to make your heart the powerful pump that it is.

Another organ is your stomach. It also has several kinds of tissues. Muscle tissue in the stomach makes food move in and through the stomach. Special tissues make chemicals that help digest your food. Connective tissue holds the stomach together, and nervous tissue carries messages back and forth between the stomach and the brain. Other organs include the intestines, brain, and lungs.

Plants also have different kinds of tissues that work together as organs. The leaf of a plant is an organ that contains tissue that traps sunlight energy to make food. Other examples of organs in plants are stems and roots.

Standards Check What is an organ? 7.5.a

tissue (TISH oo) a group of similar cells that perform a common function

organ (AWR guhn) a collection of tissues that carry out a specialized function of the body

A Pet Protist
Imagine that you have a tiny, box-shaped protist for a pet. To care for your pet protist properly, you have to figure out how much to feed it. The dimensions of your protist are roughly 25 μm × 20 μm × 2 μm. If seven food particles can enter through each square micrometer of surface area per second, how many particles can your protist eat in 1 min? Record you work in your **Science Journal.**

Organ Systems: The Fourth Level of Organization

A group of organs working together to perform a particular function is called an **organ system.** Each organ system has a specific job to do in the body. The cardiovascular system, shown in **Figure 5,** includes organs and tissues, such as the heart and blood vessels. The job of the cardiovascular system is to transport blood throughout the body.

The digestive system is an organ system made up of several organs, including the stomach and intestines. The digestive system's job is to break down food into small particles. Other parts of the body then use these small particles as fuel. In turn, the digestive system depends on the respiratory and cardiovascular systems for oxygen.

Plants also have organ systems. They include leaf systems, root systems, and stem systems.

Organisms

Multicellular organisms, such as plants and animals, have levels of organization. Cells form the tissues, the tissues form the organs, and the organs form the organ systems of a multicellular organism. The levels of organization in a multicellular organism are shown in **Figure 6.**

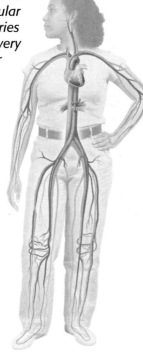

Figure 5 *The cardiovascular system carries blood to every cell in your body.*

organ system (AWR guhn SIS tuhm) a group of organs that work together to perform body functions

Standards Check List the four levels of organization in multicellular organisms. 🐻 **7.5.a**

| **Figure 6** | **Levels of Organization** |

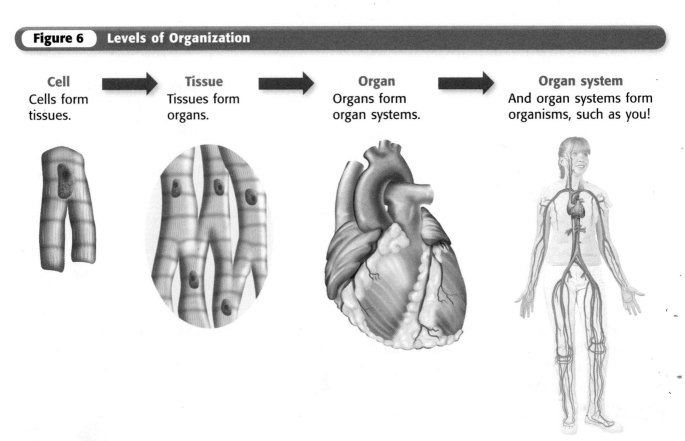

| **Cell** | **Tissue** | **Organ** | **Organ system** |
| Cells form tissues. | Tissues form organs. | Organs form organ systems. | And organ systems form organisms, such as you! |

Unicellular Organization

Prokaryotes, most protists, and some kinds of fungi are unicellular. Although some of these organisms live in colonies, they are still unicellular. These unicellular organisms live together, and each cell in the colony is the same. However, each cell must carry out all life processes in order for that cell to survive. In contrast, even the simplest multicellular organism has specialized cells that depend on each other in order to survive.

A slime mold is shown in **Figure 7.** A slime mold is a unicellular organism in which individual cells can come together to form a large group.

Figure 7 *Slime molds eat small organisms and break down organic matter.*

Using Vocabulary

1. Use *tissue, organ,* and *multicellular* in separate sentences.

Understanding Concepts

2. **Describing** Describe the four levels of organization in multicellular organisms.

3. **Applying** Explain how different types of tissues work together in the heart, an organ.

4. **Demonstrating** The layer between the outside of a plant leaf and the inside of the leaf contains specialized cells called *guard cells.* How does the structure of guard cells relate to the function of guard cells?

Critical Thinking

5. **Predicting Consequences** What would happen if the cells of a developing plant did not differentiate into guard cells?

6. **Making Inferences** Why can multicellular organisms be more complex than unicellular organisms?

7. **Making Comparisons** Organisms need to perform life functions. How do the ways in which a multicellular organism and a unicellular organism perform life functions differ?

Math Skills

8. **Analyzing Shapes** Multicellular organism A is a cube. Each of its sides is 3 cm long. The volume of each of its cells is 1 cm³. How many cells does the organism have?

Challenge

9. **Applying Concepts** Think of an environment on Earth in which you would expect to find unicellular organisms but no multicellular organisms. Why are unicellular organisms able to survive in this environment?

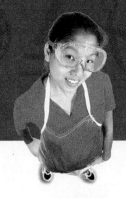

Skills Practice Lab

Cells Alive!

You have probably used a microscope to look at single-celled organisms such as those shown below. These organisms can be found in pond water. In the following exercise, you will look at algae of the genus *Protococcus*, which form a greenish stain on tree trunks, wooden fences, flowerpots, and buildings.

OBJECTIVES

Observe the structure of a eukaryotic organism.

Compare the structure of several organisms.

MATERIALS

- algae of the genus *Protococcus* (or other algae)
- eyedropper
- microscope
- saucer
- slide, microscope, and coverslip
- water

SAFETY

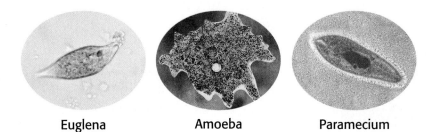

Euglena   Amoeba   Paramecium

Procedure

① Locate some algae of the genus *Protococcus*. Scrape a small sample into a container. Bring the sample to the classroom. If you can't find these algae outdoors, look for algae on the glass in an aquarium. Such algae may not be members of the genus *Protococcus* but will be very good substitutes.

② Mix the scraping in a few drops of water in a saucer. Draw up the mixture with an eyedropper, and carefully squeeze one or two drops onto a slide.

③ Place one edge of the coverslip on one end of the slide face. Hold the coverslip at about a 45° angle to the slide.

7.1.b Students know the characteristics that distinguish plant cells from animal cells, including chloroplasts and cell walls.
7.1.c Students know the nucleus is the repository for genetic information in plant and animal cells.

Investigation and Experimentation
7.7.a Select and use appropriate tools and technology (including calculators, computers, balances, spring scales, microscopes, and binoculars) to perform tests, collect data, and display data.
7.7.d Construct scale models, maps, and appropriately labeled diagrams to communicate scientific knowledge (e.g., motion of Earth's plates and cell structure).

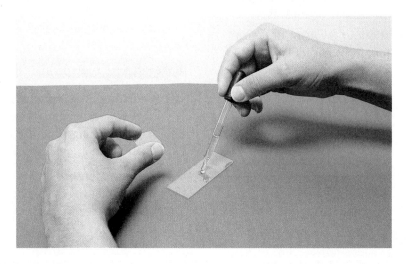

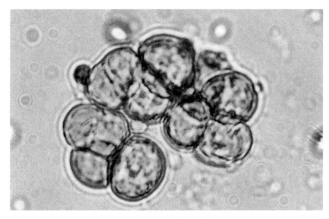

Protococcal cells

4 Draw the edge of the coverslip along the slide until the edge comes into contact with the liquid. Gently lower the coverslip onto the slide. Avoid trapping any air bubbles under the coverslip.

5 Set the microscope on low power to examine the algae. Draw the cells that you see.

6 Switch to high power to examine a single cell. Draw the cell on a separate sheet of paper.

7 You will probably see several chloroplasts in each cell. Label a chloroplast on your drawing. What is the function of the chloroplast?

8 Another structure that should be clearly visible in all the algae cells is the nucleus. Find a cell's nucleus, and label it on your drawing. What is the function of the nucleus?

9 What does the cytoplasm look like? Describe any movement that you see inside the cells.

Analyze the Results

10 **Examining Data**   Is a protococcus unicellular or multicellular?

11 **Examining Data**   How does a protococcus differ from an amoeba?

12 **Identifying Patterns**   How can you tell if a protococcus is eukaryotic or prokaryotic?

Draw Conclusions

13 **Interpreting Results**   Discuss how the shape of the cells and the structures within the cells differ between a protococcus and an amoeba.

14 **Interpreting Results**   How does a protococcus get its nutrition? Is this method different from the method used by an amoeba?

15 **Making Predictions**   If there were no light for some time, predict whether the protococcus or the amoeba would survive more easily, and explain why.

Big Idea Question

16 **Drawing Conclusions**   What cell parts were you able to observe in the algae? Are these cell parts found in all living organisms? Explain your answer.

Science Skills Activity

Scientific Methods	Research	Data Analysis	Models, Maps & Diagrams

Constructing Scale Diagrams

▶ **Tutorial**

 Investigation and Experimentation
7.7.d Construct scale models, maps, and appropriately labeled diagrams to communicate scientific knowledge (e.g., motion of Earth's plates and cell structure).

Procedure

When a scientist needs to study objects that are too big or too small to fit on a piece of paper, he or she uses a scale diagram. A scale diagram shows the relationship between the size of the object shown on the diagram and the actual size of the object. The following procedure explains how to construct a scale diagram.

1 Find the actual size of the object. You can measure the object if it is big enough, or do research to find its size. For example, if you wanted to draw a scale diagram of a yeast cell, you might research yeast cells and find that the longest yeast cell is 10 μm long.

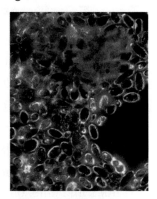

Yeast The longest individual cell is 10 μm long.

2 Once you determine the scale, the actual measurement divided by the scale gives you the measurement of the object in scale units. For example, to draw a scale diagram of a yeast cell, you might decide that one square unit, or scale unit on a piece of graph paper, is equal to 2 μm. Therefore, a yeast cell that is 10 μm in length would equal 5 scale units on a piece of graph paper.

Scale: 1 scale unit:2 μm
10 μm ÷ 2 μm = 5 scale units

3 Mark the dimensions of your object in scale units on a piece of graph paper. Draw the object so that it begins and ends on the spots that you marked.

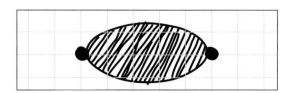

▶ **You Try It!**

Procedure

Scale diagrams can be used to compare objects. Construct a scale diagram of each cell shown below. The photos were taken using a microscope. Each photo has a different magnification. Use the actual dimensions of the cells to determine the measurement of the cells in scale units. Construct your diagram on graph paper using the following scale: 1 scale unit = 5 μm.

Euglena The average individual cell is 100 μm long.

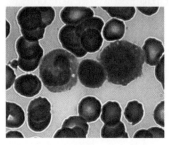

Red blood cell The average diameter is 7 μm.

Chapter Summary

go.hrw.com
SUPER SUMMARY
KEYWORD: HY7CELS

The Big Idea
All organisms are composed of one or more cells.

Section

Vocabulary

1 The Characteristics of Cells

Key Concept Cells function similarly in all living organisms.

- The cell theory explains why cells are important for living things.
- All cells have a cell membrane, cytoplasm, and DNA.
- Prokaryotic cells and eukaryotic cells differ in how their genetic information is contained.

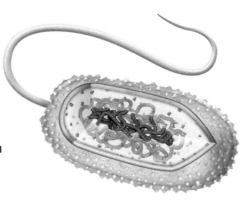

A bacterium is a prokaryotic cell.

cell p. 114
cell membrane p. 117
organelle p. 117
nucleus p. 117
prokaryote p. 118
eukaryote p. 119

2 Eukaryotic Cells

Key Concept Eukaryotic cells have organelles that perform important functions.

- Eukaryotic cells have many cell parts—such as cell membranes, a nucleus, and ribosomes—in common.
- Plant cells and animal cells have some cell parts that are different.

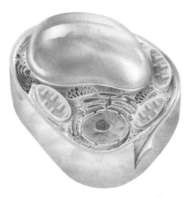

A plant cell is made of many cell parts, such as cell walls and chloroplasts.

cell wall p. 120
cytoskeleton p. 122
ribosome p. 123
endoplasmic reticulum p. 123
mitochondrion p. 124
chloroplast p. 124
Golgi complex p. 125
vesicle p. 125
lysosome p. 126

3 The Organization of Living Things

Key Concept As multicellular organisms develop, their cells differentiate and form levels of organization.

- Unicellular organisms are made up of one cell, and multicellular organisms are made up of many cells.
- The cells of multicellular organisms can differentiate to become specialized types of cells.
- The levels of organization in multicellular organisms are cells, tissues, organs, and organ systems.

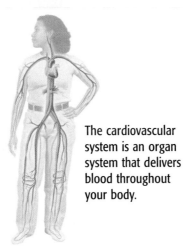

The cardiovascular system is an organ system that delivers blood throughout your body.

organism p. 128
function p. 130
structure p. 130
tissue p. 131
organ p. 131
organ system p. 132

Chapter Review

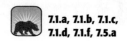

7.1.a, 7.1.b, 7.1.c, 7.1.d, 7.1.f, 7.5.a

Organize

Layered Book   Review the FoldNote that you created at the beginning of the chapter. Add to or correct the FoldNote based on what you have learned.

Using Vocabulary

1. **Academic Vocabulary**   Which of the following words is the closest in meaning to the word *structure?*
   a. evidence   **c.** duty
   b. shape   **d.** location

Complete each of the following sentences by choosing the correct term from the word bank.

cell	organ
cell membrane	prokaryote
organelles	differentiate
cell wall	tissue

2. A(n) ___ is the smallest structural and functional unit of living things.

3. Two types of ___ are ribosomes and mitochondria.

4. During development, the cells of a multicellular organism ___, which allows them to be specialized.

5. A(n) ___ is a group of cells working together to perform a specific function.

Understanding Concepts

Multiple Choice

6. Which of the following best describes an organ?
   a. a group of cells that work together to perform a specific job
   b. a group of tissues that belong to different systems
   c. a group of tissues that work together to perform a specific job
   d. a body structure, such as muscles or lungs

7. In eukaryotic cells, which organelle contains the DNA?
   a. nucleus   **c.** smooth ER
   b. Golgi complex   **d.** vacuole

8. Which of the following statements is part of the cell theory?
   a. All cells suddenly appear by themselves.
   b. All cells come from other cells.
   c. All organisms are multicellular.
   d. All cells have identical parts.

9. The surface area–to–volume ratio of a cell limits
   a. the number of organelles that the cell has.
   b. the size of the cell.
   c. where the cell lives.
   d. the types of nutrients that a cell needs.

10. Two types of organisms whose cells do NOT have a nucleus are
    a. prokaryotes and eukaryotes.
    b. plants and animals.
    c. bacteria and archaea.
    d. single-celled and multicellular organisms.

Short Answer

11. **Listing**   Describe the four levels of organization in multicellular organisms.

INTERPRETING GRAPHICS   Use the diagram below to answer the next three questions.

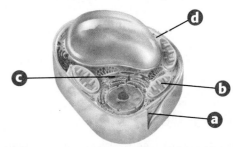

12. **Analyzing**   Is this a plant or an animal cell?

13. **Identifying**   Which letter identifies the structure that captures sunlight energy for photosynthesis?

14. **Applying**   Which letter identifies the structure that makes proteins and lipids and that contains passageways through which substances move from place to place in the cell?

Writing Skills

15 Creative Writing   Write a paragraph from the perspective of an organelle in a plant cell. Describe which organelle you are and what you do for the cell. Include information about how your structure relates to your function.

Critical Thinking

16 Concept Mapping   Use the following terms to create a concept map: *cells, organisms, Golgi complex, organ systems, organs, nucleus, organelle,* and *tissues.*

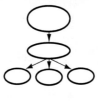

17 Making Comparisons   Compare the functions of the endoplasmic reticulum with the functions of the Golgi complex.

18 Evaluating Hypotheses   One of your classmates states a hypothesis that all organisms must have organ systems. Is your classmate's hypothesis valid? Explain your answer.

19 Predicting Consequences   What would happen if all of the ribosomes in your cells disappeared?

INTERPRETING GRAPHICS   Use the diagram below to answer the next question.

20 Making Inferences   Describe what could happen to an organism if the organ system shown above failed to function properly.

21 Making Comparisons   Compare how a plant cell retains its shape to how an animal cell retains its shape. Be sure to include in your explanation which cell parts are used by each type of cell to maintain its shape.

22 Making Comparisons   Compare how a eukaryote stores DNA to how a prokaryote stores DNA.

23 Applying Concepts   If you used a microscope to observe a heart cell and a skin cell, would you find that the two cells are exactly the same? Explain your answer.

24 Expressing Opinions   How do you think cell differentiation affects an organism? Support your answer with examples.

Math Skills

INTERPRETING GRAPHICS   Use the diagram below to answer the next question.

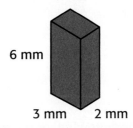

6 mm

3 mm   2 mm

25 Analyzing Shapes   What is the surface area-to-volume ratio for a cell that has the shape depicted in the diagram?

Challenge

26 Making Inferences   A plant cell has chloroplasts that capture sunlight for photosynthesis. Plant cells have mitochondria that release energy that the cell can use to do work. Animal cells have mitochondria but do not have chloroplasts. How do animal cells get the sugars that mitochondria use to release energy?

REVIEWING ACADEMIC VOCABULARY

1 **Which of the following words is the closest in meaning to the word *liberate*?**

A constrain

B tolerate

C protect

D free

2 **Choose the appropriate form of the word *differentiate* for the following sentence: When cells ___ , they become specialized.**

A different

B differentiate

C differ

D differentiation

3 **Which of the following is the noun form of the word *illustrate?*￼**

A illustrated

B illustrate

C illustration

D illustrating

4 **Which of the following words means "the arrangement of the parts of a whole"?**

A structure

B function

C inclusion

D container

5 **Which of the following words means "something that can be seen"?**

A dominant

B visible

C identical

D process

REVIEWING CONCEPTS

6 **The cell theory has three parts. The first states that all organisms are made up of one or more cells. The second states that the cell is the basic unit of all living things. What does the third part state?**

A Cells were discovered by accident.

B Single-celled organisms are protists.

C All cells come from existing cells.

D DNA is contained in a cell's nucleus.

7 **Some cells have nuclei, and some do not. Cells that have nuclei are called**

A prokaryotic. C eukaryotic.

B archaea. D ribosomes.

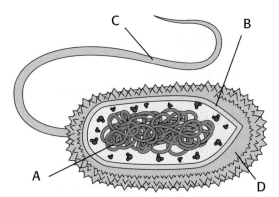

8 **Which part of the cell is pictured at point A in the diagram above?**

A cell wall C DNA

B flagellum D cell membrane

9 **Eukaryotic plant and animal cells have many of the same organelles, but how do these cells differ?**

A Animal cells have cytoskeletons, and plant cells do not.

B Animals cells have phospholipids, and plant cells do not.

C Plant cells have ribosomes, and animal cells do not.

D Plant cells have cell walls, and animal cells do not.

10 Mitochondria are important organelles within a cell. What would most likely happen if a cell's mitochondria were not functioning properly?

A The cell would use lysosomes to release energy.

B The cell's level of ATP would decrease.

C The cell would create new mitochondria by cell division.

D The cell's level of sugar would decrease.

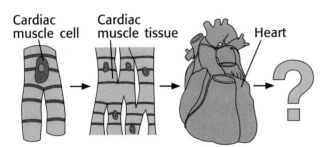

Cardiac muscle cell   Cardiac muscle tissue   Heart

11 Which of the following choices correctly completes the diagram above?

A Cardiac organ

B Connective tissue

C Cardiovascular organ system

D Human organism

12 What types of cells differentiate to become specialized?

A the cells of multicellular organisms

B prokaryotic cells

C bacterial cells

D the cells of unicellular organisms

13 Why are a plant cell's chloroplasts green?

A because they trap sunlight

B because they contain chlorophyll

C because they make sugar

D because they have DNA

REVIEWING PRIOR LEARNING

14 Some unicellular organisms are decomposers. Others, including some bacteria, are

A protists.   **C** eukaryotes.

B organelles.   **D** producers.

15 Plants make their food through photosynthesis. What substances must plants have in order to begin photosynthesis?

A sunlight, oxygen, and water

B sunlight, carbon dioxide, and water

C water and carbon dioxide

D sunlight and oxygen

16 Multicellular plants have many specialized structures. What function does the xylem perform in multicellular vascular plants?

A The xylem transports water and minerals from the roots to the leaves.

B The xylem is the place where photosynthesis takes place in a plant.

C The xylem breaks down sugar into a form that plant cells can use.

D The xylem is a woody tissue that fills the stem of a plant.

17 How does energy enter an ecosystem?

A as sunlight

B as ATP

C as food

D as prokaryotes

Standards Assessment

Science in Action

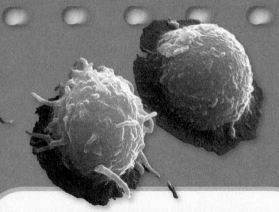

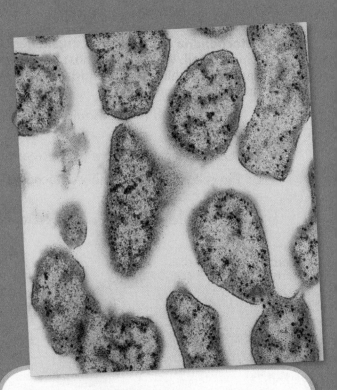

Scientific Discoveries

Discovery of the Stem Cell

What do Parkinson's disease, diabetes, aplastic anemia, and Alzheimer's disease have in common? All of these diseases are diseases for which stem cells may provide treatment or a cure. Stem cells are unspecialized cells from which all other kinds of cells can grow. And research on stem cells has been going on almost since microscopes were invented. But scientists have been able to culture, or grow, stem cells in laboratories for only about the last 20 years. Research during these 20 years has shown scientists that stem cells can be useful in treating—and possibly curing—a variety of diseases.

Weird Science

Extremophiles

Are there organisms on Earth that can give scientists clues about possible life elsewhere? Yes, there are! Such organisms are called *extremophiles*. They live where the environment is extreme in some way, such as in temperature. Some extremophiles live in the hot volcanic thermal vents of the deep ocean. Other extremophiles live in the extreme cold of Antarctica. Most extremophiles are archaea, but some are bacteria, fungi, or animals.

Language Arts ACTIVITY

Imagine that you are a doctor who treats diseases such as Parkinson's disease. Design and create a pamphlet or brochure that you could use to explain some of the methods used to treat Parkinson's disease. Include a description of how stem cells might be used to treat one of your patients who has Parkinson's disease. Be sure to include information about Parkinson's disease.

Social Studies ACTIVITY

Do some research about an extremophile, and make a poster showing what you learned about it, including where it can be found, under what conditions it lives, how it survives, and how it is used.

Caroline Schooley

Microscopist Imagine that your assignment is the following: Go outside. Look at 1 ft² of the ground for 30 min. Make notes about what you observe. Be prepared to describe what you see. If you look at the ground with just your naked eyes, you may quickly run out of things to see. But what would happen if you used a microscope to look? How much more would you be able to see? And how much more would you have to talk about? Caroline Schooley could tell you.

Caroline Schooley joined a science club in middle school. That's when her interest in looking at things through a microscope began. Since then, Schooley has spent many years at the University of California at Berkeley teaching about the study of life through a microscope. Schooley is a microscopist. A *microscopist* is someone who uses a microscope to explore the world of small things that cannot be seen by the naked eye. And with today's powerful electron microscopes, microscopists can study things that we could never see before, such as atoms.

Math ACTIVITY

An average bacterium is about 0.000002 m long. A pencil point is about 0.001 m wide. Approximately how many bacteria lined up end to end would fit across a pencil point? Record your work in your **Science Journal.**

Internet Resources

- To learn more about careers in science, visit **www.scilinks.org** and enter the SciLinks code HY70225.

- To learn more about these Science in Action topics, visit **go.hrw.com** and type in the keyword HY7CELF.

- Check out articles related to this chapter by visiting **go.hrw.com**. Just type in the keyword HY7CELC.

Improving Comprehension

Graphic Organizers are important visual tools that can help you organize information and improve your reading comprehension. The Graphic Organizer below is called a *cause-and-effect map*. Instructions for creating other types of Graphic Organizers are located in the **Study Skills** section of the Appendix.

How to Make a Cause-and-Effect Map

❶ Draw a box, and write a cause in the box. You can have as many cause boxes as you want. The diagram shown here is one example of a cause-and-effect map.

❷ Draw another box to the right of the cause box to represent an effect. You can have as many effect boxes as you want. Draw arrows from each cause box to the appropriate effect boxes.

❸ In the cause boxes, explain the process that makes up the cause. In the effect boxes, write a description of the effect or details about the effect.

When to Use a Cause-and-Effect Map

A cause-and-effect map is a useful tool for illustrating a specific type of scientific process. Use a cause-and-effect map when you want to describe how, when, or why one event causes another event. As you read, look for events that are either causes or results of other events, and draw a cause-and-effect map that shows the relationships between the events.

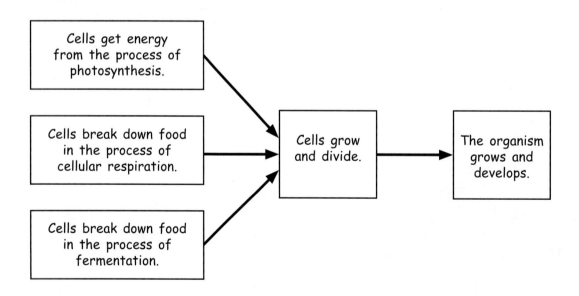

You Try It!

This Reading Strategy can also be used within the chapter that you are about to read. Practice making your own *cause-and-effect map* as directed in the Reading Strategy for Section ❶. Record your work in your **Science Journal.**

Unpacking the Standards

The information below "unpacks" the standards by breaking them down into basic parts. The higher-level, academic vocabulary is highlighted and defined to help you understand the language of the standards. "What It Means" restates the standards as simply as possible.

California Standard	Academic Vocabulary	What It Means
7.1.b Students know the characteristics that distinguish plant cells from animal cells, including chloroplasts and cell walls.		Plant cells have some unique structures that make plant cells different from animal cells. These structures include chloroplasts and a cell wall.
7.1.d Students know that mitochondria **liberate** energy for the work that cells do and that chloroplasts capture sunlight **energy** for photosynthesis.	**liberate** (LIB uhr AYT) to release; to set free **energy** (EN uhr jee) the capacity to do work	Mitochondria release energy from sugar to power the cell's life processes. Chloroplasts use energy from the sun to produce sugars and oxygen.
7.1.e Students know cells divide to increase their numbers through a **process** of mitosis, which results in two daughter cells with **identical** sets of chromosomes.	**process** (PRAH ses) a set of steps, events, or changes **identical** (ie DEN ti kuhl) being exactly the same	Cells split to make more cells through a process called mitosis. Through this process, a single cell becomes two cells that have the same genetic material.
7.2.e Students know DNA (deoxyribonucleic acid) is the genetic material of living organisms and is **located** in the chromosomes of each cell.	**located** (LOH KAYT id) to be in a certain place	DNA is the material that determines what traits are passed from one generation of living things to the next. DNA is found in the chromosomes of each cell.

5

The Cell in Action

The Big Idea

Cells carry out important life functions, such as obtaining energy, growing, and making new cells.

California Standards

Focus on Life Sciences

7.1 All living organisms are composed of cells, from just one to many trillions, whose details usually are visible only through a microscope. (Sections 1 and 2)

7.2 A typical cell of any organism contains genetic instructions that specify its traits. Those traits may be modified by environmental influences. (Section 2)

Investigation and Experimentation

7.7 Scientific progress is made by asking meaningful questions and conducting careful investigations. (Science Skills Activity)

Math
7.1.1 Mathematical Reasoning
7.1.3 Number Sense

English–Language Arts
7.2.1 Writing
7.2.3 Reading

About the Photo

This *Elodea* plant cell has been magnified to be over 400 times as large as its actual size. At this magnification, cell walls and round, green chloroplasts are visible. Chloroplasts are the site of photosynthesis, the process by which plants use energy from the sun to make food.

Organize

Layered Book

Before you read this chapter, create the FoldNote entitled "Layered Book." Label the tabs of the layered book with "Photosynthesis," "Cellular respiration," "Fermentation," and "The cell cycle." As you read the chapter, write information that you learn about each category on the appropriate tab.

Instructions for creating FoldNotes are located in the Study Skills section on p. 580 of the Appendix.

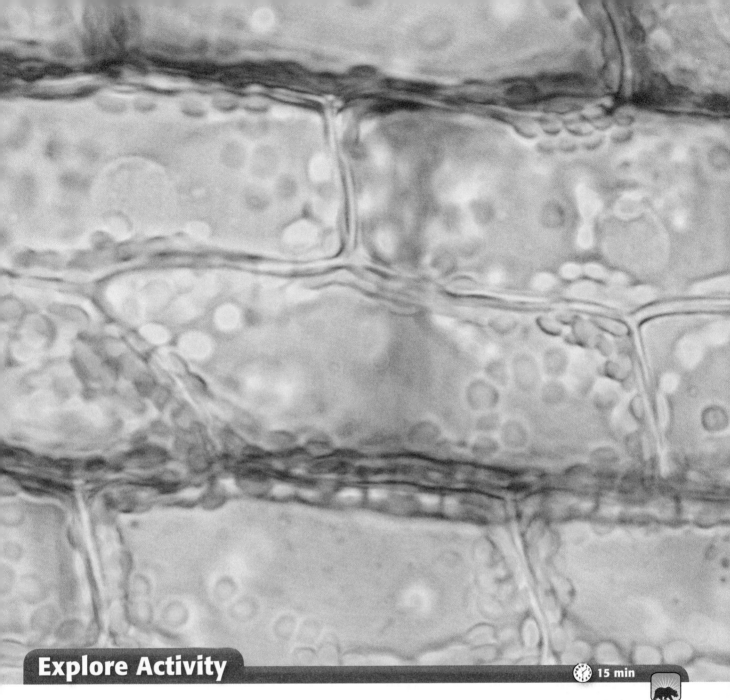

Explore Activity

🕐 15 min

The Purpose of Pigment

Chlorophyll is a green pigment found in the chloroplasts of plant cells. Chlorophyll gives plants their green color. Sunlight stimulates the formation of chlorophyll. Chlorophyll is important for photosynthesis because chlorophyll absorbs energy from the sun. In this activity, you will observe how chlorophyll affects the appearance of a plant.

Procedure

1. Gather a **large, presoaked lima bean** and a **magnifying lens.** A lima bean is actually the seed of the lima bean plant.

2. Carefully remove the softened outer shell that covers the seed. Gently separate the two larger halves of the seed.

3. Use the magnifying lens to examine the small plant between the two halves. Draw what you see.

7.1.d

4. Examine the **seedling** supplied by your teacher. Draw what you see.

Analysis

5. Compare the size and appearance of the two plants.

6. Both of these samples are the same type of plant. Why are they different colors?

7. Which plant is capable of absorbing energy from the sun? Explain your answer.

Cell Energy

Key Concept   All cells need energy to carry out cell functions. However, cells may obtain and process energy in different ways.

photosynthesis
(FOHT oh SIN thuh sis) the process by which plants, algae, and some bacteria use sunlight, carbon dioxide, and water to make food
  Wordwise   The root *phot-* means "light."

  Wordwise   **chloroplast**
The root *chlor-* means "green." The root *plast-* means "to form."

► Why do you get hungry? Feeling hungry is your body's way of telling you that your cells need energy. All cells need energy to live, grow, and reproduce. Plant cells get their energy from the sun. Many animal cells get their energy from food.

From Sun to Cell

Nearly all of the energy that fuels life comes from the sun. Plants absorb energy from the sun and change the energy into food through a process called **photosynthesis.** The food that plants make gives them energy. This food also becomes a source of energy for the organisms that eat the plants.

Photosynthesis

Plant cells have molecules that absorb light energy. These molecules are called *pigments*. Chlorophyll (KLAWR uh FIL), the main pigment used in photosynthesis, gives plants their green color. Chlorophyll is found in *chloroplasts.*

Plants cannot use energy directly from the sun to perform life processes. Instead, they use the sun's energy to change carbon dioxide and water into food. The food is in the form of the simple sugar glucose. Glucose can be stored and used by the plant's cells. Photosynthesis also produces oxygen. The chemical equation for photosynthesis is shown in **Figure 1.**

Standards Check   What kind of cell has chloroplasts? **7.1.b**

Figure 1   *Photosynthesis takes place in chloroplasts. Chloroplasts are found inside plant cells.*

Photosynthesis

$$6CO_2 + 6H_2O + \text{light energy} \longrightarrow C_6H_{12}O_6 + 6O_2$$
Carbon   Water   Glucose   Oxygen
dioxide

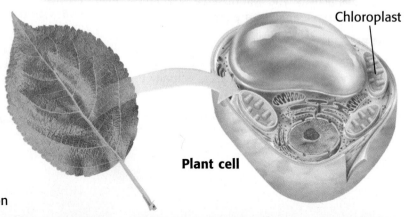

Chloroplast

Plant cell

Getting Energy from Food

Animal cells cannot make their own food. Animals must eat to get food. No matter how an organism gets food, the food must be broken down in the organism's cells in order to free the energy stored in the food. Even plant cells must break down the food that they make during photosynthesis.

Cells can break down food in two ways. The first way is **cellular respiration,** a process that uses oxygen. The second way does not use oxygen. This process is called **fermentation.** Cellular respiration releases more energy from food than fermentation does. Most complex organisms, such as plants and animals, get most of their energy through cellular respiration.

Cellular Respiration

The word *respiration* means "breathing," but cellular respiration is different from breathing. Cellular respiration is a chemical process that happens in cells. In prokaryotic cells, cellular respiration happens in the cell membrane. In eukaryotic cells, cellular respiration takes place mostly in the mitochondria.

During cellular respiration, food (such as glucose) is broken down into CO_2 and H_2O, and energy is liberated, or freed. In animals, most of the freed energy is used to keep a constant body temperature. Some of the energy is used to form **a**deno-sine **tri**phosphate (ATP). Molecules of ATP supply readily available energy that fuels cell activities, such as growth.

The process of cellular respiration is shown in **Figure 2.** Does the equation in the figure remind you of the equation for photosynthesis? On the next page, **Figure 3** shows how photosynthesis and respiration are related.

Standards Check Where does the process of cellular respiration take place in eukaryotes, such as plants and animals? **7.1.d**

cellular respiration
(SEL yoo luhr RES puh RAY shuhn) the process by which cells use oxygen to produce energy from food

fermentation (fuhr muhn TAY shuhn) the breakdown of food without the use of oxygen

Cellular respiration

$$C_6H_{12}O_6 + 6O_2 \rightarrow 6CO_2 + 6H_2O + \text{energy (ATP)}$$

Glucose   Oxygen   Carbon dioxide   Water

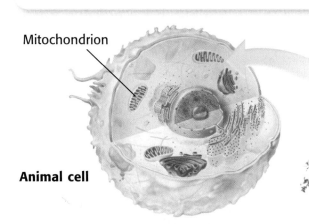

Mitochondrion

Animal cell

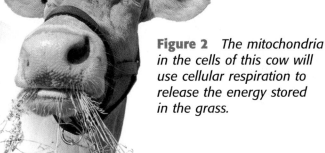

Figure 2 *The mitochondria in the cells of this cow will use cellular respiration to release the energy stored in the grass.*

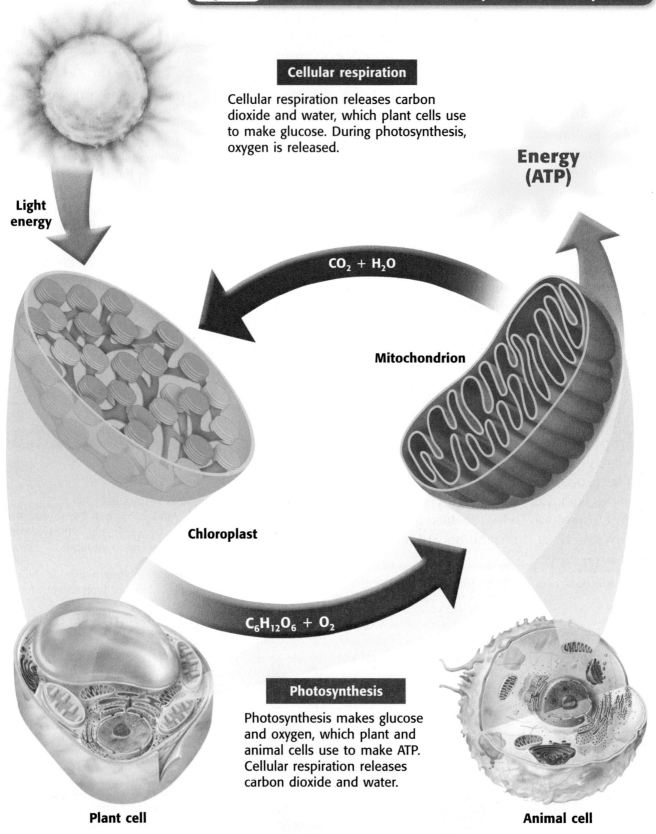

Figure 3 The Connection Between Photosynthesis and Respiration

Cellular respiration

Cellular respiration releases carbon dioxide and water, which plant cells use to make glucose. During photosynthesis, oxygen is released.

Energy (ATP)

Light energy

$CO_2 + H_2O$

Mitochondrion

Chloroplast

$C_6H_{12}O_6 + O_2$

Photosynthesis

Photosynthesis makes glucose and oxygen, which plant and animal cells use to make ATP. Cellular respiration releases carbon dioxide and water.

Plant cell

Animal cell

Connection Between Photosynthesis and Respiration

As shown in **Figure 3,** photosynthesis changes CO_2 and H_2O into glucose. During photosynthesis, cells use energy from the sun to make glucose. The process also releases O_2. During cellular respiration, cells use O_2 to break down glucose and to free energy and CO_2. Each process makes the materials that are needed for the other process to occur.

Standards Check List the products of cellular respiration. 7.1.d

Fermentation

Have you ever had a burning feeling in your leg muscles while you were running? You may have these feelings during short, fast races. When muscle cells cannot get the oxygen that they need for cellular respiration, they use the process of fermentation to get energy. One kind of fermentation takes place in your muscles and makes lactic acid. The buildup of this acid leads to muscle fatigue and causes a burning feeling. This kind of fermentation also happens in the muscle cells of other animals and in some fungi and bacteria.

Calories and Energy

Mitochondria in your cells change energy from the food that you eat into ATP. Packaged food lists the energy in food but not in units of ATP. Instead, the energy is listed as Calories. Ask an adult to help you find the number of Calories in each serving of your favorite food.

ACTIVITY

SECTION Review

 7.1.b, 7.1.d

Summary

- Most of the energy that fuels life comes from the sun.
- The sun's energy is changed into food by the process of photosynthesis, which occurs in the chloroplasts of plant cells.
- Cellular respiration breaks down glucose into water, carbon dioxide, and energy.
- Cellular respiration takes place in the mitochondria of plant and animal cells.
- Fermentation is a way that cells get energy from their food without using oxygen.

Using Vocabulary

1. Write an original definition for *cellular respiration.*

Understanding Concepts

2. **Applying** How are photosynthesis and cellular respiration related?

3. **Concluding** What type of cell has chloroplasts? How do chloroplasts affect the functions of the cell?

Critical Thinking

4. **Analyzing Relationships** Why are plants important for the survival of other organisms?

5. **Predicting Consequences** What would happen to an animal if all of its mitochondria disappeared?

Math Skills

6. **Making Conversions** Cells of plant A make 120 molecules of glucose per hour. Cells of plant B make half as many molecules of glucose as cells of plant A do. How many molecules of glucose does plant B make per minute?

Challenge

7. **Applying Concepts** Your classmate suggests that chlorophyll is not the only pigment contained in plant cells. Is your classmate correct? Explain your answer.

Internet Resources

For a variety of links related to this chapter, go to www.scilinks.org

Topic: Cell Energy; Photosynthesis
SciLinks code: HY70237; HY71140

The Cell Cycle

Key Concept The cell cycle results in daughter cells, two new cells that are exact copies of the original cell.

What You Will Learn

- Before a cell divides, it must make a copy of its DNA.
- To increase their numbers, eukaryotic cells divide through the processes of mitosis and cytokinesis.
- Mitosis has four phases.
- Cytokinesis differs in animals and plants.
- Cancer occurs when cells replicate abnormally.

Why It Matters

Problems within the cell cycle can lead to cancer.

Vocabulary

- cell cycle
- chromosome
- mitosis
- cytokinesis
- cancer

READING STRATEGY

Prediction Guide Before reading this section, write each heading from this section in your **Science Journal.** Below each heading, write what you think you will learn.

cell cycle (SEL SIE kuhl) the life cycle of a cell

chromosome (KROH muh SOHM) in a eukaryotic cell, one of the structures in the nucleus that are made up of DNA and protein; in a prokaryotic cell, the main ring of DNA

mitosis (mie TOH sis) in eukaryotic cells, a process of cell division that forms two new nuclei, each of which has the same number of chromosomes

cytokinesis (SIET oh ki NEE sis) the division of the cytoplasm of a cell

In the time that it takes you to read this sentence, your body will have made millions of new cells! Making new cells allows you to grow and to replace cells that have died. Your stomach is so acidic that the cells lining the inside must be replaced every few days. Other cells are replaced less often, but your body is always making new cells.

The Life of a Cell

As you grow, you pass through different stages in life. Your cells also pass through different stages in their life cycle. The life cycle of a cell is called the **cell cycle.**

The cell cycle begins when the cell is formed and ends when the cell divides and forms new cells. Before a cell divides, it must make a copy of its **d**eoxyribo**n**ucleic **a**cid (DNA). DNA is the hereditary material that directs all cell activities, including the making of new cells. The DNA of a cell is organized into structures called **chromosomes.** Chromosomes are made up of DNA and proteins. Copying chromosomes ensures that each new cell receives all of the DNA of the parent cell. Each new cell will be an exact copy of its parent cell. How a cell makes more cells depends on whether the cell is prokaryotic (has no nucleus) or eukaryotic (has a nucleus).

Making More Prokaryotic Cells

Prokaryotic cells are less complex than eukaryotic cells. Bacteria, which are prokaryotes, have a single, circular chromosome. Also, they do not have membrane-enclosed organelles. Cell division in bacteria is called *binary fission,* which means "splitting into two parts." Binary fission results in two cells, each of which has one copy of the circle of DNA. A few of the bacteria in **Figure 1** are undergoing binary fission.

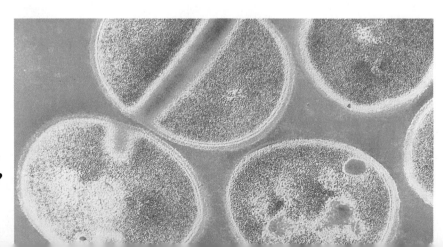

Figure 1 *Bacteria reproduce by binary fission.* **How will the new cells compare to the parent cell?**

Eukaryotic Cells and Their DNA

Prokaryotic cells have a single chromosome, but eukaryotic cells have many chromosomes. Eukaryotes have more DNA than prokaryotes do. Different kinds of eukaryotes have different numbers of chromosomes. More-complex eukaryotes do not always have more chromosomes than simpler eukaryotes do. For example, fruit flies have 8 chromosomes, potatoes have 48, and humans have 46. **Figure 2** shows the 46 chromosomes of a human body cell lined up in pairs. These pairs are made up of similar chromosomes known as *homologous chromosomes* (hoh MAHL uh guhs KROH muh SOHMZ). Although chromosomes vary in size, the homologous chromosomes in each pair will be very similar.

Standards Check How many chromosomes are in the cells of the human body?  **7.2.e**

Making More Eukaryotic Cells

The eukaryotic cell cycle has three stages. In the first stage, called *interphase,* the cell grows and copies its organelles and chromosomes. After each chromosome is duplicated, the two copies are called *chromatids.* Chromatids are held together at a region called the *centromere.* The joined chromatids condense into an X shape, as shown in **Figure 3.** After this step, the cell enters the second stage of the cell cycle.

In the second stage, the chromatids separate. The process by which chromosomes separate is called **mitosis.** During mitosis, each new cell receives a copy of each chromosome. Mitosis is divided into four phases: prophase, metaphase, anaphase, and telophase.

In the third stage, cytokinesis, the cell splits into two cells called *daughter cells.* **Cytokinesis** is the division of cytoplasm and all of the materials in the cytoplasm. The new daughter cells are exactly the same as each other and as the original cell. For example, each daughter cell receives exactly the same number of chromosomes.

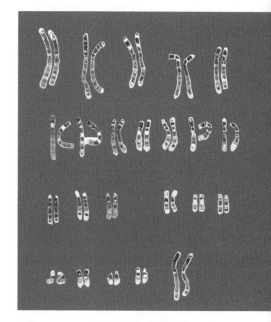

Figure 2 *Human body cells have 46 chromosomes, or 23 pairs of chromosomes.*

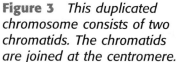

Mitosis Adventure

How does a cell change during a cell cycle? Describe cell division from inside the cell. Go to **go.hrw.com,** and type in the keyword HY7ACTW.

Figure 3 *This duplicated chromosome consists of two chromatids. The chromatids are joined at the centromere.*

Chromatids

Centromere

7.1.b Students know the characteristics that distinguish plant cells from animal cells, including chloroplasts and cell walls.
7.1.e Students know cells divide to increase their numbers through a process of mitosis, which results in two daughter cells with identical sets of chromosomes.
7.2.e Students know DNA (deoxyribonucleic acid) is the genetic material of living organisms and is located in the chromosomes of each cell.

Figure 4 The Cell Cycle

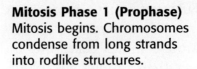

Interphase Before mitosis begins, chromosomes are copied. Each chromosome becomes two chromatids.

Mitosis Phase 1 (Prophase) Mitosis begins. Chromosomes condense from long strands into rodlike structures.

Mitosis Phase 2 (Metaphase) The nuclear membrane is dissolved. Paired chromatids align at the cell's equator.

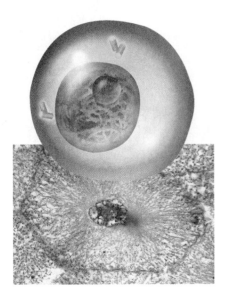

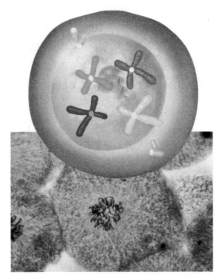

Mitosis and the Cell Cycle

Figure 4 shows the cell cycle and the phases of mitosis in an animal cell. Mitosis has four phases, as shown and described above. This diagram shows only four chromosomes to make it easy to see what's happening inside the cell.

Cytokinesis

In animal cells and other eukaryotes that do not have cell walls, division of the cytoplasm begins at the cell membrane. The cell membrane begins to pinch inward to form a groove. Eventually, the cell is pinched in half, and two daughter cells form. Cytokinesis is shown at the last step of **Figure 4.**

Eukaryotic cells that have a cell wall—such as the cells of plants, algae, and fungi—go through cytokinesis differently. In this kind of cell, a *cell plate* forms in the middle of the cell. The cell plate contains the materials for the new cell membranes and for the new cell walls that will separate the new cells. After the cell splits in two, a new cell wall forms where the cell plate was. The cell plate and a late stage of cytokinesis in a plant cell are shown in **Figure 5.**

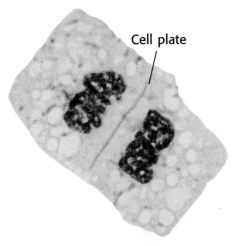

Cell plate

Figure 5 *When a plant cell divides, a cell plate forms and the cell splits into two cells.*

Standards Check What is the difference between cytokinesis in an animal cell and cytokinesis in a plant cell? 7.1.b

Mitosis Phase 3 (Anaphase)
The paired chromatids separate and move to opposite sides of the cell.

Mitosis Phase 4 (Telophase)
A nuclear membrane forms around each set of chromosomes, and the chromosomes decondense. Mitosis is complete.

Cytokinesis In a cell that lacks a cell wall, the cell pinches in two. In a cell that has a cell wall, a cell plate forms and separates the cells into two new cells.

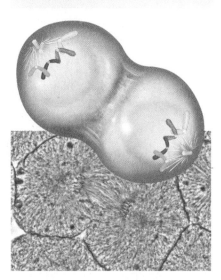
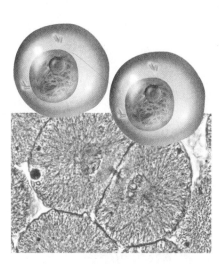

Quick Lab

The Mitosis Flipbook

The process of mitosis involves four phases, but the transition from one phase to the next involves many intermediate stages. In this activity, you will illustrate and assemble a flipbook. The flipbook will show the phases and intermediate stages of mitosis.

1. Punch two holes near the upper edge of **20 index cards.**

2. Take four cards from your stack. List a different phase of mitosis on each card.

3. Review the images above. Draw a diagram of each phase of mitosis on the correct card.

4. Use **colored pencils** to make each chromosome a different color. On each card where the cell part is present, label one example of the chromosome, centromere, and nuclear membrane.

5. On the blank cards, draw the intermediate stages between each phase. Show the gradual transitions of mitosis by making small changes on each card.

6. Put your cards in order. Place a **brad** in each hole to assemble your flipbook.

7. In what phase of mitosis does the nuclear membrane dissolve?

8. This flipbook shows the actions of chromosomes, centromeres, and the nuclear membrane during mitosis. Is it acceptable to leave out what is happening to the rest of the cell's organelles? Explain your answer.

9. Why is it important for eukaryotic cells to undergo mitosis?

7.1.e
7.7.d

30 min

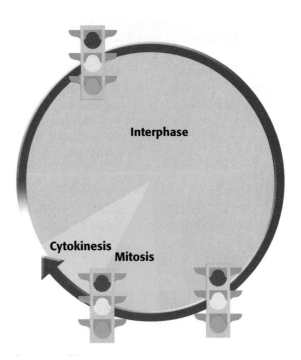

Figure 6 *The feedback switches of cells work like traffic signals. A "go" signal, like a green light, tells a cell to start or continue a process. A "stop" signal, like a red light, tells a cell to end a process.*

Interphase

Cytokinesis Mitosis

cancer (KAN suhr) a tumor in which the cells begin dividing at an uncontrolled rate and can become invasive

Control of the Cell Cycle

Most of a cell's life is spent in interphase. During interphase, parent cells replicate their chromosomes and organelles. But what causes a cell to start or stop making copies of organelles and chromosomes? These activities are controlled by feedback switches.

Feedback Switches

Babies cry when they are hungry. Once they are fed, they stop crying. Crying is a baby's way of reporting conditions. Cells report conditions in messages called *feedback*. A cell may report that it needs more, has enough, or has too much of a certain molecule. This feedback turns on a set of switches that work like traffic lights. For example, if feedback indicates that there is too much of a molecule, proteins assembling that molecule get a "stop" signal. Thus, the production of the molecule stops. At the same time, proteins that break down the molecule may get a "go" signal. Thus, the breakdown of the molecule begins. This process continues until feedback indicates that levels of the molecule are ideal.

The cell cycle is controlled by the feedback switches shown in **Figure 6.** When feedback indicates that the cell is healthy and large enough for division, proteins get the first "go" signal. Organelles and chromosomes are copied. Then, the cell prepares for division.

Standards Check What feedback does the cell need in order to prepare for cell division? **7.1.e**

Cancer

The feedback switches that control the "stop" and "go" signals are proteins. A cell's DNA carries the information needed to make proteins. If the DNA is changed, the proteins also may be changed. Thus, the proteins may not be able to control cell growth and division. Cells may reproduce rapidly and form clumps called *tumors*. **Cancer** occurs when tumors affect the normal functions of the body.

There are more than a hundred kinds of cancer. All cancers are caused by the uncontrolled growth of cells. **Figure 7** shows *melanoma*, the most deadly kind of skin cancer. Wearing sunscreen and checking skin for abnormal moles may help prevent skin cancer.

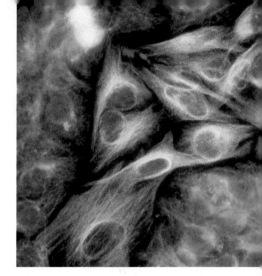

Figure 7 *Cancer cells, such as these melanoma cells, are growing uncontrollably.*

SECTION Review

7.1.b, 7.1.e, 7.2.e

Summary

- The life cycle of a cell is the cell cycle.
- A cell copies its chromosomes during interphase.
- Mitosis produces two nuclei that have the same number of chromosomes.
- Mitosis has four phases: prophase, metaphase, anaphase, and telophase.
- After mitosis, the cytoplasm is divided by cytokinesis into two daughter cells.
- In plant cells, a cell plate forms between the two new cells during cytokinesis.
- Cancer is a disorder of cell division.

Understanding Concepts

1 **Comparing** Compare the organization of DNA in prokaryotic and eukaryotic cells.

2 **Analyzing** Why must chromosomes be copied before cells divide?

3 **Describing** Describe mitosis.

4 **Summarizing** Summarize the control methods of the cell cycle.

Critical Thinking

5 **Predicting Consequences** What would happen if cytokinesis occurred without mitosis?

6 **Applying Concepts** How does mitosis ensure that a new cell is identical to its parent cell?

7 **Making Comparisons** Compare the processes that animal cells and plant cells use to make new cells. How are the processes different?

8 **Identifying Relationships** Do more-complex organisms always have more chromosomes than simpler organisms do? How do you know?

INTERPRETING GRAPHICS Use the diagram below to answer the next question.

9 **Evaluating Data** What step of mitosis does this image show? Describe what is happening.

Math Skills

10 **Solving Problems** Cell A takes 6 h to complete division. Cell B takes 8 h to complete division. After 24 h, how many more copies of cell A than copies of cell B are there?

Internet Resources

For a variety of links related to this chapter, go to www.scilinks.org

Topic: Cell Cycle
SciLinks code: HY70235

Skills Practice Lab

Phases of Mitosis

Cell division is a step-by-step process that results in the formation of two identical daughter cells. All of the material inside the parent cell must be replicated before the new daughter cells can form. A cell's nucleus is replicated by the process of mitosis. Mitosis has four phases: prophase, metaphase, anaphase, and telophase. During each phase of mitosis, cell parts follow a routine that results in the formation of two identical nuclei. You can observe mitosis in the cells of onion-root tips. These cells reproduce often, so you can observe a large number of them in the stages of cell reproduction.

Procedure

1. Use the microscope's low-power setting to examine a prepared slide of an onion root tip.

2. Locate the growing region of the root tip.

3. Switch to the high-power setting.

4. Select the cells that are the best representatives of each of the four phases of mitosis. Draw each cell on a separate sheet of paper. Label the chromosomes, centromeres, and the nuclear membrane on your drawings.

7.1.e Students know cells divide to increase their numbers through a process of mitosis, which results in two daughter cells with identical sets of chromosomes.

7.2.e Students know DNA (deoxyribonucleic acid) is the genetic material of living organisms and is located in the chromosomes of each cell.

Investigation and Experimentation

7.7.d Construct scale models, maps, and appropriately labeled diagrams to communicate scientific knowledge (e.g., motion of Earth's plates and cell structure).

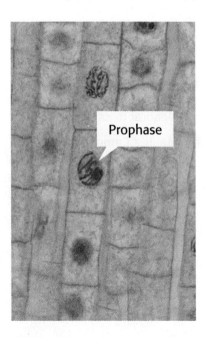

Prophase

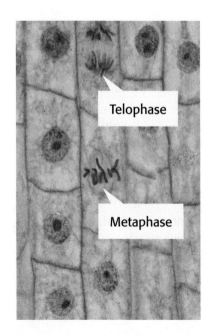

Telophase

Metaphase

Analyze the Results

5 Analyzing Data   Which phase(s) have visible chromosomes? In which phase(s) are the chromosomes invisible?

6 Recognizing Patterns   What feature of metaphase is most visible?

7 Examining Data   During which phase do the two separate nuclei appear?

8 Examining Data   In which phase(s) does the cell have a visible nuclear membrane?

Draw Conclusions

9 Evaluating Results   Explain why the nuclear membrane is visible in some phases of mitosis but not in others.

10 Interpreting Information   Although chromosomes are not visible during interphase, the cell still contains DNA. Where is the DNA and why can't it be seen?

11 Making Predictions   The cell's DNA doubles during interphase. Suppose this increase in DNA never occurred. How would this affect the daughter cells produced during mitosis?

Big Idea Question

12 Interpreting Information   Explain what the term *cycle* means and how the meaning applies to the cell cycle. Besides mitosis, what are the stages of the cell cycle?

Science Skills Activity

Scientific Methods | Research | Data Analysis | Models, Maps & Diagrams

Investigation and Experimentation

7.7.c Communicate the logical connection among hypotheses, science concepts, tests conducted, data collected, and conclusions drawn from the scientific evidence.

Drawing Conclusions from Data

▶ Tutorial

After scientists analyze the data from an experiment, they can draw conclusions. Conclusions reveal what was discovered through the experiment.

1 First, determine which question you want to answer. Use your question to form a hypothesis. Then, plan and carry out your experiment.

2 Collect data and other observations during your experiment. Your observations should also include any problems that you encountered during your experiment.

3 Analyze your data. Complete mathematical calculations if necessary. Be sure to use the correct units.

4 Begin your conclusions with a brief summary of your data. Describe what your data show.

5 Explain how your data relate to the question you were trying to answer. Be sure to use the data that you collected, not the data that you expected to collect.

6 Explain any errors or problems that occurred during experimentation. Major problems can result in incorrect data. Incorrect data can lead to incorrect conclusions.

▶ You Try It!

Why do we put food in the refrigerator? Perishable foods—foods that can go bad, such as meat—can support the growth of thousands of bacteria. Some bacteria, such as *Escherichia coli,* can cause sickness and even death when people eat foods contaminated by these bacteria. At cool temperatures, the chemical processes that lead to cell growth and division are slowed down or stopped. This environment helps control bacterial populations. Use the data in the table below to draw conclusions and to answer the following questions.

Bacterial Growth on Food X at Various Temperatures		
Starting temperature (°C)	**Growth after 24 h (% increase)**	**Observations of refrigerator performance**
30	42	normal
20	20	normal
15	5	normal
10	9	broke down

1 Drawing Conclusions Analyze the table. Write a conclusion paragraph about the data. Begin with a summary of the data. What do the data show?

2 Examining Data Explain any problems that occurred in the data. Are the data valid? Why or why not?

3 Defending Conclusions Explain why each of the following conclusions CANNOT be drawn from the data: (a) bacteria grow faster on food X than on food Y, (b) you will get sick if you eat food X left at 30°C for one day, and (c) storing food X at a temperature of 15°C leads to fewer bacteria than storing it at 10°C.

4 Applying Conclusions Does this experiment indicate that refrigeration slows the processes of cell growth and division? Explain your answer.

Chapter Summary

go.hrw.com
SUPER SUMMARY
KEYWORD: HY7ACTS

The Big Idea
Cells carry out important life functions, such as obtaining energy, growing, and making new cells.

Section

Vocabulary

1 Cell Energy

Key Concept All cells need energy to carry out cell functions. However, cells may obtain and process energy in different ways.

- In plant cells, chloroplasts capture energy from the sun in order to make food during photosynthesis.
- Cells release energy from food through either cellular respiration or fermentation.

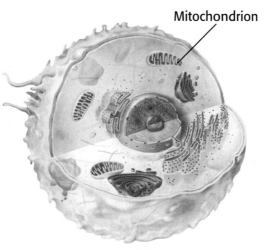

Mitochondrion

Eukaryotic cells, such as this animal cell, carry out cellular respiration in mitochondria.

photosynthesis p. 148
cellular respiration p. 149
fermentation p. 149

2 The Cell Cycle

Key Concept The cell cycle results in daughter cells, two new cells that are exact copies of the original cell.

- Before a cell divides, it must make a copy of its DNA.
- To increase their numbers, eukaryotic cells divide through the processes of mitosis and cytokinesis.
- Mitosis has four phases.
- Cytokinesis differs in animals and plants.
- Cancer occurs when cells replicate abnormally.

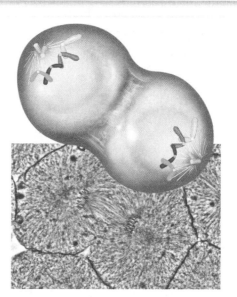

Telophase is the last phase of mitosis.

cell cycle p. 152
chromosome p. 152
mitosis p. 153
cytokinesis p. 153
cancer p. 157

Chapter Review

Organize

Layered Book Review the Fold-Note that you created at the beginning of the chapter. Add to or correct the FoldNote based on what you have learned.

Using Vocabulary

1 **Academic Vocabulary** In the sentence "The process of photosynthesis converts energy from the sun into food," what does the word *process* mean?

Complete each of the following sentences by choosing the correct term from the word bank.

cellular respiration
photosynthesis
fermentation

2 Plants use ___ to make glucose.

3 During ___, oxygen is used to break down food molecules, releasing large amounts of energy.

For each pair of terms, explain how the meanings of the terms differ.

4 *cytokinesis* and *mitosis*

5 *cellular respiration* and *fermentation*

Understanding Concepts

Multiple Choice

6 What is the result of mitosis and cytokinesis?
a. two identical cells
b. two nuclei
c. two chloroplasts
d. two different cells

7 Before a cell can use the energy in food, the energy must be transferred to molecules of
a. proteins.
b. carbohydrates.
c. DNA.
d. ATP.

8 Which of the following cells would form a cell plate during the cell cycle?
a. a human cell
b. a prokaryotic cell
c. a plant cell
d. All of the above

Short Answer

9 **Identifying** Name the cell structures that are needed for photosynthesis and the cell structures that are needed for cellular respiration.

10 **Describing** Describe the three stages of the cell cycle of a eukaryotic cell.

11 **Listing** List in order the four phases of mitosis.

12 **Evaluating** How many pairs of chromosomes do humans have?

INTERPRETING GRAPHICS The picture below shows a cell. Use the picture to answer the next question.

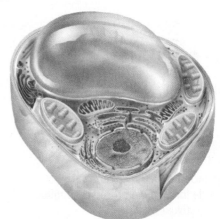

13 **Classifying** Does the picture show a plant cell or an animal cell? How do you know?

Writing Skills

14 **Writing a Biography** Write and illustrate the biography of a cell. The biography can be humorous or serious, but it should include accurate descriptions of how cells grow and reproduce.

Critical Thinking

15 **Concept Mapping** Use the following terms to create a concept map: *chromosome duplication, cytokinesis, prokaryote, mitosis, cell cycle, binary fission,* and *eukaryote.*

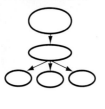

16 **Applying Concepts** A parent cell has 10 chromosomes. How many chromosomes will each new cell have after the parent cell divides?

17 **Identifying Relationships** How is DNA related to cancer? How are chromosomes related to cancer?

18 **Analyzing Processes** How is ATP involved in cellular respiration? What would happen to cells if ATP did not exist?

19 **Making Comparisons** How are chlorophyll and chloroplasts related, and where are they found?

20 **Applying Concepts** How are mitochondria related to ATP?

INTERPRETING GRAPHICS Use the table below to answer the next two questions.

Cell Characteristics		
Cell	Number of chromosomes	Presence of chloroplasts
A	12	no
B	12	yes
C	10	yes
D	12	yes

21 **Evaluating Data** Two of these cells came from the division of one parent cell. Which two cells came from the same parent cell? Explain your answer.

22 **Applying Concepts** Which of the cells does NOT form a cell plate during cytokinesis? How do you know?

23 **Predicting Consequences** What would happen to a cell if it were unable to use feedback?

INTERPRETING GRAPHICS The image below shows a cell. Use the image to answer the next four questions.

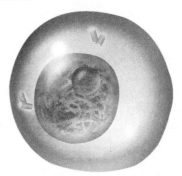

24 **Applying Concepts** Is the cell prokaryotic or eukaryotic?

25 **Evaluating Data** Which stage of the cell cycle is this cell in?

26 **Identifying Relationships** What will happen to the cell after this stage is complete?

27 **Applying Concepts** Assume that 12 chromatids are present in the image above. How many chromosomes will be present in each of the new cells after the cell divides?

Math Skills

28 **Making Calculations** Cell A converts 80% of its food into usable fuel. Cell B is not as efficient as cell A. Cell B converts only half the amount of food into fuel as cell A does. What percentage of food does cell B convert into fuel? How many grams of fuel will cell B make if cell B starts with 150 g of food?

Challenge

29 **Identifying Relationships** Describe the path of energy conversions, beginning with light energy from the sun and ending with the energy in your muscles.

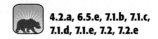
REVIEWING ACADEMIC VOCABULARY

1 Which of the following words is the closest in meaning to the word *identical*?

A related

B common

C duplicate

D woven

2 Choose the appropriate form of the word *locate* for the following sentence: Genetic information is ___ in the nucleus of a cell.

A locates

B locative

C located

D location

3 Which of the following sets of words best completes the following sentence: A cell's traits may be ___ the environment.

A modify with

B modified by

C modifying

D modifies in

4 Which of the following words means "to release or to set free"?

A liberate

B characterize

C function

D specify

REVIEWING CONCEPTS

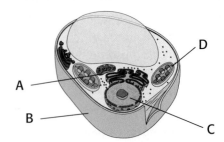

5 The diagram above shows a plant cell. Where in the diagram does the process of photosynthesis take place?

A part A   **C** part C

B part B   **D** part D

6 Which of the following best describes a major difference between plant cells and animal cells?

A Only plant cells use cellular respiration.

B Only plant cells have a nucleus containing DNA.

C Unlike plant cells, animal cells cannot make their own food.

D Only animal cells have a cell wall.

7 What is the life cycle of a cell called?

A mitosis   **C** cell cycle

B centromere   **D** chromatid

8 What is the purpose of the process of mitosis?

A to produce two identical nuclei

B to split a cell into two identical cells

C to copy each chromosome in a cell

D to create deoxyribonucleic acid in a cell

9 A parent cell has 24 chromosomes at the beginning of interphase. How many chromatids will it have during prophase?

A 48   **C** 12

B 24   **D** 6

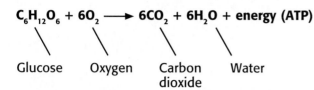

$$C_6H_{12}O_6 + 6O_2 \longrightarrow 6CO_2 + 6H_2O + energy\ (ATP)$$

Glucose   Oxygen   Carbon dioxide   Water

10 Above is the chemical equation for a process that occurs in cells. What process is described by the chemical equation?

A cytokinesis

B cellular respiration

C fermentation

D photosynthesis

11 How are the processes of photosynthesis and cellular respiration connected?

A Both processes begin with oxygen.

B Both processes require sunlight.

C Each process takes place only in plant cells.

D Each process makes the material needed in the other process.

12 Which of the following is true of cytokinesis in the cells of a plant?

A A cell plate forms and separates the cytoplasm into two new cells.

B The cell divides its cytoplasm by a process called *binary fission.*

C The cell membrane pinches the cytoplasm of the cell in two.

D At this stage, the nuclear membrane of the cell dissolves.

13 Which of the following best describes the chromosomes of eukaryotic cells?

A More-complex eukaryotes have more chromosomes than simpler ones do.

B Different kinds of eukaryotes have different numbers of chromosomes.

C The chromosomes in a pair contain very different genetic information.

D Each of the chromosomes contains one copy of circular DNA.

REVIEWING PRIOR LEARNING

14 Where is DNA found within a eukaryotic cell?

A the Golgi apparatus

B the mitochondria

C the smooth endoplasmic reticulum

D the nucleus

15 Offspring are created by either sexual or asexual reproduction. How are the two kinds of offspring similar?

A Both share traits of two parents.

B Both have DNA.

C Both have multiple cells.

D Both are identical to one parent.

16 Which of the following is an abiotic factor that may affect the types and numbers of animals that can live in an area?

A the range of temperatures experienced in the area

B the types of plants available for food sources

C the number and types of predators in the area

D the number of plants available for food sources

17 What are the primary sources of energy and matter in most food chains?

A primary consumers

B decomposers

C plants

D carnivores

Science in Action

New branches of blood vessels supply nutrients to this tumor.

Science Fiction

"Contagion" by Katherine MacLean

A quarter mile from their spaceship, the *Explorer,* a team of doctors walk carefully along a narrow forest trail. Around them, the forest looks like a forest on Earth in the fall—the leaves are green, copper, purple, and fiery red. But it is not fall. And the team is not on Earth.

Minos is enough like Earth to be the home of another colony of humans. But Minos might also be home to unknown organisms that could cause severe illness or death among the crew of *Explorer.* These diseases might be enough like diseases on Earth to be contagious, but they might be different enough to be very difficult to treat.

Something large moves among the shadows—it looks like a man. What happens next? Read Katherine MacLean's "Contagion" in the *Holt Anthology of Science Fiction* to find out.

Language Arts ACTIVITY

In your **Science Journal,** write two to three paragraphs that describe what you think might happen next in the story.

HOLT ANTHOLOGY OF
Science Fiction

HOLT, RINEHART AND WINSTON

Scientific Discoveries

"Smart Bombs" Can Fight Cancer?

There are more than 100 types of cancer. Cancer cells multiply rapidly in clumps called *tumors.* Current cancer treatment involves harsh side effects. However, Dr. David Cheresh of the University of California, San Diego, may have a better way to fight cancer.

In order to survive, cancer cells need nutrients supplied by the blood. As the number of cells in tumors grow, new branches of blood vessels form nearby. Without these blood vessels, tumors would have no access to blood. The new cancer treatment, called "smart bombs," destroys the new branches of blood vessels that supply blood to tumors. Although the "smart bombs" are still being tested, this new method of fighting cancer seems to be promising!

Math ACTIVITY

Cell A requires 18 h to complete division. When cell A experiences abnormal cell growth, cell division takes one-third of that time. How many hours will it take for 32 cells to be present? Solve the problem in your **Science Journal.**

Jerry Yakel

Neuroscientist Jerry Yakel credits a sea slug for making him a neuroscientist. In a college class studying neurons, or nerve cells, Yakel got to see firsthand how ions move across the cell membrane of *Aplysia californica*, also known as a *sea hare*. He says, "I was totally hooked. I knew that I wanted to be a neurophysiologist then and there. I haven't wavered since."

Today, Yakel is a senior investigator for the National Institute of Environmental Health Sciences, which is part of the U.S. government's National Institutes of Health. "We try to understand how the normal brain works," says Yakel of his team. "Then, we look at a diseased brain; we train to understand where the deficits are. Eventually, someone will have an idea about a drug that will tweak the system in this or that way."

Yakel studies the ways in which nicotine affects the human brain. "It is one of the most prevalent and potent neurotoxins in the environment," says Yakel. "I'm amazed that it isn't higher on the list of worries for the general public."

Social Studies ACTIVITY

Research a famous or historical figure in science. In your **Science Journal,** write a short report that outlines how he or she became interested in science.

Internet Resources

- To learn more about careers in science, visit **www.scilinks.org** and enter the SciLinks code HY70225.

- To learn more about these Science in Action topics, visit **go.hrw.com** and type in the keyword HY7ACTF.

- Check out articles related to this chapter by visiting go.hrw.com. Just type in the keyword HY7ACTC.

UNIT 3

TIMELINE

Heredity and Genes

How do organisms acquire their traits? The inheritance of traits is the subject of this unit. You will learn how characteristics are passed from one generation to another, how DNA contains genetic information, and how genes influence traits.

Many important discoveries have been made in the field of genetics. This timeline will give you an idea of some of the discoveries that have been made so far.

Around 250

Mayan farmers build terraces to control the flow of water to crops.

1860

Abraham Lincoln is elected the 16th president of the United States.

1865

Gregor Mendel publishes the results of his studies of genetic inheritance in pea plants.

1953

James Watson and Francis Crick figure out the structure of DNA.

1990

Ashanti DeSilva's white blood cells are genetically engineered to treat her immune deficiency disease.

1620
The Pilgrims settle Plymouth Colony.

1859
Charles Darwin suggests that natural selection is a mechanism of evolution.

1905
Nettie Stevens describes how human gender is determined by the X and Y chromosomes.

1941
George Beadle and Edward Tatum discover that genes control the chemical reactions in cells by directing protein production.

1951
Rosalind Franklin photographs DNA.

1997
A sheep named Dolly becomes the first animal to be cloned from a single body cell.

2002
An international team decodes the DNA sequences for both the protist that causes malaria and the mosquito that carries this protist. As a result, the door to more-effective antimalaria drugs is opened.

2003
The Human Genome Project is completed. Scientists spent 13 years mapping out the 3 billion DNA subunits of chromosomes.

Improving Comprehension

Graphic Organizers are important visual tools that can help you organize information and improve your reading comprehension. The Graphic Organizer below is called *combination notes*. Instructions for creating other types of Graphic Organizers are located in the **Study Skills** section of the Appendix.

How to Make Combination Notes

1 Draw a table like the one shown below. Draw the columns to be as long as you want them to be.

2 Write the topic of your notes in the section at the top of the table.

3 In the left column, write important phrases or sentences about the topic. In the right column, draw diagrams or pictures that illustrate the information in the left column.

When to Use Combination Notes

Combination notes let you express scientific information in words and pictures at the same time. Use combination notes to express information that a picture could help explain. The picture could be a diagram, a sketch, or another useful visual representation of the written information in your notes.

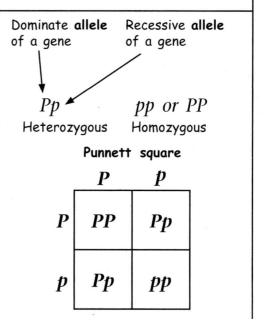

Heredity

- Gregor Mendel helped establish the basics of modern genetics.

- Mendel discovered that an offspring inherits two **alleles** for each gene, one allele from each parent.

- Through **meiosis** and sexual reproduction, genetic material combines.

- **Punnett squares** are used to predict the possible **genotypes** for a particular combination of genes.

You Try It!

This Reading Strategy can also be used within the chapter that you are about to read. Practice making your own *combination notes* as directed in the Reading Strategies for Section **2** and Section **3**. Record your work in your **Science Journal.**

Unpacking the Standards

The information below "unpacks" the standards by breaking them down into basic parts. The higher-level, academic vocabulary is highlighted and defined to help you understand the language of the standards. "What It Means" restates the standards as simply as possible.

California Standard	Academic Vocabulary	What It Means
7.2.b Students know **sexual** reproduction produces offspring that inherit half their genes from each parent.	**sexual** (SEK shoo uhl) having to do with sex	Offspring that are produced through sexual reproduction get half of their genetic material from one parent and half of their genetic material from the other parent.
7.2.c Students know an inherited trait can be determined by one or more genes.		A feature that is passed from parent to offspring can be caused by one gene or by the interaction of two or more genes.
7.2.d Students know plant and animal cells contain many thousands of different genes and typically have two copies of every gene. The two copies (or alleles) of the gene may or may not be **identical,** and one may be dominant in determining the phenotype while the other is recessive.	**identical** (ie DEN ti kuhl) being exactly the same	Plant and animal cells have many different genes and usually have two copies of each gene. The two copies of the gene, called alleles, may be the same or may be different. One of the two copies may be more important than the other in causing the features of the plant or animal.
7.2.e Students know DNA (deoxyribonucleic acid) is the genetic material of living organisms and is **located** in the chromosomes of each cell.	**located** (LOH KAYT id) to be in a certain place	DNA is the material that determines what traits are passed from one generation of living things to the next. DNA is found in the chromosomes of each cell.

6

Heredity

The Big Idea
Heredity is the passing of the instructions for traits from one generation to the next.

 California Standards

Focus on Life Sciences
7.2 A typical cell of any organism contains genetic instructions that specify its traits. Those traits may be modified by environmental influences. (Sections 1, 2, and 3)

Investigation and Experimentation
7.7 Scientific progress is made by asking meaningful questions and conducting careful investigations. (Science Skills Activity)

Math
6.1.2 Number Sense
6.3.2 Statistics, Data Analysis, and Probability

English–Language Arts
7.1.3 Reading
7.2.5 Writing

About the Photo
The parrot on the left has orange feathers. Three of the parrots have red feathers. The parrot that has yellow feathers is the only parrot that has a black beak. Why do these parrots look different from one another? The colors of their feathers and of their beaks were determined before they were born. These are just two of the many traits determined by genetic information. Genetic information is passed on from parents to their offspring.

Organize

Key-Term Fold
Before you read this chapter, create the FoldNote entitled "Key-Term Fold." Write a key term from the chapter on each tab of the key-term fold. As you read the chapter, write the definition of each key term under the appropriate tab.

Instructions for creating FoldNotes are located in the Study Skills section on p. 581 of the Appendix.

Explore Activity

7.2.d

Modeling Traits

In this activity, you will model how the combination of different traits creates variation.

Procedure

1. Your teacher will gather three boxes. Then, your teacher will place five hats in the first box, five gloves in the second box, and five scarves in the third box.

2. Your teacher will allow students to select items from each box without looking in the boxes. Record the three items, or "outfit," each student chooses. Replace the clothes in the appropriate boxes. Repeat this process until each student in the class has picked an outfit.

Analysis

3. Were any two outfits exactly alike? Did you see all possible combinations? Explain your answer.

4. Choose a partner. Using your outfits, how many different combinations could you make by giving a third person one of your hats, gloves, and scarves? How is this process like parents passing traits to their children?

5. Based on what you have learned in this activity, why do you think parents often have children who look very different from each other?

173

Mendel and His Peas

Key Concept The work of Gregor Mendel explains the rules of heredity and is the foundation of modern genetics.

▶ Imagine a puppy. The puppy has long, floppy ears like his mother has, and the puppy has dark brown fur like his father has. How did the puppy get these traits? The passing of traits from parents to offspring is called **heredity.** About 100 years ago, Gregor Mendel performed experiments about heredity that helped establish the field of *genetics*. Genetics is the study of how traits are inherited.

Before Mendel

Offspring often look a little like their mother and a little like their father. This observation led people to think that each trait of the offspring was the result of the traits of both parents mixed together. The idea that each trait of the offspring is a mixture of traits of both parents is called *blending inheritance*. According to the idea of blending inheritance, if a brown rabbit mates with a white rabbit, the offspring would be tan. And if a tan rabbit mates with a brown rabbit, the offspring would be dark tan.

However, when a brown rabbit and a white rabbit mate, the offspring often have brown fur. And when two brown rabbits mate, a white rabbit might be born. So, blending inheritance is not a good explanation of heredity. The experiments of Gregor Mendel provide evidence that blending inheritance is incorrect for many traits. Mendel's results have changed the way people think about inheritance.

Standards Check What is blending inheritance? 🐘 **7.2.d**

Gregor Mendel's Work

Gregor Mendel, shown in **Figure 1,** was born in 1822 in Heinzendorf, Austria. Mendel grew up on a farm and learned a lot about flowers and fruit trees. When he was 21 years old, Mendel entered a monastery. A monastery is a place where monks study religion. The monks also taught science and performed scientific experiments.

As a monk, Mendel put most of his energy into research. Mendel decided to study only one kind of organism. Garden peas were a good choice because they grow quickly and because there are many varieties.

Figure 1 *Gregor Mendel discovered the principles of heredity while studying pea plants.*

Self-Pollinating Peas

Pea plants, like many flowering plants, have both male and female reproductive structures. Many flowering plants reproduce through cross-pollination. In *cross-pollination,* sperm (in pollen) from one plant fertilizes the eggs (in an ovule) of a different plant. Pollen from one plant may be carried by insects, bats, birds, or other organisms to a flower on a different plant. Pollen can also be carried by the wind from one flower to another.

Most flowering plants cross-pollinate and therefore need another plant to reproduce. But a pea plant can reproduce through cross-pollination or self-pollination. In *self-pollination,* sperm from one plant fertilizes the eggs of the same plant.

What happens when pea plants self-pollinate? When a *true-breeding plant* self-pollinates, its offspring will have the same trait as the parent. For example, a true-breeding plant that has purple flowers will always have offspring that have purple flowers. Self-pollination is important because Mendel was able to grow true-breeding plants for his experiments. **Figure 2** shows flowers reproducing by cross-pollination and by self-pollination.

Describing Traits

How would you describe yourself? Are you tall or short, or do you have curly hair or straight hair? In your **Science Journal,** make a list of your physical traits. Then, make a list of traits that you were not born with, such as "caring" or "good at soccer." Talk to your family about your lists. Does your family agree with your descriptions?

heredity (hee RED i tee) the passing of genetic traits from parent to offspring

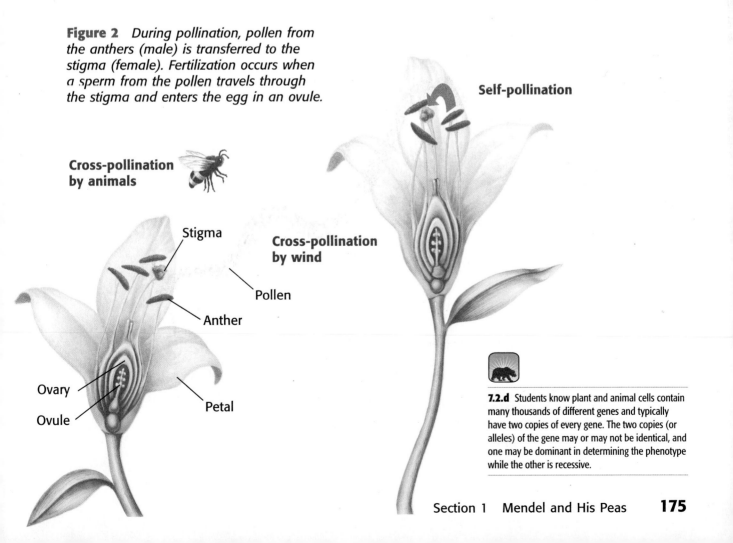

Figure 2 *During pollination, pollen from the anthers (male) is transferred to the stigma (female). Fertilization occurs when a sperm from the pollen travels through the stigma and enters the egg in an ovule.*

Self-pollination

Cross-pollination by animals

Stigma

Cross-pollination by wind

Pollen

Anther

Ovary

Ovule

Petal

7.2.d Students know plant and animal cells contain many thousands of different genes and typically have two copies of every gene. The two copies (or alleles) of the gene may or may not be identical, and one may be dominant in determining the phenotype while the other is recessive.

Characteristics

Mendel studied one characteristic at a time. A *characteristic* is a feature that has different forms in a population. For example, hair color is a characteristic in humans. The different forms, or colors, such as brown or red hair, are called *traits*. Mendel used plants that had different traits for each of the characteristics he studied. For instance, for the characteristic of flower color, he chose plants that had purple flowers and plants that had white flowers. Mendel also studied other characteristics such as seed shape, pod color, and plant height.

Mix and Match

Mendel was careful to use plants that were true breeding for each of the traits he was studying. By choosing these plants, he would know what to expect if his plants were to self-pollinate. He decided to find out what would happen if he bred, or crossed, two plants that had different traits of a single characteristic. To be sure the plants cross-pollinated, he removed the anthers of one plant so that the plant could not self-pollinate. Then, he used pollen from another plant to fertilize the plant, as **Figure 3** shows. This step allowed Mendel to select which plants would be crossed to produce offspring.

dominant trait (DAHM uh nuhnt TRAYT) the trait observed in the first generation when parents that have different traits are bred

recessive trait (ri SES iv TRAYT) a trait that reappears in the second generation after disappearing in the first generation when parents with different traits are bred

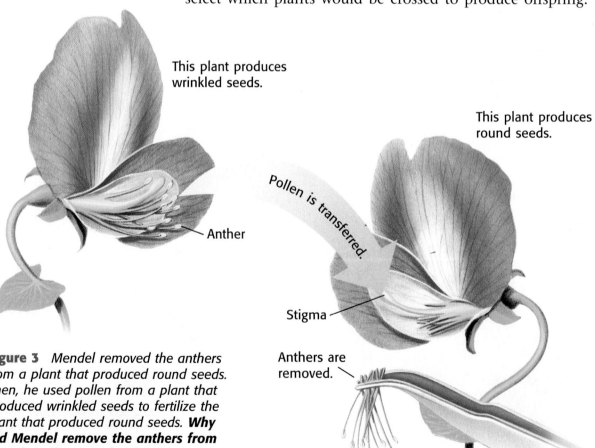

This plant produces wrinkled seeds.

This plant produces round seeds.

Pollen is transferred.

Anther

Stigma

Anthers are removed.

Figure 3 *Mendel removed the anthers from a plant that produced round seeds. Then, he used pollen from a plant that produced wrinkled seeds to fertilize the plant that produced round seeds.* **Why did Mendel remove the anthers from the plant that was fertilized?**

Mendel's First Experiments

In his first experiments, Mendel crossed pea plants to study seven different characteristics. In each cross, Mendel used plants that were true breeding for different traits for each characteristic. For example, he crossed plants that had purple flowers with plants that had white flowers. The offspring from such a cross are called *first-generation plants*. All of the first-generation plants in this cross had purple flowers. Are you surprised by the results? What happened to the trait for white flowers?

Mendel got similar results for each cross. One trait was always present in the first generation, and the other trait seemed to disappear. Mendel chose to call the trait that appeared the **dominant trait.** Because the other trait seemed to fade into the background, Mendel called it the **recessive trait.** To *recede* means "to go away or back off." To find out what might have happened to the recessive trait, Mendel decided to do another set of experiments.

Mendel's Second Experiments

Mendel allowed the first-generation plants to self-pollinate. **Figure 4** shows what happened when a first-generation plant that had purple flowers was allowed to self-pollinate. As you can see, the recessive trait for white flowers reappeared in the second generation.

Mendel did this same experiment on seven different characteristics. In each case, some of the second-generation plants had the recessive trait.

Standards Check Describe the second set of experiments performed by Mendel. 7.2.d

Quick Lab

Flower Cross   7.2.d

1. Use **colored pencils** and **paper** to draw a plant that has two varieties: plants that have yellow flowers and plants that have red flowers.

2. Draw a picture of what the offspring would look like if you bred the two plants according to the idea of blending inheritance.

3. What would the offspring look like if you did the same cross but bred the plants according to Mendelian genetics?

4. How do the two crosses differ?

⏱ 15 min

Parent Generation

Pollen transfer

First Generation
All flowers are purple.

A mature plant is allowed to self-pollinate.

Second Generation
For every three plants that have purple flowers, there is one plant that has white flowers.

Figure 4 *Mendel used the pollen from a plant that had purple flowers to fertilize a plant that had white flowers. Then, he allowed the offspring to self-pollinate.*

Ratios in Mendel's Experiments

Mendel then decided to count the number of plants that had each trait and that turned up in the second generation. He hoped that this might help him explain his results. Take a look at Mendel's results shown in **Table 1.**

As you can see, the recessive trait did not show up as often as the dominant trait. Mendel decided to figure out the ratio of dominant traits to recessive traits. A *ratio* is a relationship between two different numbers that is often expressed as a fraction. Calculate the dominant-to-recessive ratio for each characteristic. (If you need help, look at the Math Practice at left.) Do you notice anything interesting about the ratios? Round to the nearest whole number. Are the ratios all the same, or are they different?

Standards Check What is a ratio? 7.2.d

Table 1	Mendel's Results		
Characteristic	**Dominant traits**	**Recessive traits**	**Ratio**
Flower color	705 purple	224 white	3.15:1
Seed color	6,002 yellow	2,001 green	?
Seed shape	5,474 round	1,850 wrinkled	?
Pod color	428 green	152 yellow	?
Pod shape	882 smooth	299 bumpy	?
Flower position	651 along stem	207 at tip	?
Plant height	787 tall	277 short	?

Gregor Mendel—Gone but Not Forgotten

Mendel realized that his results could only be explained if each plant had two sets of instructions for each characteristic. Therefore, he concluded that each parent gives one set of instructions to the offspring. The offspring's traits are then determined by the dominant set of instructions.

In 1865, Mendel published his findings. But good ideas are sometimes overlooked or misunderstood at first. It was not until after his death, more than 30 years later, that Mendel's work was widely recognized. Once Mendel's ideas were rediscovered and understood, the door was opened to modern genetics. Genetic research, as shown in **Figure 5,** is one of the fastest changing fields in science today.

Figure 5 *This researcher is continuing the work started by Gregor Mendel more than 100 years ago.*

SECTION Review

 7.2.d

Summary

- Heredity is the passing of traits from parents to offspring.
- Before Mendel's ideas were accepted, people explained inheritance as the blending of traits from each parent.
- Gregor Mendel's experiments using pea plants eventually changed the way people thought about heredity.
- When parents with different traits are bred, dominant traits are always present in the first generation. Recessive traits are not visible in the first generation but reappear in the second generation.
- Mendel found a 3:1 ratio of dominant-to-recessive traits in the second generation.
- Mendel's ideas are the foundation of modern genetics.

Using Vocabulary

1. Use *heredity, dominant trait,* and *recessive trait* in separate sentences.

Understanding Concepts

2. **Summarizing** Explain the difference between self-pollination and cross-pollination.

3. **Comparing** What is the difference between a trait and a characteristic? Give one example of each.

4. **Describing** Describe Mendel's first set of experiments.

5. **Describing** Describe Mendel's second set of experiments.

Critical Thinking

6. **Predicting Consequences** If Mendel had used plants that were not true breeding, do you think he would have discovered dominant and recessive traits? Explain your answer.

7. **Applying Concepts** Cats may have normal or curly ears. A curly-eared cat mated with a normal-eared cat, and all of the kittens had curly ears. Are curly ears a dominant or recessive trait? Explain your answer.

Math Skills

8. **Number Sense** Of the 52 students eating lunch, 17 students are eating a sandwich. The rest of the students are eating pizza. What is the ratio of students who are eating sandwiches to students eating pizza?

Challenge

9. **Predicting Consequences** If blending inheritance explained how flowers inherit traits, would you expect to see more flower colors? Explain your answer.

Internet Resources

For a variety of links related to this chapter, go to www.scilinks.org

Topic: Heredity; Dominant and Recessive Traits

SciLinks code: HY70738; HY70423

Traits and Inheritance

Key Concept Genes are the instructions for inherited traits.

▶ What did Mendel's experiments tell him about how traits are passed from parents to offspring?

A Great Idea

Mendel knew from his experiments with pea plants that there must be two sets of instructions for each characteristic. The first-generation plants carried the instructions for both the dominant trait and the recessive trait. Scientists now call these instructions for an inherited trait **genes.** Each parent gives one set of genes to the offspring. The offspring then has two versions, or forms, of the same gene for every characteristic—one from each parent. The different versions (often dominant and recessive) of a gene are known as **alleles.** Dominant alleles are shown as capital letters. A single dominant allele masks the expression of the instructions held on a recessive allele. When an organism has a dominant allele, the organism has the dominant trait. Recessive alleles are shown as lowercase letters. An organism has a recessive trait when two copies of the recessive allele are present in the organism.

Standards Check Compare the terms gene and allele. ▨ **7.2.d**

Phenotype

Genes affect the traits of offspring. An organism's appearance is known as the organism's **phenotype. Figure 1** shows the possible phenotypes for the characteristic of flower color in pea plants. The pea plants Mendel studied had either purple flowers or white flowers. The phenotypes for seed color are yellow and green. Phenotypes for humans also describe characteristics. For example, you most likely have a phenotype of either curly hair or straight hair.

Figure 1 *Purple flowers and white flowers are the two possible phenotypes for the characteristic of flower color in pea plants.*

Genotype

Both inherited alleles together form an organism's **genotype.** Because the allele for purple flowers (*P*) is dominant, only one *P* allele is needed for the plant to have purple flowers. A plant with two dominant or two recessive alleles is said to be *homozygous* (HOH moh ZIE guhs). A plant that has the genotype *Pp* is said to be *heterozygous* (HET uhr OH ZIE guhs).

Punnett Squares

A Punnett square is used to predict the possible genotypes of offspring in a particular cross. **Figure 2** shows a Punnett square for a cross of a true-breeding, purple-flowered plant and a true-breeding, white-flowered plant. The alleles for a true-breeding, purple-flowered plant are written as *PP*. The alleles for a true-breeding, white-flowered plant are written as *pp*. Offspring get one allele from each parent. All of the offspring from this cross will have the same genotype: *Pp*. Because of the dominant allele, *P*, in the genotype, all of the offspring will have purple flowers.

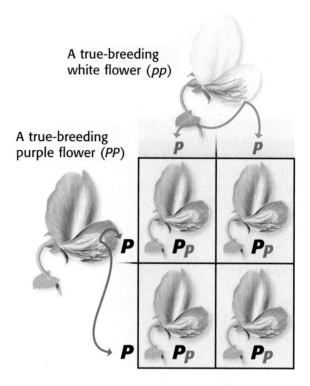

A true-breeding white flower (*pp*)

A true-breeding purple flower (*PP*)

Figure 2 *All of the offspring for this cross have the same genotype—Pp.*

genotype (JEE nuh TIEP) the entire genetic makeup of an organism; *also* the combination of genes for one or more specific traits

Quick Lab

Completing a Punnett Square

7.2.d
7.7.d

1. Draw a square. Divide it into four sections.

2. Write the letters that represent alleles from one parent along the top of the square.

3. Write the letters that represent alleles from the other parent along the side of the square.

4. Fill in each column in the square with the letter on the top of that column.

5. Fill in each row in the square with the letter on the side of that row.

6. The cross shown at right is between two plants that produce round seeds. The genotype for each plant is *Rr*. Round seeds (*R*) are dominant, and wrinkled seeds (*r*) are recessive. Follow the arrows to see how the inside of the square was filled. The resulting alleles inside the square show the possible genotypes for the offspring from this cross.

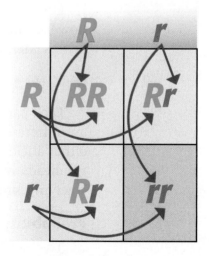

7. What are the possible phenotypes of the offspring from the cross above?

 15 min

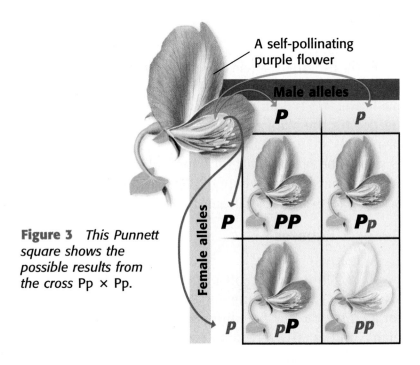

A self-pollinating purple flower

Figure 3 *This Punnett square shows the possible results from the cross Pp × Pp.*

More Evidence for Inheritance

In his second experiments, Mendel allowed the first-generation plants to self-pollinate. **Figure 3** shows a self-pollination cross of a plant that has the genotype *Pp*. What are the possible genotypes of the offspring?

Notice that one square shows the genotype *Pp*, while another shows *pP*. These are exactly the same genotype. The other possible genotypes of the offspring are *PP* and *pp*. The combinations *PP*, *Pp*, and *pP* have the same phenotype—purple flowers. The combinations have the same phenotype because each contains at least one dominant allele (*P*).

Only one combination, *pp*, produces plants that have white flowers. The ratio of dominant alleles to recessive alleles is 3:1, just as Mendel calculated from his data.

What Are the Chances?

Each parent has two alleles for each gene. When these alleles are different, as in *Pp*, offspring are equally likely to receive either allele. Think of a coin toss. There is a 50% chance you'll get heads and a 50% chance you'll get tails. The chance of receiving one allele or another is as random as a coin toss.

Probability

The mathematical chance that something will happen is known as **probability.** Probability is most often written as a fraction or percentage. If you toss a coin, the probability of tossing tails is 1/2—you will get tails half the time.

Standards Check What is probability? 7.2.d

probability (PRAHB uh BIL uh tee) the likelihood that a possible future event will occur in any given instance of the event

Probability

If you roll a pair of dice, what is the probability that you will roll 2 threes?

Step 1: Count the number of faces on one die. Put this number in the denominator: 6.

Step 2: Count how many ways you can roll a three with one die. Put this number in the numerator: 1/6.

Step 3: To find the probability that you will throw 2 threes, multiply the probability of throwing the first three by the probability of throwing the second three:
$1/6 \times 1/6 = 1/36$.

Now It's Your Turn

If you roll a single die, what is the probability that you will roll an even number?

Calculating Probabilities

To find the probability that you will toss two heads in a row, multiply the probability of tossing the first head (1/2) by the probability of tossing the second head (1/2). The probability of tossing two heads in a row is 1/4.

Genotype Probability

To have white flowers, a pea plant must receive a *p* allele from each parent. Each offspring of a *Pp* × *Pp* cross has a 50% chance of receiving either allele from either parent. So, the probability of inheriting two *p* alleles is $1/2 \times 1/2$, which equals 1/4, or 25%. The traits Mendel chose to examine in pea plants are easy to predict because there were only two choices for each trait. Mendel studied sets of traits such as purple or white flowers and round or wrinkled seeds. Look at **Figure 4.** Do you see only two distinct choices for fur color?

Selective Breeding

Is breeding organisms for a particular characteristic an acceptable practice? Argue for or against selective breeding. Go to **go.hrw.com,** and type in the keyword HY7HERW.

Figure 4 *These kittens inherited one allele from their mother for each trait.*

Figure 5 *The gene that gave this tiger white fur also influenced its eye color.*

More About Traits

Things are often more complicated than they first appear to be. Gregor Mendel uncovered the basic principles of how genes are passed from one generation to the next. But as scientists learned more about heredity, they began to find exceptions to Mendel's principles.

One Gene, Many Traits

In the traits that Mendel studied, one gene determined one trait. But sometimes one gene influences more than one trait. An example of this is shown by the white tiger in **Figure 5.** The white fur is caused by a single gene, but this gene influences more than just fur color. If you look closely, you will see that the tiger has blue eyes. Here, the gene that controls fur color also influences eye color.

Genetic disorders can be the result of an error on one allele of one gene. In some cases, the gene may affect many traits. For example, the genetic disorder sickle cell anemia is caused by an error on an allele of a single gene. This gene carries instructions for the structure of a protein in red blood cells. When a person has an allele with the error, she produces a protein with the wrong shape. This protein causes red blood cells to collapse into sickle-shapes, as **Figure 6** shows.

Sickle-shaped blood cells do not carry oxygen through the body as well as normal red blood cells do. Also, sickle-shaped blood cells can become stuck in small blood vessels. Both the ability of the cell to carry oxygen and the ability of the cell to move through the body are affected by the error in the alleles for this one gene.

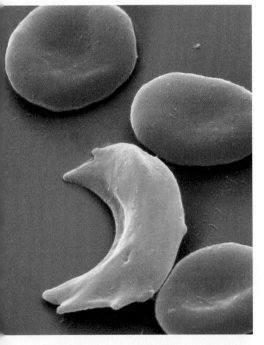

Figure 6 *One out of 500 African Americans has sickle cell anemia, which is caused by a mutation in the alleles for a gene that carries instructions for the protein hemoglobin.*

Figure 7 *At least two genes determine human eye color. That's why many shades of a single color are possible.*

Many Genes, One Trait

Some traits, such as the color of your skin, hair, and eyes, are the result of several genes acting together. Different combinations of alleles result in different eye-color shades, as shown in **Figure 7.** Multiple genes also affect many internal traits. For example, multiple genes influence how people break down food for energy. Because there is not always a one-to-one correspondence between trait and gene, many traits do not have simple patterns of inheritance.

Standards Check Give an example of many genes affecting one trait. 7.2.c

The Importance of Environment

Genes are not the only influences on traits. Traits are also determined by an organism's internal and external environment. For example, height is influenced by nutrition, which is an internal environmental condition. Also, skin color can be influenced by exposure to the sun, which is an external environmental condition.

Sometimes, the environment can have a great effect on an organism's phenotype. Look at the two grasshoppers in **Figure 8.** Would you believe that the grasshoppers are the same species? These grasshoppers develop a different coloration depending on the kind of food available when they are young. Some grasshoppers eat certain plants that make them poisonous to predators. Grasshoppers that eat these plants have a yellow and black coloration. Other grasshoppers that eat different kinds of plants will not be poisonous. They have a green coloration.

Figure 8 *These grasshoppers develop different colorations based on what they eat.*

Figure 9 *Genetic variation explains why these corn snakes are different colors.*

Genetic Variation

How many genes do you have? Would you guess that you have a hundred genes or a thousand genes? Scientists estimate that humans have approximately 30,000 genes. For most genes, a person has two alleles, or copies. Because there are different alleles for most genes, every person has a unique set of alleles. One reason people look different from each other is that they do not have the same set of alleles. The differences in the sets of alleles between individuals in a population is called *genetic variation.*

Genetic variation is found in many populations. An example of genetic variation in a population of corn snakes is shown in **Figure 9.** The phenotypes of the corn snakes differ for the trait of skin color. Because skin color in corn snakes is determined by the alleles for skin color, you can see that there must be a large amount of genetic variation in the population of corn snakes shown in **Figure 9.**

Genes affect many things that are not easy to see. Some genes affect traits inside of your body. All of the enzymes, hormones, and other chemicals that your body makes are affected by genes. Different alleles direct the cells in your body to make different versions of these chemicals. So, even when two people look similar, the alleles for each of their genes may be very different.

Standards Check Approximately how many genes do people have?
🐻 7.2.d

Summary

- Instructions for an inherited trait are called *genes.* For each gene, there are two alleles, one inherited from each parent. Both alleles make up an organism's genotype.
- An organism's phenotype is the organism's observable characteristics.
- Punnett squares show all possible offspring genotypes.
- Probability can be used to describe possible outcomes in offspring and the likelihood of each outcome.
- Some genes influence more than one trait.
- Some traits are influenced by many genes.
- The environment can influence how genes are expressed.
- Scientists estimate that humans have approximately 30,000 genes.

Using Vocabulary

1. Use *gene* and *allele* in the same sentence.

2. Write an original definition for *genotype* and *phenotype*.

Understanding Concepts

3. **Describing** How are genes and alleles related to genotype and phenotype?

4. **Summarizing** What are three exceptions to Mendel's observations?

5. **Applying** What is the probability of rolling a five on one die three times in a row?

Critical Thinking

6. **Applying Concepts** The allele for a cleft chin, *C,* is dominant in humans. What are the possible results of a cross between parents that have genotypes *Cc* and *cc*?

7. **Evaluating Hypotheses** A student in your class believes that the number of genes an organism has is equal to the number of traits that organism has. Evaluate this hypothesis.

INTERPRETING GRAPHICS The Punnett square shows the alleles for fur color in rabbits. Black fur, *B,* is dominant over white fur, *b.* Use the Punnett square below to answer the next two questions.

	B	B
b	?	?
b	?	?

8. **Applying Concepts** What are the possible genotypes of the offspring from the cross above?

9. **Applying Concepts** What are the possible phenotypes of the offspring from the cross above?

Math Skills

10. **Making Calculations** In pea plants, the allele for purple flowers (*P*) is dominant. The allele for white flowers (*p*) is recessive. If you cross two flowers that have a genotype of *Pp*, what is the probability that the offspring will inherit a *PP* genotype?

Challenge

11. **Making Inferences** Some wild roses produce bigger flowers than other wild roses do. How could people use the genetic variation in wild roses to create roses that produce large flowers?

Internet Resources

For a variety of links related to this chapter, go to www.scilinks.org

Topic: Genotypes; Phenotypes
SciLinks code: HY70664; HY71135

Meiosis

Key Concept Meiosis and sexual reproduction allow for the combination of genetic material from two different cells.

What You Will Learn

- In sexual reproduction, offspring receive half of their genetic material from each parent.
- Homologous chromosomes contain the same genes but may have different alleles for each gene.
- Meiosis results in the production of haploid cells that have half the number of chromosomes that diploid cells do.

Why It Matters

The combination of genetic material during sexual reproduction allows for genetic variation.

Vocabulary

- homologous chromosomes
- diploid
- haploid
- meiosis

READING STRATEGY

Graphic Organizer In your **Science Journal,** create Combination Notes about meiosis.

homologous chromosomes
(hoh MAHL uh guhs KROH muh SOHMZ) chromosomes that have the same sequence of genes and the same structure

diploid (DIP LOYD) a cell that contains two haploid sets of chromosomes
  Wordwise The root *dipl-* means "twice" or "double."

haploid (HAP LOYD) describes a cell, nucleus, or organism that has only one set of unpaired chromosomes

7.2.b Students know sexual reproduction produces offspring that inherit half their genes from each parent.
7.2.e Students know DNA (deoxyribonucleic acid) is the genetic material of living organisms and is located in the chromosomes of each cell.

Offspring receive genetic information, or DNA, from their parents. In asexual reproduction, one parent contributes genetic information to its offspring. The offspring has the same genotype as the parent.

In sexual reproduction, two parents contribute genetic information to their offspring. Before sexual reproduction can occur, each parent must reduce his or her genetic material by half in a process called meiosis. Therefore, when the genetic information from two parents combine, the offspring will have the same amount of genetic information as each of its parents. Genetic information is located on structures called *chromosomes*.

Chromosome Numbers

Most species have a specific number of chromosomes in their body cells. For example, human cells usually have 46 chromosomes, corn cells usually have 20 chromosomes, and dog cells usually have 78 chromosomes. Most of the time, the chromosomes are spread out in long strands. Before a cell divides, the chromosomes in the cell condense and become shorter and thicker. **Figure 1** shows the 46 chromosomes of a human body cell that are visible during cell division.

Standards Check How many chromosomes does a human body cell have? **7.2.e**

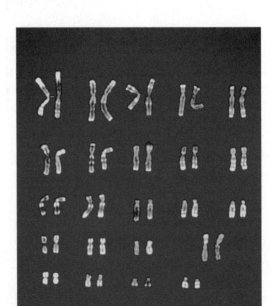

Figure 1 *This karyotype shows the 46 chromosomes from a human body cell.*

Homologous Chromosomes

Organisms who reproduce sexually have two kinds of cells, body cells and sex cells. In body cells, the chromosomes are found in pairs that carry similar genetic information and have a similar structure. These chromosomes, that carry the same sets of genes, are called **homologous chromosomes.** Homologous chromosomes carry the same genes, but the chromosomes may have different alleles for those genes. **Figure 2** shows a diagram of a homologous pair of chromosomes.

Chromosomes in Reproduction

Cells that have homologous pairs of chromosomes are called **diploid.** Body cells are diploid cells. Before an organism can reproduce sexually, it must make *sex cells.* Sex cells have one copy of each chromosome. Sex cells do not have homologous chromosomes because the homologous chromosomes separate during the production of sex cells. So, each sex cell only has one copy of each gene. A cell that does not have homologous chromosomes is called **haploid.** Sex cells are haploid cells.

Figure 3 shows the role haploid sex cells play in the reproduction of diploid organisms. The male makes sex cells called *sperm.* The female makes sex cells called *eggs.* The sperm and eggs are haploid cells. Fertilization occurs when a sperm cell and an egg cell combine. A diploid cell is formed when the chromosomes from the sperm cell and the egg cell combine. The diploid cell divides and creates more diploid cells through the process of mitosis. These cells can develop into a new organism.

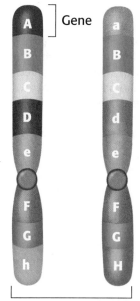

Homologous chromosomes

Figure 2 *Homologous chromosomes have the same genes. Genes can be the same version, or allele, such as the "B" allele found on both chromosomes. The genes can also be different alleles, such as the "A" and "a" alleles.*

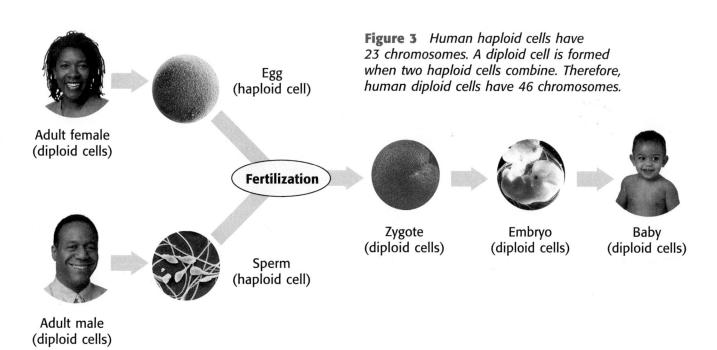

Figure 3 *Human haploid cells have 23 chromosomes. A diploid cell is formed when two haploid cells combine. Therefore, human diploid cells have 46 chromosomes.*

Egg
(haploid cell)

Adult female
(diploid cells)

Fertilization

Sperm
(haploid cell)

Adult male
(diploid cells)

Zygote
(diploid cells)

Embryo
(diploid cells)

Baby
(diploid cells)

Meiosis

meiosis (mie OH sis) a process in cell division during which the number of chromosomes decreases to half the original number by two divisions of the nucleus, which results in the production of sex cells (gametes or spores)

Sex cells are made during meiosis. **Meiosis** is a copying process that produces cells that have half the usual number of chromosomes. Each sex cell receives one-half of each homologous pair. For example, a human egg cell has 23 chromosomes, and a sperm cell has 23 chromosomes. The new cell that forms when an egg cell and a sperm cell join has 46 chromosomes.

Standards Check How many chromosomes does a human egg cell have?  **7.2.b**

The Steps of Meiosis

The steps of meiosis for a cell that has four chromosomes are shown in **Figure 4.** Before meiosis begins, each chromosome is copied. The original chromosome and the new copy form *chromatids,* which are joined together. The chromosomes shorten and thicken, which makes them visible under a microscope. During meiosis, the nucleus divides twice. The first time the nucleus divides, the homologous chromosomes separate. The second time the nucleus divides, the identical chromatids separate. Finally, meiosis results in four sex cells, which have half the number of chromosomes as the original cell.

Figure 4 Steps of Meiosis

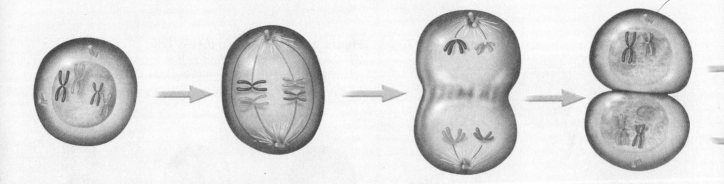

❶ The chromosomes are copied before meiosis begins. The identical copies, or chromatids, are joined together.

❷ After the nuclear membrane disappears, pairs of homologous chromosomes line up along the equator of the cell.

❸ The chromosomes separate from their homologous partners and then move to opposite ends of the cell.

❹ The nuclear membrane re-forms, and the cell divides. The paired chromatids are still joined.

Meiosis Skit

After studying the steps of meiosis, perform a skit with your class about how a diploid cell that has four chromosomes undergoes meiosis.

1. To play the part of the genetic material, use four colors of **paper streamers** that are each 1 m long. Fold the streamers in half to represent chromosomes.

2. Students who are not holding genetic material can be the cell membrane by standing in a circle around the chromosomes. After the chromosomes separate, the membrane pinches to form separate cells.

3. As a group, you will act out each step of meiosis. For example, start with four students each holding one chromosome. When the chromosomes replicate before meiosis begins, four more students with chromosomes should enter the cell.

4. Continue the steps of meiosis until haploid cells are produced.

5. How many chromosomes are in each haploid cell?

🕐 **20 min**

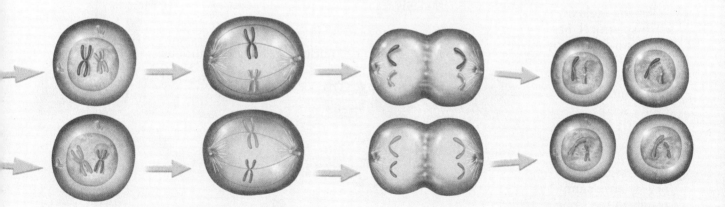

5 Each cell contains one member of the homologous chromosome pair. The chromosomes are not copied again between the two cell divisions.

6 The nuclear membrane disappears, and the chromosomes line up along the equator of each cell.

7 The chromatids pull apart and move to opposite ends of the cell. The nuclear membranes re-form, and the cells divide.

8 The result is that four new haploid cells have formed from the original diploid cell. Each new cell has half the number of chromosomes present in the original cell.

Meiosis and Mendel

The steps in meiosis explain Mendel's results. **Figure 5** shows what happens to chromosomes during meiosis and fertilization. The cross shown is between a plant that is true breeding for round seeds and a plant that is true breeding for wrinkled seeds. All of the sperm formed by the male parent during meiosis have the wrinkled-seed allele, *r*, and all of the female parent's eggs have the round-seed allele, *R*. Each fertilized egg has one dominant allele and one recessive allele for seed shape. So, only one genotype, *Rr*, is possible for the offspring. Because the round-seed allele is dominant and the wrinkled-seed allele is recessive, the offspring have the round-seed phenotype.

Figure 5   Meiosis and Dominance

Male Parent In the plant-cell nucleus below, each homologous chromosome has an allele for seed shape, and each allele carries the same instructions: to make wrinkled seeds.

Female Parent In the plant-cell nucleus below, each homologous chromosome has an allele for seed shape, and each allele carries the same instructions: to make round seeds.

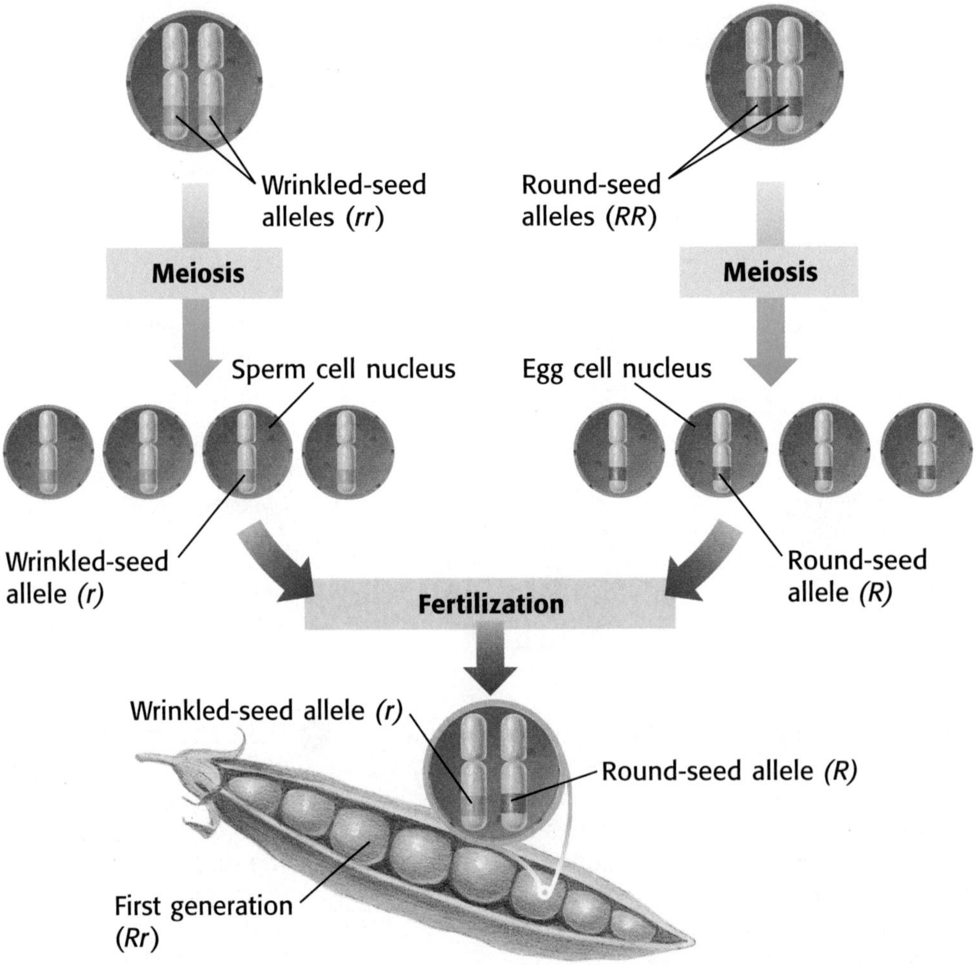

Wrinkled-seed alleles (*rr*)

Round-seed alleles (*RR*)

Meiosis

Meiosis

a Following **meiosis,** each sperm cell has a recessive allele for wrinkled seeds, and each egg cell has a dominant allele for round seeds.

Sperm cell nucleus

Egg cell nucleus

Wrinkled-seed allele (*r*)

Round-seed allele (*R*)

Fertilization

b **Fertilization** of any egg by any sperm results in the same genotype (*Rr*) and the same phenotype (round). This result is exactly what Mendel found in his studies.

Wrinkled-seed allele (*r*)

Round-seed allele (*R*)

First generation (*Rr*)

Meiosis and Inheritance

In sexual reproduction, sex cells combine to produce off-spring. Therefore, approximately half of the offspring's genetic material comes from its biological mother, and approximately half comes from its biological father. In eukaryotes, most of the genetic information is located in the nucleus. However, mitochondria, shown in **Figure 6,** also contain genetic material. Mitochondria are organelles that release energy. In most cases, all of an organism's mitochondria come from its mother. Therefore, mitochondrial DNA in the cells of offspring is the same as the mitochondrial DNA in the cells of the offspring's mother.

Standards Check From which parent does an offspring receive its mitochondrial DNA? 🐻 **7.2.b**

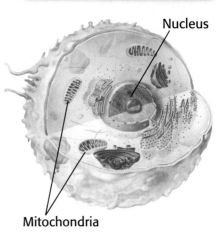

Figure 6 Animal Cell

Nucleus

Mitochondria

SECTION Review

7.2.b, 7.2.e

Summary

- Homologous pairs of chromosomes contain the same genes. The alleles for each gene may be the same or they may be different.

- Diploid cells have homologous pairs of chromosomes. Haploid cells do not.

- The process of meiosis produces haploid sex cells.

- During sexual reproduction, haploid sex cells combine to form a new diploid organism.

- Meiosis explains how organisms inherit one-half of their genetic information from each parent.

Using Vocabulary

1. Use *meiosis* and *sex cells* in the same sentence.

2. Write an original definition for the term *homologous chromosomes.*

Understanding Concepts

3. **Classifying** Are your body cells diploid or haploid?

4. **Describing** How many times does the nucleus divide during meiosis?

5. **Applying** If there are 14 chromosomes in pea plant cells, how many chromosomes are present in a sex cell of a pea plant?

6. **Describing** Approximately how much of an organism's genetic material is contributed by its mother?

7. **Describing** How many pairs of homologous chromosomes are found in human body cells?

Critical Thinking

8. **Identifying Relationships** Put the following in order of smallest to largest: chromosome, gene, and cell.

9. **Applying Concepts** A pea plant has purple flowers. What alleles for flower color could the sex cells carry?

Challenge

10. **Making Comparisons** Is the mitochondrial DNA in a baby more like the mitochondrial DNA from his mother's mother or the mitochondrial DNA from his father's mother? Explain your answer.

Model-Making Lab

Modeling Space Bug Genetics

Imagine that you are working with a team of scientists that has discovered a new organism. The organism shares many characteristics with insects, but the species also has some very strange traits. Because the new organisms look like bugs from outer space, your team has decided to call the new organisms "space bugs." Space bugs inherit traits according to the principles of genetics discovered by Gregor Mendel. In this activity, you will use your knowledge of genetics to construct models of space bugs. You will then construct models of the offspring that could be created by crossing space bugs that have different traits.

Procedure

1 Seven characteristics of space bugs are shown in the table below. For each characteristic, there are two traits. The allele for the dominant trait is written with a capital letter. The allele for the recessive trait is written with a lowercase letter.

2 Create a table like the one entitled "Space Bug Family Traits." Notice that the genotypes of the parents are already entered into the table.

3 Determine the phenotype of each parent by using the table below and the genotypes listed for each parent. Enter the phenotypes in the table that you created.

OBJECTIVES

Build models to further your understanding of inheritance.

Examine the traits of a population of offspring.

MATERIALS

- cup, paper
- gumdrops, green and black (feet)
- map pins (eyes)
- marshmallows, large (head and body segments)
- pipe cleaners (tails)
- pushpins, green and blue (noses)
- scissors
- toothpicks, red and green (antennae)

SAFETY

7.2.b Students know sexual reproduction produces offspring that inherit half their genes from each parent.
7.2.d Students know plant and animal cells contain many thousands of different genes and typically have two copies of every gene. The two copies (or alleles) of the gene may or may not be identical, and one may be dominant in determining the phenotype while the other is recessive.

Investigation and Experimentation
7.7.c Communicate the logical connection among hypotheses, science concepts, tests conducted, data collected, and conclusions drawn from the scientific evidence.
7.7.d Construct scale models, maps, and appropriately labeled diagrams to communicate scientific knowledge (e.g., motion of Earth's plates and cell structure).

Space Bug Traits and Alleles		
Characteristic	**Traits and Alleles**	
Antennae color	red antennae (*R*)	green antennae (*r*)
Number of body segments	three body segments (*S*)	two body segments (*s*)
Tail Shape	curly tail (*C*)	straight tail (*c*)
Number of leg pairs	three pairs of legs (*L*)	two pairs of legs (*l*)
Nose color	blue nose (*B*)	green nose (*b*)
Foot color	green feet (*G*)	black feet (*g*)
Number of eyes	two eyes (*E*)	three eyes (*e*)

Space Bug Family Traits						
Characteristic	Female genotype	Female phenotype	Male genotype	Male phenotype	Offspring genotype	Offspring phenotype
Antennae color	Rr		rr			
Number of body segments	ss		Ss			
Tail shape	cc		CC			
Number of leg pairs	Ll		Ll			
Nose color	BB		Bb			
Foot color	Gg		Gg			
Number of eyes	Ee		ee			

DO NOT WRITE IN BOOK

4 In a group of four students, two students will construct a model of the female space bug and two students will construct a model of the male space bug. (Toothpicks can be used to hold body segments together and can be used as legs to attach the feet to the body.)

5 Based on the model that you created, determine which traits the offspring will inherit from the parent. First, write the parent's alleles for one characteristic on separate, small pieces of paper. For example, if your space bug has the genotype *Rr* for antennae, you will write "*R*" on one piece of paper and "*r*" on a second piece of paper.

6 Fold the pieces of paper, and place them in the paper cup. Without looking, draw one piece of paper. This is the allele that the offspring has inherited from the parent that you created. The other members of your group will tell you which allele the offspring has inherited from the other parent.

7 In your table, record the genotype of the offspring. Continue drawing alleles for the other characteristics.

8 Use the table entitled "Space Bug Traits and Alleles" and the genotype to determine the phenotype of the offspring.

9 As a group, construct a model of the offspring.

Analyze the Results

10 **Organizing Data** Take a poll of the traits of the offspring in your class. What are the ratios for each trait?

11 **Examining Data** Do any of the offspring models look the same? How many different models of offspring are there in your class?

Draw Conclusions

12 **Interpreting Information** Is it possible for an offspring to have a trait that neither of its parents have? If so, how could this occur?

Big Idea Question

13 **Drawing Conclusions** How does the inheritance of traits in the bug models you built represent how traits are inherited in humans?

Science Skills Activity

Investigation and Experimentation

7.7.e Communicate the steps and results from an investigation in written reports and oral presentations.

Giving Oral Presentations

▶ Tutorial

Communicating your results is an important part of any scientific investigation. Results from an investigation can be communicated through written reports or oral presentations. In this tutorial, you will learn the steps for preparing and giving an oral presentation.

Procedure

1 The first step is to research the topic you will be discussing. Ask your teacher which sources you should use for the assignment. Sources might include newspapers, magazines, interviews, or information from the Internet.

2 To guide your research, make a list of topics you want to discuss in your presentation. You can update this list as you continue to gather information. Remember to take good notes!

3 When you have completed your research, think about the order in which you will discuss the information. Create an outline that lists the order of topics.

4 Consider what your introduction and conclusion will be. Your introduction should get your audience interested in your presentation. Your conclusion should review the information you have discussed.

5 Practice giving your presentation to family members. You can also practice your presentation in front of a mirror.

6 Use your outline as a guide when you give your presentation, but do not forget to make eye contact with your audience. Remember to stand up straight, to stay still, and to speak loudly and clearly.

▶ You Try It!

Procedure

Germs or other things in the environment can cause many health problems. But some health problems are inherited. A genetic disorder is a health condition that results from inheriting alleles that do not function properly. Research a genetic disorder, and give a presentation about it to your class. Your presentation should include information that answers the following questions:

1 What are the symptoms of this genetic disorder?

2 What treatment is available?

3 How is the genetic disorder inherited? Is it a dominant allele or a recessive allele?

4 How common is the genetic disorder in the human population?

Chapter Summary

The Big Idea Heredity is the passing of the instructions for traits from one generation to the next.

| **Section** | **Vocabulary** |

1 Mendel and His Peas

Key Concept The work of Gregor Mendel explains the rules of heredity and is the of foundation of modern genetics.

- Heredity is the passing of genetic traits from parent to offspring.
- Gregor Mendel's experiments with pea plants led to the discovery of dominant and recessive traits.

Gregor Mendel discovered many properties of heredity.

heredity p. 174
dominant trait p. 177
recessive trait p. 177

2 Traits and Inheritance

Key Concept Genes are the instructions for inherited traits.

- Genes exist in multiple versions called alleles.
- An organism's phenotype is affected by the organism's genotype.
- Punnett squares are used to predict the possible genotypes of the offspring from particular parents.
- Patterns of inheritance can be more complicated than one gene influencing one trait.

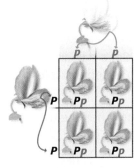

Punnett squares predict the possible genotypes for the offspring of a cross.

gene p. 180
allele p. 180
phenotype p. 180
genotype p. 181
probability p. 182

3 Meiosis

Key Concept Meiosis and sexual reproduction allow for the combination of genetic material from two different cells.

- In sexual reproduction, offspring receive half of their genetic information from each parent.
- Homologous chromosomes contain the same genes but may have different alleles for each gene.
- Meiosis results in the production of haploid cells that have half the number of chromosomes that diploid cells do.

The alleles for genes are found on chromosomes.

homologous chromosomes p. 189
diploid p. 189
haploid p. 189
meiosis p. 190

Organize

Key-Term Fold   Review the FoldNote that you created at the beginning of the chapter. Add to or correct the FoldNote based on what you have learned.

Using Vocabulary

1   **Academic Vocabulary**   In the sentence "The allele for round seeds is dominant to the allele for wrinkled seeds," what does the word *dominant* mean?

Complete each of the following sentences by choosing the correct term from the word bank.

diploid	genotype
haploid	alleles
phenotype	meiosis

2   Meiosis produces ___ cells.

3   The ___ is the expression of a trait and is determined by the combination of alleles called the ___.

4   ___ produces cells that have half the normal number of chromosomes found in body cells.

5   Different versions of the same genes are called ___.

Understanding Concepts

Multiple Choice

6   Genes carry information that determines
   a. alleles.
   b. ribosomes.
   c. chromosomes.
   d. traits.

7   The process that produces sex cells is
   a. mitosis.
   b. photosynthesis.
   c. meiosis.
   d. probability.

8   A male guinea pig that has long, orange fur mated with a female guinea pig that has short, black fur. The litter consisted of guinea pigs that have only long, black fur. Which of the following is probably dominant for both traits?
   a. short, orange fur
   b. long, orange fur
   c. long, black fur
   d. short, black fur

9   Which of the following statements about meiosis is true?
   a. Chromosomes are copied twice.
   b. The nucleus divides once.
   c. Four cells are produced from a single cell.
   d. Two cells are produced from a single cell.

Short Answer

10   **Identifying**   What are the two methods of sexual reproduction used by pea plants?

INTERPRETING GRAPHICS   Use the Punnett square below to answer the next three questions.

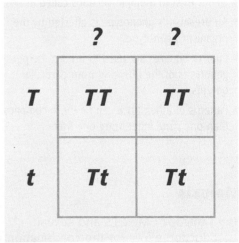

11   **Applying**   What is the unknown genotype?

12   **Analyzing**   If *T* represents the allele for tall pea plants and *t* represents the allele for short pea plants, what is the phenotype of each parent and of the offspring?

13   **Concluding**   If each of the offspring were allowed to self-fertilize, what are the possible genotypes in the next generation?

14 Communicating Concepts Write a paragraph that describes Mendel's experiments with pea plants. Include information about how Mendel performed the experiments, what his results were, and what conclusions he made from the results.

Critical Thinking

15 Concept Mapping Use the following terms to create a concept map: *genes, dominant, heredity, homologous chromosomes, recessive,* and *alleles.*

16 Applying Concepts If a child does not have freckles and both of her parents have freckles, what does that tell you about the allele for freckles? Explain.

17 Applying Concepts In Mendel's experiments with pea plants, each trait was influenced by one gene. Describe an example in which there is not a one-to-one correspondence between trait and gene.

18 Identifying Relationships Explain the relationship between the alleles for a gene and homologous chromosomes.

19 Evaluating Hypotheses When two organisms that have different traits are crossed, some traits disappear in the offspring. But these traits can reappear in later generations. If the theory of blending inheritance explained how traits are inherited, could traits disappear and reappear? Explain your answer.

20 Analyzing Ideas How do the steps of meiosis explain Mendel's results?

21 Identifying Relationship How does the inheritance of mitochondrial DNA differ from the inheritance of DNA found in the nucleus of cells?

22 Applying Concepts Punnett squares can be used to predict many traits of offspring based on the traits of the offspring's parent. Why is it difficult to use a Punnett square to determine certain traits, such as eye color?

Math Skills

23 Making Calculations In pea plants, the allele for yellow seeds, *Y,* is dominant to the allele for green seeds, *y.* If a plant that has the genotype *Yy* is crossed with a plant that has the genotype *yy,* what is the probability that the offspring will have green seeds?

INTERPRETING GRAPHICS Use the table below to answer the next question.

Survey of Traits		
Trait	Number of students with trait	Number of students without trait
Dimples	9	21
Ability to roll tongue	23	7

24 Analyzing Data What is the ratio of students with dimples to students without dimples?

Challenge

25 Evaluating Hypotheses Hydrangeas are flowers that can produce either pink flowers or blue flowers. Your neighbor thinks that the color of the flowers is determined by the type of soil in which the hydrangeas are grown. Your friend thinks the color is determined by the plant's alleles. How could you perform an experiment to prove which hypothesis best explains how the flower color of hydrangeas is determined?

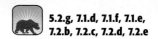
REVIEWING ACADEMIC VOCABULARY

1 **Which of the following words is the closest in meaning to the word _instructions_?**

A information

B advice

C directions

D threats

2 **In the sentence "Traits may be modified by environmental influences," what does the word _modified_ mean?**

A changed

B exaggerated

C erased

D preserved

3 **Which of the following words means "a way of doing something"?**

A method

B product

C evaluation

D market

4 **Choose the appropriate form of the word _locate_ for the following sentence: DNA _____ in the chromosomes of each cell.**

A was location

B is located

C have located

D locate

REVIEWING CONCEPTS

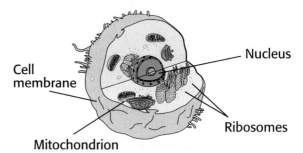

Cell membrane

Nucleus

Ribosomes

Mitochondrion

5 **In which of the cell parts is DNA located?**

A the mitochondrion

B the cell membrane

C the ribosomes

D the nucleus

6 **Which cells are created during meiosis in humans?**

A diploid cells with 46 chromosomes

B diploid cells with 23 chromosomes

C haploid cells with 46 chromosomes

D haploid cells with 23 chromosomes

7 **How many genes do humans have?**

A 1,000 to 2,000

B 3,000 to 6,000

C 20,000 to 30,000

D 100,000 to 200,00

8 **Which statement best describes inheritance in humans?**

A Offspring inherit two alleles for each gene from both parents.

B Offspring inherit two alleles for each gene from one parent.

C Offspring inherit one allele for each gene from both parents.

D Offspring inherit one gene for each allele from both parents.

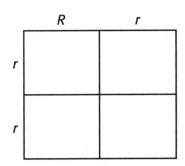

9 The Punnett square above shows a cross between a pea plant that has round seeds (*Rr*) and a pea plant that has wrinkled seeds (*rr*). What are the possible genotypes of the offspring of this cross?

A *RR, Rr, rr*

B *RR, rr*

C *Rr, rr*

D *RR, Rr*

10 Why do identical twins have the same genotype?

A They have all the same sets of alleles.

B They come from two identical eggs.

C They look exactly like one another.

D They have heterozygous genotypes.

11 What is the best explanation for the many shades in human eye color?

A Eye color is determined by more than one gene.

B Blended inheritance creates offspring with mixed eye colors.

C One gene sometimes influences more than one characteristic.

D Many recessive alleles exist for different shades of eye color.

12 Which structure(s) contains DNA and protein?

A a genotype   C a nucleus

B chromosomes   D organelles

13 What is the purpose of mitosis?

A to transform haploid sex cells into diploid cells

B to produce copies of cells

C to change cells in response to the environment

D to create sex cells for sexual reproduction

14 Why is cell differentiation necessary as a multicellular animal develops?

A to keep cells multiplying so that the animal will grow more quickly

B to create tissues, organs, and organ systems that keep the animal alive

C to prevent genetic disorders and other health problems from occurring

D to help the animal adapt to its environment as it grows to adulthood

15 Which structures in plant cells capture sunlight for photosynthesis?

A chloroplasts

B chromosomes

C genotypes

D nuclei

16 What is the process by which cells break down sugar molecules and release energy?

A sexual reproduction

B meiosis

C photosynthesis

D cellular respiration

Standards Assessment

Science in Action

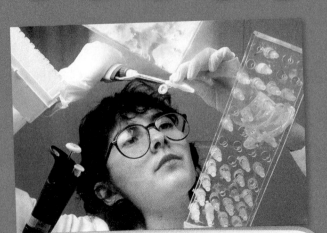

This is a normal fruit fly under a scanning electron microscope.

This fruit fly has legs growing where its antennae should be.

Science, Technology, and Society

Mapping the Human Genome

In 2003, scientists finished one of the most ambitious research projects in history. Researchers with the Human Genome Project (HGP) mapped the human body's complete set of genetic instructions, which is called the *genome*. You might be wondering whose genome the scientists are decoding. Actually, it doesn't matter—only 0.1% of each person's genetic material is unique. The researchers' goals are to identify how tiny differences in that 0.1% make each of us who we are and to begin to understand how some differences can cause disease. Scientists are already using the map to think of new ways to treat genetic diseases, such as asthma, diabetes, and kidney disease.

Weird Science

Lab Rats with Wings

Drosophila melanogaster (droh SAHF i luh muh LAN uh GAS tuhr) is the scientific name for the fruit fly. This tiny insect has played a big role in helping scientists understand many illnesses. Because fruit flies reproduce every 2 weeks, scientists can alter a fruit fly gene and see the results of the experiment very quickly. Another important reason for using these "lab rats with wings" is that their genetic code is simple and well understood. Fruit flies have approximately 13,000 genes, but humans may have approximately 30,000. Scientists use fruit flies to find out about diseases such as cancer, Alzheimer's disease, and muscular dystrophy.

Language Arts ACTiViTY

The mythical creature called the *Chimera* (kie MIR uh) was said to be part lion, part goat, and part serpent. According to legend, the Chimera terrorized people for years until it was killed by a brave hero. The word *chimera* now refers to any organism that has parts from many organisms. Write a short story about the Chimera that describes what it looks like and how it came to be.

Social Studies ACTiViTY

Research DNA fingerprinting. Write a short report that describes how DNA fingerprinting has affected the way criminals are caught.

Stacey Wong

Genetic Counselor If your family had a history of a particular disease, what would you do? Would you eat healthier foods, get more exercise, or visit your doctor regularly? All of those are good ideas, but Stacey Wong went a step farther. Her family's history of cancer helped her decide to become a genetic counselor. As a genetic counselor in Los Angeles, California, Wong is part of a team of health professionals that includes physicians, nurses, dieticians, social workers, laboratory personnel, and others. "If a diagnosis is made by the geneticist," says Wong, "then I provide genetic counseling." When a patient visits a genetic counselor, the counselor asks many questions and builds a family medical history. Although counseling involves discussing what it means to have a genetic condition, Wong says "the most important part is to get to know the patient or family we are working with, listen to their concerns, gain an understanding of their values, help them to make decisions, and be their advocate."

Math

The probability of inheriting genetic disease *A* is 1/10,000. The probability of inheriting genetic disease *B* is also 1/10,000. What is the probability that one person would inherit both genetic diseases *A* and *B*?

Internet Resources

- To learn more about careers in science, visit **www.scilinks.org** and enter the SciLinks code HY70225.

- To learn more about these Science in Action topics, visit **go.hrw.com** and type in the keyword HY7HERF.

- Check out articles related to this chapter by visiting **go.hrw.com**. Just type in the keyword HY7HERC.

Improving Comprehension

Graphic Organizers are important visual tools that can help you organize information and improve your reading comprehension. The Graphic Organizer below is called a *concept map*. Instructions for creating other types of Graphic Organizers are located in the **Study Skills** section of the Appendix.

How to Make a Concept Map

1. Identify main ideas from the text, and write the ideas as short phrases or single words.
2. Select a main concept. Place this concept at the top or center of a piece of paper.
3. Place other ideas under or around the main concept based on their relationship to the main concept. Draw a circle around each idea.
4. Draw lines between the concepts, and add linking words to connect the ideas.

When to Use a Concept Map

Concept maps are useful when you are trying to identify how several ideas are connected to a main concept. Concept maps may be based on vocabulary terms or on main topics from the text. The concept map below shows how the important concepts of this chapter are related. As you read about science, look for terms that can be organized in a concept map.

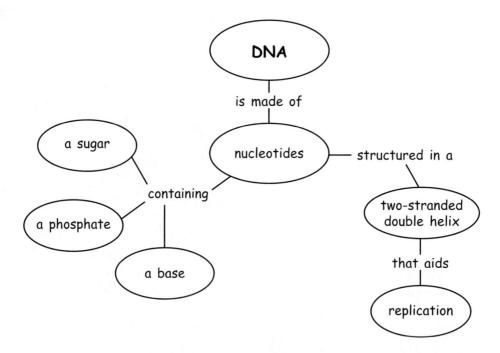

You Try It!

This Reading Strategy can also be used within the chapter that you are about to read. Practice making your own *concept map* as directed in the Reading Strategy for Section ②. Record your work in your **Science Journal.**

Unpacking the Standards

The information below "unpacks" the standards by breaking them down into basic parts. The higher-level, academic vocabulary is highlighted and defined to help you understand the language of the standards. "What It Means" restates the standards as simply as possible.

California Standard	Academic Vocabulary	What It Means
7.1.a Students know cells **function similarly** in all living organisms.	**function** (FUHNGK shuhn) to work **similarly** (SIM uh luhr lee) in almost the same way	Cells perform the same actions in all living things.
7.2.e Students know DNA (deoxyribonucleic acid) is the genetic material of living organisms and is **located** in the chromosomes of each cell.	**located** (LOH kayt id) to be in a certain place	DNA is the material that determines what traits are passed from one generation of living things to the next. DNA is found in the chromosomes of each cell.

Genes and DNA

The Big Idea

DNA is the genetic material of living organisms and is located in the chromosomes of each cell.

 California Standards

Focus on Life Sciences

7.1 All living organisms are composed of cells, from just one to many trillions, whose details usually are visible only through a microscope. (Section 2)

7.2 A typical cell of any organism contains genetic instructions that specify its traits. Those traits may be modified by environmental influences. (Sections 1 and 2)

Investigation and Experimentation

7.7 Scientific progress is made by asking meaningful questions and conducting careful investigations. (Science Skills Activity)

Math

7.1.1, 7.1.2 Number Sense

English–Language Arts

7.1.3 Reading

7.2.5 Writing

About the Photo

In the cells of these adult mice, the genes that normally carry the signal to grow hair are not working. The genes were "turned off" by scientists who have learned to control the function of some genes. Scientists study defective genes in mice in order to learn more about a variety of medical problems, including cancer.

Organize

Tri-Fold

Before you read this chapter, create the FoldNote entitled "Tri-Fold." Write what you know about the structure of DNA in the column labeled "Know." Then, write what you want to know about the structure of DNA in the column labeled "Want." As you read the chapter, write what you learn about the structure of DNA in the column labeled "Learn."

Instructions for creating FoldNotes are located in the Study Skills section on p. 582 of the Appendix.

Explore Activity

Fingerprint Identification

One way to identify people is by taking their fingerprints. Does it really work? Are everyone's fingerprints unique? Try this activity to find out.

Procedure

1. Rub the tip of a **pencil** back and forth across a **piece of tracing paper.** Make a large, dark mark.

2. Rub the tip of one of your fingers on the pencil mark. Then place a small **piece of transparent tape** over the darkened area on your finger.

3. Remove the tape, and stick it on a **piece of white paper.** Repeat steps 1–3 for the rest of your fingers.

4. Look at the fingerprints with a **magnifying lens.** What patterns do you see?

Analysis

5. Compare your fingerprints with those of your classmates. Do any two people in your class have the same prints? Try to explain your findings.

7.2.e
7.7.c

What Does DNA Look Like?

Key Concept The structure of DNA is a double helix, which is shaped like a twisted ladder.

DNA (DEE EN AYE) **d**eoxyribo**n**ucleic **a**cid, a molecule that is present in all living cells and that contains the information that determines the traits that a living thing inherits and needs to live

nucleotide (NOO klee oh TIED) in a nucleic-acid chain, a subunit that consists of a sugar, a phosphate, and a nitrogenous base

▶ The study of heredity helped scientists understand how genetic information is transferred from parents to offspring. But what is genetic information made of, and how does it work?

Inherited characteristics are determined by genes, and genes are passed from one generation to the next. Genes are found on *chromosomes,* which are structures located in the nucleus of cells. Chromosomes are made of protein and DNA. **DNA** stands for *deoxyribonucleic acid* (dee AHKS ee RIE boh noo KLEE ik AS id). DNA is the genetic material of living things. It determines inherited characteristics. So, what does DNA look like?

The Pieces of the Puzzle

Scientists knew that the material that makes up genes must be able to do two things. First, it must be able to give instructions for building and maintaining cells. Second, it must be able to be copied each time a cell divides so that each cell contains identical genes. The structure of DNA allows for these two functions to occur.

Standards Check What are two functions of DNA? 🐻 **7.2.e**

Nucleotides: The Subunits of DNA

DNA is made of subunits called nucleotides. A **nucleotide** consists of a sugar, a phosphate, and a base. The nucleotides are identical except for the base. The four bases are *adenine, thymine, guanine,* and *cytosine.* Each base has a different shape. Scientists often refer to a base the first letter of the base—*A, T, G,* and *C.* **Figure 1** shows models of the four nucleotides.

Figure 1 The Four Nucleotides of DNA

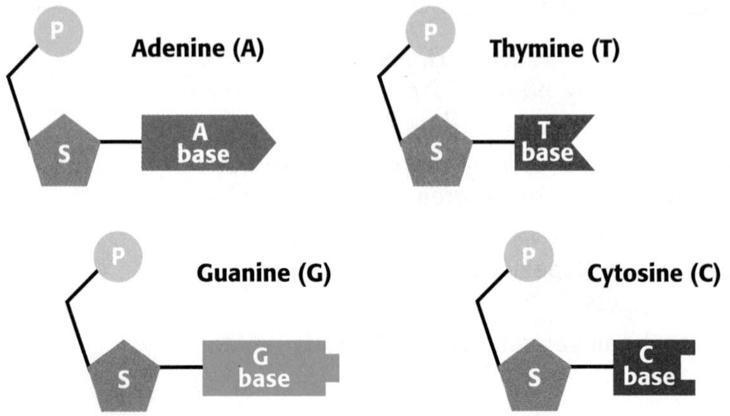

Adenine (A)

Thymine (T)

Guanine (G)

Cytosine (C)

Chargaff's Rules

In the 1950s, a biochemist named Erwin Chargaff found that the amount of adenine in DNA always equals the amount of thymine. He also found that the amount of guanine always equals the amount of cytosine. His findings are now known as *Chargaff's rules*. At the time of his discovery, no one knew the importance of these findings. But Chargaff's rules later helped scientists understand the structure of DNA.

Franklin's Discovery

More clues about the structure of DNA came from scientists in Britain. There, chemist Rosalind Franklin, shown in **Figure 2,** was able to make images of DNA molecules. She used a process known as *X-ray diffraction* to make these images. In this process, X rays are aimed at the DNA molecule. When an X ray hits a part of the molecule, the ray bounces off. The pattern made by the bouncing rays is captured on film. Franklin's images suggested that DNA has a spiral shape.

Watson and Crick's Model

At about the same time, two other scientists were also trying to solve the mystery of DNA's structure. They were James Watson and Francis Crick, shown in **Figure 3.** After seeing Franklin's X-ray images, Watson and Crick concluded that DNA must look like a long, twisted ladder. They were then able to build a model of DNA by using simple materials from their laboratory. Their model perfectly fit with both Chargaff's and Franklin's findings. The model eventually helped explain how DNA is copied and how it functions in the cell.

Figure 2 *Rosalind Franklin used X-ray diffraction to make images of DNA that helped reveal the structure of DNA.*

Figure 3 *This photo shows James Watson (left) and Francis Crick (right) with their model of DNA.*

DNA's Double Structure

The shape of DNA is shown in **Figure 4.** As you can see, a strand of DNA looks like a twisted ladder. This shape is known as a *double helix* (DUB uhl HEE LIKS). The two sides of the ladder are made of alternating sugar parts and phosphate parts. The rungs of the ladder are made of a pair of bases. Adenine on one side of a rung always pairs with thymine on the other side. Guanine always pairs with cytosine.

Notice how the double helix structure matches Chargaff's observations. When Chargaff separated the parts of a sample of DNA, he found that the matching bases were always present in equal amounts. To model how the bases pair, Watson and Crick tried to match Chargaff's observations. They also used information from chemists about the size and shape of each of the nucleotides. They found that the width of the DNA ladder matches the combined width of the matching bases. Only the correct pairs of bases fit within the ladder's width.

DNA Replication

The pairing of bases allows the cell to *replicate,* or make copies of, DNA. Each base always bonds with only one other base. Thus, pairs of bases are *complementary* to each other, and both sides of a DNA molecule are complementary. For example, the sequence CGAC will bond to the sequence GCTG.

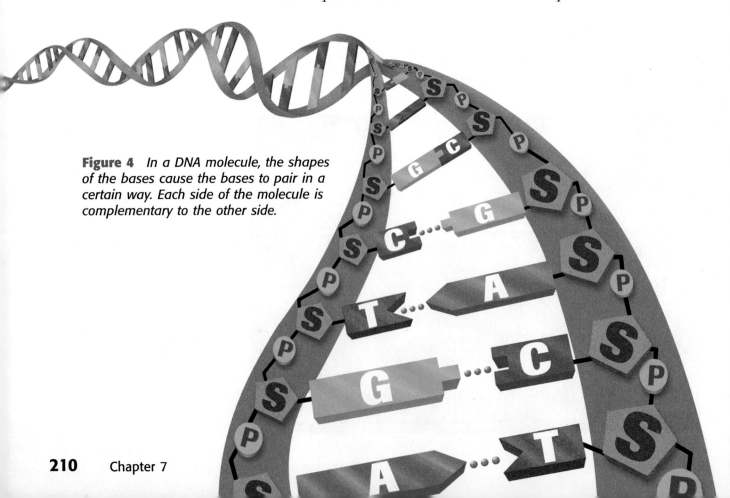

Figure 4 *In a DNA molecule, the shapes of the bases cause the bases to pair in a certain way. Each side of the molecule is complementary to the other side.*

How Copies Are Made

During replication, a DNA molecule is split down the middle, as shown in **Figure 5.** The bases on each side of the molecule are used as a pattern for a new strand. As the bases on the original molecule are exposed, complementary nucleotides are added. Finally, two DNA molecules are formed. Half of each of the molecules is old DNA, and half is new DNA.

When Copies Are Made

DNA is copied every time that a cell divides. Each new cell gets a complete copy of all the DNA. The job of unwinding, copying, and rewinding the DNA is done by proteins within the cell. So, DNA is usually found with several kinds of proteins. Other proteins help with the process of carrying out the instructions written in the code of the DNA.

Standards Check What functions do proteins perform in DNA replication? 📖 **7.2.e**

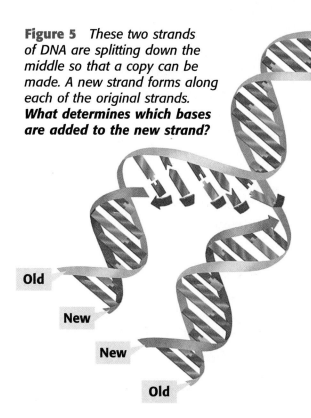

Figure 5 *These two strands of DNA are splitting down the middle so that a copy can be made. A new strand forms along each of the original strands.* ***What determines which bases are added to the new strand?***

Old

New

New

Old

SECTION
Review

📖 **7.2.e**

Summary

- DNA is the material that makes up genes.

- Investigations by Chargaff, Franklin, Watson, and Crick led to the discovery of DNA's structure and function.

- The DNA molecule looks like a twisted ladder, or double helix. The two halves are long strings of nucleotides.

- In DNA, adenine always pairs with thymine, and guanine always pairs with cytosine.

- The structure of DNA allows it to be replicated accurately.

Understanding Concepts

1 **Describing** What is the relationship between DNA and chromosomes?

2 **Listing** What are three important events that led to understanding the structure of DNA?

3 **Listing** What substance is the genetic material of living things?

Critical Thinking

4 **Identifying Relationships** How are proteins involved in DNA replication?

5 **Analyzing Processes** How does the structure of DNA allow cells to replicate?

INTERPRETING GRAPHICS Use the diagram of DNA below to answer the next question.

6 **Applying Concepts** What would the complementary strand of DNA be for the sequence of bases shown?

Challenge

7 **Analyzing Processes** What scientific methods were used by the scientists who studied the structure of DNA?

How DNA Works

Key Concept DNA stores a code that carries the instructions for making proteins. Proteins cause most of the differences among organisms.

What You Will Learn

- DNA is bundled with proteins to form chromosomes.
- DNA stores genetic information in the form of a code.
- Cells use the DNA code to make proteins. Proteins affect traits.
- A mutation is the result of a change in the genetic code.

Why It Matters

Your DNA code directs the growth and survival of your body.

Vocabulary

- RNA
- ribosome
- mutation

READING STRATEGY

Graphic Organizer In your **Science Journal,** create a Concept Map by using the terms *DNA, proteins, RNA, traits, mutations,* and *chromosomes.*

▶ Almost every cell in your body contains about 2 m of DNA. How does all of the DNA fit in a cell? And how does the DNA contain a code that affects your traits?

Unraveling DNA

Large amounts of DNA can fit inside a cell because DNA is packaged tightly by proteins. The proteins found around DNA help support the structure and function of DNA. Together, the DNA molecule and the proteins it winds around make up a chromosome. In eukaryotic cells, chromosomes are usually spread out, and DNA and proteins exist as long strands called *chromatin.* Chromatin is bundled up to make chromosomes more compact before a cell divides. **Figure 1** shows how DNA is packaged with proteins so that it can fit inside a cell.

The structure of DNA allows DNA to contain information. The order of the bases on one side of DNA is a code that carries information. A *gene* consists of a string of nucleotides that give the cell information about how to make a specific trait.

Standards Check What is the function of a gene? 🐻**7.2.e**

Figure 1 **Unraveling DNA**

ⓐ A typical skin cell has a diameter of about 0.0025 cm. The DNA in the nucleus of each cell codes for proteins. Proteins are involved in many aspects of how your body looks and how it works.

ⓑ The DNA in the nucleus is part of a material called *chromatin.* Long strands of chromatin are usually bundled loosely within the nucleus.

7.1.a Students know cells function similarly in all living organisms.
7.2.e Students know DNA (deoxyribonucleic acid) is the genetic material of living organisms and is located in the chromosomes of each cell.

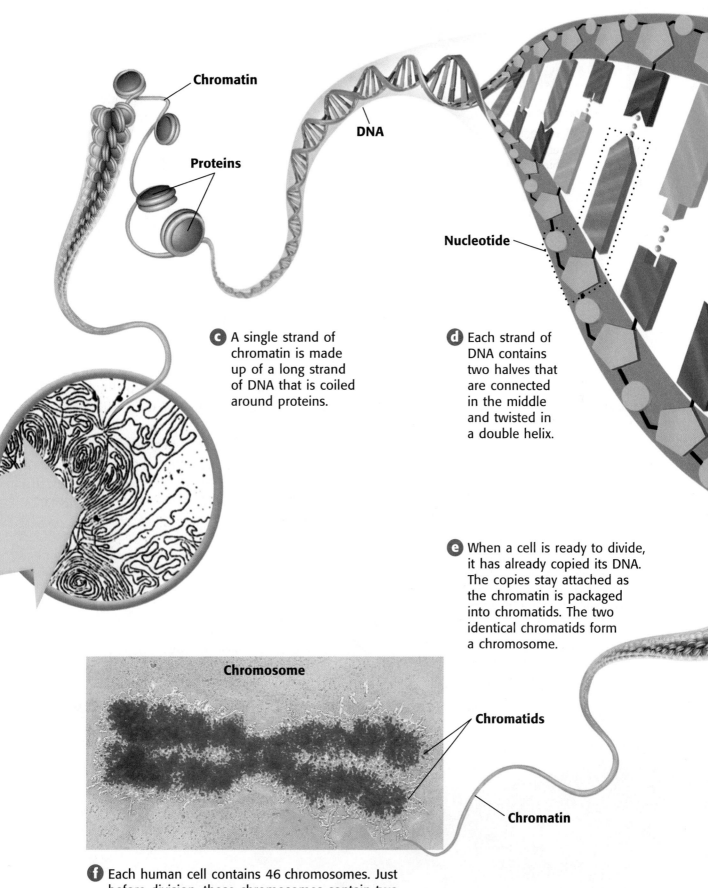

Chromatin

DNA

Proteins

Nucleotide

c A single strand of chromatin is made up of a long strand of DNA that is coiled around proteins.

d Each strand of DNA contains two halves that are connected in the middle and twisted in a double helix.

e When a cell is ready to divide, it has already copied its DNA. The copies stay attached as the chromatin is packaged into chromatids. The two identical chromatids form a chromosome.

Chromosome

Chromatids

Chromatin

f Each human cell contains 46 chromosomes. Just before division, these chromosomes contain two identical copies of all of the cell's genetic material.

Genes and Proteins

The DNA code is read like a book. Each gene has a starting point and an ending point, with DNA being read in one direction. The bases form the alphabet of the code. Groups of three bases are the codes for specific amino acids. A long string of amino acids forms a protein. Thus, each gene is usually a set of instructions for making a particular protein.

Proteins and Traits

How are proteins related to traits? Proteins are found throughout cells and cause most of the differences that you can see among organisms. Proteins act as chemical triggers and messengers for many of the processes within cells. Proteins help determine what colors you can see and whether your hair is curly or straight. A single organism typically has thousands of genes that code for thousands of proteins.

Help from RNA

Another type of molecule that helps make proteins is called **RNA,** or *ribonucleic acid* (RIE boh noo KLEE ik AS id). RNA is so similar to DNA that RNA can serve as a temporary copy of a DNA sequence. However, one difference between DNA and RNA is that RNA contains the base *uracil* (YOOR uh SIL) instead of thymine. Uracil is often referred to as *U*. **Figure 2** shows the forms of RNA that help in the process of changing the DNA code into proteins.

INTERNET ACTIVITY

Anton Van Leeuwenhoek

How did Anton Van Leeuwenhoek help science advance? Write a biography about Anton Van Leeuwenhoek. Go to **go.hrw.com,** and type in the keyword HY7DNAW.

RNA (AHR EN AY) ribonucleic acid, a molecule that is present in all living cells and that plays a role in protein production

Figure 2 *Proteins are built in the cytoplasm by using RNA copies of genes, which are segments of DNA. The order of the bases on the RNA determines the order of amino acids that are assembled at the ribosome.*

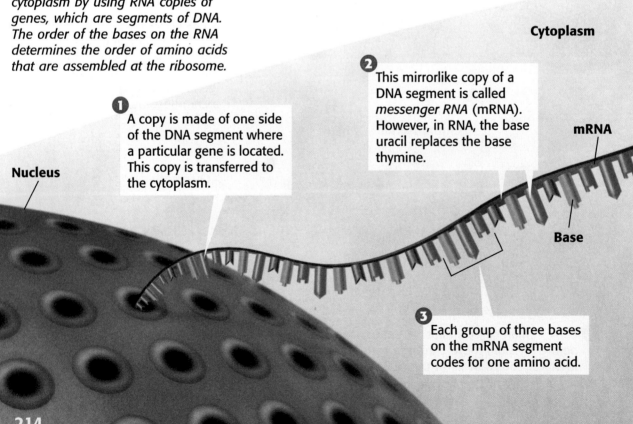

1 A copy is made of one side of the DNA segment where a particular gene is located. This copy is transferred to the cytoplasm.

2 This mirrorlike copy of a DNA segment is called *messenger RNA* (mRNA). However, in RNA, the base uracil replaces the base thymine.

3 Each group of three bases on the mRNA segment codes for one amino acid.

Cytoplasm

mRNA

Base

Nucleus

214

The Making of a Protein

The first step in making a protein is to copy one side of the segment of DNA containing a gene. A mirrorlike copy of the DNA segment is made out of RNA. This copy of the DNA segment is called *messenger RNA* (mRNA). It moves out of the nucleus and into the cytoplasm of the cell.

In the cytoplasm, the messenger RNA is fed through a protein assembly line. The "factory" that runs this assembly line is known as a ribosome. A **ribosome** is a cell organelle composed of RNA and protein. The messenger RNA is fed through the ribosome. Then, molecules of *transfer RNA* (tRNA) translate the RNA message. Each transfer RNA molecule picks up a specific amino acid from the cytoplasm. Inside the ribosome, bases on the transfer RNA match up with bases on the messenger RNA like pieces of a puzzle. The transfer RNA molecules then release their amino acids. The amino acids become linked in a growing chain. As the entire segment of messenger RNA passes through the ribosome, the growing chain of amino acids folds up into a new protein molecule.

Standards Check How are proteins made inside cells? 7.1.a

Code Combinations

A given sequence of three bases codes for one amino acid. For example, AGU and ACU are two possible sequence combinations. How many different sequences of the four RNA bases (adenine, guanine, uracil, and cytosine) are possible? (Hint: Make a list.)

ribosome (RIE buh SOHM) a cell organelle composed of RNA and protein; the site of protein synthesis

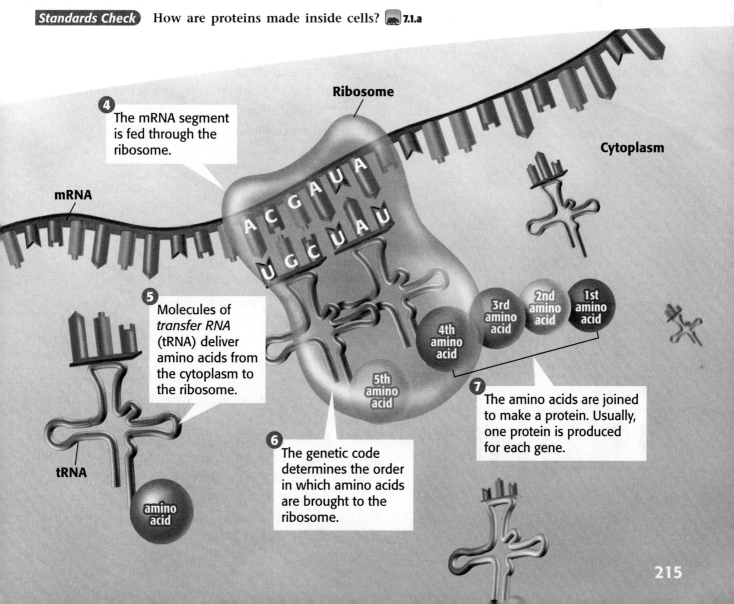

Ribosome

4 The mRNA segment is fed through the ribosome.

Cytoplasm

mRNA

5 Molecules of *transfer RNA* (tRNA) deliver amino acids from the cytoplasm to the ribosome.

7 The amino acids are joined to make a protein. Usually, one protein is produced for each gene.

3rd amino acid — 2nd amino acid — 1st amino acid

4th amino acid

5th amino acid

6 The genetic code determines the order in which amino acids are brought to the ribosome.

tRNA

amino acid

215

Cracking the Code

In messenger RNA, genetic information is stored in a code of four different bases: uracil (U), adenine (A), cytosine (C), and guanine (G). In this activity, you will crack a similar type of code.

▶ **Try It!**

1. Begin by tying a knot in one end of a **pipe cleaner.**

2. The code below shows the order in which **beads** should be placed on the pipe cleaner. Use the key to determine which color bead each group of three letters in the code represents.

Key	
Code	**Color**
CUU	blue
CCU	red
UUC	green
UCC	yellow
GUC	orange
CUA	blue

Code:
C C U C U U C C U G U C C U A U C C C U U

▶ **Think About It!**

3. Compare your string of beads with those of your classmates. Are the beads in the same order?

4. How is the code for the beads similar to the genetic code? What do the beads represent?

15 min

Changes in Genes

mutation (myoo TAY shuhn) a change in the nucleotide-base sequence of a gene or DNA molecule

Wordwise The root *mut-* means "to change." Another example is *mutant.*

Read the following sentence: "Put the book on the desk." Replace the letter *o* in the word *on* with the letter *i* and read the sentence again. Now replace the letter *b* in the word *book* with the letter *z* and read the sentence. Changing a letter in a sentence can change what the sentence means or keep the sentence from making any sense at all.

A change in the DNA sequence, like a change in the letters of a sentence, can affect the protein that DNA codes for. A change in the nucleotide-base sequence of DNA is called a **mutation.**

How Do Mutations Happen?

Mutations happen regularly because of random errors when DNA is copied. **Figure 3** shows what could happen if a nucleotide base were changed during DNA replication.

In addition, damage to DNA can be caused by things in the environment. Any physical or chemical agent that can cause a mutation in DNA is called a *mutagen.* Examples of mutagens include high-energy radiation from X rays and ultraviolet radiation. Ultraviolet radiation is one type of energy in sunlight. It is responsible for suntans and sunburns. Other mutagens include asbestos and the chemicals in cigarette smoke.

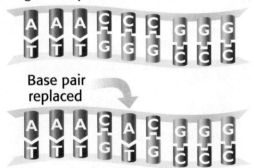

Figure 3 *The original base sequence on the top has been changed to show what happens when a nucleotide base is changed in DNA.*

Do Mutations Matter?

Changes in DNA can cause an improved trait, no change, or a harmful trait. A mutation that makes an organism more likely to survive during a drought is an example of an improved trait. If a mutation does not change the protein that a gene codes for, then there will be no change to the trait.

Mutations can produce harmful traits. For example, a mutation that makes an animal a brighter color can make the animal easier for predators to find. Cells make proteins that detect and repair mutations. But not all errors are repaired correctly. If a mutation occurs in sex cells, the changed gene can be passed from one generation to the next.

SECTION Review

7.1.a, 7.2.e

Summary

- A gene is a set of instructions for making a protein. DNA stores these genetic instructions.

- Every organism has DNA in its cells. Humans have about 2 m of DNA in each cell.

- Traits of organisms are typically determined by proteins, which are coded for by segments of DNA called genes.

- Within a gene, each group of three bases codes for one amino acid. A sequence of amino acids is linked to make a protein.

- Proteins are built within the cytoplasm of cells.

- A mutation is a change in the DNA that can affect the traits of an organism.

Understanding Concepts

1 **Identifying** What structures in cells contain DNA and proteins?

2 **Describing** Explain how proteins help support the structure and function of DNA.

INTERPRETING GRAPHICS The illustration shows a sequence of bases on one strand of a DNA molecule. Use the illustration below to answer the next three questions.

3 **Applying** How many amino acids are coded for by the sequence on side A of this DNA strand?

4 **Demonstrating** What is the order of bases on side B, from left to right?

5 **Demonstrating** If *G* replaced *A* as the first base on side A, what would the order of bases be on side B of this DNA strand?

Critical Thinking

6 **Forming Hypotheses** What would happen if the proteins that support a DNA molecule failed to function?

7 **Applying Concepts** In which cell type could a mutation be passed from generation to generation? Explain.

8 **Analyzing Ideas** How does DNA store information in a code?

Challenge

9 **Forming Hypotheses** A beetle inherits a mutation that makes the beetle a darker green color than other beetles of its species. Explain how having the dark green trait could be a harmful trait or an improved trait for the beetle.

Internet Resources

For a variety of links related to this chapter, go to www.scilinks.org

Topic: Genes and Traits

SciLinks code: HY70647

Skills Practice Lab

Extracting DNA

Every living thing has DNA. Within the nucleus of eukaryotic cells, DNA can be found in chromosomes. In chromosomes, strands of DNA are tightly packed and organized around several different proteins. DNA is packed so efficiently that if the DNA from one of your cells were unraveled, it would be about 2 m long! In this activity, you'll use common household items to release, unravel, and collect DNA. You will be extracting DNA from raw wheat germ, which is part of the seed of a wheat plant. Wheat germ is included in many products, such as whole wheat flour.

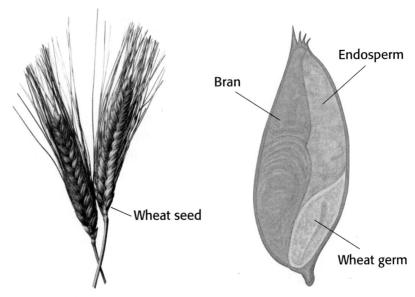

Bran

Endosperm

Wheat seed

Wheat germ

Wheat　　　　**Cross section of wheat seed**

Procedure

1 Measure 1 g of raw wheat germ. Place the raw wheat germ in a beaker.

2 Use a separate beaker to measure about 50 mL of hot tap water. Add the water to the beaker containing the wheat germ. **Caution:** Be careful when handling hot water.

3 Using a pipet, add 2 mL of detergent to the wheat-germ mixture. Use a stirring rod to gently stir the mixture for 30 s. The detergent will help break down the cell membranes of the wheat germ.

7.2.e Students know DNA (deoxyribonucleic acid) is the genetic material of living organisms and is located in the chromosomes of each cell.

4 Pour the contents of the beaker into several test tubes. Fill each test tube so it is about one-third full.

5 Holding a test tube at an angle, gently pour chilled isopropyl alcohol so that it runs down the inner surface of the test tube. Add enough alcohol so that the test tube is half full. The alcohol will form a layer on top of the wheat-germ mixture.

6 Place the test tubes in a test-tube rack. Observe the white strands that form in the alcohol layer. These strands are clumps of DNA. DNA is drawn to the alcohol layer. Most cell parts, including proteins that organize DNA, are drawn to the water level. Do not disturb the contents of the test tubes for several minutes.

7 Reshape a paper clip into a long, straight shaft with a hook on one end. Twirl the hook in the alcohol to collect the white stringy masses. The stringy masses are clumps of wheat DNA.

Analyze the Results

8 **Recognizing Patterns** What two materials make up chromosomes? What are their functions?

9 **Examining Data** Why was it important to tilt the test tube when introducing the alcohol?

Draw Conclusions

10 **Making Predictions** What other materials might be good sources of DNA? What materials would not be good to use for a DNA extraction?

11 **Evaluating Methods** Meat tenderizer contains chemicals that break down proteins. Explain why this substance may be used in some DNA extractions.

Big Idea Question

12 **Drawing Conclusions** How is it possible for a single cell to contain more than 2 m of DNA?

Science Skills Activity

Investigation and Experimentation

7.7.c Communicate the logical connection among hypotheses, science concepts, tests conducted, data collected, and conclusions drawn from the scientific evidence.

Connecting Scientific Methods

▶ Tutorial

You can evaluate an investigation by examining whether scientific methods were properly used. For example, you can evaluate if the procedure of an investigation successfully tested the hypothesis.

The following questions can help you examine the scientific methods used in an investigation. But keep in mind that not all investigations will use the same scientific methods in the same order.

Procedure

1 Ask a Question What question did the investigation set out to answer?

2 Make Observations What was learned about the subject by observing it?

3 Form a Hypothesis What was the hypothesis? What predictions were made?

4 Test the Hypothesis How was the hypothesis tested? The answer to this question can include a description of the experiments performed, data collected, and observations made.

5 Analyze the Results How was the data organized and analyzed?

6 Draw Conclusions Did the results of the investigation support the hypothesis? Why or why not?

7 Communicate Results How were the results shared?

▶ You Try It!

Procedure

Read the following description of a scientific experiment. Then, use the procedure in the tutorial to examine the scientific methods used in the investigation. Finally, use your answers to write a short evaluation of the investigation.

Michele's Investigation

When Michele was studying DNA, she learned that all living things have DNA in their cells. She used the Internet to find a procedure for extracting DNA. She learned that DNA forms white, threadlike clumps when it is extracted from cells. Michele wondered if she could extract the DNA from a strawberry. She predicted yes, because if strawberries are made of cells, then strawberries should have DNA. Michele placed a strawberry into a plastic bag, sealed the bag, and smashed the strawberry. She opened the bag and added 15 mL of dish detergent and 100 mL of warm water to the bag. After sealing the bag, Michele mixed the contents by gently shaking the bag. Next, Michele poured the contents of the bag into a test tube. She then poured 20 mL of cold isopropyl alcohol into the test tube. Michele observed that the alcohol floated on top of the water. She could see a white, threadlike substance floating in the alcohol. Michele reasoned that the white substance was many strands of DNA clumped together.

Chapter Summary

The Big Idea DNA is the genetic material of living organisms and is located in the chromosomes of each cell.

Section	Vocabulary

1 What Does DNA Look Like?

Key Concept The structure of DNA is a double helix, which is shaped like a twisted ladder.

- The discovery of the structure and function of DNA is a major achievement in life science.
- DNA is made up of nucleotides arranged in two strands. Together, the two strands form a double helix.
- The structure of DNA relates to how it functions, including how it is replicated.

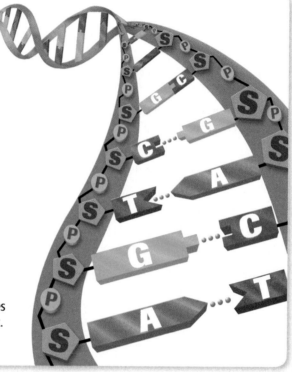

DNA is made of complementary nucleotides arranged in a double helix.

DNA p. 208
nucleotide p. 208

2 How DNA Works

Key Concept DNA stores a code that carries the instructions for making proteins. Proteins cause most of the differences among organisms.

- DNA is bundled with proteins to form chromosomes.
- DNA stores genetic information in the form of a code.
- Cells use the DNA code to make proteins. Proteins affect traits.
- A mutation is the result of a change in the genetic code.

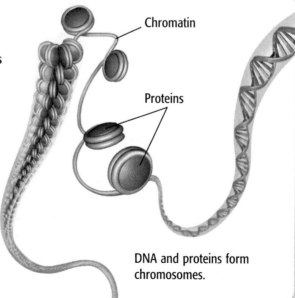

Chromatin

Proteins

DNA and proteins form chromosomes.

RNA p. 214
ribosome p. 215
mutation p. 216

Organize

Tri-Fold Review the FoldNote that you created at the beginning of the chapter. Add to it or correct it based on what you have learned.

Using Vocabulary

1 **Academic Vocabulary** In the sentence "DNA is located in the chromosomes of cells," what does the word *locate* mean?

Correct each statement by replacing the underlined term.

2 The information in DNA is coded in the order of <u>amino acids</u> along one side of the DNA molecule.

3 The "factory" that puts together proteins based on the DNA code is called a <u>gene</u>.

Understanding Concepts

Multiple Choice

4 A gene can be all of the following EXCEPT
   a. a set of instructions for a trait.
   b. a complete chromosome.
   c. instructions for making a protein.
   d. a portion of a strand of DNA.

5 James Watson and Francis Crick
   a. took X-ray pictures of DNA.
   b. discovered that genes are in chromosomes.
   c. bred pea plants to study heredity.
   d. made models to figure out DNA's shape.

6 Within the cell, where are proteins made?
   a. the cytoplasm
   b. the nucleus
   c. the amino acids
   d. the chromosomes

7 Which of the following statements about DNA is NOT true?
   a. DNA is found in all organisms.
   b. DNA is made up of five subunits.
   c. DNA has a structure like a twisted ladder.
   d. Mistakes can be made when DNA is copied.

INTERPRETING GRAPHICS Use the illustration below to answer the next question.

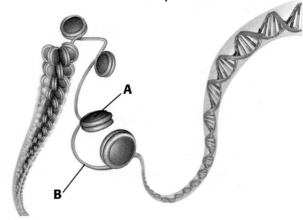

8 What molecule does A identify?
   a. protein
   b. RNA
   c. DNA
   d. ribosome

Short Answer

9 **Comparing** What is the difference between DNA and RNA?

INTERPRETING GRAPHICS Use the illustration below to answer the next two questions.

10 **Demonstrating** What is the order of bases on strand B, from left to right?

11 **Applying** How many amino acids are coded for by the sequence on strand A of this DNA strand?

12 **Communicating Concepts** Write a paragraph explaining how the DNA in genes relates to the traits of an organism. Be sure to include information about where DNA is found and describe how it stores information in the form of a code.

Critical Thinking

13 **Concept Mapping** Use the following terms to create a concept map: *bases, adenine, thymine, nucleotides, guanine, DNA,* and *cytosine.*

14 **Analyzing Processes** What role did scientific methods, such as communicating results, play in the discovery of the structure of DNA?

15 **Evaluating Hypotheses** Your classmate states that mutations to DNA are always harmful. Evaluate this statement.

INTERPRETING GRAPHICS The illustration shows the process of replication of a DNA strand. Use the illustration below to answer the next two questions.

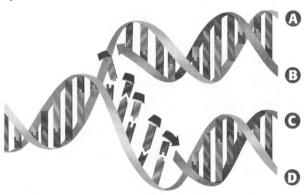

Ⓐ
Ⓑ
Ⓒ
Ⓓ

16 **Applying Concepts** Which letters identify the two new strands that are being added to the original strands?

17 **Applying Concepts** How does the structure of DNA allow it to complete the process of replication?

18 **Making Comparisons** You are using a microscope to observe a cell that is ready to divide. What does the DNA look like? What does the DNA look like in a cell that is not ready to divide?

19 **Making Inferences** Why do governments make laws about the use of chemicals that are known to be mutagens?

Math Skills

20 **Making Calculations** The 46 chromosomes in a human cell contain 3.2 billion pairs of DNA bases in sequence. On average, about how many pairs of bases are in each chromosome?

21 **Making Calculations** Each cell in your body contains approximately 2.0 m of DNA. Your body has approximately 100 trillion cells. How long would the DNA in your body be if you laid it out end to end? Express your answer in scientific notation.

Challenge

22 **Forming Hypotheses** A house cat and a tiger have many similar traits, such as retractable claws and special teeth for tearing meat. A lion also shares these traits with a house cat. In addition, a lion and a tiger share other traits, such as the ability to roar and their large size. If you compared the sequence of nucleotide bases in a house cat, lion, and tiger, between which animals would you expect to find the most similarities? Explain your answer.

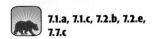
REVIEWING ACADEMIC VOCABULARY

1 Which of the following terms means "to be in a certain place"?

A provide

B locate

C rest

D give

2 Which of the following words best completes the following sentence: Cells function _____ in all living organisms.

A periodically

B sporadically

C irregularly

D similarly

3 Which of the following words is the closest in meaning to the word *functioning*?

A thinking

B developing

C working

D dividing

4 Which of the following words means "able to be seen"?

A visible

B audible

C tangible

D sensible

5 Which of the following words is the closest in meaning to the word *instructions*?

A tests

B directions

C questions

D investigations

REVIEWING CONCEPTS

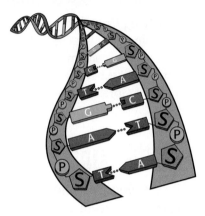

6 In the diagram above, what do the letters *S* and *P* stand for?

A sugars and proteins

B sucrose and proteins

C sugars and protons

D sugars and phosphates

7 What did Rosalind Franklin's experiment about DNA reveal?

A DNA has a spiral shape.

B DNA absorbs X rays.

C DNA is composed of X rays.

D DNA has an oval shape.

8 What is a gene?

A an organelle that makes proteins

B a molecule that makes copies of DNA

C the material outside the nucleus

D a segment of DNA that codes for proteins

9 What are the four nucleotide bases that form the genetic code?

A adenine, thymine, guanine, and cytoid

B adenine, thymine, guanine, and cytosine

C adenine, thyroid, guanine, and cytosine

D adenoid, thymine, guanine, and cytosine

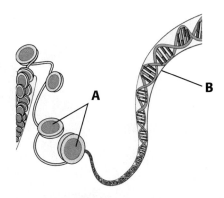

A

B

10 **What is the material identified by letter A in the diagram above?**

A proteins

B chromatin

C DNA

D chromosomes

11 **What did Watson and Crick discover?**

A DNA has two strands that form a branched chain called a *branched helix.*

B DNA is in the shape of a twisted ladder called a *double helix.*

C DNA is in the shape of a straight ladder called a *double helix.*

D DNA has three strands that form a *triple helix.*

12 **What is a change in the nucleotide-base sequence of DNA called?**

A variance

B ribosome

C chromatin

D mutation

13 **What are the structures that are in the nuclei of most cells and that are made of protein and DNA?**

A cytosine

B molecules

C chromosomes

D protons

14 **Which type of reproduction leads to offspring that share characteristics of two parents?**

A binary fission

B asexual reproduction

C budding

D sexual reproduction

15 **Where is DNA stored in an animal cell?**

A mitochondria

B nucleus

C chloroplast

D Golgi complex

16 **If you are conducting research about how scientists study cells, what would be the best source to consult?**

A a Web site maintained by a cell research group

B a Web site written by a student who has written an essay on cell structure

C a Web site about the composition of molecules

D a Web site written by someone who is interested in cell research

17 **If you wanted to show cell structure, what would be the best way to show the information?**

A a flowchart showing what composes cells

B a model of what the cell looks like

C a chart listing the cell's function

D a list showing the amount of each molecule in the cell

Standards Assessment

Science in Action

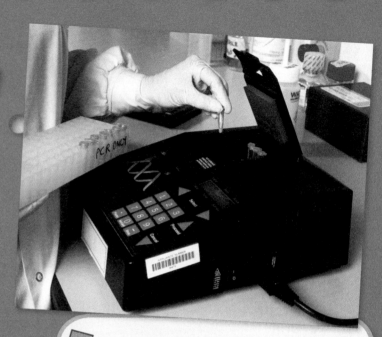

Scientific Debate

Supersquash or Frankenfruit?

Some food that you buy may have been developed in a new way. Food producers may use genetic engineering to make food crops easier to grow or sell, more nutritious, or resistant to pests and disease. More than half of the packaged foods sold in the United States are likely to contain ingredients from genetically modified organisms.

The U.S. government has stated that research shows that these foods are safe. But some people are concerned that genes introduced into crop plants could cause new environmental or health problems. For example, some people worry that crops engineered to be pest resistant might kill insects that are not pests, such as butterflies.

Scientific Discoveries

Using PCR to Analyze DNA

Scientists analyze DNA to learn about an individual's identity and ancestors. It was once very difficult to analyze DNA because a large amount of DNA is usually needed to yield good results. But in 1983, California scientist Kary Mullis made a discovery that revolutionized DNA analysis. Mullis discovered how to take tiny amounts of DNA and duplicate, or "amplify," them. The technique worked like a copy machine for DNA. Mullis called it *polymerase chain reaction* (PCR). PCR has many uses. For example, PCR is used in forensics to study clues left at a crime scene. Scientists can also use PCR to study the DNA of the remains of organisms that have been dead for thousands of years!

Math ACTIVITY

In a study measuring insect damage, 100 acres of land were planted with 32,000 corn plants per acre. Insects damaged an average of 19,200 corn plants per acre. What percentage of the corn plants survived? Record your work in your **Science Journal.**

Language Arts ACTIVITY

Research the use of PCR in forensics. In your **Science Journal,** write a newspaper article about an imaginary crime that was solved by using DNA analysis.

Lydia Villa-Komaroff

Genetic Researcher   When Lydia Villa-Komaroff was young, science represented "a kind of refuge" for her. She grew up in a very large family that lived in a very small house. "I always wanted to find things out. I was one of those kids who took things apart."

In college, Villa-Komaroff became interested in the process of embryonic development: how a simple egg grows into a complex animal. This interest led her to study genes and the way that genes code for proteins. For example, insulin is a protein that is normally produced by the human body. Often, people who suffer from diabetes lack the insulin gene, so their bodies can't make insulin. These people may need to inject insulin into their blood as a drug treatment.

Before the research by Villa-Komaroff's team was done, insulin was difficult to produce. Villa-Komaroff's team isolated the human gene that codes for insulin. Then, the scientists inserted the normal human insulin gene into the DNA of bacteria. This inserted gene caused the bacteria to produce insulin. This technique was a new and more efficient way to produce insulin. Now, most of the insulin used for diabetes treatment is made in this way. Many genetic researchers dream of making breakthroughs such as the one that Villa-Komaroff made in her work with insulin.

Social Studies ACTiViTY

Do some research about several women, such as Marie Curie, Barbara McClintock, or Maxine Frank Singer, who have done important scientific research. In your **Science Journal,** write a short biography about one of these women.

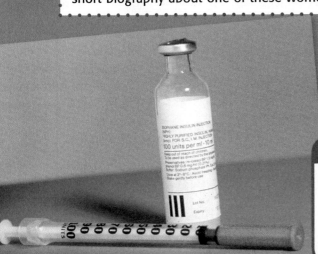

Internet Resources

- To learn more about careers in science, visit **www.scilinks.org** and enter the SciLinks code HY70225.

- To learn more about these Science in Action topics, visit **go.hrw.com** and type in the keyword HY7DNAF.

- Check out articles related to this chapter by visiting **go.hrw.com**. Just type in the keyword HY7DNAC.

TIMELINE

Earth and Life History

The rocks under your feet have a story to tell about what things have been like on Earth for the last three billion to four billion years! In this unit, you will learn how studying rocks helps us understand Earth and life history, how living things are classified based on their characteristics, and how these characteristics help living things survive. The timeline shows some events that have helped scientists understand Earth and life history.

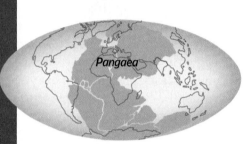

245 Million
Years Ago

The supercontinent Pangaea exists. Millions of years later, Pangaea breaks apart and the continents move to their current positions.

1864

Louis Pasteur uses heat to eliminate microbes. This process is later called *pasteurization*.

1913

Arthur Holmes develops a new technique for finding the absolute age of rocks and fossils.

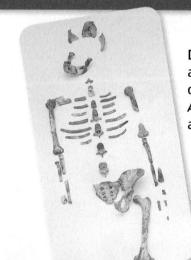

1974

Donald Johanson discovers a fossilized skeleton of one of the first hominids, *Australopithecus afarensis*, also called "Lucy."

1693

John Ray correctly identifies whales as mammals.

1753

Carolus Linnaeus publishes the first of two volumes containing the classification of all known species.

1960

Mary and Jonathan Leakey discover fossil bones of the human ancestor *Homo habilis* in Olduvai Gorge, Tanzania.

1969

Apollo 11 lands on the moon. Neil Armstrong becomes the first person to walk on the lunar surface.

1990

The most complete and largest known *Tyrannosaurus rex* skeleton is discovered. The skeleton is named Tyrannosaurus Sue.

2003

Researchers find that individual cloned pigs behave in very different ways. This finding shows that environmental conditions affect behavior.

Improving Comprehension

Graphic Organizers are important visual tools that can help you organize information and improve your reading comprehension. The Graphic Organizer below is called a *process chart*. Instructions for creating other types of Graphic Organizers are located in the **Study Skills** section of the Appendix.

How to Make a Process Chart

1 Draw a box. In the box, write the first step of a process, chain of events, or cycle.

2 Under the box, draw another box, and draw an arrow to connect the two boxes. In the second box, write the next step of the process or the next event in the timeline.

3 Continue adding boxes until each step of the process, chain of events, or cycle is written in a box. For cycles only, draw an arrow to connect the last box and the first box.

When to Use a Process Chart

Science is full of processes. A process chart shows the steps that a process takes to get from one point to another point. Timelines, chains of events, and cycles are examples of the kinds of information that can be organized well in a process chart. As you read, look for information that is described in steps or in a sequence, and draw a process chart that shows the progression of the steps or sequence.

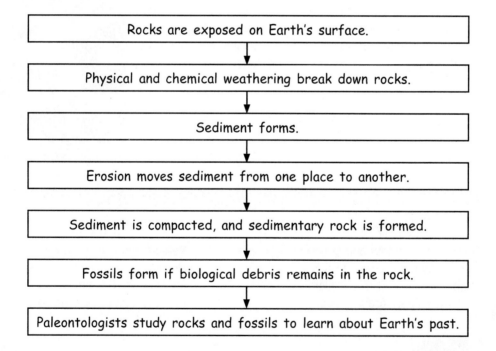

Rocks are exposed on Earth's surface.

↓

Physical and chemical weathering break down rocks.

↓

Sediment forms.

↓

Erosion moves sediment from one place to another.

↓

Sediment is compacted, and sedimentary rock is formed.

↓

Fossils form if biological debris remains in the rock.

↓

Paleontologists study rocks and fossils to learn about Earth's past.

You Try It!

This Reading Strategy can also be used within the chapter that you are about to read. Practice making your own *process chart* as directed in the Reading Strategy for Section **1**. Record your work in your **Science Journal.**

Unpacking the Standards

The information below "unpacks" the standards by breaking them down into basic parts. The higher-level, academic vocabulary is highlighted and defined to help you understand the language of the standards. "What It Means" restates the standards as simply as possible.

California Standard	Academic Vocabulary	What It Means
7.3.c Students know how independent lines of **evidence** from geology, fossils, and comparative anatomy provide the bases for the theory of evolution.	**evidence** (EV uh duhns) information showing whether an idea or belief is true or valid	The theory of evolution is based on several kinds of information that was gathered by studying rocks and fossils and by comparing the bodies of living and extinct organisms.
7.4.a Students know Earth **processes** today are **similar** to those that **occurred** in the past and slow geologic processes have large cumulative effects over long **periods** of time.	**process** (PRAH ses) a set of steps, events, or changes **similar** (SIM uh luhr) almost the same **occur** (uh KUHR) to happen **period** (PIR ee uhd) an interval or unit	Earth processes that happen today also happened in the past. These slow processes can cause large changes over long periods of time.
7.4.b Students know the history of life on Earth has been disrupted by **major** catastrophic events, such as major volcanic eruptions or the **impacts** of asteroids.	**major** (MAY juhr) of great importance or large scale **impact** (IM PAKT) a striking together; collision	The history of life on Earth has been changed or upset by large-scale, disastrous events, such as the eruption of volcanoes or the impact of asteroids.
7.4.c Students know that the rock **cycle** includes the formation of new sediment and rocks and that rocks are often found in **layers,** with the oldest generally on the bottom.	**cycle** (SIE kuhl) a repeating series of changes **layer** (LAY uhr) a separate or distinct portion of matter that has thickness	The rock cycle includes the breakdown of rock into smaller fragments that may form new rock. Rocks are often found in layers, in which the oldest rock is usually on the bottom.
7.4.e Students know fossils provide evidence of how life and **environmental** conditions have changed.	**environment** (en VIE ruhn muhnt) the surrounding natural conditions that affect an organism	Fossils can be used to understand how living things and the environment have changed over time.

Studying Earth's Past

The Big Idea

The rock record can be used to determine the relative and absolute ages of rocks, which can be used to study Earth's history.

California Standards

Focus on Life Sciences

7.3 Biological evolution accounts for the diversity of species developed through gradual processes over many generations. (Sections 2 and 3)

7.4 Evidence from rocks allows us to understand the evolution of life on Earth. (Sections 1, 2, and 3)

Investigation and Experimentation

7.7 Scientific progress is made by asking meaningful questions and conducting careful investigations. (Science Skills Activity)

Math

6.3.3 Statistics, Data Analysis, and Probability
7.1.1 Mathematical Reasoning
7.2.1 Measurement and Geometry

English–Language Arts

7.2.3 Reading
7.1.1, 7.1.2 Writing

About the Photo

The Barringer Meteorite Crater in the Arizona desert has a diameter of more than 1 km. The crater formed when an asteroid hit Earth about 40,000 years ago. Most geologic processes are slow and cause change on Earth over long periods of time. But rare catastrophic events can reshape Earth's surface suddenly and leave evidence, such as this crater.

Organize

Three-Panel Flip Chart

Before you read this chapter, create the FoldNote entitled "Three-Panel Flip Chart." Label each flap with the title of one of the sections in the chapter. As you read the chapter, write information from each section under the appropriate flap.

Instructions for creating FoldNotes are located in the Study Skills section on p. 581 of the Appendix.

Explore Activity

🤿 🦺   🕐 **20 min**

Model Craters

Craters are part of the surface of many bodies in our solar system, including Earth! In this activity, you will make your own craters and observe what happens as the craters form.

Procedure

1. Fill a **bowl, basin,** or **tray** with **flour** to a depth of at least 7 cm.

2. Sprinkle **colored gelatin powder** over the flour's surface to produce a thin, uniform coating.

3. Using a **meterstick,** position a **marble** about 10 cm above the basin or tray. Release the marble, but do not throw it! The marble should not bounce out of the tray. Describe, measure, and sketch the appearance of the model crater.

4. Repeat step 3, positioning the marble at heights of 20 cm and 50 cm above areas of the undisturbed gelatin surface.

7.4.b

Analysis

5. How did the impact affect the flour and gelatin?

6. Did the height of the dropped marble have any effect on the crater's appearance? Explain.

7. How might such an event have affected Earth's surface?

The Study of Earth's History

Key Concept Slow geologic processes and major catastrophic events have shaped Earth's surface in the past and continue to shape Earth today.

What You Will Learn

- Uniformitarianism describes uniform change in Earth's geology, and catastrophism describes sudden change.
- Modern geology describes most change as gradual but acknowledges rare, sudden changes.

Why It Matters

Understanding the processes that shape Earth's surface today help us understand Earth's past.

Vocabulary

- uniformitarianism
- catastrophism
- paleontology

READING STRATEGY

Graphic Organizer In your **Science Journal,** create a Process Chart that shows how the theory of Earth's geologic history has changed over time.

▶ How do mountains form? How old is Earth? Have you ever asked these questions? Nearly 250 years ago, a Scottish farmer and scientist named James Hutton did. Searching for answers to his questions, Hutton spent more than 30 years studying rock formations in Scotland and England.

The Early Study of Geology

In 1788, James Hutton collected his notes and wrote *Theory of the Earth.* In *Theory of the Earth,* he stated that the key to understanding Earth's history is all around us. In other words, processes that we observe today—such as erosion and deposition—do not change over time. This idea is now called uniformitarianism. **Uniformitarianism** is the idea that the same geologic processes that shape Earth today have been at work during all of Earth's history. **Figure 1** shows some of the observations that Hutton used to develop the idea of uniformitarianism.

Standards Check What is uniformitarianism? 7.4.a

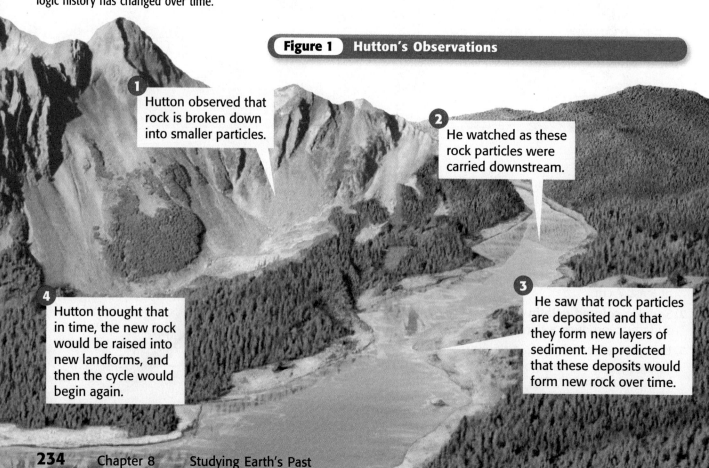

Figure 1 Hutton's Observations

1 Hutton observed that rock is broken down into smaller particles.

2 He watched as these rock particles were carried downstream.

3 He saw that rock particles are deposited and that they form new layers of sediment. He predicted that these deposits would form new rock over time.

4 Hutton thought that in time, the new rock would be raised into new landforms, and then the cycle would begin again.

Figure 2 *This photograph shows Siccar Point on the coast of Scotland. Siccar Point is one of the places where Hutton observed the results of gradual geologic processes.*

Uniformitarianism Versus Catastrophism

In Hutton's time, most people thought that Earth was only a few thousand years old. To explain Earth's history, most scientists supported catastrophism. **Catastrophism** is the idea that geologic change happens suddenly. Supporters of catastrophism thought that Earth's surface is shaped mainly by rare, sudden events. These unpredictable events caused rapid geologic change over large areas—sometimes over the whole planet.

Scientists debated Hutton's theory because it suggested that Earth is much older than most people thought it was. A few thousand years was not nearly enough time for the gradual geologic processes that Hutton described. Hutton thought that very slow processes needed a very long time to produce large effects. For example, the rocks that he saw at Siccar Point, shown in **Figure 2,** were deposited and folded. Hutton thought that the rock took a long time to form and to be deformed.

Standards Check What is catastrophism? **7.4.b**

A Victory for Uniformitarianism

Despite Hutton's work, most scientists continued to believe in catastrophism. Only after the work of British geologist Charles Lyell did people begin to think of uniformitarianism as geology's most important principle. From 1830 to 1833, Lyell published three books called *Principles of Geology*. In those books, he wrote about uniformitarianism. Using Hutton's notes and new evidence of his own, Lyell successfully challenged the principle of catastrophism. Lyell supported the idea that major geologic change happened gradually. For at least a century after Lyell's work, most geologists agreed with uniformitarianism and not catastrophism.

uniformitarianism
(YOON uh FAWRM uh TER ee uhn IZ uhm) a principle that geologic processes that occurred in the past can be explained by current geologic processes

catastrophism (kuh TAS truh FIZ uhm) a principle that states that geologic change occurs suddenly

Wordwise The prefix *cata-* means "against" or "very." The root *stroph-* means "to turn." The suffix *-ism* means "a belief in."

7.4.a Students know Earth processes today are similar to those that occurred in the past and slow geologic processes have large cumulative effects over long periods of time.
7.4.b Students know the history of life on Earth has been disrupted by major catastrophic events, such as major volcanic eruptions or the impacts of asteroids.
7.4.e Students know fossils provide evidence of how life and environmental conditions have changed.

Section 1   The Study of Earth's History   **235**

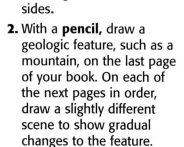
Modern Geology—A Happy Medium

During the late 1900s, scientists such as Stephen J. Gould challenged uniformitarianism. They thought that catastrophes can play an important role in shaping Earth's surface. Today, scientists realize that neither uniformitarianism nor catastrophism accounts for all geologic change during Earth's history. Most geologic change is slow and uniform, but catastrophes that cause sudden changes have also happened during Earth's history. For example, craters have been found where meteorites, asteroids, and comets are thought to have struck Earth.

Catastrophes can affect small areas or the whole Earth. They can have short-term or long-term effects on climate. Some scientists think that an asteroid strike about 65 million years ago may have contributed to the disappearance of the dinosaurs. **Figure 3** shows an imaginary re-creation of this asteroid strike. The asteroid impact could have thrown debris into the atmosphere. The debris spread around the whole planet and fell to Earth for decades. This global debris cloud may have blocked the sun's rays, causing a cooling of Earth's climate that doomed the dinosaurs. A volcanic eruption that injects debris into the atmosphere can cause similar changes in climate.

Standards Check What is one way that a catastrophe has disrupted the history of life on Earth? 🐻 **7.4.b**

Figure 3 *Today, scientists think that sudden events are responsible for some changes during Earth's past. An asteroid hitting Earth, for example, may have contributed to the disappearance of the dinosaurs about 65 million years ago.*

Paleontology—The Study of Past Life

Studying the rate of geologic change provides only part of the picture of Earth's past. To get a fuller picture, scientists also study the organisms that lived on Earth and the conditions in which they lived. The science that deals with the study of past life is called **paleontology.** Scientists who study this life are called *paleontologists,* and the data they use are fossils. *Fossils* are the remains of organisms preserved by geologic processes.

Paleontologists study fossils to see how the environment has changed. Fossils of sea life may be found almost anywhere on Earth. They may be found in a rock layer in the desert or on a mountain peak. These fossils are evidence that the rock layer formed when the area was part of the ocean. Fossils also provide evidence of how life has changed. As conditions on Earth's surface changed, organisms changed or died out. For example, the fossil record contains evidence of animals that no longer exist, such as saber-toothed cats and woolly mammoths.

Standards Check What are two things for which fossils can provide evidence? 🐻 **7.4.e**

MATH PRACTICE

The Age of Earth
Today, geologists estimate that Earth is about 4.6 billion years old. How many times older is this age than early estimates of about 6,000 years? Record your work in your **Science Journal.**

paleontology
(PAY lee uhn TAHL uh jee) the scientific study of fossils
  Wordwise The root *paleo-* means "old." The suffix *-logy* means "the science of."

SECTION Review

 7.4.a, 7.4.b, 7.4.e

Summary

- Uniformitarianism assumes that geologic change is gradual. Catastrophism is based on the idea that geologic change is sudden.

- Modern geology is based on the idea that gradual geologic change is interrupted by catastrophes.

- Using fossils to study past life is called paleontology.

Using Vocabulary

1. Write an original definition for *uniformitarianism, catastrophism,* and *paleontology.*

Understanding Concepts

2. **Comparing** Compare catastrophism with uniformitarianism.

3. **Identifying** Give one example of catastrophic global change.

Critical Thinking

4. **Analyzing Methods** Describe how fossils can provide evidence of how environmental conditions and life have changed during Earth's history.

5. **Identifying Relationships** Why did many scientists disagree with the idea of uniformitarianism?

Math Skills

6. **Making Calculations** An impact crater left by an asteroid strike has a radius of 85 km. What is the area of the crater? (Hint: The area of a circle is πr^2.)

Challenge

7. **Analyzing Ideas** Imagine that you are explaining uniformitarianism and catastrophism to a friend. Describe an example of two related events that happen within the span of a human lifetime that demonstrate these two ideas.

Internet Resources

For a variety of links related to this chapter, go to www.scilinks.org
Topic: Earth's Story
SciLinks code: HY70450

Relative Dating

Key Concept Scientists can interpret the sequence of events in Earth's history by studying rock layers.

If you were a detective investigating a crime scene, what would you do? You might dust the scene for fingerprints or search for witnesses. As a detective, you must figure out the sequence of events that took place before you reached the crime scene.

Geologists have a similar goal when investigating Earth. They try to determine the order in which events have happened during Earth's history. But instead of relying on fingerprints and witnesses, geologists rely on rocks and fossils to help them. Determining whether an object or event is older or younger than other objects or events is called **relative dating.**

The Rock Cycle

Geologic history, from Earth's formation to the present, includes a record of rocks and of changes in life on Earth. This geologic history is sometimes called the *geologic record.* The rock cycle is an important process in the development of the geologic record. **Figure 1** shows how each type of rock can become any other type of rock through the rock cycle. For example, all rock can melt to form magma. *Igneous rock* forms when magma cools. *Metamorphic rock* forms when any type of solid rock changes into another type of rock because of temperature or pressure changes. **Sedimentary rock** is the kind of rock that forms from fragments of other types of rocks. Sedimentary rocks are the most useful rocks for relative dating.

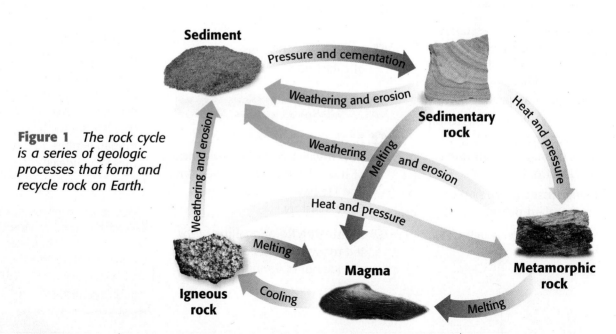

Figure 1 *The rock cycle is a series of geologic processes that form and recycle rock on Earth.*

Figure 2 *These mountains in Death Valley have been weathered, and the sediment has been eroded. The sediment has been deposited in a flat layer below the mountains.*

Weathering, Erosion, and Deposition

When rocks are exposed on Earth's surface, they can be broken down into smaller pieces, or *weathered*. Rocks can be weathered when physical processes crack and break the rock. Chemical weathering can take place as rock material reacts with water or air. Through weathering, all three rock types can break down to form sediment. *Sediment* is composed of rock fragments, material dissolved in water, and sometimes, biological debris.

Erosion is the process that moves sediment from one place to another. Water, wind, ice, and gravity can cause erosion. Eventually, sediment is deposited in a new location. Deposition is the process in which material is laid down or dropped. Because the sediment is loose when it is deposited, it settles into relatively flat layers. A new, flat layer of sediment rests on top of whatever rock or other sediment is already in place. So, new layers of sedimentary rock are almost always flat. The results of erosion and deposition in Death Valley in California are shown in **Figure 2.**

relative dating (REL uh tiv DAYT ing) any method of determining whether an event or object is older or younger than other events or objects

sedimentary rock (SED uh MEN tuhr ee RAHK) a rock that forms from compressed or cemented layers of sediment

Formation of Sedimentary Rock

After loose sediment is deposited, it may be *lithified*, or hardened, into sedimentary rock. In this process, the sediment is compacted and the grains of sediment are cemented together. Fossils form if biological debris or a trace of animal activity remains in a rock. The fossils are a record of the kind of life that existed where the sediment was deposited. And the type of rock that forms with a fossil can give clues about the environment in which the organism lived.

The type of rock that forms in any area depends on local conditions. So, no single rock layer is found in all areas of Earth. And during any one period of geologic time, many types of rock were forming in different areas of Earth. Therefore, no single area or history of an area can contain the geologic record for all of Earth.

7.3.c Students know how independent lines of evidence from geology, fossils, and comparative anatomy provide the bases for the theory of evolution.
7.4.c Students know that the rock cycle includes the formation of new sediment and rocks and that rocks are often found in layers, with the oldest generally on the bottom.

The Principle of Superposition

Suppose that you have a brother who takes a lot of pictures of your family and piles them in a box. Over the years, he adds new pictures to the top of the stack. Think about the family history recorded in those pictures. Where are the oldest pictures—the ones taken when you were a baby? Where are the most recent pictures—those taken last week?

Superposition in Rock Layers

Layers of sedimentary rock, such as the ones shown in **Figure 3,** are like stacked photographs. As you move from top to bottom, the layers get older. The principle that states that younger rocks lie above older rocks in undisturbed sequences is called **superposition.** Superposition helps geologists determine the relative ages of rock layers.

Superposition also helps geologists determine the relative ages of fossils. Fossils represent organisms that lived when sediment collected to form sedimentary rock. So, fossils found in a younger rock layer are younger than fossils found in an older rock layer. And fossils found in lower, or older, rock layers are older than fossils found in higher, or younger, rock layers.

Standards Check What does the principle of superposition state about rocks that are found in layers? **7.3.c, 7.4.c**

superposition
(soo puhr puh ZISH uhn) a principle that states that younger rocks lie above older rocks if the layers have not been disturbed

Figure 3 *These rock layers are in Red Rock Canyon in California. Rock layers are like pictures stacked over time—the younger ones are at the top of the stack over the older ones.*

Figure 4 How Rock Layers Become Disturbed

Folding *Folding* occurs when rock layers bend and buckle from forces inside Earth.

Tilting *Tilting* occurs when forces inside Earth slant rock layers.

Faults A *fault* is a break in Earth's crust along which blocks of rock slide relative to one another.

Intrusions An *intrusion* is molten rock from Earth's interior that squeezes into existing rock and cools.

Disturbed Rock Layers

Gravity causes sediment to be deposited in horizontal layers. So, if rock layers are not horizontal, something must have disturbed them after they formed. Sometimes, rock layers are even overturned by powerful forces in Earth's crust. In these sequences, older layers lie on top of younger layers.

Processes That Disturb Rock Layers

Folding and tilting are two events that disturb rock layers. *Folding* is the bending of rock layers that results from stress. *Tilting* happens when Earth's forces move rock layers so that they are slanted. Folding and tilting are shown in **Figure 4.**

Features That Cut Across Rock Layers

Geologists often find features that cut across existing layers of rock. These features include faults and intrusions. A *fault* is a break or crack in Earth's crust along which rocks shift position. An *intrusion* is a mass of igneous rock that forms when magma is injected into rock and then cools and solidifies. A fault and an intrusion are shown in **Figure 4.**

Gaps in the Record

Sometimes, layers of rock are missing, so there is a gap in the geologic record. To think of this another way, let's say that you stack your newspapers every day after reading them. Now, let's suppose that you want to look at a paper you read 10 days ago. You know that the paper should be 10 papers deep in the stack. But when you look, the paper is not there. What happened? Perhaps you didn't put the paper in the stack. Or maybe someone removed the paper. The same principles apply to a missing rock layer and the missing newspaper.

Unconformities

Missing rock layers create breaks in rock-layer sequences. An **unconformity** is a surface that represents a break in or a missing part of the geologic record. Unconformities also represent missing time—time that was not recorded in layers of rock. When geologists find an unconformity, they question whether the "missing layer" was never present or whether it was there once and was somehow removed. Unconformities can form when deposition stops after a supply of sediment is cut off. Unconformities also form when erosion removes layers. **Figure 5** shows these two processes.

unconformity
(uhn kuhn FAWRM uh tee) a break in the geologic record created when rock layers are eroded or when sediment is not deposited for a long period of time

law of crosscutting relationships
(LAW UHV KRAWS KUHT ing ri LAY shuhn SHIPS) the principle that a fault or body of rock is younger than any other body of rock that it cuts through

---

Figure 5 **How Unconformities Form**

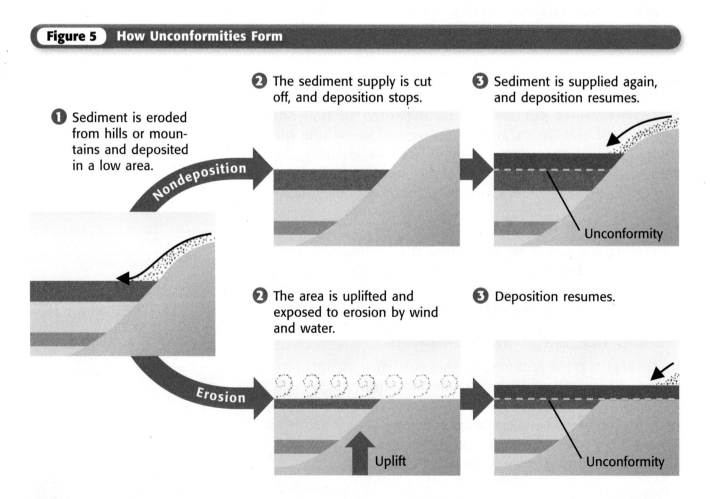

1 Sediment is eroded from hills or mountains and deposited in a low area.

Nondeposition

2 The sediment supply is cut off, and deposition stops.

3 Sediment is supplied again, and deposition resumes.

Unconformity

Erosion

2 The area is uplifted and exposed to erosion by wind and water.

Uplift

3 Deposition resumes.

Unconformity

Rock-Layer Puzzles

The principle of superposition states that younger layers of sedimentary rock are found on top of older layers if the layers have not been overturned. But what if the rock layers are more than just a stack of horizontal layers?

Geologists often find rock-layer sequences that have been affected by more than one process. Determining the order of events that led to the arrangement of these rock layers is like piecing together a puzzle. Geologists study rock-layer sequences to help piece together the history of Earth as told by the rock record.

The Law of Crosscutting Relationships

The **law of crosscutting relationships** states that a fault or a body of rock, such as an intrusion, is younger than any feature or layer of rock that the fault or rock body cuts through. For example, if a fault cuts through an unconformity, the fault is younger than the rock layers on either side of the unconformity. Remember that layers of rock have to be in place before anything can disturb them.

Standards Check How does the law of crosscutting relationships help with relative dating of rock layers and features? 🐾 **7.4.c**

Relative Ages of Rock Layers and Features

Figure 6 shows four stages in the formation of rock layers that contain an igneous intrusion, an unconformity, and a fault. A geologist studying rock layers has only the fourth view to look at when piecing together a rock-layer puzzle. Look at the bottom picture to see what the geologist is studying.

Now, start at the top to see the history of this area. You can see that the bottom three layers of sedimentary rock were formed first. Next, an intrusion cut through the three layers. The layers had to be there first before the intrusion could cut through them. An unconformity formed when the top of the sequence was eroded away. Then, two more layers of sediment were deposited. These layers were lithified and formed sedimentary rock. Finally, a fault cut through all of the sedimentary layers and the igneous intrusion.

Figure 6 A Rock-Layer Sequence

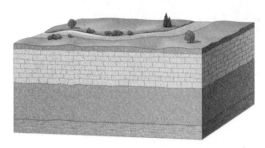

❶ Three layers of sedimentary rock form.

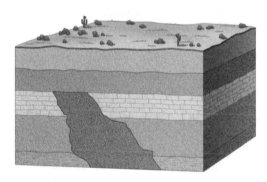

❷ An igneous intrusion cuts through the three rock layers.

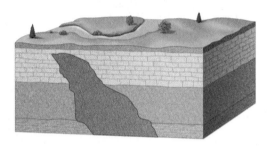

❸ Erosion removes some of the top layer and some of the intrusion. Then, more sedimentary rock forms.

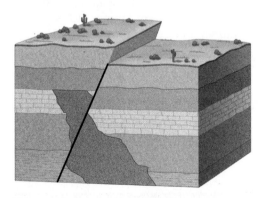

❹ Tectonic forces cause a fault to form.

Order of Events

Geologists use superposition and crosscutting relationships to find the relative ages of rocks. Relative dating makes clear the order in which events happened. But relative dating does not tell scientists exactly when those events took place.

To form a more complete picture of Earth's history, geologists combine relative dating with information that can establish actual dates. For example, imagine that you are digging in layers of soil at the edge of a river. You know from superposition that the layers near the top were deposited more recently than the layers farther down. But without more information, you can't tell when any of the layers were deposited. Now, imagine that in one layer, you find a coin dated 1965. You can now tell that the layer in which you found the coin could not have been deposited before 1965. And you know that the layers above the coin were deposited in 1965 or in a later year.

Standards Check What information do geologists obtain from relative dating? 7.4.c

Looking at Rock Layers

With a parent or guardian, look at road cuts, beaches, or other areas where rock layers are visible. Sketch the rock layers in your **Science Journal.** Discuss which rock layers are the oldest with your parent or guardian. Hypothesize what processes have affected the rocks since the rocks formed.

ACTIVITY

Quick Lab

Solve a Rock-Layer Puzzle!

In this activity, you will put your scientific skills to work to determine the relative ages of the layers and features of this rock-layer puzzle.

▶ Try It!

1. On a **piece of paper,** use a **pencil** to draw 10 horizontal lines. Write "Youngest" above the top line and "Oldest" below the bottom line.

2. Study the rock layers shown in the drawing to the right. Use what you know about superposition and crosscutting relationships to determine the order in which layers and features A through J formed.

3. List the oldest layer or feature on the bottom line, and list the youngest feature or layer on the top line.

4. Fill in all 10 letters to show the relative ages of all of the layers and features. When you have finished, each line should contain one letter.

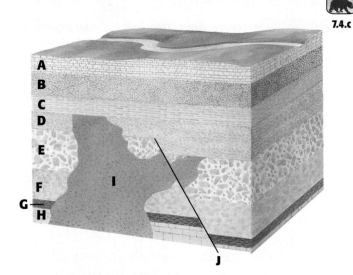

▶ Think About It!

5. Do the layers and features best represent geologic change as described by uniformitarianism or catastrophism? Explain your answer.

6. Can you tell how old any of the features or layers in this illustration are? If so, give the ages. If not, explain why not.

 20 min

Summary

- Geologists use relative dating to determine the order in which events happen.

- The rock cycle describes processes that form and recycle rock on Earth.

- Sedimentary rock forms when layers of sediment are lithified. Fossils may be preserved in sedimentary rock.

- The principle of superposition states that in undisturbed rock sequences, younger sedimentary rock layers lie above older layers.

- Folding and tilting are two events that disturb rock layers. Faults and intrusions are two features that cut across rock layers.

- Unconformities occur when rock layers are eroded or when sediment is not deposited for a long time.

- The law of crosscutting relationships states that structures and features that cut across rock layers are younger than the rock layers.

- Superposition and crosscutting relationships allow geologists to determine the order in which rock layers and features form but not the age in years of rock layers and features.

Using Vocabulary

1 Write an original definition for *relative dating, superposition, sedimentary rock,* and *unconformity.*

Understanding Concepts

2 **Summarizing** What does the rock cycle demonstrate about the three types of rocks?

3 **Listing** What are two ways unconformities can form?

4 **Justifying** Explain how scientists use the law of crosscutting relationships to determine the relative ages of rock layers and a fault that cuts through the layers.

Critical Thinking

5 **Analyzing Processes** Put the following terms in the order in which they would likely occur as sedimentary rock forms: *weathering, lithification, deposition,* and *erosion.* Explain what happens during each of these steps.

6 **Analyzing Ideas** Does the law of crosscutting relationships involve sedimentary rock only? Explain why or why not.

INTERPRETING GRAPHICS Use the illustration below to answer the next three questions.

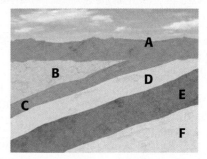

7 **Analyzing Processes** What process appears to have disturbed rock layers B, C, D, E, and F?

8 **Identifying Relationships** List the relative ages of these rock layers from youngest to oldest.

9 **Evaluating Data** There is an unconformity in this rock sequence. Describe its location, and describe how it may have formed.

Math Skills

10 **Making Calculations** Sediment in one area is deposited at a rate of 3 mm per year. At this rate, how many years must pass for 12 cm of sediment to be deposited?

Challenge

11 **Making Comparisons** Describe an example of something around your home or school that demonstrates superposition. Explain how you could use superposition to determine the order of events at home or at school.

Absolute Dating

Key Concept Because radioactive decay occurs at a constant rate, the age of a rock can be estimated by analyzing the amounts of different isotopes in a rock.

What You Will Learn

- Radioactive decay is the process by which a radioactive isotope changes into a stable isotope.
- Radiometric dating is the process in which parent and daughter isotopes are analyzed to determine the age of rocks and fossils.

Why It Matters

Estimating the age of rocks and fossils helps tell the story of Earth's past.

Vocabulary

- absolute dating
- radioactive decay
- radiometric dating
- half-life

READING STRATEGY

Clarifying Concepts Take turns reading this section out loud with a partner. Stop to discuss ideas that seem confusing.

absolute dating (AB suh LOOT DAYT ing) any method of measuring the age of an event or object in years

radioactive decay (RAY dee oh AK tiv dee KAY) the process in which a radioactive isotope tends to break down into a stable isotope of the same element or another element

7.3.c Students know how independent lines of evidence from geology, fossils, and comparative anatomy provide the bases for the theory of evolution.

7.4.d Students know that evidence from geologic layers and radioactive dating indicates Earth is approximately 4.6 billion years old and that life on this planet has existed for more than 3 billion years.

▶ If you want to know exactly how old a person is, you can ask the person. But how can you find out the age of a rock? Finding the age of an object by determining the number of years the object has existed is called **absolute dating.** Read on to see how unstable atoms are used in one method of absolute dating.

Radioactive Decay

Atoms of the same element that have the same number of protons but have different numbers of neutrons are called *isotopes*. Most isotopes are stable, meaning that they stay in their original form. But some isotopes are unstable. Scientists call unstable isotopes *radioactive*. The breakdown of a radioactive isotope into a stable isotope of the same element or another element is called **radioactive decay. Figure 1** shows one example of how radioactive decay can happen.

Each kind of unstable isotope decays at a different rate. The rate of radioactive decay for a given isotope can be determined experimentally. For each kind of isotope, the rate of decay is constant. So, certain naturally occurring radioactive isotopes can be used as a kind of "clock" to find the ages of rocks that contain these isotopes.

Standards Check What is radioactive decay? 🐻 **7.4.d**

Figure 1 Radioactive Decay

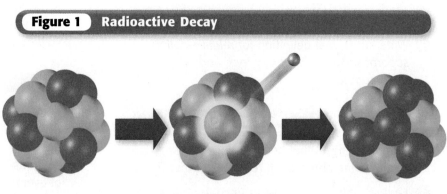

Unstable Isotope
6 protons,
8 neutrons

Radioactive Decay
When some unstable isotopes decay, a neutron is converted into a proton. In the process, an electron is released.

Product of Decay: Stable Isotope
7 protons,
7 neutrons

Dating Rocks—Parent and Daughter Isotopes

An unstable radioactive isotope is called a *parent isotope*. The stable isotope produced by radioactive decay is called the *daughter isotope*. Radioactive decay can occur as a single step or a series of steps. In either case, the rate of decay is constant.

To date rock, scientists compare the amount of parent isotope with the amount of daughter isotope. The more daughter isotope there is, the older the rock is. For this reason, radiometric dating works only on rocks that contained either no daughter isotope or a known amount of daughter isotope at the time the rock formed.

Radiometric Dating

If you know the rate of decay for a radioactive element in a rock, you can figure out the absolute age of the rock. Determining the absolute age of a sample based on the ratio of parent material to daughter material is called **radiometric dating.** For example, let's say that a rock sample contains an isotope with a half-life of 10,000 years. A **half-life** is the time needed for one-half of a radioactive sample to decay. In this rock sample, after 10,000 years, half of the parent material will have decayed and become daughter material. You analyze the sample and find equal amounts of parent material and daughter material. Half of the original radioactive isotope has decayed, so the sample must be about 10,000 years old. **Figure 2** shows how this steady decay happens.

The Most Useful Rock Samples

Igneous rocks are the best types of rock samples to use for radiometric dating. When igneous rock forms, elements are separated into different minerals in the rock. Thus, when they form, minerals in igneous rocks often contain only a parent isotope and none of the daughter isotope.

Radioactive Benefits
Can radioactivity be a good thing? Write an essay that describes how radioactivity can be beneficial. Go to **go.hrw.com,** and type in the keyword HY7RADW.

radiometric dating (RAY dee oh MET rik DAYT ing) a method of determining the age of an object by estimating the relative percentages of a radioactive (parent) isotope and a stable (daughter) isotope

half-life (HAF lief) the time required for half of a sample of a radioactive isotope to break down by radioactive decay to form a daughter isotope

Figure 2 *After every half-life, the amount of parent material decreases by one-half.* **What fraction of parent material remains after two half-lives?**

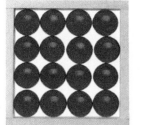

0 years
Parent isotope = 16 mg
Daughter isotope =
0 mg

10,000 years
Parent isotope = 8 mg
Daughter isotope =
8 mg

20,000 years
Parent isotope = 4 mg
Daughter isotope =
12 mg

30,000 years
Parent isotope = 2 mg
Daughter isotope =
14 mg

Using Radiometric Dating

Scientists use different radiometric-dating techniques based on the estimated age of a sample. The half-life of an isotope determines how the isotope can be used for dating. The older the rock is, the more daughter material there will be in the rock. Isotopes with long half-lives can be used to date old rocks but not young rocks. For isotopes with long half-lives, younger rocks do not contain enough daughter material to allow accurate measurements.

Methods of Radiometric Dating

One isotope used for radiometric dating is potassium-40. Potassium-40 has a half-life of 1.3 billion years. It decays to argon and calcium. Geologists measure argon as the daughter material. This method can be used to date rocks older than 100,000 years.

Uranium-238 is a radioactive isotope that decays to lead-206. The half-life of uranium-238 is 4.5 billion years. Uranium-lead dating can be used to date rocks older than 10 million years.

Half Dome, in Yosemite National Park, is shown in **Figure 3.** This dome is composed of igneous rock. After the rock formed, it was uplifted and shaped by glaciers. Uranium-lead dating shows that the rock in Half Dome formed about 85 million years ago. So, geologists can use relative dating to determine that the uplift and glacial erosion happened sometime in the last 85 million years.

Figure 3 *Half Dome in California's Yosemite National Park formed when a large mass of magma cooled very slowly below Earth's surface.*

Quick Lab

Radioactive Decay

1. Use a **clock** or **watch with a second hand** to record the time. Wait 20 s, and then use **scissors** to carefully cut a **sheet of paper** in half. Select one piece, and set the other piece aside.

2. Repeat step 1 until nine 20 s intervals have elapsed.

3. What does the whole piece of paper used in this lab represent?

4. What do the pieces of paper you set aside in each step represent?

5. How much of your paper isotope was left after the first interval? after three intervals? after nine intervals? Express your answers as percentages.

7.4.d

6. What is the half-life of your paper isotope?

 10 min

The Age of Our Solar System

Can radiometric dating be used to find the age of Earth? Yes, but not by dating rocks from Earth. The first rocks that formed on Earth have been recycled by plate tectonics and erosion. Therefore, there are no Earth rocks left that are as old as our planet. But other bodies in space contain rock that is as old as our solar system.

For example, the moon and some meteorites contain rock that formed as our solar system, including Earth, was forming. *Meteorites* are small, rocky bodies that have traveled through space and fallen to Earth's surface. Geologists have found meteorites on Earth. Rocks from the moon have also been collected, as shown in **Figure 4.** Radiometric dating has been done on these rocks from other parts of our solar system. The absolute ages of these samples show that our solar system, including Earth, is about 4.6 billion years old.

Standards Check Approximately how old are Earth and the solar system? What is the evidence for this age? 7.4.d

Figure 4 *Scientist-astronaut Harrison Schmitt collects samples of rock on the moon with the lunar rake during the* Apollo 17 *mission.*

SECTION Review

7.3.c, 7.4.d

Summary

- During radioactive decay, an unstable isotope decays and becomes a stable isotope of the same element or a different element.

- Radiometric dating, based on the ratio of parent to daughter material, is used to determine the absolute age of a sample.

- The method of radiometric dating is chosen based on the estimated age of the sample.

- Earth and the solar system are about 4.6 billion years old.

Using Vocabulary

① Use *absolute dating, radioactive decay, radiometric dating,* and *half-life* in separate sentences.

Understanding Concepts

② **Describing** Explain how radioactive decay occurs.

③ **Summarizing** How does radioactive decay relate to radiometric dating?

④ **Analyzing** In order for radiometric dating to be accurate, what must be true about the daughter material at the time a rock formed?

⑤ **Evaluating** How do geologists know that Earth and the solar system are approximately 4.6 billion years old?

Critical Thinking

⑥ **Analyzing Methods** Explain why radioactive decay must be constant in order for radiometric dating to be accurate.

⑦ **Making Inferences** Why are there rocks on the moon that are older than any rocks on Earth?

Challenge

⑧ **Applying Concepts** Could the potassium-argon method of radiometric dating be used to date rock that is estimated to have formed 1,000 years ago? Explain why or why not.

Internet Resources

For a variety of links related to this chapter, go to www.scilinks.org
Topic: Absolute Dating
SciLinks code: HY70003

Skills Practice Lab

The Half-Life of Pennies

Uranium-238—or U-238—is a radioactive isotope of the element uranium. Uranium-238 decays to lead-206, which is a stable isotope of the element lead. The half-life of uranium-238 is 4.5 billion years. So, every 4.5 billion years, half of the uranium-238 in a sample will decay to lead-206. In other words, during any 4.5-billion-year period, the probability that a particular uranium-238 atom will decay is 1/2.

The absolute age of a rock can be found by analyzing the rock for uranium-238 and lead-206. Knowing the amounts of both of these isotopes enables scientists to calculate how long ago the rock formed. In the following experiment, you will use pennies to model radioactive decay.

Procedure

1 Place 100 pennies in a large, covered container. Shake the container several times, and remove the cover. Carefully empty the pennies onto a flat surface. Make sure that the pennies don't roll away.

7.4.d Students know that evidence from geologic layers and radioactive dating indicates Earth is approximately 4.6 billion years old and that life on this planet has existed for more than 3 billion years.

Investigation and Experimentation
7.7.c Communicate the logical connection among hypotheses, science concepts, tests conducted, data collected, and conclusions drawn from the scientific evidence.

2 Remove all of the pennies that have the "head" side of the coin turned upward. In a data table similar to the one below, record the number of pennies that you removed and the number of pennies that remain.

Shake number	Number of pennies remaining	Number of pennies removed
0	100	0
1		
2		

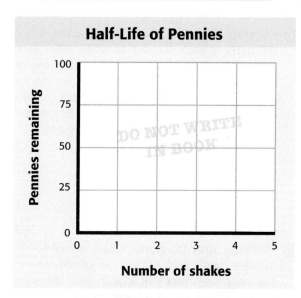

Half-Life of Pennies

3 Repeat the process until no pennies are left in the container. Remember to remove only the pennies showing "heads."

4 Draw a graph similar to the one entitled "Half-Life of Pennies." Label the x-axis "Number of shakes," and label the y-axis "Pennies remaining." Plot the data from your table on the graph.

Analyze the Results

5 Examining Data Examine the graph entitled "Half-Life of Uranium-238." Compare the graph you have made for pennies with the one for U-238. Explain any similarities.

Draw Conclusions

6 Evaluating Results Recall that the probability of landing "heads" in a coin toss is 1/2. Use this information to explain why the remaining number of pennies is reduced by about half each time the pennies are shaken and tossed.

7 Evaluating Models Assume that pennies represent U-238 and lead-206 isotopes. In this model, which isotope does the "head" side of the pennies represent? Which isotope is represented by the "tail" side of the pennies?

8 Applying Conclusions If a "sample" of pennies contained 75 heads and 25 tails, how many half-lives would have passed since the "sample" formed? Explain your answer.

Big Idea Question

9 Interpreting Information Imagine that you are studying an area where two horizontal layers of sedimentary rock are cut by an igneous intrusion. Radiometric dating indicates that the igneous intrusion formed about 15 million years ago. What would you conclude about the history of the three rock formations? Explain your conclusions.

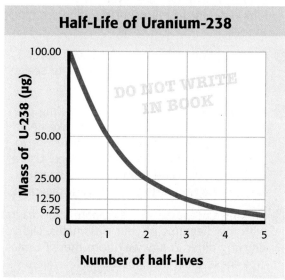

Half-Life of Uranium-238

Science Skills Activity

Investigation and Experimentation
7.7.d Construct scale models, maps, and appropriately labeled diagrams to communicate scientific knowledge (e.g., motion of Earth's plates and cell structure).

Constructing Labeled Diagrams

▶ Tutorial

A diagram illustrates an item or place and shows how the parts of the item or place are related. Scientists use diagrams to show many things that may be hard to describe in words. When diagrams are drawn to scale, they can show the relative sizes of items. If a diagram is well labeled, it will be easy to see what makes up the item or place that is being illustrated. To construct a labeled diagram, follow these steps:

1 Choosing Your Scale Decide on the scale. The scale is the ratio of the size of the diagram to the size of the item or place being drawn. You will use the scale to determine the size of each part of your diagram. For example, imagine that you are making a diagram of a hill that is 20 m high. To fit it on a page, you choose a scale of 0.5 cm = 1 m. The hill will be 10 cm high in your diagram.

2 Planning Your Diagram Use a pencil to sketch a rough draft of your diagram on a scrap of paper. Plan how to make the parts of your diagram look different from one another.

3 Drawing Your Diagram If you know the overall size of your diagram, sketch the outlines. If not, start with the bottom or main part and build the rest of your diagram to scale around the first part.

4 Labeling Your Diagram After drawing all of the parts of your diagram to scale, label each part. Make neat labels for each part of the diagram close to where that part appears on the page. Use a ruler to draw a line from the label to the correct part of the diagram. Remember to put a title at the top of your diagram.

▶ You Try It!

A team of scientists has studied sedimentary rock layers exposed in a canyon. The team left notes about the layers but did not make any drawings. You have been asked to make a diagram of the layers so that others can see what the canyon wall looks like. Use these notes to make your diagram:

Layer 1 (bottom of canyon wall): sandstone, 18 m high
Layer 2: limestone, 32 m high
Layer 3: shale, 10 m high
Layer 4: dolomite, 45 m high
Layer 5: sandstone, 45 m high

1 Choosing Your Scale Decide what scale you will use so that your entire diagram will fit on a page. The total height of the layers in the canyon wall is 150 m.

2 Planning Your Diagram Use a pencil to make a rough draft on a scrap of paper to see how the layers will look in your diagram. Plan how to make the layers in your diagram look different to represent the different types of rock.

3 Drawing Your Diagram Start with Layer 1, and build the rest of your diagram to scale around that layer.

4 Labeling Your Diagram After drawing the layers of your diagram to scale, make neat labels for each part of the diagram close to where that part appears on the page. Use a ruler to draw a line from the label to each layer. Put a title at the top of your diagram.

5 Making Comparisons Compare your diagram with the diagrams of your classmates. Did your drawing differ in any way from theirs? Explain why these differences occurred.

Chapter Summary

go.hrw.com
SUPER SUMMARY
KEYWORD: HY7STUS

The Big Idea The rock record can be used to determine the relative and absolute ages of rocks, which can be used to study Earth's history.

Section

Vocabulary

1 The Study of Earth's History

Key Concept Slow geologic processes and major catastrophic events have shaped Earth's surface in the past and continue to shape Earth today.

- Uniformitarianism describes uniform change in Earth's geology, and catastrophism describes sudden change.
- Modern geology describes most change as gradual but acknowledges rare, sudden changes.

Most geologic features are the result of gradual processes.

uniformitarianism p. 234
catastrophism p. 235
paleontology p. 237

2 Relative Dating

Key Concept Scientists can interpret the sequence of events in Earth's history by studying rock layers.

- The rock cycle includes the formation and recycling of rock.
- Relative dating establishes the order in which rocks formed or events took place.
- The principle of superposition states that younger rocks lie above older rocks if the layers are undisturbed.

If things are found in undisturbed layers, the order of events can be determined.

relative dating p. 238
sedimentary rock p. 238
superposition p. 240
unconformity p. 242
law of crosscutting relationships p. 243

3 Absolute Dating

Key Concept Because radioactive decay occurs at a constant rate, the age of a rock can be estimated by analyzing the amounts of different isotopes in a rock.

- Radioactive decay is the process by which a radioactive isotope changes into a stable isotope.
- Radiometric dating is the process in which parent and daughter isotopes are analyzed to determine the age of rocks and fossils.

The half-life of an isotope is the time it takes for half of a sample to decay.

absolute dating p. 246
radioactive decay p. 246
radiometric dating p. 247
half-life p. 247

Chapter Review

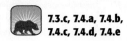

Organize

Three-Panel Flip Chart   Review the FoldNote that you created at the beginning of the chapter. Add to or correct the FoldNote based on what you have learned.

Using Vocabulary

1 **Academic Vocabulary**   In the sentence "Younger rocks lie above older rocks if the layers have not been disturbed," what does the word *layers* mean?

For each pair of terms, explain how the meanings of the terms differ.

2 *uniformitarianism* and *catastrophism*

3 *relative dating* and *absolute dating*

4 *radioactive decay* and *radiometric dating*

5 *superposition* and *law of crosscutting relationships*

Understanding Concepts

Multiple Choice

6 Paleontologists study
  a. craters on the moon and Earth.
  b. the history of life on Earth.
  c. the use of radioactivity for electric power.
  d. erosion and deposition.

7 To determine relative ages, geologists use
  a. the principle of superposition.
  b. radiometric dating.
  c. half-lives.
  d. catastrophism.

8 Rock layers that are cut by a fault formed
  a. after the fault.
  b. before the fault.
  c. at the same time as the fault.
  d. There is not enough information to determine the answer.

9 An unconformity is
  a. evidence of past life.
  b. a tilted rock layer.
  c. an isotope that has no half-life.
  d. a gap in a rock-layer sequence.

10 The rock cycle describes
  a. how round mineral crystals form.
  b. how to find the absolute age of a rock.
  c. how to find the relative age of a rock.
  d. how rock changes to form new rock.

11 Sedimentary rock
  a. forms from layers of sediment.
  b. forms when sediment is cemented.
  c. can be heated and squeezed to form metamorphic rock.
  d. All of the above

Short Answer

12 **Identifying**   Identify the role of uniformitarianism in Earth science.

13 **Summarizing**   Describe the role of paleontology in the study of Earth's history.

14 **Justifying**   Approximately how old is our solar system? What evidence supports this estimate?

15 **Applying**   How do geologists use the principle of superposition?

INTERPRETING GRAPHICS   Use the table below to answer the next question.

Isotope Ratios		
	Parent isotope (mg)	**Daughter isotope (mg)**
Rock forms	8	0
Sample time A	4	4
Sample time B	2	6

16 **Applying**   How many half-lives have elapsed at sample time A? at sample time B?

Writing Skills

17 **Outlining Topics**   Describe how life on Earth has been affected by major catastrophic events.

Critical Thinking

18 **Concept Mapping** Use the following terms to create a concept map: *age, half-life, absolute dating, radioactive decay, radiometric dating, relative dating, superposition,* and *isotopes.*

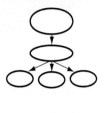

19 **Analyzing Methods** How could relative dating and absolute dating be used together?

20 **Identifying Relationships** How do geologists know that an intrusion is younger than the layers it cuts across?

21 **Making Inferences** What could you conclude about the formation of a sedimentary rock layer if you observed ripple marks preserved in the rock?

22 **Making Inferences** What might have happened in the atmosphere in the time just after the Barringer Meteorite Crater formed?

23 **Analyzing Methods** Would the uranium-lead method of radiometric dating be appropriate for determining the absolute age of a rock that is estimated to be between 1 million and 2 million years old? Explain your answer.

24 **Analyzing Ideas** Hutton's theory has been summarized in the statement "The present is the key to the past." Explain how this statement applies to studying Earth's history.

25 **Identifying Relationships** What are the source materials for sedimentary rocks?

26 **Identifying Relationships** Why are sedimentary rocks often found in layers? Why are the oldest layers generally on the bottom?

27 **Making Comparisons** Scientists are studying two sedimentary rock layers. One layer has no fossils in it, and the other layer has numerous fossils. Explain how fossils can provide evidence of how life and environmental conditions have changed. What might scientists be able to conclude about the layer with fossils that they cannot conclude about the layer with no fossils?

INTERPRETING GRAPHICS Use the diagram below to answer the next four questions.

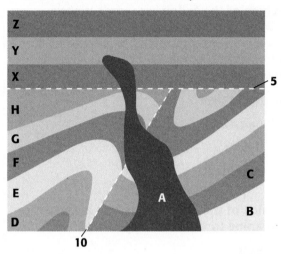

28 **Applying Concepts** Is intrusion A younger or older than layer X? Explain your answer.

29 **Applying Concepts** What is feature 5?

30 **Making Comparisons** Is intrusion A younger or older than feature 10? Explain your answer.

31 **Analyzing Relationships** Other than the intrusion and faulting, what event happened in layers B, C, D, E, F, G, and H? Number this event, the intrusion, and the fault in the order that they happened.

Math Skills

32 **Making Calculations** The half-life of uranium-238 is 4.5 billion years. How many years will three-fourths of a sample of uranium-238 take to decay?

Challenge

33 **Evaluating Data** Scientists discover a crater that has layers of sedimentary rock exposed on the inside walls of the crater. A layer of sandstone is visible near the bottom of the crater wall. A layer of limestone is visible above the sandstone. Both layers are below the edge of the crater. Describe the order of events that is most likely to have formed the limestone layer, the sandstone layer, and the crater.

REVIEWING ACADEMIC VOCABULARY

1 Which of the following words means "an explanation of many related observations supported by a large body of evidence acquired through scientific investigation"?

A hypothesis

B question

C theory

D statement

2 Which of the following words is closest in meaning to the word *approximately*?

A exactly

B some

C about

D never

3 In the sentence "Students must know how to communicate the connection between a hypothesis and a theory," what does the word *communicate* mean?

A exchange ideas

B follow a series of steps

C be connected to

D make known or tell

4 In the sentence "The scientist found the fossil in the first layer of rock," what does the word *layer* mean?

A a single thickness lying above or below another

B a person who lays tile or bricks in horizontal sheets

C a single sheet of glass

D a depth or level of meaning

REVIEWING CONCEPTS

5 What is the main idea of the theory of uniformitarianism?

A Earth's surface is shaped by sudden events.

B Geologic change happens gradually.

C Fossils show how Earth has changed.

D Earth is approximately 4,000 years old.

6 Paleontologists believe that dinosaurs became extinct 65 million years ago. How do scientists explain this phenomenon?

A A volcanic eruption sent ash into the air, and Earth's climates cooled.

B A gradual global climate change caused extinctions of many of Earth's species.

C An asteroid hit Earth, and a debris cloud formed that blocked the light from the sun.

D Scientists have discovered fossils of the dinosaurs that lived on Earth 65 million years ago.

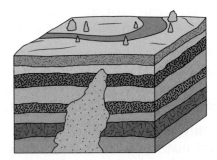

7 Determine what sequence of events occurred in the rock layers shown above.

A An intrusion formed, and then the rock layers formed around the intrusion.

B First, the bottom rock layer formed. Then, the intrusion formed. Finally, the other rock layers formed.

C The rock layers were folded, and then an intrusion cut through the layers.

D The rock layers formed, and then an intrusion cut through some of the layers.

Isotope Ratios		
	Parent isotope (mg)	Daughter isotope (mg)
Rock forms	20	0
20,000 years	10	10
40,000 years		

8 According to the table above, what will the composition of the rock be in 40,000 years?

A The rock will contain 3.75 mg of the parent isotope and 16.25 mg of the daughter isotope.

B The rock will contain 5 mg of the parent isotope and 15 mg of the daughter isotope.

C The rock will contain 3.75 mg of the parent isotope and 18.75 mg of the daughter isotope.

D The rock will contain 5 mg of the parent isotope and 17.5 mg of the daughter isotope.

9 Which of the following methods has helped scientists determine the age of our solar system?

A relative dating

B radiometric dating

C geologic columns

D radioactive decay

10 What method is used to determine whether an object or event is older or younger than other objects or events?

A relative dating

B superposition

C crosscutting

D unconformity

REVIEWING PRIOR LEARNING

11 Rock that is formed by the process of lithification is called

A sedimentary rock.

B igneous rock.

C metamorphic rock.

D volcanic rock.

12 Which of the following processes best explains a mountain that has a smooth, rounded peak?

A an earthquake

B chemical erosion

C wind erosion

D volcanic eruption

13 Which of the following would most likely cause a volcano to form?

A tectonic plates sliding past each other horizontally

B tectonic plates becoming stuck against each other

C tectonic plates colliding and crumpling

D one tectonic plate sliding beneath another

14 Which of the following is the most important process in shaping Earth's landscape?

A water running downhill

B wind blowing across mountain ranges

C glaciers sliding downhill

D ocean waves striking the beach

15 Heat from Earth's interior reaches Earth's surface mostly through

A conduction.

B surface waves.

C convection.

D longitudinal waves.

Science in Action

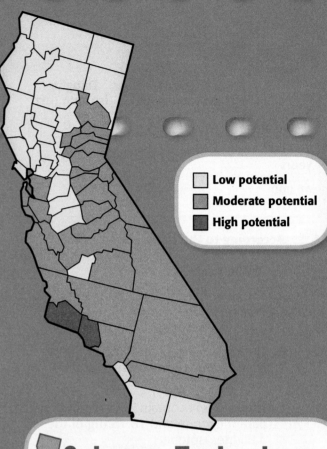

Low potential
Moderate potential
High potential

Weird Science

Nuclear-Powered Bacteria

Deep under Earth's surface, there is no light. Temperatures are high, water is scarce, and oxygen is difficult to find. For many years, scientists thought that nothing could live under these extreme conditions. But in 1989, a team of scientists found bacteria living in rocks that are 500 m below Earth's surface. Since then, bacteria have been found living in rocks that are as deep as 3.5 km below Earth's surface! These bacteria seem to get their food from an unusual source. The compounds they use for food are formed by the energy produced during the radioactive decay of uranium. The idea that the energy from radioactive decay can produce a food source is new to science and is changing the way that scientists think about life.

Science, Technology, and Society

Radon in California

An invisible, radioactive gas produced in some soils is the second leading cause of lung cancer. The name of the gas is *radon*, and it is present in some parts of California. Radioactive elements in California's bedrock and soil decay into radon. Radon gas can seep through cracks in a building's foundation. Over time, exposure to radon can damage lungs or cause lung cancer. Luckily, inexpensive tests can detect radon, and repairs can often fix the problem.

Math ACTIVITY

How deep is 3.5 km? To help you imagine this depth, calculate how many Statues of Liberty could be stacked in a hole that is 3.5 km deep. The Statue of Liberty in New York is about 46 m tall.

Social Studies ACTIVITY

The development of simple smoke detectors and radon-detection kits has led to their wide use. Write a short essay in your **Science Journal** about how these technological advances have benefited society.

Marie and Pierre Curie

A Great Team You may have heard the saying "Two heads are better than one." For scientific discoveries, this saying is often true. The husband and wife team Pierre and Marie Curie put their heads together and discovered the elements radium and polonium. Their work also helped them describe radioactivity.

Working side by side for long hours under poor conditions, Marie and Pierre Curie studied the mysterious rays given off by the element uranium. They processed huge amounts of an ore called *pitchblende* to collect the uranium from it. Strangely, the leftover material was more radioactive than uranium was. They spent several more months working with the material and discovered an element that was 300 times as radioactive as uranium was. Marie called it *polonium* in honor of Poland, the country in which she was born. For their research on radiation, the Curies were awarded the Nobel Prize in physics in 1903.

Language Arts ACTIVITY

Think of a time when you and a friend solved a problem together that neither of you could solve alone. Write a one-page story in your **Science Journal** about how you each helped solve the problem.

Internet Resources

- To learn more about careers in science, visit **www.scilinks.org** and enter the SciLinks code HY70225.

- To learn more about these Science in Action topics, visit **go.hrw.com** and type in the keyword HY7STUF.

- Check out articles related to this chapter by visiting **go.hrw.com**. Just type in the keyword HY7STUC.

Improving Comprehension

Graphic Organizers are important visual tools that can help you organize information and improve your reading comprehension. The Graphic Organizer below is called a *spider map*. Instructions for creating other types of Graphic Organizers are located in the **Study Skills** section of the Appendix.

How to Make a Spider Map

1. Draw a diagram like the one shown below. In the circle, write the main topic.

2. From the circle, draw legs to represent the main ideas or characteristics of the topic. Draw as many legs as you want to draw. Write an idea or characteristic along each leg.

3. From each leg, draw horizontal lines. As you read the chapter, write details about each idea on the idea's horizontal lines. To add more details, make the legs longer and add more horizontal lines.

When to Use a Spider Map

A spider map is an effective tool for classifying the details of a specific topic in science. A spider map divides a topic into ideas and details. As you read about a topic, look for the main ideas or characteristics of the topic. Within each idea, look for details. Use a spider map to organize the ideas and details of each topic.

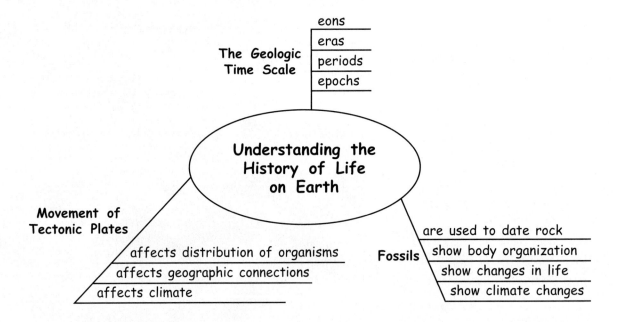

You Try It!

This Reading Strategy can also be used within the chapter that you are about to read. Practice making your own *spider map* as directed in the Reading Strategies for Section 1 and Section 2. Record your work in your **Science Journal.**

Unpacking the Standards

The information below "unpacks" the standards by breaking them down into basic parts. The higher-level, academic vocabulary is highlighted and defined to help you understand the language of the standards. "What It Means" restates the standards as simply as possible.

California Standard	Academic Vocabulary	What It Means
7.3.c Students know how independent lines of **evidence** from geology, fossils, and comparative anatomy provide the bases for the theory of evolution.	**evidence** (EV uh duhns) information showing whether an idea or belief is true or valid	The theory of evolution is based on several kinds of information that was gathered by studying rocks and fossils and by comparing the bodies of living and extinct organisms.
7.4.c Students know that the rock **cycle** includes the formation of new sediment and rocks and that rocks are often found in **layers,** with the oldest generally on the bottom.	**cycle** (SIE kuhl) a repeating series of changes **layer** (LAY uhr) a separate or distinct portion of matter that has thickness	The rock cycle includes the breakdown of rock into smaller fragments that may form new rock. Rocks are often found in layers, in which the oldest rock is usually on the bottom.
7.4.d Students know that **evidence** from geologic **layers** and radioactive dating **indicates** Earth is **approximately** 4.6 billion years old and that life on this planet has existed for more than 3 billion years.	**indicate** (IN di KAYT) to be or give a sign of; to show **approximately** (uh PRAHK suh mit lee) almost; about	Rock layers and dating methods that use radioactive elements suggest that Earth is about 4.6 billion years old and that Earth has supported life for more than 3 billion years.
7.4.e Students know fossils provide evidence of how life and **environmental** conditions have changed.	**environment** (en VIE ruhn muhnt) the surrounding natural conditions that affect an organism	Fossils can be used to understand how living things and the environment have changed over time.
7.4.f Students know how movements of Earth's continental and oceanic plates through time, with associated changes in climate and geographic connections, have **affected** the past and present **distribution** of organisms.	**affect** (uh FEKT) to change; to have an effect on; to influence **distribution** (DIS tri BYOO shuhn) the relative arrangement of objects or organisms in time or space	The movement of large chunks of Earth's lithosphere has caused changes in climate and changes in how landmasses are connected. These changes have affected where living things have existed on Earth in the past and where they live today.
7.4.g Students know how to explain **significant** developments and extinctions of plant and animal life on the geologic time scale.	**significant** (sig NIF uh kuhnt) important	You must know how to explain how, when, and why different plants and animals appeared and disappeared throughout Earth's history.

The following identifies other standards that are covered in this chapter and where you can go to see them unpacked: **7.4.a** (Chapter 8)

The History of Life on Earth

The Big Idea

Evidence from rocks allows us to understand the evolution of life on Earth.

 California Standards

Focus on Life Sciences
7.3 Biological evolution accounts for the diversity of species developed through gradual processes over many generations. (Sections 1 and 2)
7.4 Evidence from rocks allows us to understand the evolution of life on Earth. (Sections 1, 2, and 3)

Investigation and Experimentation
7.7 Scientific progress is made by asking meaningful questions and conducting careful investigations. (Science Skills Activity)

Math
6.1.2, 6.2.1 Number Sense
7.1.2 Number Sense
6.2.1, 6.2.3 Algebra and Functions
7.1.1, 7.2.2 Mathematical Reasoning

English–Language Arts
7.1.3 Reading
7.2.5 Writing

About the Photo

Watch out! Saber-toothed cats, such as this *Smilodon,* were daunting predators in California long ago. This fossil skeleton was found in the sticky La Brea Tar Pits in Los Angeles, California. Predators were probably trapped as they ventured into the tar pits to eat animals already stuck there. *Smilodon* was about the size of a tiger and had sharp, dagger-like teeth, as you can see!

Organize

Four-Corner Fold

Before you read this chapter, create the FoldNote entitled "Four-Corner Fold." Label each flap of the four-corner fold with "Fossils," "Changes in Earth's environments," "Changes in life on Earth," and "The geologic time scale." As you read the chapter, add details about each topic under the appropriate flap.

Instructions for creating FoldNotes are located in the Study Skills section on p. 581 of the Appendix.

Explore Activity

🕐 20 min

Making Fossils

How do scientists learn from fossils? In this activity, you will study "fossils" and identify the object that made each fossil.

Procedure

1. You and three or four of your classmates will be given **several pieces of modeling clay** and a **paper sack** containing a **few small objects.**

2. Press each object into a piece of clay, and then remove the object from the clay. Try to leave a "fossil" imprint showing as much detail as possible.

3. Trade your model fossils with another group.

4. On a **sheet of paper,** describe the fossils you have received. List as many details as possible. What patterns and textures do you observe?

5. Work as a group to identify each fossil, and check your results. Were you right?

7.3.c
7.4.c

Analysis

6. What kinds of evidence were important in identifying your fossils? What kinds of evidence were not preserved in the imprints? For example, can you tell what materials the objects were made of or what colors the objects were?

7. Why do you think fossils are sometimes called a "partial record" of past life?

Looking at Fossils

Key Concept Fossils provide evidence of how life and environmental conditions have changed.

▶ A paleontologist named Luis Chiappe found a dinosaur nesting ground in Argentina. How did he know the area had been a dinosaur nest? He studied fossil eggs found there.

Fossilized Organisms

The trace or remains of an organism that lived long ago is called a **fossil.** Fossils can form in several ways. The ways in which fossils form are outlined below.

Fossils in Rocks

When an organism dies, either it begins to decay or it is eaten by other organisms. Sometimes, however, organisms are quickly buried by sediment when they die. The sediment slows down decay and preserves the organisms. Hard parts, such as shells, teeth, and bones, are more resistant to decay than soft parts are. So, the hard parts of organisms are more often preserved than soft parts are. The fossils are preserved when sediment hardens to form sedimentary rock.

Standards Check How is evidence of past life preserved in sedimentary rock? 🐻 **7.4.c, 7.4.e**

Fossils in Amber

Imagine that an insect is caught in soft, sticky tree sap. Suppose that the insect is covered by more sap. If the sap hardens quickly enough, it preserves the insect inside. Hardened tree sap is called *amber.* Some of the best insect fossils are found in amber, as shown in **Figure 1.** Frogs and lizards have also been found in amber.

Figure 1 *These insects are preserved in amber. They are more than 38 million years old.*

7.3.c Students know how independent lines of evidence from geology, fossils, and comparative anatomy provide the bases for the theory of evolution.

7.4.c Students know that the rock cycle includes the formation of new sediment and rocks and that rocks are often found in layers, with the oldest generally on the bottom.

7.4.e Students know fossils provide evidence of how life and environmental conditions have changed.

Figure 2 *Scientist Vladimir Eisner studies the upper molars of a 20,000-year-old woolly mammoth found in Siberia, Russia. The almost perfectly preserved male mammoth was excavated from a block of ice in October 1999.*

Frozen Fossils

In October 1999, scientists removed a 20,000-year-old woolly mammoth from the frozen ground of the Siberian tundra. Some of the remains of this mammoth are shown in **Figure 2.** Woolly mammoths, which are relatives of modern elephants, became extinct about 10,000 years ago. Cold temperatures slow down decay. So, many frozen fossils are preserved from the last ice age. By studying the fossils, scientists hope to learn more about the mammoth and its environment.

Fossils in Asphalt

There are places where asphalt wells up at Earth's surface in thick, sticky pools. The asphalt deposits known as the La Brea Tar Pits in Los Angeles, California, for example, are at least 38,000 years old. These pools of thick, sticky asphalt have trapped and preserved many kinds of organisms for the past 38,000 years. From these fossils, scientists have learned about the past environment of southern California.

fossil (FAHS uhl) the trace or remains of an organism that lived long ago, most commonly preserved in sedimentary rock

Petrification

Organisms buried in sediment are sometimes preserved by petrification. *Petrification* is the filling or replacement of an organism's tissues with minerals that have different chemical compositions than the original tissues did. In one form of petrification, the space in an organism's hard tissue—for example, bone—is filled with a mineral. In another form of petrification, the organism's tissues are completely replaced by minerals. Petrified wood has undergone this type of replacement.

Standards Check What is petrification? 7.3.c

Figure 3 *These dinosaur tracks are located in Arizona. They show that the dinosaur was running when it made these tracks.*

trace fossil (TRAYS FAHS uhl) a fossilized structure, such as a footprint or a coprolite, that formed in sedimentary rock by animal activity on or within soft sediment

Other Types of Fossils

Besides their hard parts—and in rare cases their soft parts—do organisms leave behind any other clues? What other evidence of past life do paleontologists look for? Many fossils are not body parts at all!

Trace Fossils

Any fossilized evidence of animal activity is called a **trace fossil.** Tracks, such as the ones shown in **Figure 3,** are an example of a trace fossil. These fossils form when animal footprints fill with sediment and are preserved in rock. Tracks reveal a lot about the animal that made them, including how big it was and how fast it was moving. Scientists have found parallel paths of tracks showing that a group of dinosaurs moved in the same direction. These discoveries have led paleontologists to hypothesize that some dinosaurs moved in herds.

Burrows are another kind of trace fossil. Burrows are shelters made by animals, such as clams, that bury themselves in sediment. Like tracks, burrows are preserved when they are filled with sediment and are buried quickly. A *coprolite* (KAHP roh LIET), a third kind of trace fossil, is preserved animal dung.

Standards Check Name three kinds of trace fossils. 🐻 **7.4.e**

Molds and Casts

Molds and casts are two more kinds of fossils. The impression left in sediment or in rock where a plant or animal was buried is called a *mold*. **Figure 4** shows two types of molds from the same organism—an internal mold and an external mold. A *cast* is an object that forms when sediment fills a mold and becomes rock. Like a mold, a cast can show what the inside or the outside of an organism looked like.

Figure 4 *The fossil on the left is the internal mold of an ammonite. It formed when sediment filled the ammonite's shell. The shell later dissolved away. On the right is the external mold of the ammonite. It shows the external features of the shell.*

Using Fossils to Interpret the Past

All of the fossils that have been discovered on Earth are part of the fossil record. The *fossil record* is the history of life in the geologic past as indicated by the traces or remains of living things. Read on to find out more about the fossil record, including what scientists can learn from it.

The Information in the Fossil Record

The fossil record offers only a partial history of life on Earth. Some parts of this history are more complete than others. For example, scientists know more about organisms that had hard body parts than about organisms that had only soft body parts. Scientists also know more about organisms that lived in environments that favored fossilization. The fossil record is incomplete because most organisms never became fossils. And many fossils have not been discovered yet.

A History of Environmental Changes

Would you expect to find marine fossils on the mountain shown in **Figure 5**? The presence of marine fossils means that the rocks in these mountains formed in a very different environment. They formed at the bottom of an ocean.

Fossils can also contain evidence of climate change. For example, scientists have found fossil evidence of forests and freshwater organisms in Antarctica. The climate must have been warmer in the past for forests to grow and for fresh water to remain unfrozen. So, fossils are evidence of climate change in Antarctica. By studying life in the fossil record, scientists can tell what climates were like in the past.

Figure 5 *This scientist has found fossils of marine life at the top of mountains in the Yoho National Park in Canada. The marine fossils are evidence that these rocks were pushed up from below sea level.*

Quick Lab

Connecting Fossils to Climates

7.4.e

1. Imagine that you go on an expedition to a desert near your home and find the two fossils shown here. Write a description of each fossil.

2. Formulate a hypothesis about the type of organism each fossil represents.

3. Formulate a hypothesis about the environment in which these organisms lived.

4. Is the environment you described in step 3 different from the desert environment in which the fossils were found? If so, how would you explain this difference?

15 min

index fossil (IN DEKS FAHS uhl) a fossil that is used to establish the age of a rock layer because the fossil is distinct, abundant, and widespread and the species that formed that fossil existed for only a short span of geologic time

Figure 6 *Paleontologists know that any rock layer that contains a fossil of the trilobite* Phacops *is about 400 million years old.*

A History of Changing Organisms

To determine how life on Earth has changed, scientists look for similarities between different fossils. Scientists also look for similarities between fossils and living organisms. By studying these relationships, scientists can interpret how life has changed over time. However, only a small fraction of the organisms that have existed in Earth's history have been fossilized. As a result, the fossil record is incomplete. So, it does not provide paleontologists with a continuous record of changes in life on Earth.

Dating the Fossil Record

To understand the history of life on Earth, paleontologists put fossils in order based on age. In some cases, scientists can use absolute dating methods, such as radiometric dating, to determine the age of fossils. More commonly, they use relative dating methods, especially superposition, to establish the relative ages of fossils. Fossils found in older layers of rock are from more ancient life-forms. Fossils found in younger rock layers are from organisms that lived more recently.

Standards Check Would you expect to find fossils of an organism that lived recently in very old rock layers or in younger rock layers? Why? **7.3.c**

Using Fossils to Date Rocks

Scientists have found that some types of fossils appear all over the world, but only in certain rock layers. Scientists date the rock layers above and below these fossils. Then, scientists can determine the time span in which the organisms that formed the fossils lived. These types of fossils are called index fossils. **Index fossils** are fossils of organisms that lived during a relatively short, well-defined geologic time span. To be considered an index fossil, a fossil must be found in rock layers throughout the world. It must also be easy to identify, and many fossils of that organism must exist. Scientists use index fossils to date rock layers in which the fossils are found.

Trilobites as Index Fossils

Fossils in a group of trilobites (TRIE loh BIETS) called *Phacops* are an example of an index fossil. Trilobites are extinct. Their closest living relatives are horseshoe crabs, spiders, and scorpions. Through the dating of rock, paleontologists have determined that *Phacops* lived approximately 400 million years ago. So, when scientists find *Phacops* in rock layers anywhere on Earth, they know that the rock layers are approximately 400 million years old. A *Phacops* fossil is shown in **Figure 6.**

Ammonites as Index Fossils

Ammonites (AM uh NIETS), another index fossil, were marine mollusks similar to a modern squid. Ammonites were common in ancient oceans and lived in coiled shells. A genus of ammonites called *Tropites*, shown in **Figure 7,** is a common index fossil. *Tropites* lived between 230 million and 208 million years ago. So, it is an index fossil for that period of time. If scientists find *Tropites* in a rock layer, they know the rock layer formed between 230 and 208 million years ago.

Figure 7 Tropites *is a kind of coiled ammonite.* Tropites *existed for only about 20 million years, which makes it a good index fossil.*

SECTION Review

 7.3.c, 7.4.c, 7.4.e

Summary

- Fossils are the traces or remains of an organism that lived long ago.
- Fossils can be preserved in sedimentary rock, amber, asphalt, or ice and by petrification.
- Trace fossils are any naturally preserved evidence of animal activity. Tracks, burrows, and coprolites are examples of trace fossils.
- Scientists study fossils to determine how environments and organisms have changed over time.
- An index fossil is a fossil that can be used to establish the age of rock layers.

Using Vocabulary

1. Use *fossil, trace fossil,* and *index fossil* in separate sentences.

Understanding Concepts

2. **Listing** Describe five ways fossils can form.

3. **Applying** Explain how an index fossil can be used to date rock.

4. **Demonstrating** How can fossils be used to provide evidence of how life and environmental conditions on Earth have changed?

5. **Concluding** Explain why the fossil record contains an incomplete record of the history of life on Earth.

Critical Thinking

6. **Making Inferences** You find a fossil of clam A in rock layer A and a fossil of clam B in rock layer B. If rock layer B is older than rock layer A, what can you infer about the relative ages of clams A and B?

7. **Applying Concepts** What could you conclude if you found a fossil of a tropical plant in a rock that is in a polar climate?

Math Skills

8. **Solving Problems** If a scientist finds the remains of a plant between a rock layer that contains 400 million–year-old *Phacops* fossils and a rock layer that contains 230 million–year-old *Tropites* fossils, how old could the plant fossil be?

Challenge

9. **Applying Concepts** Imagine that you have discovered a dinosaur fossil in Antarctica. What types of information would you look for in order to determine the environment in which the dinosaur lived?

Internet Resources

For a variety of links related to this chapter, go to www.scilinks.org

Topic: Looking at Fossils
SciLinks code: HY70886

Earth's Changing Continents

Key Concept Movements of Earth's tectonic plates have affected climate, geographic connections, and the distribution of organisms.

▶ The surface of Earth on which we live is constantly moving. Sometimes, we feel this movement as earthquakes. But did you know that Earth's surface has changed so much during Earth's long history that the continents have changed locations?

Plate Tectonics

The thin, cool "skin" of Earth is called the *lithosphere.* This layer is broken into several smaller blocks called *tectonic plates.* These plates rest on a thick layer of solid rock called the *mantle.* Earth's mantle is solid, but it moves very slowly. As the mantle moves, it drags on the bottom of the cold tectonic plates lying on top of it. As a result, the tectonic plates move. Earth's surface currently has about 12 large plates and many small ones. Some of the large plates are labeled in **Figure 1.** Most plates move as fast as your fingernails grow—between 2 cm and 5 cm per year. Over geologic time scales, this movement can cause large cumulative effects—plate movements may total thousands of miles. The theory that explains how Earth's tectonic plates move and change shape is called **plate tectonics.**

Standards Check What is plate tectonics? 🐻 **7.4.a, 7.4.f**

Figure 1 Earth's Tectonic Plates

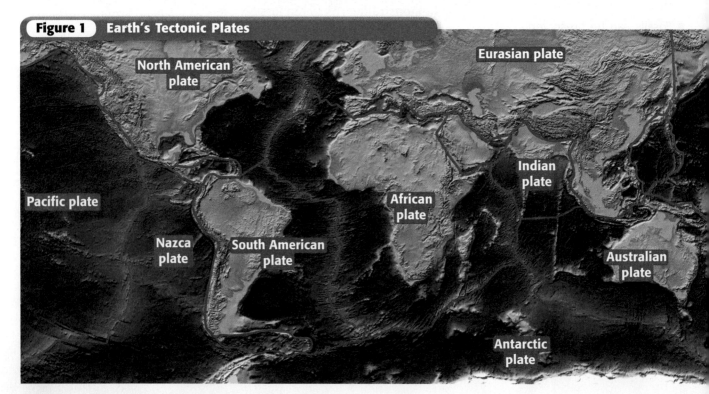

North American plate

Eurasian plate

Pacific plate

Nazca plate

South American plate

African plate

Indian plate

Australian plate

Antarctic plate

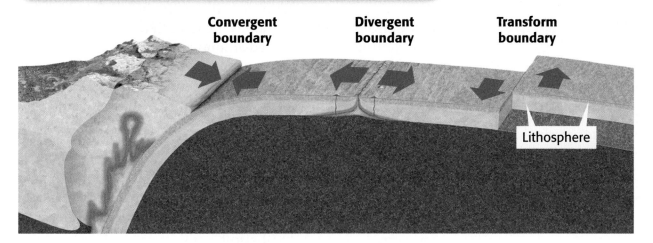

Figure 2 Tectonic Plate Boundaries

Convergent boundary   Divergent boundary   Transform boundary

Lithosphere

Where Tectonic Plates Meet

Tectonic plates may contain oceanic lithosphere, continental lithosphere, or both types of lithosphere. As tectonic plates move, they collide, separate, and grind past each other. Places where two or more tectonic plates meet are called *plate boundaries*. There are three main types of plate boundaries. The type of plate boundary that forms is a result of how the plates move relative to each other.

Convergent Boundaries

Plates move toward each other at a *convergent boundary*, as shown in **Figure 2.** If both plate edges are continental lithosphere, the rocks are forced together until they crumple to make great mountain belts. But if one plate is thin, dense oceanic lithosphere, it may sink downward into the mantle. As the plate sinks, surrounding rock may melt. Some of this molten rock rises to the surface and makes a line of volcanoes.

Divergent Boundaries

Plates move apart at a *divergent boundary*, as shown in **Figure 2.** This process forms a rift—a giant crack in the lithosphere. Volcanic eruptions fill the crack with lava that cools to form new oceanic lithosphere. If a rift tears apart a continent and then widens for millions of years, a new sea forms. The sea may gradually grow into a new ocean.

Transform Boundaries

Two plates slide horizontally past each other along a *transform boundary*, as shown in **Figure 2.** The movement of the plates can cause earthquakes in the area of a transform boundary. One of the world's most well known transform boundaries is the San Andreas fault, which cuts right across California.

plate tectonics (PLAYT tek TAHN iks) the theory that explains how large pieces of Earth's outermost layer, called *tectonic plates,* move and change shape

7.4.a Students know Earth processes today are similar to those that occurred in the past and slow geologic processes have large cumulative effects over long periods of time.

7.4.e Students know fossils provide evidence of how life and environmental conditions have changed.

7.4.f Students know how movements of Earth's continental and oceanic plates through time, with associated changes in climate and geographic connections, have affected the past and present distribution of organisms.

Tectonic Motion

Tectonic plates move slowly but may be in motion for millions of years. If a plate moves 4 cm per year, how many kilometers would it move in 1 million years? Record your work in your **Science Journal**.

continental drift (KAHN tuh NENT'l DRIFT) the hypothesis that a single large landmass broke up into smaller landmasses to form the continents, which then drifted to their present locations; the movement of continents

Continental Drift

As the tectonic plates move, they carry the continents along as passengers. **Continental drift** is the term that is used to describe how continents have moved around Earth's surface throughout Earth's history. As a continent moves across Earth's surface, it carries rocks and fossils with it. Sometimes, the rocks and fossils provide evidence of how the continent has moved.

Geologic Evidence of Continental Drift

Rocks in India show scratches and scars that formed when glaciers ground over their surfaces. So, at one time, India must have been covered by ice. Such a thick layer of ice could not form at sea level in the tropical zone where India is today. Southern Africa and Brazil also have ice-scratched rocks of the same age. This evidence suggests that at one time, the rocks were joined and were located in a colder climate. Scientists now know that India, South America, and Africa were part of a single landmass that was located near the South Pole about 280 million years ago.

Fossil Evidence of Continental Drift

A fossil of a little reptile called *Mesosaurus* is shown in **Figure 3.** Mesosaurs ate fishes in rivers and lakes about 270 million years ago. Today, *Mesosaurus* fossils are found in South America and southwestern Africa. These areas are separated by 3,000 miles of ocean. Mesosaurs could not have swum across this ocean. And there is no evidence of land bridges between these continents. Thus, mesosaurs must have lived at a time when the two continents were joined. This fossil evidence supports continental drift.

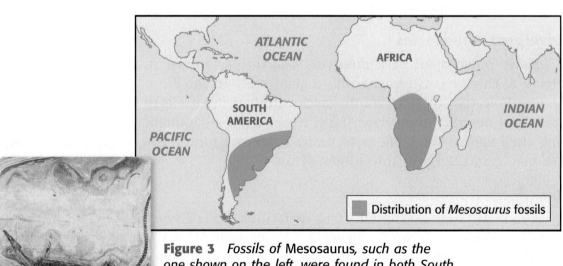

Figure 3 *Fossils of* Mesosaurus, *such as the one shown on the left, were found in both South America and southwestern Africa.*

History of Continental Drift

By putting together all of the evidence, scientists can draw maps that show how Earth's geography has changed over time. For example, all of Earth's continents made up a supercontinent called *Pangaea* (pan JEE uh) about 245 million years ago. At the same time, Earth also had a single super-ocean. Pangaea split into several new plates beginning about 200 million years ago. As the plates drifted apart, those new continents separated, and new oceans formed between them. The breakup of Pangaea is shown in **Figure 4.**

These huge changes moved rocks and fossils all over Earth. The rocks and fossils give scientists evidence of the plate movements. In addition, plate movements changed Earth's climate and affected *evolution*, or how populations of species have changed over time.

Changes in Climate

As continents moved, they changed the way land and sea were placed on Earth's surface. If continents moved toward the equator, they received more energy from the sun and developed warmer climates. Continental drift caused ocean currents and winds to flow differently. These changes affected heat flow. As a result, temperature and precipitation patterns around the planet changed.

For example, Antarctica was not frozen 40 million years ago. But as the other continents moved, Antarctica was left surrounded by the cold water near the South Pole. As cold water currents moved around Antarctica, the polar icecap formed. Antarctica slowly became the icy land we see today.

Changes in Life

When Pangaea split apart, the organisms living on each continent were separated. As their environments changed, the organisms that lived in those environments also changed. And as new oceans formed, changes also occurred in sea life. This explains why different organisms live on different continents. It also explains why fossils of the same organisms are found on different continents.

Standards Check How have tectonic plate motions affected the distribution of organisms? **7.4.f**

Figure 4 The Breakup of Pangaea

About 245 million years ago The continents were one giant landmass called Pangaea.

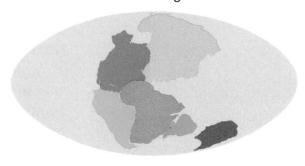

About 135 million years ago As Pangaea broke apart, the North Atlantic and Indian Oceans began to form.

About 65 million years ago The continents continued to drift apart toward their modern locations.

Today The continents continue to move at a rate of about 2 cm to 5 cm per year.

Case Study: The Panama Land Bridge

North and South America drifted close together about 3 million years ago. At that time, a narrow strip of land joined North and South America for the first time, as shown in **Figure 5.** This strip of land was called the Panama Land Bridge.

Changes in Life

Animals could now walk across the Panama Land Bridge. As they migrated, they competed with one another. Many animals became extinct, but successful ones flourished. Opossums and armadillos invaded North America, whereas camels and cats invaded South America. At the same time, creatures in the sea were separated by the new land bridge. Some populations of clams, corals, whales, and sea urchins evolved into separate species on the Pacific and Caribbean coasts of Panama.

Standards Check How did the formation of the Panama Land Bridge affect the distribution of organisms in the Americas? 🐻 **7.4.f**

Changes in Climate

The land bridge forced warm, tropical water that had once flowed between the continents to flow around the Gulf of Mexico and north past Florida. The new flow of water formed the Gulf Stream—a strong ocean current. The Gulf Stream changed the climate of western Europe by transporting warm water across the Atlantic Ocean. This water heats the air and makes climates milder.

Figure 5 *After North and South America were joined by the Panama Land Bridge, animals migrated across the bridge and ocean currents changed dramatically.*

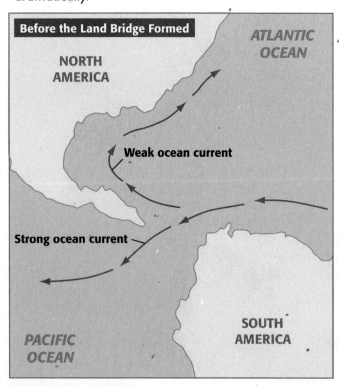

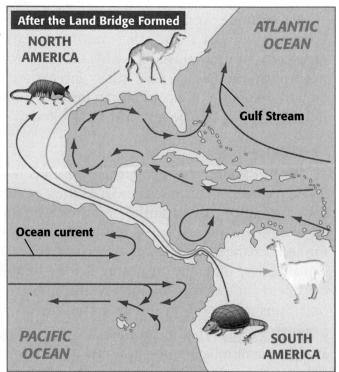

Quick Lab

Climate Changes

1. Each lab group will receive **two pictures** of environments on Earth. Describe each environment. Describe each climate, making estimates about the temperature and precipitation patterns in each environment.

2. Now, imagine that your two pictures represent the same place during different times in Earth's history. Discuss with your lab group how the climate in your first picture could have changed into the one shown in your second picture.

3. With your lab group, discuss the kinds of animal and plant life that might be found in each of your environments.

7.4.f

⏱ **20 min**

SECTION Review

7.4.a, 7.4.e, 7.4.f

Summary

- Earth's tectonic plates drift over time, moving continents and changing oceans.

- Evidence from rocks and fossils shows how Earth's continents have drifted and how climate and life have changed as a result.

- The breakup of Pangaea about 245 million years ago divided Earth's land into separate continents.

- The movement of continents alters climates by changing the patterns of air currents and ocean currents.

- The formation of the Panama Land Bridge is an example of how the movement of tectonic plates affects the distribution of organisms on Earth.

Using Vocabulary

1. Use *continental drift* and *plate tectonics* in separate sentences.

Understanding Concepts

2. **Describing** Name the three types of plate boundaries, and describe how plates move at each type of boundary.

3. **Summarizing** Name two types of evidence for continental drift, and give examples of each type.

4. **Identifying** How do tectonic plate movements affect climate?

5. **Applying** Describe a change in geographic connections that has affected the distribution of organisms during Earth's history.

Critical Thinking

6. **Applying Concepts** How do fossils of extinct species provide evidence of how life on Earth has changed?

7. **Analyzing Processes** Explain how the slow process of continental drift has a large effect over long periods of time.

Evaluating Assumptions

8. What assumption do scientists make when they state that if continents separate, the land animals on the continents are separated from each other?

Math Skills

9. **Solving Problems** The San Andreas fault moves 5 cm per year in some areas. Which of the following is more likely—that in 1,000 years the fault will move 50 m or that it will move 50 km?

Challenge

10. **Predicting Consequences** Imagine that the Panama Land Bridge eroded and water began flowing between North and South America. Predict changes that might occur in the climate and the distribution of organisms.

Internet Resources

For a variety of links related to this chapter, go to www.scilinks.org

Topic: Earth's Story; Plate Tectonics
SciLinks code: HY70450; HY71171

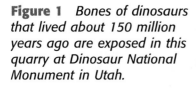

Time Marches On

Key Concept Life has changed through Earth's history as life-forms have developed, or evolved, and become extinct.

What You Will Learn

- The geologic time scale organizes Earth's history into intervals of time.
- Life first appeared on Earth more than 3.6 billion years ago.
- Life-forms changed as environmental changes happened during the Paleozoic, Mesozoic, and Cenozoic Eras.

Why It Matters

Understanding the history of life on Earth will help you understand how life-forms evolve.

Vocabulary

- geologic time scale
- extinction

READING STRATEGY

Outlining In your **Science Journal,** create an outline of the section. Use the headings from the section in your outline.

▶ Try to think of Earth's history in "fast forward." If you could watch Earth change in this way, you would see mountains rise up like wrinkles in fabric and quickly wear away. You would see life-forms appear, change, and disappear, or become extinct. In this section, you will learn that geologists must "fast forward" Earth's history when they write or talk about it. You will also learn about some incredible events in the history of life on Earth.

The Geologic Time Scale

Fossils of dinosaurs that lived 150 million years ago are shown in **Figure 1.** You may think that 150 million years is a very long time. But 150 million years is less than 3% of the time Earth has existed. All together, geologists study 4.6 billion years of Earth's history! To help keep track of this history, geologists have developed the geologic time scale, shown in **Figure 2.** The **geologic time scale** divides Earth's 4.6 billion–year history into distinct intervals of time. Each interval is distinct because life and environments have changed throughout Earth's history.

Standards Check Define the term *geologic time scale.* **7.4.g**

Figure 1 *Bones of dinosaurs that lived about 150 million years ago are exposed in this quarry at Dinosaur National Monument in Utah.*

7.4.d Students know that evidence from geologic layers and radioactive dating indicates Earth is approximately 4.6 billion years old and that life on this planet has existed for more than 3 billion years.
7.4.e Students know fossils provide evidence of how life and environmental conditions have changed.
7.4.g Students know how to explain significant developments and extinctions of plant and animal life on the geologic time scale.

Geologic Time Scale

Eon	Era	Period	Epoch	Millions of years ago
PHANEROZOIC	Cenozoic	Quaternary	Holocene	0.01
			Pleistocene	1.8
		Tertiary	Pliocene	5.3
			Miocene	23.0
			Oligocene	33.9
			Eocene	55.8
			Paleocene	65.5
	Mesozoic	Cretaceous		146
		Jurassic		200
		Triassic		251
	Paleozoic	Permian		299
		Carboniferous		359
		Devonian		416
		Silurian		444
		Ordovician		488
		Cambrian		542
PROTEROZOIC				
ARCHEAN	These three eons together are known as *Precambrian time* because they came before the Cambrian Period.			
HADEAN				4,600

Divisions of Time

Geologists have divided Earth's history into chunks of time, as shown on the geologic time scale in **Figure 2.** The largest divisions of geologic time are *eons* (EE AHNZ). Together, the first three eons of Earth's history are known as Precambrian time. The Phanerozoic Eon is divided into three *eras,* which are the second-largest divisions of geologic time. The three eras are further divided into *periods.* Periods are divided into *epochs* (EP uhks).

The boundaries between geologic time intervals usually correspond to significant changes in Earth's history. Most boundaries are defined by the appearance or disappearance of a significant number of species. Some boundaries are defined by the appearance or disappearance of index fossils. Other boundaries are defined by major changes in Earth's surface or climate, such as the advance or retreat of glaciers.

Figure 2 *The geologic time scale is divided into four major parts called eons. Dates given for intervals on the geologic time scale are approximate.* **What percentage of Earth's history does the Cenozoic Era represent?**

geologic time scale (JEE uh LAHJ ik TIEM SKAYL) the standard method used to divide Earth's long natural history into manageable parts

Figure 3 Hallucigenia, named for its "bizarre and dreamlike quality," was one of numerous marine organisms to make its appearance during the early Cambrian Period.

The Appearance and Disappearance of Organisms

At certain times in Earth's history, the number of different kinds of organisms has increased or decreased dramatically. These increases can happen because of increases in competition or environmental changes. *Hallucigenia,* shown in **Figure 3,** appeared in the Cambrian Period, when the number of different kinds of marine organisms greatly increased.

extinction (ek STINGK shuhn) the death of every member of a species

The diversity of organisms can decrease dramatically over a short period of time during a mass extinction. **Extinction** is the death of every member of a certain kind of organism. Gradual events, such as climate change and changes in ocean currents, can cause mass extinctions. Catastrophic events, such as the impact of an asteroid, can also cause mass extinctions.

Quick Lab

Timeline of Earth's History

7.4.d
7.4.g

1. Lay a **5 m strip of adding machine paper** flat on a hard surface. With a **pencil,** put a mark at the top of the paper. Near this mark write "Present time."

2. Using a **meterstick,** measure off 1 m sections from your first mark. At the first mark beyond "Present time," write "1 bya" (1 billion years ago), and at the second, write "2 bya." Continue marking 1 m sections until you have a mark labeled "4 bya."

3. Make a mark 4.6 m from "Present time," and label this mark "Earth forms, 4.6 bya."

4. Use a **colored pencil** to mark off and label the Cenozoic Era from the present time to 0.065 bya (6.5 cm from "Present time").

5. Use **another colored pencil** to mark off and label the Mesozoic Era from 0.065 bya to 0.25 bya (from the beginning of "Cenozoic Era" to 25 cm from the "Present time" mark).

6. Use **another colored pencil** to mark off and label the Paleozoic Era from 0.25 bya to 0.54 bya (from the beginning of "Mesozoic Era" to 54 cm from the "Present time" mark).

7. Use **another colored pencil** to mark off and label Precambrian time from 4.6 bya to 0.54 bya (from the beginning of "Paleozoic Era" to the "Earth forms, 4.6 bya" mark).

8. What percentage of the geologic time scale does Precambrian time represent?

9. Add to your timeline as you learn about events and life-forms in Precambrian time and in the Paleozoic, Mesozoic, and Cenozoic Eras.

 30 min

Precambrian Time—Life Develops

Precambrian time is the time from the formation of Earth 4.6 billion years ago to about 542 million years ago. Early Earth was very different from today's Earth. The early atmosphere did not contain oxygen as it does today. Intense radiation from the sun bombarded Earth's surface. Life on Earth began during this time. The first organisms appeared in Earth's oceans more than 3.6 billion years ago. These organisms were *prokaryotes*, or single-celled organisms that lack a nucleus.

Standards Check   When did life first appear on Earth?   7.4.d, 7.4.g

Life and Oxygen

Cyanobacteria, a kind of prokaryotic organism, were some of the first organisms on Earth. Some cyanobacteria are shown in **Figure 4.** Cyanobacteria use sunlight to produce their own food through a process called *photosynthesis*. During this process, the cyanobacteria make oxygen. Cyanobacteria began to release oxygen gas into the oceans and the air.

Oxygen began to accumulate in the atmosphere. Some of the oxygen formed a new layer of gas in the upper atmosphere. This gas, called *ozone*, absorbs harmful radiation from the sun, as shown in **Figure 5.** Before ozone formed, life existed only in the oceans and underground. The new ozone layer reduced the amount of radiation that reached Earth's surface. The decrease in radiation allowed life to survive on land.

Organisms That Are More Complex

After about 1 billion years, organisms that were larger and more complex than prokaryotes appeared in the fossil record. These organisms, known as *eukaryotes*, contain a nucleus and other structures in their cells. Eukaryotes may have evolved into more complex multicellular organisms.

A Fossil's Life
Can you discover how an organism lived by studying its fossil? Describe a day in the life of an extinct organism. Go to **go.hrw.com,** and type in the keyword HY7FOSW.

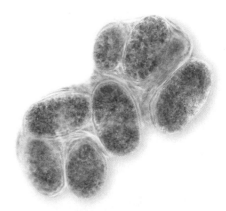

Figure 4 *Cyanobacteria are the simplest living organisms that use the sun's energy to produce their own food. They are still common on Earth and are very similar to the cyanobacteria that existed on Earth billions of years ago.*

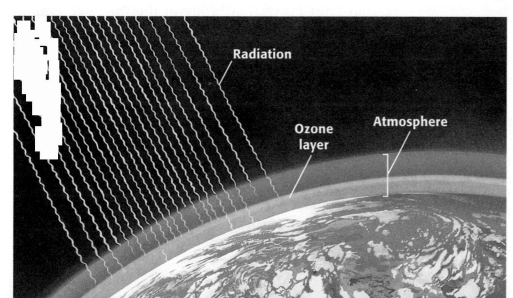

Radiation

Ozone layer

Atmosphere

Figure 5 *Oxygen in the atmosphere formed a layer of ozone, which absorbs harmful radiation from the sun.*

The Paleozoic Era

The Paleozoic Era (PAY lee OH ZOH ik ER uh) began about 542 million years ago and ended about 251 million years ago. The word *Paleozoic* comes from Greek words that mean "ancient life." When scientists first named this era, they thought it held the earliest forms of life. Scientists now know that earlier forms of life existed, but less is known about those life-forms. Before the Paleozoic Era, most organisms lived in the oceans and left few fossils.

The Cambrian Explosion

The Cambrian Period was the first period in the Paleozoic Era. Many marine life-forms appeared during this period in what scientists call the "Cambrian explosion." This event was not an actual explosion. It was the appearance of many new and more-complex life-forms. For the first time, some had preservable hard parts such as shells and exoskeletons.

Life on Land

Rocks from the Paleozoic Era are rich in fossils of animals such as sponges, corals, snails, squids, and trilobites. Fishes, the earliest animals with backbones, also appeared during this era. During the middle of this era, plants, fungi, and animals colonized land.

By the end of the era, forests of giant ferns, horsetails, and conifers covered much of Earth. All major plant groups except for flowering plants appeared during this era. The plants provided food and shelter for animals. Fossils indicate that arthropods such as scorpions were the first land animals. Large salamander-like animals also evolved. Near the end of the era, reptiles and insects appeared. **Figure 6** is an artist's depiction of life in the Paleozoic Era.

The Permian Extinction

The largest known mass extinction was the Permian extinction. It took place about 251 million years ago, at the end of the Permian Period of the Paleozoic Era. Earth's continents had joined to form Pangaea, and shallow inland seas had disappeared. As many as 90% of marine species and 78% of land species had become extinct. The fossil record shows that groups such as reptiles and amphibians survived the Permian extinction.

Figure 6 *Organisms that first appeared in the Paleozoic Era include reptiles, amphibians, fishes, worms, and ferns.*

The Mesozoic Era

The *Mesozoic Era* (MES oh ZOH ik ER uh) began about 251 million years ago. *Mesozoic* comes from Greek words meaning "middle life." Scientists think that the reptiles that survived the Permian extinction evolved into many reptile species in the Mesozoic Era. Therefore, the Mesozoic Era is commonly called the *Age of Reptiles*.

Life in the Mesozoic Era

Dinosaurs are the most well-known reptiles that lived during the Mesozoic Era. Dinosaurs dominated Earth for about 150 million years. Some had unique adaptations, such as ducklike bills for feeding or large spines on their bodies for defense. In addition to dinosaurs on land, giant marine reptiles swam in the oceans. The first birds also appeared during the Mesozoic Era. Scientists think that some dinosaurs were the ancestors of birds. The first mammals also appeared during the Mesozoic Era.

The most important plants during the early part of the Mesozoic Era were conifers, which formed large forests. Flowering plants appeared later in the Mesozoic Era. Some of the organisms of the Mesozoic Era are illustrated in **Figure 7.**

The Cretaceous-Tertiary Extinction

The Mesozoic Era ended about 65 million years ago. Around this time, all of the dinosaurs and about half of the animal and plant species became extinct. This event is called the *Cretaceous-Tertiary* (or *K-T) extinction* because it defines the boundary between the Cretaceous and Tertiary Periods. Scientists find evidence for this mass extinction in the disappearance of many types of fossils from the fossil record during this time.

What happened? According to one hypothesis, an object from our solar system hit Earth. The impact formed giant dust clouds and enough heat to cause worldwide fires. The dust and smoke blocked out some sunlight and caused many plants to die out. Without enough plants to eat, the plant-eating dinosaurs died out. As a result, the meat-eating dinosaurs that fed on the plant-eating dinosaurs died.

Standards Check What fossil evidence is there for the Cretaceous-Tertiary extinction? 🐻 **7.4.e, 7.4.g**

Figure 7 *The Mesozoic Era ended with the mass extinction of many of the large animals, such as the ankylosaur and the aquatic plesiosaur shown above.*

Figure 8 *Many types of mammals, including humans, appeared during the Cenozoic Era.*

The Cenozoic Era

The *Cenozoic Era* (SEN uh ZOH ik ER uh) began about 65 million years ago and continues today. *Cenozoic* comes from Greek words meaning "recent life." Scientists have more information about the Cenozoic Era than about any of the previous eras. Because Cenozoic rocks formed on top of rocks from previous eras, many Cenozoic fossils are closer to Earth's surface. The closer the fossils are to the surface, the more likely they are to be found.

During the Cenozoic Era, many kinds of mammals, birds, insects, and flowering plants appeared. Some organisms that appeared in the Cenozoic Era are shown in **Figure 8.**

The Age of Mammals

The Cenozoic Era is sometimes called the *Age of Mammals.* Mammals have dominated the Cenozoic Era the way reptiles dominated the Mesozoic Era. Early Cenozoic mammals were small forest dwellers. Larger mammals appeared later in the era. Some of these larger mammals had long legs for running, teeth that were specialized for eating different kinds of food, and large brains. Cenozoic mammals have included mastodons, saber-toothed cats, camels, giant ground sloths, and horses. Humans appeared very late in the Cenozoic Era.

Standards Check What significant organisms appeared during the Cenozoic Era? 🐻 **7.4.g**

The Cenozoic Era Today

The environment and landscapes that we see around us today developed during the Cenozoic Era. For example, the Alps and the Himalayas formed during this era. The climate has also changed many times during the Cenozoic Era. Earth's history includes some lengths of time called *ice ages,* during which the climate was very cold. During the ice ages, ice sheets and glaciers extended from Earth's poles. To survive, many organisms migrated toward the equator. Other organisms adapted to the cold or became extinct.

We are currently living in the Cenozoic Era. When will this era end? No one knows. In the future, geologists might draw the line at a time when life on Earth again undergoes major changes.

Summary

- The geologic time scale divides Earth's 4.6 billion–year history into time intervals. These intervals include eons, eras, periods, and epochs.

- At certain times in Earth's history, the number of different kinds of organisms has increased or decreased dramatically.

- Life on Earth developed more than 3.6 billion years ago, during Precambrian time. After cyanobacteria added oxygen to the atmosphere, more-complex forms of life evolved.

- A variety of marine organisms appeared at the beginning of the Paleozoic Era in what is called the Cambrian explosion. Near the end of the Paleozoic Era, the Permian extinction resulted in the disappearance of many organisms from the fossil record.

- Dinosaurs dominated Earth during the Mesozoic Era. They all became extinct during the Cretaceous-Tertiary extinction.

- Mammals have dominated the Cenozoic Era. Modern humans appeared during this era.

Using Vocabulary

1 Write an original definition for *extinction* and *geologic time scale.*

Understanding Concepts

2 **Listing**   What are the major types of time intervals represented by the geologic time scale?

3 **Describing**   Explain how cyanobacteria were important to the development of life on Earth.

4 **Listing**   What kinds of environmental changes can cause mass extinctions?

5 **Describing**   Describe the types of life that were common in the Paleozoic, Mesozoic, and Cenozoic Eras.

6 **Concluding**   How do scientists study life-forms that are extinct?

7 **Applying**   What environmental changes may have caused the Cretaceous-Tertiary extinction? What may have caused the changes?

8 **Identifying**   About how much time elapsed between the formation of Earth and the appearance of the first life-forms?

Critical Thinking

9 **Making Inferences**   Name three possible reasons why less is known about Precambrian life-forms than is known about more recent life.

10 **Analyzing Ideas**   Why do scientists think the first organisms did not need oxygen to survive?

Math Skills

INTERPRETING GRAPHICS   Use the figure below to answer the next question.

Phanerozoic Eon   Hadean Eon

Proterozoic Eon   Archean Eon

11 **Making Calculations**   On the Earth-history clock shown, 1 h equals 383 million years, and 1 min equals 6.4 million years. In millions of years, how much more time is represented by the Proterozoic Eon than by the Phanerozoic Eon?

Challenge

12 **Making Comparisons**   Describe a future event or sequence of events that might mark the end of the Cenozoic Era.

Internet Resources

For a variety of links related to this chapter, go to www.scilinks.org

Topic: Geologic Time; Geologic Time Scale

SciLinks code: HY70668; HY70669

Skills Practice Lab

Interpreting Fossil Finds

At a remote desert site, a scientist searched for fossils in two layers of sedimentary rock. In addition to identifying each fossil, she recorded its location by using map coordinates consisting of a letter and a number. She also noted whether the fossil was found in the upper or lower rock layer. The data she collected are shown in Table 1.

Table 1	Locations of Fossils Uncovered at Site		
Rock layer	**Shark**	**Crab**	**Fern**
Upper layer	A4, B1, C2, C5, D3, E1	A5, B6, C6, D4, F1, F3	B9, E8, H5, H9, I2, J7
Lower layer	A1, B4, D2, D7, E5, E10, G3, G6, I2, J5	G7, G9, H10, I6, J7	I8, J9, J10

Procedure

1. Use your graph paper to create two maps of the fossil site, similar to Table 2. Each map will be formed by a grid pattern made up of 10 rows and 10 columns. The two maps should be the same size.

Table 2	Location of Fossils in Rock Layer								
	A	B	C	D	E	F	G	H	I	J
1										
2										
3										
4										
5										
6										
7										
8										
9										
10										

DO NOT WRITE IN BOOK

7.4.e Students know fossils provide evidence of how life and environmental conditions have changed.

Investigation and Experimentation
7.7.d Construct scale models, maps, and appropriately labeled diagrams to communicate scientific knowledge (e.g., motion of Earth's plates and cell structure).

2 Use letters *A* through *J* to label the columns along the top of each grid. Use numbers 1 through 10 to label the rows along the side of each grid.

3 Label one grid "Location of Fossils in the Upper Rock Layer." Label the other grid "Location of Fossils in the Lower Rock Layer."

4 Begin with the map of the upper rock layer. For each fossil, mark a letter in pencil (*S* for a shark fossil, *C* for a crab fossil, and *F* for a fern fossil) in the square that corresponds to the coordinates listed in Table 1.

5 Repeat step 4 on your other map for the lower rock layer.

Analyze the Results

6 **Classifying** Describe the environment in which each organism was likely to have lived.

7 **Examining Data** Examine the map of the fossils found in the upper layer. According to the fossil distribution, which part of this site was probably underwater when these organisms died? How can you tell? Color this area of your map blue.

8 **Examining Data** Examine the map of the fossils found in the lower layer. Which part of this site was probably underwater when these organisms died? How can you tell? Color this area blue.

Draw Conclusions

9 **Drawing Conclusions** Which is older, the upper layer or the lower layer of sedimentary rock? Explain your answer.

10 **Drawing Conclusions** Which came first in Earth's history, the organisms and environment in the upper layer or those in the lower layer of sedimentary rock? Explain your answer.

11 **Interpreting Information** Before mapping the fossil finds, one scientist thought that sea level had risen between the time that the two rock layers formed. Did the fossil distribution support her hypothesis? Explain your answer.

Big Idea Question

12 **Applying Conclusions** How can fossils provide evidence of how environmental conditions change over time?

Horseshoe crab fossil

Fossilized shark teeth

Fern fossil

Science Skills Activity

Scientific Methods | Research | Data Analysis | Models, Maps & Diagrams

Investigation and Experimentation

7.7.d Construct scale models, maps, and appropriately labeled diagrams to communicate scientific knowledge (e.g., motion of Earth's plates and cell structure).

Constructing Models

▶ Tutorial

The following general instructions will show you one way to understand and model a process. You can also communicate scientific knowledge to others this way.

1 **Research** Read about the process in which you are interested. Start with your textbook and encyclopedias. Then, find written information in other places, including your library and the Internet. Be sure that your information comes from reliable sources. Take notes as you read to help you understand and remember what you have learned. Do more research with maps, videos, and other resources. If possible, talk with someone knowledgeable who can tell you about the process.

2 **Make a Model** Make a model of your process. A model could be
- a physical model such as a globe, a map, or a sculpture
- a mathematical model such as a graph or an equation

3 **Use the Model for Understanding** Use your model to better understand the process that you are studying by using the model to simulate movement or interactions.

4 **Communicate** Use your model to explain the process to another person.

▶ You Try It!

Learn about the breakup of the supercontinent Pangaea, which started about 245 million years ago. Then, make a model of the process and communicate your results to others.

1 **Research** Research continental drift and the breakup of Pangaea.

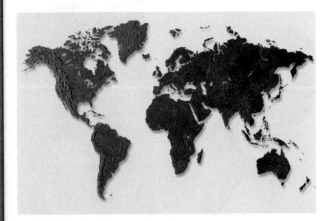

2 **Make a Model** Gather a copy of a world map that shows the Himalayas, a pencil, and a pair of scissors. Label Africa, Antarctica, Australia, Eurasia, India, North America, and South America. Cut out each continent. Cut India from Eurasia along the Himalayas.

3 **Use the Model for Understanding**
- Starting with the continents in their current positions, move them in ways that seem to make their coastlines fit together.
- Starting with the continents in the positions they occupied 245 million years ago in Pangaea, move them away from each other into their present locations.

4 **Communicate** Using your model of the continents, explain to a partner how Pangaea changed into the continents on Earth today. Then, listen to your partner's explanation of the same process. Include in your discussions evidence for continental drift and how this process affected life and climate.

Chapter Summary

go.hrw.com
SUPER SUMMARY
KEYWORD: HY7FOSS

The Big Idea Evidence from rocks allows us to understand the evolution of life on Earth.

Section	Vocabulary

1 Looking at Fossils

Key Concept Fossils provide evidence of how life and environmental conditions have changed.

- Evidence of past life is preserved as fossils in sedimentary rock and in other materials.
- The study of fossils reveals information about how Earth's environments and organisms have changed.
- Index fossils can be used to date rock layers.

Fossils provide evidence about organisms from Earth's past.

fossil p. 264
trace fossil p. 266
index fossil p. 268

2 Earth's Changing Continents

Key Concept Movements of Earth's tectonic plates have affected climate, geographic connections, and the distribution of organisms.

- Earth's continents have moved around Earth's surface throughout Earth's history and have only recently arrived at their current locations.
- Rocks and fossils provide evidence of continental drift. They also provide evidence of the changes in life and climate that have occurred during Earth's history.

Earth's continents move over Earth's surface.

plate tectonics p. 270
continental drift p. 272

3 Time Marches On

Key Concept Life has changed through Earth's history as life-forms have developed, or evolved, and become extinct.

- The geologic time scale organizes Earth's history into intervals of time.
- Life first appeared on Earth more than 3.6 billion years ago.
- Life-forms changed as environmental changes happened during the Paleozoic, Mesozoic, and Cenozoic Eras.

Many life-forms have developed and become extinct during Earth's history.

geologic time scale p. 276
extinction p. 278

Chapter Review

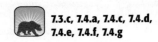

7.3.c, 7.4.a, 7.4.c, 7.4.d,
7.4.e, 7.4.f, 7.4.g

Organize

Four-Corner Fold   Review the FoldNote that you created at the beginning of the chapter. Add to or correct the FoldNote based on what you have learned.

Using Vocabulary

1 **Academic Vocabulary**   In the sentence "Fossils provide evidence of how life has changed," what does the word *evidence* mean?
   a. information presented in a legal proceeding
   b. information showing whether an idea is true or valid
   c. a separation or division
   d. a visual aid

Use a term from the chapter to correct each sentence below.

2 Continental drift is the method used to divide Earth's history into manageable parts.

3 The death of every member of a species is called an index fossil.

Understanding Concepts

Multiple Choice

4 Which of the following is a trace fossil?
   a. an insect preserved in amber
   b. a mammoth frozen in ice
   c. wood replaced by minerals
   d. a dinosaur footprint

5 The largest divisions of geologic time are called
   a. periods.
   b. eras.
   c. eons.
   d. epochs.

6 The first life on Earth appeared in
   a. Precambrian time.
   b. the Paleozoic Era.
   c. the Mesozoic Era.
   d. the Cenozoic Era.

7 In which time period are we currently living?
   a. Precambrian time
   b. the Paleozoic Era
   c. the Mesozoic Era
   d. the Cenozoic Era

8 Movements of continental and oceanic plates during Earth's history have
   a. affected the distribution of organisms.
   b. caused changes in climate.
   c. caused changes in geographic connections.
   d. All of the above

9 At a divergent plate boundary, tectonic plates
   a. move toward each other.
   b. slide horizontally against each other.
   c. move apart from each other.
   d. crumple up to form mountain ranges.

Short Answer

10 **Describing**   Describe three processes by which fossils form.

11 **Summarizing**   Explain two ways in which scientists use fossils to determine environmental change.

12 **Listing**   List two important groups of organisms that appeared during each time interval: Precambrian time, the Paleozoic Era, the Mesozoic Era, and the Cenozoic Era.

13 **Describing**   Describe the event that some scientists think caused the mass extinction at the end of the Mesozoic Era.

14 **Listing**   How long has life existed on Earth?

15 **Classifying**   Give one example of how continental drift has caused a change in geographic connections and one example of how continental drift has caused a change in climate.

16 **Describing**   Give an example of how continental drift has affected the distribution of organisms during Earth's history.

Writing Skills

17 **Writing from Research**   Find out more about *Mesosaurus*, and write a one-page report about this reptile.

Critical Thinking

18 Concept Mapping Use the following terms to create a concept map: *geologic time scale, fossils, rock record, eons, eras, periods, epochs, Earth's history, life on Earth,* and *environmental conditions.*

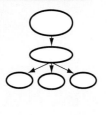

19 Applying Concepts Identify how fossil evidence supports plate tectonics and continental drift.

20 Analyzing Processes Explain how the breakup of Pangaea affected climate and organisms.

21 Making Inferences How does the fossil record provide evidence for the Cretaceous-Tertiary extinction?

INTERPRETING GRAPHICS The chart below shows data about fossilized teeth that were found within a series of rock layers. Use the chart below to answer the next two questions.

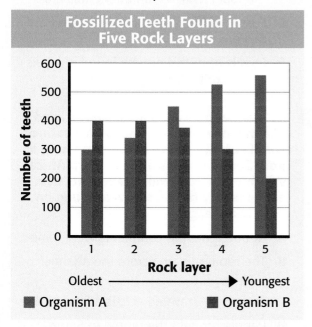

Fossilized Teeth Found in Five Rock Layers

22 Evaluating Data Describe the changes in the populations of organisms A and B that are suggested by the evidence in the chart.

23 Forming Hypotheses Develop a hypothesis to explain these population changes.

24 Identifying Relationships Describe conditions that can cause the number of species to increase dramatically and conditions that can cause the number of species to decrease dramatically.

25 Identifying Relationships How does the Cretaceous-Tertiary extinction relate to the Age of Mammals?

26 Identifying Relationships Two undisturbed rock layers are being studied by paleontologists. One of the layers is directly on top of the other, and both layers contain fossils. Describe the relative ages of the layers, and tell which layer is likely to contain fossils of life-forms that are similar to living organisms.

Math Skills

INTERPRETING GRAPHICS Use the diagram of a portion of the geologic time scale below to answer the following question.

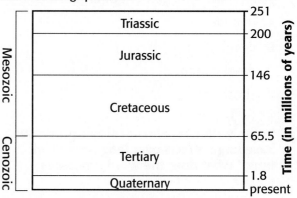

27 Making Calculations Which period shown in the diagram was the longest? How many years did that period last?

Challenge

28 Applying Concepts Identify a type of organism that is found in the fossil record of a different geologic era but that is still living on Earth today. Also identify a type of organism that has become extinct. Compare the two organisms, and try to explain why one has survived and the other has become extinct.

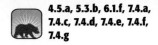
REVIEWING ACADEMIC VOCABULARY

1 Which of the following words is the closest in meaning to the word *significant*?

A minor

B signify

C identify

D important

2 In the sentence "Fossils provide evidence of how life on Earth has changed," what does the word *evidence* mean?

A data showing whether an idea is true

B signal of changes to come

C method of investigation

D description of a situation

3 Which of the following words means "the geographic arrangement of organisms"?

A remote

B distribution

C development

D classification

4 In the sentence "Slow geologic processes have large effects over long periods of time," what does the word *processes* mean?

A prepares, treats, or converts

B series of occurrences that produce change

C moves forward in an orderly way

D parts that project from the main body

5 Which of the following words means "a repeating series of changes"?

A experiment

B effect

C cycle

D occurrence

REVIEWING CONCEPTS

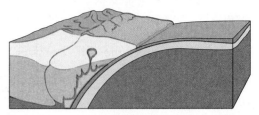

6 What type of plate boundary is shown in the diagram above?

A mantle boundary

B divergent boundary

C transform boundary

D convergent boundary

7 Why are fossils from the Cenozoic Era, which began 65 million years ago, the easiest to find?

A The number of species greatly increased during this era.

B Life on Earth, in the form of cyanobacteria, began during this era.

C Fossils of the largest creatures are from this era.

D Fossils from this era are found in layers closest to Earth's surface.

8 A small reptile called *Mesosaurus* lived 260 million years ago and is now extinct. Fossils of this reptile have been found in both South America and southern Africa. Which of the following statements best explains why the fossils were found on both continents?

A At one time, the continents were joined.

B The reptile swam across the Atlantic Ocean.

C The reptile traveled across a land bridge.

D People brought the reptile to South America.

9 Which of the following life-forms dominated the Mesozoic Era?

A mammals

B dinosaurs

C marine creatures

D one-celled organisms

10 When did the first organisms most likely appear on Earth?

A 251 million years ago

B 542 million years ago

C 3.6 billion years ago

D 4.6 billion years ago

11 Which of the following provides evidence that environmental conditions on Earth have changed?

A A fossilized footprint is found in lava rock.

B An insect fossil is found in amber.

C A marine fossil is found on a mountaintop.

D A dinosaur fossil is found in sedimentary rock.

12 If two tectonic plates form a divergent boundary on a continent and slowly move apart for millions of years, which of the following is most likely to happen?

A A new ocean will develop.

B A fault line will be created.

C A line of volcanoes will appear.

D A mountain chain will form.

13 Every year, Earth's lithospheric plates move between 2 cm and 5 cm. What causes these plates to move?

A currents in the ocean

B earthquakes in the ocean

C movement in Earth's mantle

D volcanoes under Earth's crust

14 The diagram above shows the water cycle. What process in the water cycle is found at point 2 in the diagram?

A evaporation

B transpiration

C runoff

D condensation

15 Which of these processes slowly changes Earth's surface?

A landslide

B erosion

C earthquake

D volcanic eruption

16 The San Andreas fault is a major fault line in California. Why does this fault exist?

A It is the transform boundary of tectonic plates.

B A strong earthquake split the tectonic plate.

C It is the convergent boundary of tectonic plates.

D There are volcanoes under the tectonic plate.

Standards Assessment

Science in Action

Scientific Discoveries

Feathered Dinosaurs

In 1996, a Chinese farmer broke open a rock that he found in an ancient dry lake. What he found inside the rock became one of the most exciting paleontological discoveries of the 20th century. Preserved inside were the remains of a dinosaur. The dinosaur had a large head; powerful jaws; sharp, jagged teeth; and, most importantly, a row of featherlike structures along its backbone.

Scientists named the dinosaur *Sinosauropteryx,* or "Chinese dragon wing." Since the discovery of *Sinosauropteryx,* other fossils have been found that provide evidence that some dinosaurs had feathers. These discoveries lend support to the hypothesis that birds and dinosaurs shared a common ancestor.

Place to Visit

La Brea Tar Pits

Fierce roars rumble through the air. A hungry saber-toothed cat has pounced on a young bison. Suddenly, the roars turn into panicked yowls. The big cat is stuck in asphalt! Along with the bison, she will die of exhaustion and thirst while trying to free herself.

Scenes like this happened 25,000 years ago in what is now Los Angeles, California. Natural tar deposits trapped millions of animals during the late Pleistocene Epoch. You can visit the La Brea Tar Pits and see fossils of these animals at the Page Museum. Visitors to the La Brea Tar Pits in Los Angeles can see fossils that have been discovered there, can watch scientists at work, and can watch a film that shows what scientists think downtown Los Angeles looked like when saber-toothed cats ruled!

Language Arts

Paleontologists often give dinosaurs names that describe something unusual about the animal's head, body, feet, or size. The names have Greek or Latin roots. Research the names of some dinosaurs, and find out what the names mean. In your **Science Journal,** create a list of dinosaur names and their meanings.

Math ACTiViTY

Since 1906, fossils of 231 species of vertebrate animals, 159 species of plants, and 234 species of invertebrate animals have been identified at the La Brea Tar Pits. What is the ratio of vertebrate to invertebrate fossil species that have been found? What is the ratio of plant to animal species? Show your work in your **Science Journal.**

Lizzie May

Amateur Paleontologist For Lizzie May, summer vacations have meant trips into the Alaskan wilderness with her stepfather, geologist and paleontologist Kevin May. The purpose of these trips has not been merely for fun. Instead, Kevin and Lizzie have been exploring the Alaskan wilderness for the remains of ancient life—dinosaurs, in particular.

At age 22, Lizzie May has gained the reputation of being Alaska's most famous young paleontologist. It is a reputation that is well deserved. To date, Lizzie has collected hundreds of dinosaur bones and located important sites of dinosaur, bird, and mammal tracks. In her honor and as a result of her hard work in the field, scientists named the skeleton of a dinosaur discovered by the Mays "Lizzie." "Lizzie" is a duckbill dinosaur, or hadrosaur, that lived approximately 90 million years ago. "Lizzie" is the oldest dinosaur ever found in Alaska and one of the earliest known duckbill dinosaurs in North America.

The Mays have made other, equally exciting discoveries. On one summer trip, Kevin and Lizzie located six dinosaur and bird track sites that dated back 97 million to 144 million years. On another trip, the Mays found a fossilized marine reptile more than 200 million years old—an ichthyosaur—that had to be removed with the help of a military helicopter. You have to wonder what other exciting adventures are in store for Lizzie and Kevin!

Social Studies ACTiViTY

Lizzie May is not the only young person to have made a mark in dinosaur paleontology. Using the Internet or another source, research people such as Bucky Derflinger, Johnny Maurice, Brad Riney, and Wendy Sloboda, who as young people made contributions to the field of dinosaur study. Write a short essay in your **Science Journal** summarizing your findings.

Internet Resources

- To learn more about careers in science, visit **www.scilinks.org** and enter the SciLinks code HY70225.

- To learn more about these Science in Action topics, visit **go.hrw.com** and type in the keyword HY7FOSF.

- Check out articles related to this chapter by visiting **go.hrw.com**. Just type in the keyword HY7FOSC.

Improving Comprehension

Graphic Organizers are important visual tools that can help you organize information and improve your reading comprehension. The Graphic Organizer below is called a *concept map*. Instructions for creating other types of Graphic Organizers are located in the **Study Skills** section of the Appendix.

How to Make a Concept Map

1 Identify main ideas from the text, and write the ideas as short phrases or single words.

2 Select a main concept. Place this concept at the top or center of a piece of paper.

3 Place other ideas under or around the main concept based on their relationship to the main concept. Draw a circle around each idea.

4 Draw lines between the concepts, and add linking words to connect the ideas.

When to Use a Concept Map

Concept maps are useful when you are trying to identify how several ideas are connected to a main concept. Concept maps may be based on vocabulary terms or on main topics from the text. The concept map below shows how the important concepts of this chapter are related. As you read about science, look for terms that can be organized in a concept map.

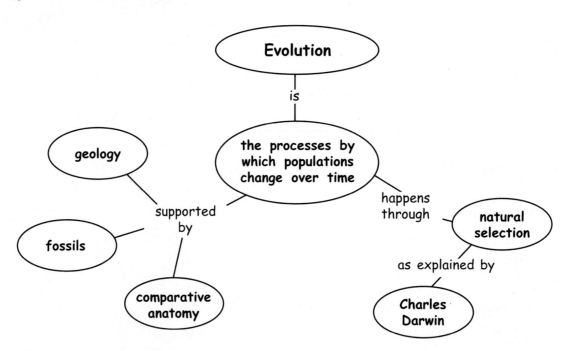

You Try It!

This Reading Strategy can also be used within the chapter that you are about to read. Practice making your own *concept map* as directed in the Reading Strategy for Section **1**. Record your work in your **Science Journal.**

Unpacking the Standards

The information below "unpacks" the standards by breaking them down into basic parts. The higher-level, academic vocabulary is highlighted and defined to help you understand the language of the standards. "What It Means" restates the standards as simply as possible.

California Standard	Academic Vocabulary	What It Means
7.3.a Students know both genetic **variation** and environmental **factors** are causes of evolution and **diversity** of organisms.	**variation** (VER ee AY shuhn) a difference in the usual form or function **factor** (FAK tuhr) a condition or event that brings about or contributes to a result **diversity** (duh VUHR suh tee) variety	Differences in the genes of individuals and the ways in which the natural surroundings affect organisms have caused living things to change and have caused many kinds of living things to develop on Earth.
7.3.b Students know the reasoning used by Charles Darwin in reaching his **conclusion** that natural **selection** is the mechanism of evolution.	**conclusion** (kuhn KLOO zhuhn) an idea developed from reasoning and investigating **selection** (suh LEK shuhn) the process of choosing	You must know what information and thought processes led Charles Darwin to form the idea that living things change over time because not all organisms survive and reproduce.
7.3.c Students know how independent lines of **evidence** from geology, fossils, and comparative anatomy provide the bases for the theory of evolution.	**evidence** (EV uh duhns) information showing whether an idea or belief is true or valid	The theory of evolution is based on several kinds of information that was gathered by studying rocks and fossils and by comparing the bodies of living and extinct organisms.
7.3.d Students know how to **construct** a simple branching diagram to classify living groups of organisms by shared **derived** characteristics and how to **expand** the diagram to include fossil organisms.	**construct** (kuhn STRUHKT) to build; to make from parts **derived** (di RIEVD) gotten from something else **expand** (ek SPAND) to make more detailed; to enlarge	You must know how to draw a simple branching diagram to sort living things into groups based on features that the organisms share. You must also know how to add extinct organisms to the branching diagram.
7.3.e Students know that extinction of a species **occurs** when the environment changes and the **adaptive** characteristics of a species are **insufficient** for its **survival**.	**occur** (uh KUHR) to happen **adaptive** (uh DAP tiv) able to adjust to changes **insufficient** (IN suh FISH uhnt) not enough **survival** (suhr VIE vuhl) the continuing to live or exist	Extinction of a species happens when the surroundings of a species change and the species does not have the right traits to allow it to survive.

The following identifies other standards that are covered in this chapter and where you can go to see them unpacked: **7.4.f** (Chapter 9)

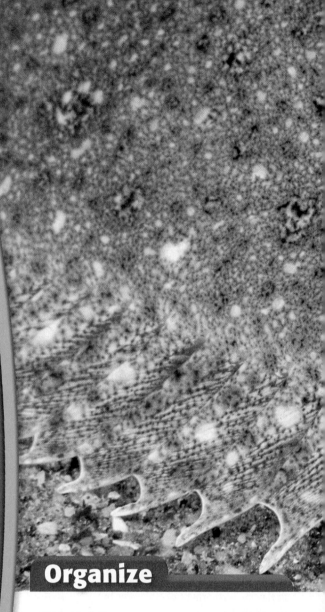

10

The Evolution of Living Things

The Big Idea

Biological evolution explains how populations change over time.

 California Standards

Focus on Life Sciences
7.3 Biological evolution accounts for the diversity of species developed through gradual processes over many generations. (Sections 1, 2, and 3)
7.4 Evidence from rocks allows us to understand the evolution of life on Earth. (Section 3)

Investigation and Experimentation
7.7 Scientific progress is made by asking meaningful questions and conducting careful investigations. (Science Skills Activity)

Math
7.1.2 Number Sense

English–Language Arts
7.1.3 Reading
7.2.5 Writing

About the Photo

Can you find two eyes and a mouth in this photo? The eyes and mouth belong to an adult flounder. Adult flounders swim on their sides and have both eyes on one side of their body. These characteristics allow flounders to lie flat and still see all of their surroundings. Flounders also look like the sandy bottoms of coastal areas. These adaptations help flounders survive in their environment.

Organize

Tri-Fold

Before you read this chapter, create the FoldNote entitled "Tri-Fold." Write what you know about evolution in the column labeled "Know." Then, write what you want to know about evolution in the column labeled "Want." As you read the chapter, write what you learn about evolution in the column labeled "Learn."

Instructions for creating FoldNotes are located in the Study Skills section on p. 582 of the Appendix.

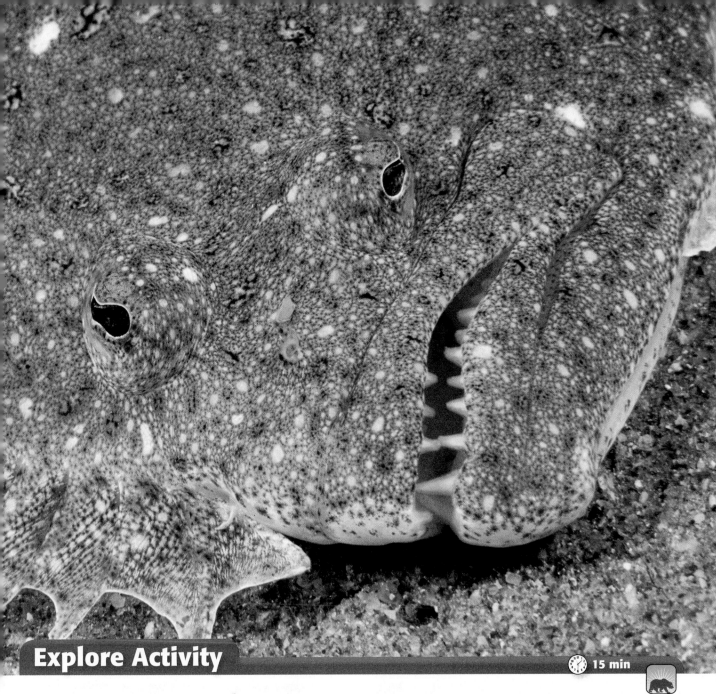

Explore Activity

🕐 **15 min**

Modeling Successful Traits

In this activity, you will see how traits can affect the success of an organism in a particular environment.

Procedure

1. Count out **25 colored marshmallows** and **25 white marshmallows.**

2. Ask your partner to look away while you spread out the marshmallows on a **white cloth.** Do not make a pattern with the marshmallows. Now, ask your partner to turn around and pick the first marshmallow that he or she sees.

3. Repeat step 2 ten times.

Analysis

7.3.a
7.7.c

4. How many white marshmallows did your partner pick? How many colored marshmallows did he or she pick?

5. What did the marshmallows and the cloth represent in your investigation? What effect did the color of the cloth have?

6. When an organism blends into its environment, the organism is *camouflaged*. How does this activity model camouflaged organisms in the wild? What are some weaknesses of this model?

Change over Time

Key Concept Independent lines of evidence from geology, fossils, and comparative anatomy provide the bases for the theory of evolution.

▶ What makes a frog a frog? Is it a frog's bulging eyes, its long hind legs, its croak, or the color of its skin?

Once you start to think about frogs, you realize that frogs differ in many ways. These differences set one kind of frog apart from another. The frogs in **Figure 1** look different from each other, yet they may live in the same area.

Differences Between Organisms

As you can see, each frog has different characteristics that may help the frog survive. A characteristic that helps an organism survive and reproduce in its environment is called an **adaptation.** Some adaptations, such as a long neck or striped fur, are physical. Other adaptations are behaviors that help an organism find food, protect itself, or reproduce.

Living things that have the same characteristics may be members of the same species. A **species** is a group of organisms that can mate with one another to produce fertile offspring. For example, all strawberry poison frogs are members of the same species. Therefore, strawberry poison frogs can mate with each other to produce fertile strawberry frogs. A group of individuals of the same species living in the same place is a *population.*

Figure 1 | **Adaptations in Species of Frogs**

The **red-eyed tree frog** hides among a tree's leaves during the day and comes out at night.

The **smokey jungle frog** blends into the forest floor.

The bright coloring of the **strawberry poison frog** warns predators that the frog is poisonous.

Do Species Change over Time?

In a single square mile of rain forest, there may be dozens of species of frogs. Across Earth, there are millions of different species of organisms. The species that live on Earth today range from single-celled bacteria and archaea to multicellular fungi, plants, and animals. Have these species always existed on Earth?

Scientists think that Earth has changed a great deal during its history and that living things have changed, too. They estimate that the planet is 4.6 billion years old. Since life first appeared on Earth, many species have died out, and many new species have appeared. **Figure 2** shows some of the species that have existed during Earth's history.

Scientists observe that species have changed over time. They also observe that the inherited characteristics in populations change over time. Scientists think that as populations change over time, new species may form. Thus, newer species descend from older species. The process in which populations change over time is called **evolution.**

7.3.c Students know how independent lines of evidence from geology, fossils, and comparative anatomy provide the bases for the theory of evolution.
7.3.d Students know how to construct a simple branching diagram to classify living groups of organisms by shared derived characteristics and how to expand the diagram to include fossil organisms.

adaptation (AD uhp TAY shuhn) a characteristic that improves an individual's ability to survive and reproduce in a particular environment

species (SPEE seez) a group of organisms that are closely related and can mate to produce fertile offspring

evolution (EV uh LOO shuhn) the process in which inherited characteristics within a population change over generations such that new species sometimes arise

Figure 2 *This diagram shows some of the many kinds of organisms that have lived on Earth since the planet formed 4.6 billion years ago.*

Figure 3 *The fossil on the left is of a trilobite, an ancient aquatic animal. The fossils on the right are of seed ferns.*

fossil (FAHS uhl) the trace or remains of an organism that lived long ago, most commonly preserved in sedimentary rock

fossil record (FAHS uhl REK uhrd) the history of life in the geologic past as indicated by the traces or remains of living things

Evidence of Changes over Time

The layers of Earth's crust are made up of different kinds of rock and soil stacked on top of each other. Evidence that organisms have changed over time is buried in sedimentary rock. *Sedimentary* rock is formed when particles of sand, dust, or soil, are deposited in horizontal layers. After a rock layer forms, newer rock layers form on top of it. So, older layers are found below younger rock layers.

Fossils

The remains or imprints of once-living organisms found in layers of rock are called **fossils.** Examples of fossils are shown in **Figure 3.** Fossils usually form when a dead organism is covered by a layer of sediment. Over time, more sediment settles on top of the organism. Minerals in the sediment may seep into the organism and gradually replace the organism with stone. If the organism rots away completely after being covered, it may leave an imprint of itself in the rock.

The Fossil Record

All of the fossils that have been found make up the **fossil record.** By examining the fossil record, scientists can learn about the history of life on Earth. Fossils found in newer layers of Earth's crust tend to be similar to present-day organisms. This similarity indicates that the fossilized organisms were close relatives of present-day organisms. Fossils from older layers are less similar to present-day organisms than fossils from newer layers are. The older fossils are of earlier life-forms, which may not exist anymore. Comparing organisms in the fossil record provides evidence for how organisms have changed over time.

Standards Check What is the fossil record? 7.3.c

Evidence of Ancestry

The fossil record provides evidence about the order in which species have existed. Scientists observe that all living organisms have characteristics in common and inherit characteristics in similar ways. So, they think that all living species descended from common ancestors. Evidence of common ancestors is found in fossils and in living organisms.

Drawing Connections

As scientists analyze fossils and living organisms, they develop hypotheses about how species are related. Scientists draw *branching diagrams* that illustrate their hypotheses. A branching diagram, such as the one shown in **Figure 4,** shows the relationships between species. The short horizontal line at the top left in the diagram represents a species that lived in the past. Each branch in the diagram represents a group of organisms that descended from that species.

Scientists think that whales and some types of hoofed mammals have a common ancestor, as **Figure 4** shows. This ancestor was probably a land mammal that lived between 50 million and 70 million years ago. The fossil record shows that many mammals appeared during this time period. The first ocean-dwelling mammals appeared about 50 million years ago. Scientists think whales evolved from these ocean-dwelling mammals.

Scientists use information about organisms to sketch a "tree of life" that includes all known living things. As scientists gather new information, they reexamine how all organisms are related.

Standards Check How do scientists use branching diagrams to show how all organisms are related? 7.3.d

Figure 4 *This diagram is a model of the proposed relationships between some modern mammals.* ***According to the diagram, which animals share the closest common ancestor with whales?***

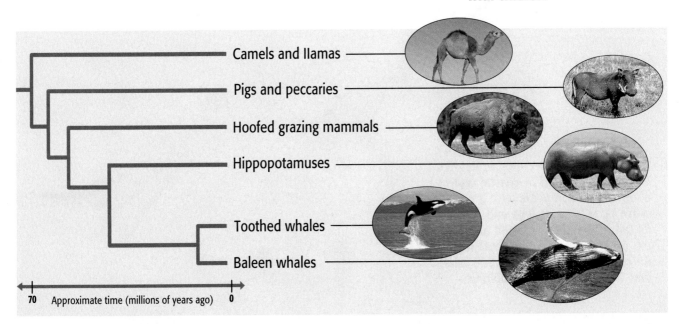

Camels and llamas

Pigs and peccaries

Hoofed grazing mammals

Hippopotamuses

Toothed whales

Baleen whales

70 Approximate time (millions of years ago) 0

Examining Organisms

Examining an organism carefully can give scientists clues about its ancestors. For example, whales seem similar to fish. But unlike fish, whales breathe air, give birth to live young, and produce milk. These traits show that whales are *mammals.* Thus, scientists think that whales evolved from ancient mammals.

Case Study: Evolution of the Whale

Scientists think that the ancient ancestor of whales was probably a mammal that lived on land and that could run on four legs. A more recent ancestor was probably a mammal that spent time both on land and in water. Comparisons between modern whales and a large number of fossils support this hypothesis. **Figure 5** shows some of this evidence.

Standards Check What evidence supports the hypothesis that the ancient ancestor of whales was a land mammal? 7.3.c

Figure 5 Evidence of Whale Evolution

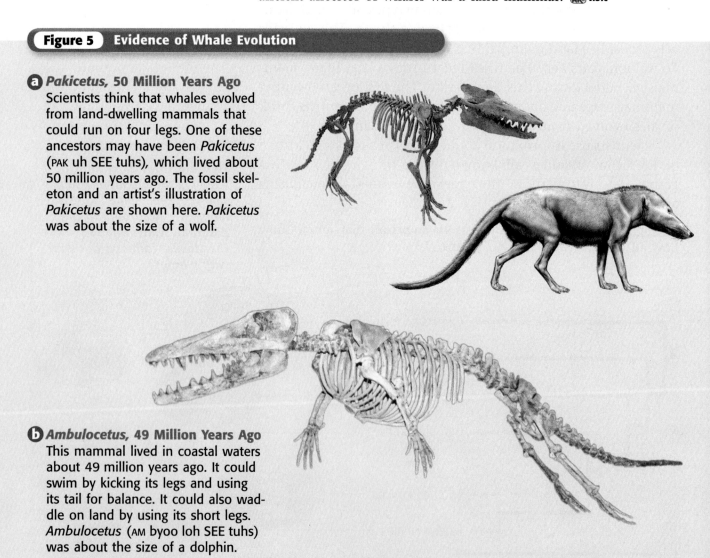

ⓐ *Pakicetus,* **50 Million Years Ago**
Scientists think that whales evolved from land-dwelling mammals that could run on four legs. One of these ancestors may have been *Pakicetus* (PAK uh SEE tuhs), which lived about 50 million years ago. The fossil skeleton and an artist's illustration of *Pakicetus* are shown here. *Pakicetus* was about the size of a wolf.

ⓑ *Ambulocetus,* **49 Million Years Ago**
This mammal lived in coastal waters about 49 million years ago. It could swim by kicking its legs and using its tail for balance. It could also waddle on land by using its short legs. *Ambulocetus* (AM byoo loh SEE tuhs) was about the size of a dolphin.

Walking Whales

The organisms in **Figure 5** form a sequence between ancient four-legged mammals and modern whales. Several pieces of evidence indicate that these species are related by ancestry. Each species shared some traits with an earlier species. Some species had new traits that were shared with later species. Each species had traits that allowed it to survive in a particular time and place in Earth's history.

Further evidence can be found inside the bodies of living whales. For example, although modern whales do not have hind limbs, they have tiny hip bones, as **Figure 5** shows. Scientists think that these hip bones were inherited from the whales' four-legged ancestors. Scientists often look at this kind of evidence when trying to determine the relationships between organisms.

Whale Measurements
Blue whales are the largest animals known to have lived on Earth. Adult blue whales can grow to be 90 ft long. Calves, or young whales, are born large. Blue whale calves are about 23 ft long at birth. Convert the lengths of blue whale adults and calves into meters. Record your work in your **Science Journal.**

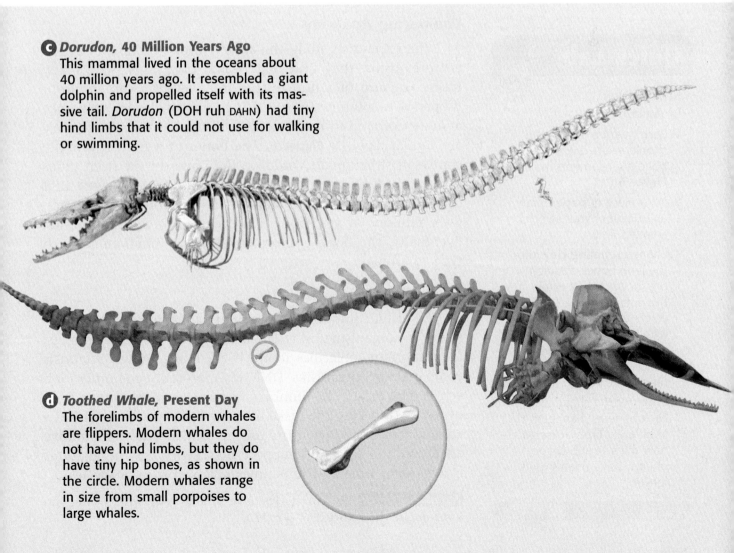

ⓒ *Dorudon,* **40 Million Years Ago**
This mammal lived in the oceans about 40 million years ago. It resembled a giant dolphin and propelled itself with its massive tail. *Dorudon* (DOH ruh DAHN) had tiny hind limbs that it could not use for walking or swimming.

ⓓ *Toothed Whale,* **Present Day**
The forelimbs of modern whales are flippers. Modern whales do not have hind limbs, but they do have tiny hip bones, as shown in the circle. Modern whales range in size from small porpoises to large whales.

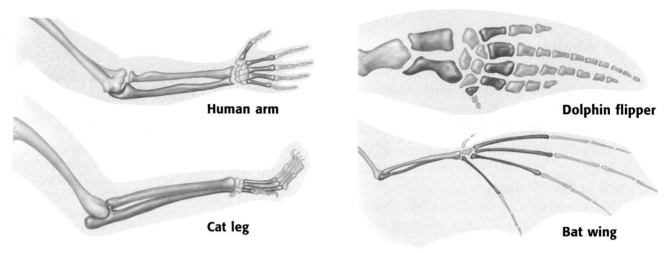

Human arm

Dolphin flipper

Cat leg

Bat wing

Figure 6 *The bones in the front limbs of humans, cats, dolphins, and bats are similar. Similar bones are shown in the same color. These limbs are not shown to scale.*

Comparing Organisms

The scientific fields of comparative anatomy and molecular biology provide evidence that organisms share common ancestors. Comparative anatomy is the study of the physical similarities and differences between organisms. Molecular biology is the study of the molecules found in living things.

Comparing Anatomy

When scientists study the anatomy, or structure, of different organisms, they find that related organisms share many traits. The arm of a human, the front leg of a cat, the front flipper of a dolphin, and the wing of a bat do not look alike and are not used in the same way. But under the surface, they are similar. Look at **Figure 6.** The bones of a human arm are similar in structure and order to the bones in the front limbs of a cat, a dolphin, and a bat. These similarities suggest that cats, dolphins, bats, and humans had a common ancestor. Over millions of years, changes occurred in the limb bones. Eventually, the bones performed different functions in each type of animal.

Comparing DNA Molecules

The genetic information stored in an organism's DNA determines the organism's traits. DNA, along with RNA and proteins, are important molecules found in all living things. Scientists compare many organisms' DNA, RNA, proteins, and other molecules. The greater the number of similarities between the DNA of any two species, the more recently the two species shared a common ancestor. Scientists use molecular data, comparative anatomy, and fossils to support the theory that populations change over time and sometimes give rise to new species.

Standards Check If two species have similar DNA, what would you infer about their ancestry? **7.3.c**

Summary

- Evolution is the process in which the inherited characteristics within a population change over generations, sometimes giving rise to new species.

- Fossils provide clues about the animals that have lived on Earth. Comparing fossils and living organisms supports the idea that organisms have changed over time.

- Scientists think that modern whales evolved from an ancient, land-dwelling mammal ancestor. Fossil organisms that support this hypothesis have been found.

- Comparing the anatomy and molecules of different organisms provides evidence of common ancestry among living organisms. The traits and DNA of species that have a common ancestor are more similar to each other than they are to the traits and DNA of distantly related species.

Understanding Concepts

1 **Describing**   What are three lines of evidence that support the theory of evolution?

2 **Sumarizing**   What evidence about the ancestors of whales do fossils provide?

3 **Describing**   How does comparative anatomy support the idea that organisms share ancestors?

Critical Thinking

4 **Making Comparisons**   Name some ways in which whales differ from fishes.

5 **Forming Hypotheses**   Is a person's DNA likely to be more similar to the DNA of his or her biological parents or to the DNA of one of his or her first cousins? Explain your answer.

6 **Evaluating Data**   A poodle and a wolf have similar physical characteristics. In addition, by using current DNA technology, scientists have learned that the DNA of a poodle is similar to the DNA of a wolf. Describe how DNA technology can be used to support the theory that poodles and wolves share a common ancestor.

7 **Making Comparisons**   Modern whales share many similarities with the animals that are thought to be their ancestors. However, whales also differ from their ancestors. Name three or more adaptations that whales have for living in water.

INTERPRETING GRAPHICS   Use the photograph of rock layers below to answer the next question.

8 **Making Inferences**   The photograph shows the layers of sedimentary rock exposed during the construction of a road. Imagine that a species that lived 200 million years ago is found in layer **b.** Would the ancestor of the species, which lived 250 million years ago, most likely be found in layer **a** or in layer **c**? Explain your answer.

Challenge

9 **Forming Hypotheses**   You are drawing a branching diagram that shows the relationships between cows, horses, and zebras. Which two organisms would you indicate as having the closest common ancestor? Explain your answer.

How Does Evolution Happen?

Key Concept   After making observations and analyzing evidence, Charles Darwin concluded that natural selection is the mechanism of evolution.

▶ Imagine that you are a scientist in the 1800s. Fossils of some very strange animals have been found. How would you explain the existence of these fossils?

In the 1800s, geologists began to realize that Earth was much older than anyone had previously thought. Evidence showed that gradual processes had changed Earth's surface over millions of years. Some scientists saw evidence of evolution in the fossil record. However, no one had been able to explain *how* evolution happens—until Charles Darwin.

Charles Darwin

In 1831, 21-year-old Charles Darwin, shown in **Figure 1,** graduated from college. Darwin didn't know what he wanted to do with his life. Although he eventually earned a degree in theology, Darwin was most interested in the study of plants and animals. So, he signed on for a five-year voyage around the world. He served as the *naturalist*—a scientist who studies nature—on the HMS *Beagle,* a British ship similar to the ship in **Figure 1.** During the trip, Darwin made observations that helped him form a theory about how evolution happens.

Figure 1   *Charles Darwin wanted to understand the natural world. He sailed around the world on a ship similar to the one shown here.*

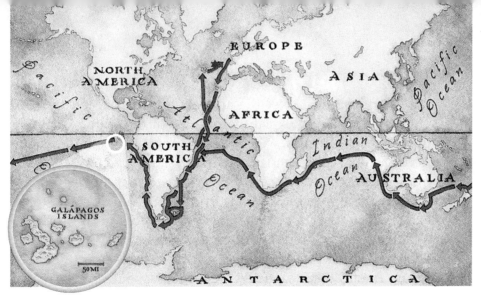

Figure 2 *The course of the HMS* Beagle *is shown by the red line. The journey began and ended in England.*

Darwin's Journey

The *Beagle*'s journey is shown in **Figure 2.** Darwin observed plants and animals from places such as the Galápagos Islands. These islands are found 965 km (600 mi) west of Ecuador, a country in South America.

Darwin's Finches

Darwin noticed that the animals and plants on the Galápagos Islands were like those in Ecuador. But the plants and animals were not identical. For example, the finches on the Galápagos Islands differed slightly from the finches in Ecuador. And the finches on each island differed from the finches on the other islands. One difference between the finches was the shape of their beaks. As **Figure 3** shows, the beak of each finch is adapted to the way the bird usually gets food.

Standards Check What did Darwin notice about the finches of Ecuador and the Galápagos Islands? 🐻 **7.3.b**

| **Figure 3** | **Some Finches of the Galápagos Islands** |

The **large ground finch** has a wide, strong beak that it uses to crack open big, hard seeds. This beak works like a nutcracker.

The **cactus finch** has a tough beak that it uses for eating cactus parts and insects. This beak works like a pair of needle-nosed pliers.

The **warbler finch** has a small, narrow beak that it uses to catch small insects. This beak works like a pair of tweezers.

Darwin's Thinking

Darwin puzzled over the animals that he had seen on his journey. He tried to explain why some of the animals, such as the Galápagos finches, were very similar yet had unique adaptations. Darwin hypothesized that the island finches descended from South American finches. He proposed that the first finches on the islands were blown there from South America by a storm. He suggested that the finches evolved adaptations for the various island environments over many generations. For example, Darwin noticed that the shape of the beak was directly related to the finch's food. Darwin's hypothesis about the Galápagos finches explained his observations.

Standards Check What structural change helped the Galápagos finches adapt to their environment? 🐻 **7.3.b**

Ideas About Breeding

In Darwin's time, farmers and breeders had produced many kinds of farm animals and plants. These plants and animals had traits that were desired by the farmers and breeders. A **trait** is a form of an inherited characteristic. For example, redness is a trait, and fruit color is the corresponding characteristic. The practice by which humans select plants or animals for breeding based on desired traits is **selective breeding.** Most pets, such as the dogs in **Figure 4,** have been bred for various desired traits. Selective breeding shows that the traits of organisms can change and that certain traits can spread through populations.

trait (TRAYT) a genetically determined characteristic

selective breeding (suh LEK tiv BREED ing) the human practice of breeding animals or plants that have certain desired traits

Figure 4 *Over the past 12,000 years, dogs have been selectively bred to produce more than 150 breeds.*

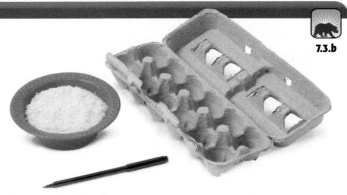

Ideas About Population

During Darwin's time, Thomas Malthus wrote *An Essay on the Principle of Population*. Malthus noted that the human population can grow more rapidly than food supplies can grow. **Figure 5** shows this relationship. Malthus also pointed out that the size of human populations is limited by problems such as starvation and disease.

After reading Malthus's work, Darwin realized that any species can produce many offspring. He also knew that the populations of all species are limited by starvation, disease, competition, and predation. Only a limited number of individuals live long enough to reproduce. Darwin reasoned that the survivors had traits that helped them survive in their environment. He also thought that some of these traits would be inherited by the offspring of the survivors.

Standards Check How did Thomas Malthus's ideas about population influence Darwin? 7.3.b

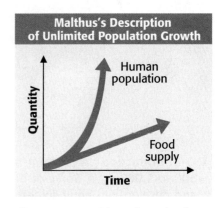

Figure 5 *Malthus thought that the human population could increase more quickly than the food supply. Such an increase would result in a worldwide food shortage.*

Ideas About Earth's History

During Darwin's time, most geologists thought that Earth was very young. But important books, such as *Principles of Geology* by Charles Lyell, were changing ideas about Earth. Lyell's book presented evidence that Earth had formed by natural processes over a long period of time. Darwin reasoned that if Earth were very old, then there would be enough time for organisms to slowly change.

Darwin's Theory of Natural Selection

After his voyage on the HMS *Beagle*, Darwin privately struggled with his ideas for about 20 years. Then, in 1858, Darwin received a letter from a naturalist named Alfred Russel Wallace. Wallace had arrived at the same ideas about evolution that Darwin had. In 1859, Darwin published a famous book called *On the Origin of Species by Means of Natural Selection*. In his book, Darwin proposed the theory that evolution happens by natural selection. **Natural selection** is the mechanism, or process by which organisms that are better adapted to their environment survive and reproduce more successfully than less well adapted organisms do. The process has four steps and is explained in **Figure 6**.

natural selection (NACH uhr uhl suh LEK shuhn) the process by which individuals that are better adapted to their environment survive and reproduce more successfully than less well adapted individuals do; a theory to explain the mechanism of evolution

Standards Check What is natural selection? 🐻 **7.3.b**

Figure 6 **Four Parts of Natural Selection**

❶ **Overproduction** A tarantula's egg sac may hold 500 to 1,000 eggs. Some of the eggs will survive and develop into adult spiders. Some will not.

❷ **Inherited Variation** Every individual has its own combination of traits. Each tarantula is similar but not identical to its parents.

❸ **Struggle to Survive** Some tarantulas may be caught by predators, such as this wasp. Other tarantulas may starve or get a disease. Only some of the tarantulas will survive to adulthood.

❹ **Successful Reproduction** The tarantulas that are best adapted to their environment are likely to have many offspring that survive.

Genetics and Evolution

Darwin knew that organisms inherit traits, but not *how* they inherit traits. He also knew that there is great variation among organisms, but not *how* that variation occurs. Today, scientists know that variation happens as genetic information is passed from parent to offspring in sexual reproduction. Some genes make an organism more likely to survive to reproduce. Natural selection happens when organisms that carry these genes survive and reproduce more than organisms that do not carry these genes. New fossil discoveries and new information about genes add to scientists' understanding of natural selection and evolution.

SECTION Review

 7.3.b

Summary

- Finch species of the Galápagos Islands evolved adaptations in response to their environment.

- Natural selection is the process by which organisms that are better adapted to their environment are more likely to survive and reproduce than less well adapted organisms do.

- The four steps of Darwin's theory of evolution by natural selection include overproduction, inherited variation, struggle to survive, and successful reproduction.

- Variation in each species is due to the exchange of genetic information as it is passed from parent to offspring.

Using Vocabulary

1. Write an original definition for *trait*.

Understanding Concepts

2. **Describing** Describe Darwin's observations about the finches on the Galápagos Islands.

3. **Describing** Describe the four parts of Darwin's theory of evolution by natural selection.

4. **Identifying** What ideas from geology influenced Darwin?

Critical Thinking

5. **Identifying Relationships** Summarize Malthus's ideas about population. How did Darwin relate Malthus's ideas to evolution by natural selection?

6. **Evaluating Assumptions** Explain overproduction in natural selection. Can a species that reproduces at a slow rate, such as a whale that produces one offspring every six years, still overproduce?

7. **Analyzing Processes** How did Darwin use scientific methods, such as making observations, analyzing data, and drawing conclusions, before presenting his ideas on the theory of evolution by natural selection?

8. **Making Comparisons** How are selective breeding and natural selection similar? How are they different?

Challenge

9. **Identifying Relationships** Although both Charles Darwin and Gregor Mendel lived during the same time period, Darwin was unaware of Mendel's work. How do Mendel's ideas about the inheritance of traits relate to Darwin's theory of evolution by natural selection?

Internet Resources

For a variety of links related to this chapter, go to www.scilinks.org

Topic: Galápagos Islands; Darwin and Natural Selection

SciLinks code: HY70631; HY70378

Natural Selection in Action

Key Concept Natural selection explains how populations become adapted to changes in their environment and why some species become extinct.

What You Will Learn

- Genetic variation and environmental factors affect evolution by natural selection.
- Separation, adaptation, and reproductive isolation can produce new species.
- Extinction occurs when the adaptations of a species are insufficient for survival in a changing environment.

Why It Matters

Natural selection accounts for the great diversity of living things.

Vocabulary

- speciation
- extinct

READING STRATEGY

Prediction Guide Before reading this section, write each heading from this section in your **Science Journal.** Below each heading, write what you think you will learn.

▶ A unique insect species lives on a particular island. A storm carries a few members of a bird species to the island. Will the birds survive in their new environment? Will the insect species survive if the birds prey on the insects?

Many factors determine if a population will survive in its environment or become extinct. Over time, a population may evolve new adaptations, which enable it to survive in its environment. The theory of evolution by natural selection explains how a population can change in response to its environment.

Changes in Populations

For natural selection to occur, a population must have genetic variation and thus a variety of traits. Environmental factors determine which traits in a population are favorable and which are unfavorable.

Genetic Variation

Genetic differences are responsible for the differences between species and between members of the same population. The *genetic variation* of a population is a measure of how much individuals in a population differ genetically. In a population that has high genetic variation, members have different *alleles,* or forms of their genes. As a result, the population will have a large variety of traits. The individuals in a population that has low genetic variation have many of the same alleles. Therefore, the population has a small variety of traits.

Genetic variation is important for the survival of a species. For example, populations of cheetahs, as shown in **Figure 1,** and other endangered species, have a low genetic variation. Populations with a low genetic variation are less likely than populations that have a high genetic variation to adapt to changes in their environment. For example, if some members of a population cannot naturally resist a disease, the species is less likely to survive a major outbreak.

Figure 1 *Cheetah populations have low genetic variation, which puts cheetahs at risk of extinction.*

Environmental Factors

Individuals in a population often have different traits. But which traits are favorable, and which traits are unfavorable? The answer depends on environmental factors. *Environmental factors* are the conditions in an environment that affect the organisms that live there.

Different environments have different environmental factors. For example, organisms that live in a desert need to be able to survive in an area that receives little water. And organisms that live near coral reefs need to be able to survive in salt water. Also, organisms living near a coral reef have different food sources and different predators than organisms in deserts do.

Certain traits are better in certain environments. For example, a snake that lives in tall, green grass may benefit from being green. In this environment, a green snake will be able to hide from predators more easily than a brown snake will. Therefore, green snakes will survive and reproduce more than brown snakes will. But being brown may be more beneficial if the snake lives on a forest floor that has a large amount of dead leaves. On a forest floor, a brown snake will probably survive and reproduce more than a green snake will.

7.3.a Students know both genetic variation and environmental factors are causes of evolution and diversity of organisms.
7.3.e Students know that extinction of a species occurs when the environment changes and the adaptive characteristics of a species are insufficient for its survival.
7.4.f Students know how movements of Earth's continental and oceanic plates through time, with associated changes in climate and geographic connections, have affected the past and present distribution of organisms.

Standards Check What are environmental factors? **7.3.a**

Quick Lab

Adaptations of Bird Beaks

The shape of a bird's beak is adapted to the way that the bird usually obtains food. In this activity, you will observe how some beak shapes are more favorable than other beak shapes based on the type of food that a bird eats.

7.3.a
7.3.e
7.7.c

▶ Try It!

1. Your teacher will provide you with a **tray of small objects,** such as nuts and rice. These objects represent different types of seeds.

2. You will also select different **tools,** such as pliers and tweezers. The tools represent different types of bird beaks.

3. Use the tools to pick up the different objects. Record which tool works best to pick up each object.

▶ Think About It!

4. Imagine an island on which all of the plants that produce small seeds are killed by a drought. Which type of bird is most likely going to be able to survive and reproduce on this island: birds that have small beaks or birds that have large beaks?

5. For the situation described in question 4, what is the important environmental factor?

6. Imagine returning to the island after many years and observing that plants that produce small seeds no longer exist. Would you expect to find more small-beaked birds or more large-beaked birds?

 20 min

Figure 2 *After squirrel populations by the Grand Canyon became separated, they formed two species: the Kaibab squirrel (left) and the Abert squirrel (right).*

Forming a New Species

Sometimes, drastic changes that can form a new species take place. A new species may form after a group becomes separated from the original population. This group forms a new population. Over time, the new population becomes adapted to its new environment. Over time, both populations evolve different adaptations. The two populations differ so greatly that they can no longer mate successfully. The new population may then be considered a new species.

speciation (SPEE shee AY shuhn) the formation of new species as a result of evolution

The formation of a new species as a result of evolution is called **speciation. Figure 2** shows two species of squirrels that live on opposite sides of the Grand Canyon. At one time, these squirrels were probably part of one population. As the Grand Canyon became larger, the population became separated and evolved into two species.

Separation

Speciation often begins when a part of a population becomes separated from the rest. The process of separation can happen in many ways. For example, a newly formed canyon, mountain range, or lake can divide a population as **Figure 3** shows. Movements of Earth's continental and oceanic plates can also affect the distribution of organisms.

Figure 3 *Populations can become separated in a variety of ways.*

Adaptation

After two groups have separated, natural selection continues to act on the groups. Over many generations, the groups may evolve different sets of traits. If the environmental conditions for each group differ, the groups' adaptations will differ. For example, a population of birds may become separated into two groups living on two different islands. The birds living on the island that has bigger, tougher seeds will probably evolve different adaptations for eating than the birds living on the island that has small, soft seeds will.

Reproductive Isolation

Natural selection can cause two separated groups to become very different. If the groups are reunited and cannot interbreed anymore, the groups have undergone *reproductive isolation*. If they cannot interbreed, the two groups are no longer the same species. **Figure 4** shows how species of Galápagos finches may have evolved through separation, adaptation, and reproductive isolation.

Standards Check What are the three parts of speciation? 🐻 **7.4.f**

INTERNET ACTIVITY

Environment and Evolution

Can you balance the need for food with the needs of the environment? Argue for or against the use of insecticides. Go to **go.hrw.com,** and type in the keyword HY7EVOW.

Figure 4 The Evolution of Species of Galápagos Finches

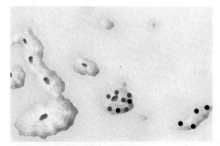

1 Some finches left the mainland and reached one of the islands (separation).

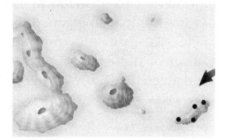

2 The finches reproduced and adapted to the environment (adaptation).

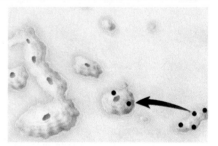

3 Some finches flew to a second island (separation).

4 These finches reproduced and adapted to the second island's environment (adaptation).

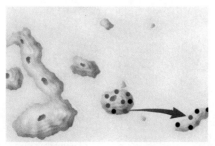

5 Some finches flew to the first island but could not interbreed with the finches there (reproductive isolation).

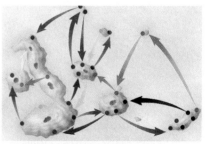

6 This process may have occurred over and over again as the finches flew to the other islands.

Extinction

Organisms have adaptive characteristics that help them survive in their environment. But what happens when the environmental factors change? Sometimes organisms can survive and reproduce after the environment has changed. However, if the adaptations of a species are not sufficient for organisms to survive, the species may become extinct. A species is **extinct** when all individuals of the species have died. Increased competition, new predators, and the loss of habitat are examples of environmental conditions that can lead to extinction.

Increased Competition

Resources such as food, water, shelter, space, or sunlight are in limited supply in the environment. Populations of different species often compete for resources. When the quantity of resources in an environment decreases, competition for the remaining resources increases. If the members of a species cannot gather the resources that they need, the species may become extinct.

New Predators

Sometimes, a new species enters an area. The new species may come from a nearby area or may be introduced by humans. For example, the European red fox, shown in **Figure 5,** was introduced to Australia by humans. Species in Australia, such as the numbat in **Figure 5,** do not have adaptations to escape foxes. So, foxes prey on numbats and have caused the population of numbats to decrease. Many species in Australia are endangered because of the introduction of new predators.

Standards Check How can a new predator cause a species to go extinct? 7.3.e

extinct (ek STINGKT) describes a species that has died out completely

Figure 5 *Since European red foxes (left) were introduced to Australia, they prey on many animals, such as numbats (right).*

Loss of Habitat

Most species get the food, water, and shelter that they need from the habitat in which they live. What happens if a habitat is destroyed? Pollution can damage a habitat so that organisms can no longer live there. Habitats can also be destroyed by natural disasters, such as floods, storms, and forest fires.

When a population loses its habitat, it may move to a new area. Sometimes, the population may not have adaptations that allow it to live in nearby environments. As a result, species may go extinct.

SECTION Review

 7.3.a, 7.3.e, 7.4.f

Summary

- A population that has high genetic variation will have many individuals with different sets of traits.

- Environmental factors determine which traits are favorable and which traits are unfavorable.

- Natural selection explains how one species evolves into another.

- Separation, adaptation, and reproductive isolation can lead to speciation.

- If environmental conditions change, a species may not be able to survive and may go extinct.

- Environmental conditions that can lead to extinction of species include increased competition, new predators, and loss of habitat.

Using Vocabulary

1. Write an original definition for *genetic variation*.

Understanding Concepts

2. **Describing** Describe how the introduction of a new predator can cause a species to go extinct.

3. **Identifying** What environmental factors may affect an organism that lives on a rocky beach?

4. **Describing** Describe how new species of Galápagos finches may have formed.

5. **Describing** Explain how genetic variation and environmental factors affect evolution by natural selection.

Critical Thinking

6. **Forming Hypotheses** Suppose that the distance between some islands is small enough for birds to fly frequently between all of the islands. Is this situation likely to lead to speciation? Explain.

7. **Making Inferences** Mass extinctions are periods in Earth's history when many species have become extinct. Some evidence suggests that major environmental changes occurred during mass extinctions. Explain how changes in the environment could be related to mass extinctions.

Challenge

8. **Forming Hypotheses** When dinosaurs were alive, most of the mammals were small. After the dinosaurs became extinct, mammals evolved into many different forms, such as cats and elephants. Explain how the extinction of dinosaurs may be related to the increase in the number of species of mammals.

Internet Resources

For a variety of links related to this chapter, go to www.scilinks.org
Topic: Species and Adaptation
SciLinks code: HY71433

OBJECTIVES

Form a hypothesis about the fate of the candy-coated chocolates.

Predict what will happen to the candy-coated chocolates.

Design and conduct an experiment to test your hypothesis.

MATERIALS

- chocolates, candy-coated, small, in a variety of colors (about 100)
- items to be determined by the students and approved by the teacher

SAFETY

Survival of the Chocolates

Imagine a world populated with candy, and hold that delicious thought in your head for just a moment. Try to apply the idea of natural selection to a population of candy-coated chocolates. According to the theory of natural selection, individuals who have favorable adaptations are more likely to survive. In the "species" of candy-coated chocolates that you will study in this experiment, the characteristics of individual chocolates may help the chocolates "survive." For example, shell strength (the strength of the candy coating) could be an adaptive advantage. Plan an experiment to find out which characteristics of the chocolates are favorable "adaptations."

Ask a Question

1 What might "survival" mean for a candy-coated chocolate? What are some ways to test which chocolates are the "strongest" or "most fit" for their environment? Also, write down any other questions that you could ask about the "survival" of the chocolates.

Form a Hypothesis

2 Form a hypothesis, and make a prediction. If you choose to study candy color, your prediction may be similar to the following: If the ___ colored shell is the strongest, then fewer of the chocolates with this color of shell will ___ when ___.

7.3.a Students know both genetic variation and environmental factors are causes of evolution and diversity of organisms.

Investigation and Experimentation
7.7.c Communicate the logical connection among hypotheses, science concepts, tests conducted, data collected, and conclusions drawn from the scientific evidence.
7.7.e Communicate the steps and results from an investigation in written reports and oral presentations.

Test the Hypothesis

3 Design a procedure to determine which type of candy-coated chocolate is most likely to survive. In your plan, be sure to include materials and tools that you may need to complete this procedure.

4 Before you begin, ask your teacher to check your experimental design. Your teacher will supply the candy and will assist you in gathering materials and tools.

5 Record your results in a data table. Be sure to organize your data in a clear and understandable way.

Analyze the Results

6 **Describing Events** Write a report that describes your experiment. Be sure to include tables and graphs of your data.

Draw Conclusions

7 **Evaluating Data** In your report, explain how your data either support or do not support your hypothesis. Include possible errors and ways to improve your procedure.

Big Idea Question

8 **Making Predictions** If the candy-coated chocolates were living things, which chocolates would survive and reproduce more than the others?

Applying Your Data

Can you think of another characteristic that can be tested to determine which type of chocolate is best adapted to survive? Explain your idea, and describe how you might test it.

Science Skills Activity

Investigation and Experimentation
7.7.c Communicate the logical connection among hypotheses, science concepts, tests conducted, data collected, and conclusions drawn from the scientific evidence.

Scientific Methods: Testing Hypotheses

▶ Tutorial

When you perform a scientific investigation, you will often start with a question and develop a hypothesis. A hypothesis is a possible answer to a question. In this tutorial, you will learn how to use a hypothesis to design an investigation.

Question: Does the size of a flowerpot affect how much fruit a tomato plant produces?

Hypothesis: If tomato plants are grown in large pots, then the plants will produce more fruit than plants grown in small pots will.

Procedure

1 Identify the Outcome The outcome describes what you will observe or measure during the investigation. The "then" part of the hypothesis includes the outcome.

Outcome: amount of tomatoes

2 Define the Outcome Sometimes you need to define how you will measure the outcome.

The number of tomatoes could be misleading because the plants could produce many small fruits or a few large fruits. I will measure the total mass of the tomatoes produced by each plant.

3 Identify Factors A factor is anything in the experiment that can influence the outcome.

Factors: amount of water, amount of sunlight, size of pot, type of soil, and temperature

4 Identify Variables A variable is a factor that can be changed. Often, you can change many of the factors. But the variable must test the hypothesis.

Variable: size of flower pot

5 Monitoring Controlled Factors In a controlled experiment, all of the factors that are not variables should be kept constant. If there are multiple variables, only one variable should be changed at a time. You may need to make a plan to keep the factors constant during the investigation.

I will use the same type of potting soil in each pot. Each plant will get 50 mL of water per day. Plants will be kept in a green house, where they will all receive the same amount of sunlight and be kept at the same temperature.

▶ You Try It!

Procedure

Insects can carry diseases that affect humans. For example, mosquitoes in tropical areas transmit malaria. One way to reduce the number of cases of diseases, such as malaria, is to use insecticides. Insecticides are chemicals that can be sprayed to kill insects.

Some populations of insects have become resistant to insecticides. Insecticide resistance is an example of natural selection in action. Some insects are naturally resistant to insecticides. In an environment where these chemicals are being used, the insects resistant to insecticides survive and reproduce more than other insects do. So,

more insects in the next generation will inherit the insecticide resistance genes.

In this activity, you will design an experiment that will test the following hypothesis: If a mosquito population is exposed to insecticides, then the number of mosquitoes that are resistant to the insecticide will increase in later generations.

1 Identify the outcome and define how you will measure it.

2 Identify controlled factors and the variables.

3 Make a plan for keeping controlled factors the same during the investigation.

Chapter Summary

The Big Idea Biological evolution explains how populations change over time.

Section

Vocabulary

1 Change over Time

Key Concept Independent lines of evidence from geology, fossils, and comparative anatomy provide the bases for the theory of evolution.

- The fossil record provides evidence that species have changed over time.
- Fossils support the hypothesis that modern whales evolved from land mammals.
- Comparing the anatomy and DNA of organisms provides evidence that organisms have common ancestors.

Trilobite fossils are the remains of an extinct species.

adaptation p. 298
species p. 298
evolution p. 299
fossil p. 300
fossil record p. 300

2 How Does Evolution Happen?

Key Concept After making observations and analyzing evidence, Charles Darwin concluded that natural selection is the mechanism of evolution.

- Darwin made many observations and was influenced by ideas from other fields.
- The four parts of natural selection are overproduction, inherited variation, struggle to survive, and successful reproduction.

Charles Darwin developed the theory of evolution by natural selection.

trait p. 308
selective breeding p. 308
natural selection p. 310

3 Natural Selection in Action

Key Concept Natural selection explains how populations become adapted to changes in their environment and why some species become extinct.

- Genetic variation and environmental factors affect evolution by natural selection.
- Separation, adaptation, and reproductive isolation can produce new species.
- Extinction occurs when the adaptations of a species are insufficient for survival in a changing environment.

The numbat is an animal that faces extinction because of new predators.

speciation p. 314
extinct p. 316

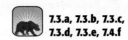
Organize

Tri-Fold Review the FoldNote that you created at the beginning of the chapter. Add to or correct the FoldNote based on what you have learned.

Using Vocabulary

1 Academic Vocabulary In the sentence "Natural selection is the mechanism of evolution," what does the term *mechanism* mean?

Complete each of the following sentences by choosing the correct term from the word bank.

adaptation   species
natural selection

2 A group of organisms that can mate with each other to produce fertile offspring is known as a(n) ___.

3 A(n) ___ makes an organism better able to survive in its environment.

Understanding Concepts

Multiple Choice

4 Charles Darwin observed variations between individuals within a population, but he did not know how variations occur. Which of the following causes variation in a population?
a. interbreeding
b. differences in food
c. genetic variation
d. selective breeding

5 The fossil record is a history of life indicated by fossils found in Earth's crust. What information about organisms in an environment can the fossil record provide?
a. how natural selection occurs
b. how organisms in an environment changed over time
c. how selective breeding occurs
d. how genetic variation occurs

6 Darwin puzzled over the various species of Galápagos finches. He eventually concluded that over time, the finches adapted to various environments on the islands. On which of the following traits did Darwin base his conclusions?
a. eye color
b. flight patterns
c. beak size and shape
d. bone structure of the wings

7 Darwin developed the theory of evolution by making careful observations and by studying ideas from different fields. Which of the following did NOT influence Darwin?
a. *Principles of Geology* by Charles Lyell
b. *An Essay on the Principle of Population* by Thomas Malthus
c. observations of selective breeding
d. evidence from molecular biology

Short Answer

8 Identifying Identify two ways that organisms can be compared to provide evidence of evolution from a common ancestor.

9 Describing Describe evidence that supports the hypothesis that whales evolved from land-dwelling mammals.

10 Comparing Why are some animals more likely to survive to adulthood than other animals are?

11 Describing Describe how environmental changes can cause species to become extinct.

INTERPRETING GRAPHICS Use the photograph below to answer the next question.

12 Identifying Identify some of the adaptations that sea turtles have for living in the ocean.

Writing Skills

13 Communicating Concepts Write a paragraph explaining how natural selection occurs. Be sure to include the four parts of natural section.

Critical Thinking

14 Concept Mapping Use the following terms to create a concept map: *struggle to survive, theory, genetic variation, Darwin, overpopulation, natural selection,* and *successful reproduction.*

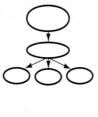

15 Analyzing Relationships A team of scientists is studying three species of frogs. How would the scientists use comparative anatomy and molecular biology to determine which two of the three species of frogs share the most recent common ancestor?

16 Analyzing Relationships Geologists have evidence that the continents were once a single giant landmass. This giant landmass eventually split apart, and the individual continents moved to their current positions. What role might this movement of continents have played in evolution?

17 Forming Hypotheses Tarantulas defend themselves by flicking hairs into the eyes of their predators. In a population of tarantulas, a few tarantulas do not have these hairs. Why are the tarantulas that have these hairs more likely to produce offspring than the hairless tarantulas are?

18 Identifying Relationships You are drawing a branching diagram to show the relationships between turtles, frogs, and alligators. Which two organisms does the diagram indicate as having the most recent common ancestor?

19 Analyzing Processes Similar species of lizards can be found on several Caribbean islands. But the species have some different traits that match the different environments in which they live. Explain how speciation could have produced the different species of lizards.

INTERPRETING GRAPHICS Use the graph below to answer the next two questions.

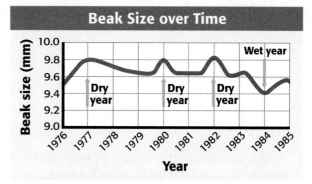

20 Evaluating Data During dry years, fewer seeds are produced. Birds have to be able to eat the large, tough seeds. How does the change of this environmental factor affect the average beak size of Galápagos finches?

21 Predicting Consequences Imagine that a storm blew some of the birds on the Galápagos Islands to a new island. The new island receives a large amount of rain. After several generations on the new island, what would you expect to happen to the average beak size of the finches?

Math Skills

22 Making Calculations A biologist studying Anaconda snakes captures five snakes of the following lengths: 8.9 m, 7.3 m, 6.6 m, 7.5 m, and 8.7 m. What is the average length of the snakes?

Challenge

23 Forming Hypotheses Whales share a more recent common ancestor with land mammals than they do with fishes. Whales breathe air, give birth to live young, and produce milk like mammals. The DNA of whales is more similar to the DNA of land mammals than it is to the DNA of fishes. Still, whales do share some characteristics with fishes. For example, both fishes and whales use flat fins to swim. How does natural selection explain how whales and fishes can have similar adaptations despite not having a recent common ancestor?

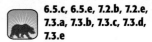
REVIEWING ACADEMIC VOCABULARY

1 **Which of the following words is the closest in meaning to the word *diversity*?**

A change

B variety

C availability

D adaptation

2 **In the sentence "The theory of evolution was first proposed by Charles Darwin," what does the word *theory* mean?**

A an idea that is not based on evidence

B a belief that guides a person's actions

C a thought or plan that exists in the mind

D an explanation developed using scientific methods

3 **Choose the appropriate form of the word *adapt* for the following sentence: Species that evolve _____ characteristics are more likely to survive environmental changes than species that do not develop these characteristics are.**

A adapt

B adapting

C adaptive

D adaptation

4 **Which of the following words means "any system or means by which something gets done"?**

A characteristic

B sequence

C attention

D mechanism

REVIEWING CONCEPTS

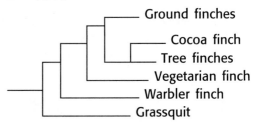

Ground finches
Cocoa finch
Tree finches
Vegetarian finch
Warbler finch
Grassquit

5 **According to the diagram above, which of the following statements about finch species is true?**

A Cocoa finches evolved from tree finches.

B Grassquits and ground finches do not have a common ancestor.

C Warbler finches are an older species than cocoa finches are.

D Tree finches are better adapted to their environment than grassquits are.

6 **Which term best describes a species in which all of the members have died?**

A evolved

B decayed

C endangered

D extinct

7 **Charles Darwin noticed that finches on different islands of the Galápagos Islands were similar but that their beaks differed. What explanation for these differences did he propose?**

A The beaks of the finches are adapted to the way the bird usually gets food.

B The beaks of the finches are randomly selected by genetic mutation.

C The different beaks would one day evolve into identical beaks.

D Beak size is related to the size of the finch.

Average Beak Measurements of Birds of the Colores Islands			
Island	Average beak length (mm)	Average beak width (mm)	Number of unique species
Verde	9.7	6.5	5
Azul	8.9	8.7	15
Rosa	5.2	8.0	10

8 The table above shows average beak measurements for birds living on three islands. Narrow beaks are best for eating insects. On which island would you expect to find the most birds that eat insects?

A Verde Island

B Azul Island

C Rosa Island

D Verde Island and Azul Island

9 Which of the following factors is necessary for natural selection to occur in a species?

A genetic variation within a population

B an abundance of food resources

C a hospitable environment

D a strong family structure

10 Scientists have noticed similarities between a bat's wings and a dolphin's flippers. What does this evidence tell us about the evolution of bats and dolphins?

A Bats probably evolved from dolphins.

B Bats and dolphins probably adapted to similar environments.

C Bats and dolphins probably have a common ancestor.

D Bats and dolphins use their wings and flippers for the same purposes.

REVIEWING PRIOR LEARNING

11 Which of the following environmental changes would directly affect primary consumers?

A the loss of plant life

B the degradation of soil

C the disappearance of insects

D the disappearance of scavengers

12 Which of the following is an abiotic factor most likely to affect the development of organisms living in a river?

A the plant life in the river

B the speed at which the river travels

C the width of the river

D the bacteria living in the river

13 What is the primary structure that contains genetic information?

A DNA

B proteins

C mitochondria

D RNA

14 Organisms that reproduce sexually contribute _____ of their genes to their offspring.

A none

B all

C about one-half

D about one-quarter

Science in Action

Scientific Discoveries

Lizards of White Sands

How did the lizards in White Sands, New Mexico become white? Erica Rosenblum, an evolutionary biologist at the University of California at Berkeley has made interesting discoveries about how natural selection has affected lizards. The lizards in White Sands are bright white, just like the environment in which they live. Except for their color, the lizards of white sands are similar to brown lizards that live in nearby brown deserts. About 6,000 years ago, winds changed the brown landscape of White Sands to bright white. At that time, the lizards were brown. Lighter lizards were better able to hide from predators than darker lizards were. Therefore, the lighter lizards survived and had more offspring. Over time, the lizards of white sands have become bright white.

Math Activity

A scientist is studying a species of lizards. Of the 150 lizards caught in a day, 24% are more than 10 cm long. How many lizards are more than 10 cm long? Record your work in your **Science Journal.**

Science Fiction

"The Anatomy Lesson" by Scott Sanders

Do you know the feeling that you get when you have an important test? A medical student faces a similar situation in this story. He needs to learn the bones of the human body for an anatomy exam the next day. He goes to the anatomy library to study. The librarian lets him check out a box of bones that are supposed to be from a human skeleton. But something is wrong. There are too many bones. They are the wrong shape. They don't fit together correctly. Somebody must be playing a joke! Find out what is going on and why the student and the librarian will never be the same. You can read "The Anatomy Lesson" in the *Holt Anthology of Science Fiction.*

Language Arts Activity

Before you read this story, predict what will happen. In your **Science Journal,** write a paragraph that "gives away" the ending that you predict. After you have read the story, listen to some of the predictions made by your classmates. Discuss your opinions about the possible endings.

Raymond Pierotti

Canine Evolution   Raymond Pierotti thinks that it is natural that he became an evolutionary biologist. He grew up exploring the desert around his home in New Mexico. He was fascinated by the abundant wildlife surviving in the bleak landscape. "One of my earliest memories is getting coyotes to sing with me from my backyard," he says.

Pierotti now studies the evolutionary relationships between wolves, coyotes, and domestic dogs. Some of his ideas come from the traditions of the Comanches. According to a Comanche creation story, humans came from wolves. Although Pierotti doesn't believe that humans evolved from wolves, he sees the creation story as a suggestion that humans and wolves have evolved together. "Wolves are very similar to humans in many ways," says Pierotti. "They live in family groups and hunt together. It is possible that wolves actually taught humans how to hunt in packs, and there are ancient stories of wolves and humans hunting together and sharing the food. I think it was this relationship that inspired the Comanche creation stories."

Social Studies ACTIVITY

Research a story of creation that comes from a Greek, Roman, or Native American civilization. In your **Science Journal,** write a paragraph summarizing the myth, and share it with a classmate.

Internet Resources

- To learn more about careers in science, visit **www.scilinks.org** and enter the SciLinks code HY70225.

- To learn more about these Science in Action topics, visit **go.hrw.com** and type in the keyword HY7EVOF.

- Check out articles related to this chapter by visiting **go.hrw.com.** Just type in the keyword HY7EVOC.

Improving Comprehension

Graphic Organizers are important visual tools that can help you organize information and improve your reading comprehension. The Graphic Organizer below is called a *pyramid chart*. Instructions for creating other types of Graphic Organizers are located in the **Study Skills** section of the Appendix.

How to Make a Pyramid Chart

1 Draw a triangle that is divided into sections like the one shown below. Draw as many sections as you need to draw.

2 Draw a box to the left of the triangle, as shown in the example. Write the topic of your pyramid chart in the box.

3 In each section of your triangle, write information about the topic in the appropriate level of the pyramid.

When to Use a Pyramid Chart

A pyramid chart is used to organize information in a hierarchy of magnitude or detail. As the shape of the pyramid suggests, the pyramid's bottom level contains information that is largest in terms of magnitude and broadest, or least specific, in terms of detail. As you read about science, look for information that you can organize into a hierarchy.

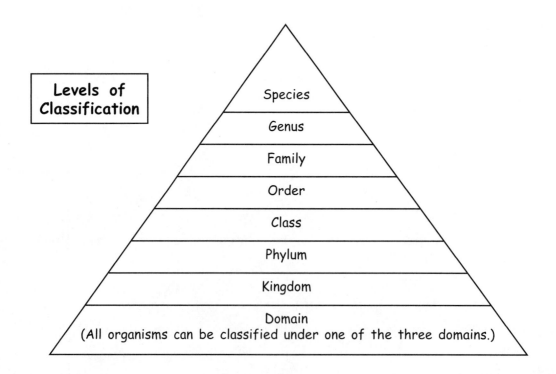

Levels of Classification

Species
Genus
Family
Order
Class
Phylum
Kingdom
Domain
(All organisms can be classified under one of the three domains.)

You Try It!

This Reading Strategy can also be used within the chapter that you are about to read. Practice making your own *pyramid chart* as directed in the Reading Strategy for Section **1**. Record your work in your **Science Journal.**

Unpacking the Standards

The information below "unpacks" the standards by breaking them down into basic parts. The higher-level, academic vocabulary is highlighted and defined to help you understand the language of the standards. "What It Means" restates the standards as simply as possible.

California Standard	Academic Vocabulary	What It Means
7.1.a Students know cells **function similarly** in all living organisms.	**function** (FUHNGK shuhn) to work **similarly** (SIM uh luhr lee) in almost the same way	Cells perform the same actions in all living things.
7.3.d Students know how to **construct** a simple branching diagram to classify living groups of organisms by shared **derived** characteristics and how to **expand** the diagram to include fossil organisms.	**construct** (kuhn STRUHKT) to build; to make from parts **derived** (di RIEVD) gotten from something else **expand** (ek SPAND) to make more detailed; to enlarge	You must know how to draw a simple branching diagram to sort living things into groups based on features that the organisms share. You must also know how to add extinct organisms to the branching diagram.

Classification

The Big Idea

Organisms can be classified into groups based on their characteristics.

 California Standards

Focus on Life Sciences

7.1 All living organisms are composed of cells, from just one to many trillions, whose details usually are visible only through a microscope. (Section 2)

7.3 Biological evolution accounts for the diversity of species developed through gradual processes over many generations. (Sections 1 and 2)

Investigation and Experimentation

7.7 Scientific progress is made by asking meaningful questions and conducting careful investigations. (Science Skills Activity)

Math

7.1.1 Measurement and Geometry
7.1.2 Number Sense

English–Language Arts

7.1.3 Reading
7.1.2 Writing

About the Photo

Look at the katydids, grasshoppers, and mantids in the photo. Every insect has a label that describes the insect. These descriptions will help a scientist find out if each insect has already been discovered and named. When scientists discover a new organism, they name the organism. The name chosen is unique and should help other scientists understand some basic facts about the organism.

Organize

Booklet

Before you read the chapter, create the FoldNote entitled "Booklet." On the front cover, title the booklet "Classification." Label each page of the booklet with "Classification," "Domain Archaea," "Domain Bacteria," and "Domain Eukarya." As you read the chapter, write what you learn about each topic on the appropriate page of the booklet.

Instructions for creating FoldNotes are located in the Study Skills section on p. 580 of the Appendix.

Explore Activity

15 min

Analyzing a Branching Diagram

Scientists use branching diagrams to show how different kinds of organisms are related to each other. The branching diagram below shows one way that clothes can be organized into groups.

Infant Toddler Preteen Teenager Adult   Elder

Procedure

7.3.d
7.7.d

1. Redraw the diagram.

2. On the branch that slopes towards the right, draw a mark between each of the other branches in your diagram. Label each mark with what changed between the branches that are on either side of the mark.

Analysis

3. Write a statement that explains what you think the diagram shows.

4. Which branch of clothing category do you fit in?

5. Which categories of clothing have you already worn?

6. Can you think of how one of these groups of clothing can be split into two new groups? Show the two new groups on your diagram.

Sorting It All Out

Key Concept An eight-level classification system and branching diagrams are two basic tools that scientists use to study living and extinct organisms.

What You Will Learn

- Scientists use classification to study organisms and how organisms are related to each other.
- The eight levels of classification are domain, kingdom, phylum, class, order, family, genus, and species.
- Each organism that has been described is given a scientific name.
- Branching diagrams show the relatedness between living and extinct organisms over time.

Why It Matters

Classifying organisms will help you identify how living and extinct organisms are related.

Vocabulary

- classification
- taxonomy

READING STRATEGY

Graphic Organizer In your **Science Journal,** make a Pyramid Chart that follows a general note-taking structure. At the top, write the topic of this section. In the next level down, ask two questions about the topic. In the next level, answer the questions. In the bottom level, add more details to your answers.

Imagine that you live in a tropical rain forest and must get your own food, shelter, and clothing from the forest. What do you need to know to survive in the forest? You need to know which plants are safe to eat and which are not. You need to know which animals you can eat and which animals might eat you. In other words, you need to study the organisms around you and organize them into categories, or classify them. **Classification** is putting things into orderly groups based on similar characteristics.

Why Classify?

For thousands of years, humans have classified organisms based on usefulness. The Chácabo people of Bolivia know of 360 kinds of plants in the forest where they live. Of these 360 plant types, 305 types are useful to the Chácabo.

Some biologists, such as those shown in **Figure 1,** classify living and extinct organisms. Scientists classify organisms to help make sense and order of the many kinds of organisms in the world. Biologists use a system to classify organisms. This system is a tool to group organisms according to the characteristics that they share. The classification of organisms allows biologists to answer many important questions, such as the following:

- What are the defining characteristics of each species?
- When did the characteristics of an organism evolve?
- What are the relationships between various species?

Standards Check What are three questions that classifying organisms can help answer? **7.3.d**

Figure 1 *These biologists are sorting rain-forest plant material.*

7.3.d Students know how to construct a simple branching diagram to classify living groups of organisms by shared derived characteristics and how to expand the diagram to include fossil organisms.

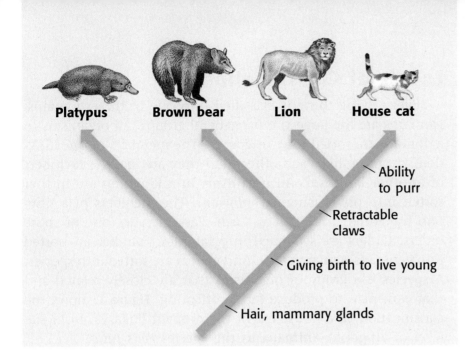

Platypus Brown bear Lion House cat

Ability to purr

Retractable claws

Giving birth to live young

Hair, mammary glands

Figure 2 *This branching diagram shows the similarities and differences between four mammals. The bottom of the branching diagram begins in the past, and the tips of the branches end in the present day.*

How Do Scientists Classify Organisms?

In the 1700s, Carolus Linnaeus (KAR uh luhs li NAY uhs), a Swedish scientist, founded modern taxonomy. **Taxonomy** is the science of describing, classifying, and naming organisms. Linnaeus classified organisms based on their structure or characteristics. Classifying organisms by their characteristics is called *systematics*. The classification system used today is based on the one that Linnaeus developed.

Classification Today

Taxonomists use an eight-level system to classify organisms by their *shared derived characteristics*. A shared derived characteristic is a characteristic that two or more kinds of organisms share with their most recent common ancestor. Scientists use these characteristics to hypothesize how closely related organisms are. The more derived characteristics organisms share, the more closely related the organisms probably are. For example, the platypus, brown bear, lion, and house cat all have hair and mammary glands. Therefore, they are grouped together as mammals.

Branching Diagrams

Branching diagrams show which characteristics organisms share and when these organisms evolved. In **Figure 2,** each characteristic listed on the branching diagram is only shared by the animals above it. All of the animals shown have hair and mammary glands. But only the bear, lion, and house cat give birth to live young. Characteristics shown higher on the diagram are more recent than the characteristics below them. Therefore, more-recent organisms are at the ends of branches that begin higher on the diagram. For example, the house cat evolved more recently than the platypus.

classification (KLAS uh fi KAY shuhn) the division of organisms into groups, or classes, based on specific characteristics

taxonomy (taks AHN uh mee) the science of describing, naming, and classifying organisms
Wordwise The root *tax-* means "to arrange" or "to put in order." The suffix *-nomy* means "the science of."

Quick Lab

Constructing a Branching Diagram
7.3.d
7.7.d

1. Construct a diagram similar to the one in **Figure 2.** On the diagram, write "frog", "snake", "kangaroo", and "rabbit" in this order, from left to right.

2. Think of one major change that happened before the frog evolved.

3. For the last three organisms, write a change that happened between one of these organisms and the other two in your diagram.

4. How does this diagram show that the organisms are related?

 15 min

Levels of Classification

Every living thing is classified into one of three domains. Domains are the largest, most general groups. All organisms in a domain are sorted into kingdoms. The members of one kingdom are more like each other than they are like the members of another kingdom. All organisms in a kingdom are further sorted into phyla (singular, *phylum*). The members of a phylum are sorted into classes. Each class includes one or more orders. Orders are separated into families. Families are sorted into genera (singular, *genus*). And genera are sorted into species. A species is a group of organisms that are closely related and that can mate to produce fertile offspring. **Figure 3** shows the classification of a house cat in the domain Eukarya, from the level of kingdom Animalia to the species *Felis catus*.

Scientific Names

By classifying organisms, biologists can give organisms scientific names. A scientific name remains the same for a specific kind of organism even if the organism has many common names. Before Linnaeus's time, scholars used names that were as long as 12 words to identify species. This system was hard to work with because the names were so long. The system was also hard to use because different scientists named organisms differently, so an organism could have more than one name.

INTERNET ACTIVITY

Kingdom Competition!

Do you have a favorite kingdom? Choose one, and write which of its characteristics you most like. Create an advertisement for your favorite kingdom! Go to **go.hrw.com,** and type in the keyword HY7CLSW.

Figure 3 *Levels of classification begin with domain, followed by kingdom, phylum, class, order, family, genus, and species. This diagram shows the levels of classification of the house cat, in domain Eukarya.*

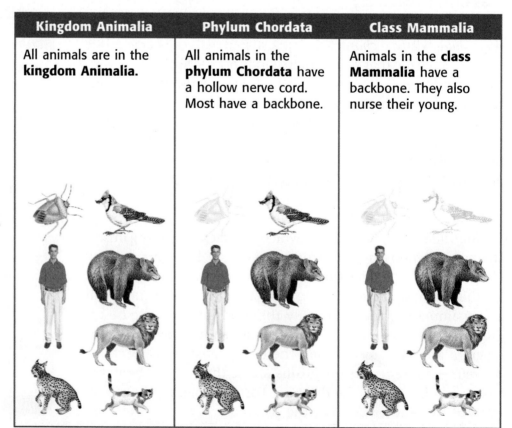

Kingdom Animalia	Phylum Chordata	Class Mammalia
All animals are in the **kingdom Animalia.**	All animals in the **phylum Chordata** have a hollow nerve cord. Most have a backbone.	Animals in the **class Mammalia** have a backbone. They also nurse their young.

Two-Part Names

Linnaeus simplified the naming of living things by giving each species a two-part scientific name. For example, the scientific name for the Asian elephant is *Elephas maximus* (EL uh fuhs MAK suh muhs). The first part of the name, *Elephas,* is the genus name. The second part, *maximus,* is the specific name. No other species has the name *Elephas maximus.* Naming rules help scientists communicate clearly about living things.

All genus names begin with a capital letter. All specific names begin with a lowercase letter. Usually, both words are underlined or italicized. But if the surrounding text is italicized, the scientific name is not, as **Figure 4** shows. These printing styles show a reader which words are genus names and specific names.

Scientific names, which are usually Latin or Greek, contain information about an organism. The name of the animal shown in **Figure 4** is *Tyrannosaurus rex. Tyrannosaurus* is a combination of two Greek words and means "tyrant lizard." The word *rex* is Latin for "king." The name tells you that this animal was probably not a passive grass eater! *Tyrannosaurus rex* can also be referred to as *T. rex.* A correct scientific name consists of the genus name (or its abbreviation) and the specific name.

Figure 4 *You would never call* Tyrannosaurus rex *just* rex!

Standards Check What are the two parts of a scientific name?

7.3.d

Order Carnivora	Family Felidae	Genus *Felis*	Species *Felis catus*
Animals in the **order Carnivora** have a backbone and nurse their young. They also have special teeth for tearing meat.	Animals in the **family Felidae** are cats. They have a backbone, nurse their young, have special teeth for tearing meat, and have retractable claws.	Animals in the **genus *Felis*** share traits with other animals in the same family. However, these cats cannot roar; they can only purr.	The **species *Felis catus*** is the common house cat. The house cat shares traits with all of the organisms in the levels above the species level, but it also has unique traits.

Extinct Organisms and Living Organisms

Extinct organisms can also be placed in a branching diagram with living organisms. Scientists identify the characteristics of an extinct organism from fossils of that organism. The more shared derived characteristics that an extinct organism has in common with a living organism, the more closely related these organisms probably are. By studying fossils scientists can better understand the evolutionary relationships between organisms or how organisms have evolved. **Figure 5** shows a branching diagram that has extinct and living genera. Notice that extinct genera never appear at the tips of branches that reach the top of the diagram.

Figure 5 *This branching diagram shows the modern horse, and other related genera. The diagram also shows how these genera have probably evolved from currently extinct genera through the epochs of the Cenozoic era.* **List all the genera that evolved from the genus Mesohippus, according to this diagram.**

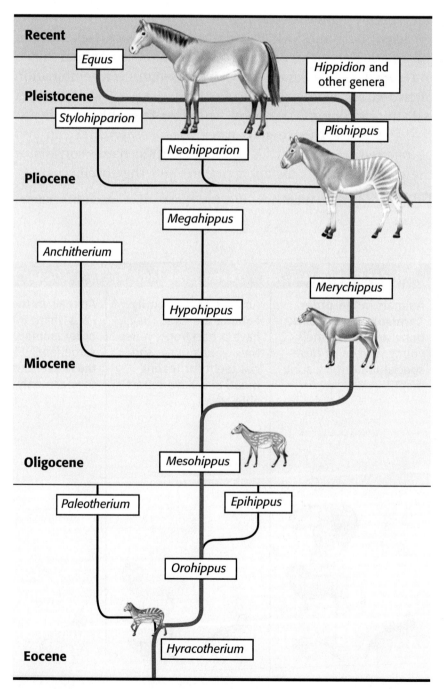

Fossils and Branching Diagrams

Branching diagrams that include fossils of extinct organisms show when the extinct organisms evolved and when those organisms became extinct. For example, as **Figure 5** shows that the members of the genus *Neohipparion* appeared near the beginning of the Pliocene Epoch and became extinct near the end of the Pliocene Epoch. In some cases, extinct organisms are on a branch that is on a direct line to other organisms. For example, the genus *Mesohippus* appeared in the Oligocene Epoch and is on a direct line to the genera *Hypohippus* and *Merychippus*.

Standards Check How are fossils of extinct organisms included in branching diagrams? 7.3.d

---

SECTION Review

 7.3.d

Summary

- Classification groups organisms based on their shared derived characteristics.
- Classification is a tool that helps us understand the relationships between organisms.
- The are eight levels of classification.
- The scientific name of an organism has two parts.
- Branching diagrams show evolutionary relationships between extinct and living organisms.

Using Vocabulary

1 Write an original definition for *classification* and *taxonomy*.

Understanding Concepts

2 **Analyzing** Why do scientists use scientific names for organisms?

3 **Listing** What are the eight levels of classification?

INTERPRETING GRAPHICS Use the branching diagram below to answer the next two questions.

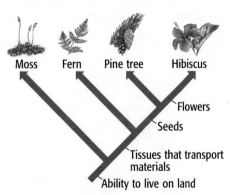

Moss Fern Pine tree Hibiscus

Flowers
Seeds
Tissues that transport materials
Ability to live on land

4 **Identifying** Which kind of organism evolved earliest? Which kind of organism evolved most recently?

5 **Inferring** Which organisms have tissues that transport materials?

Critical Thinking

6 **Analyzing Processes** You have found a fossil of an organism. The organism has characteristics that have never been described. What would you have to do to identify this fossil?

7 **Making Inferences** What is the difference between organisms that share many derived characteristics and organisms that do not?

8 **Applying Concepts** There is an organism halfway up a branch in a branching diagram, and a different organism at the tip of the branch. What can you infer about these organisms?

9 **Making Inferences** In branching diagrams, what can you infer about the organisms at the tips of the branches that do not reach the tops of the diagrams?

Domains and Kingdoms

Key Concept All organisms can be classified into three domains based on their shared derived characteristics.

What You Will Learn

- Classification systems change as greater numbers of different organisms are described.
- All prokaryotes are divided into one of two domains, domain Archaea or domain Bacteria.
- All eukaryotes are classified into the domain Eukarya, which is divided into four kingdoms.

Why It Matters

Learning about the characteristics of organisms in each domain and kingdom can help you recognize similarities and differences between organisms.

Vocabulary

- Archaea
- Bacteria
- Eukarya
- Protista
- Fungi
- Plantae
- Animalia

READING STRATEGY

Summarizing Read this section silently. In pairs, take turns summarizing the material. Stop to discuss ideas and words that seem confusing.

Archaea (ahr KEE uh) in a modern taxonomic system, a domain made up of prokaryotes that differ from other prokaryotes in the makeup of their cell walls and in their genetics

For hundreds of years, all organisms were classified as either plants or animals. But over time, scientists discovered species that did not fit easily into these two kingdoms. For example, an organism of the genus *Euglena,* has characteristics of both plants and animals. How would you classify this organism?

Three Domains

Organisms are classified by their shared derived characteristics. Euglena are single-celled organisms that live in pond water. Euglena perform photosynthesis, move around, and can feed on other organisms. Therefore, euglena are neither plants nor animals. Scientists solved this classification problem by adding another kingdom, the kingdom Protista, for organisms such as euglena. However, scientists soon realized that new kingdoms could not solve some larger problems in classification.

As greater differences among organisms were discovered, scientists had to create a new level of classification, the level of domain. **Figure 1** shows the three domains in the eight-level classification system that is used today. Domains represent the largest differences among organisms. At each level of classification, organisms within a group are more like other organisms in the same group than organisms that belong to different groups. Therefore, organisms in each domain are more like each other than organisms in another domain. Domains are subdivided into kingdoms. Scientists are still working to describe the kingdoms in each of the three domains.

Standards Check What do scientists use to classify organisms today?

 7.3.d

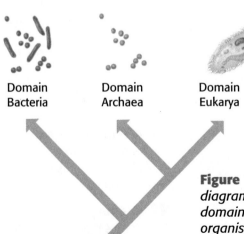

Domain Bacteria   Domain Archaea   Domain Eukarya

Figure 1 *This branching diagram shows the three domains into which all organisms are classified.*

7.1.a Students know cells function similarly in all living organisms.
7.3.d Students know how to construct a simple branching diagram to classify living groups of organisms by shared derived characteristics and how to expand the diagram to include fossil organisms.

Figure 2 *The Grand Prismatic Spring in Yellowstone National Park contains water that is about 90°C (194°F). The spring is home to archaea that thrive in its hot water.*

Domain Archaea

The domain **Archaea** is made up entirely of archaea. Archaea are one of two kinds of prokaryotes. *Prokaryotes* (proh KAR ee OHTS) are single-celled organisms that do not have a nucleus. Archaea were first discovered living in extreme environments, where other organisms could not survive. **Figure 2** shows a hot spring in Yellowstone National Park. The yellow and orange rings around the edge of the hot spring are made up of the billions of archaea that live there. Some archaea can also be found in more-moderate environments, such as the open ocean.

Bacteria (bak TIR ee uh) in a modern taxonomic system, a domain made up of prokaryotes that differ from other prokaryotes in the makeup of their cell walls and in their genetics

Domain Bacteria

All bacteria belong to the domain **Bacteria.** Bacteria are another kind of prokaryote. Bacteria can be found in the soil, in water, and even on and inside the human body! For example, *Escherichia coli* (ESH uh RIK ee uh KOH LIE), pictured in **Figure 3,** is present in large numbers in human intestines, where it produces vitamin K. One kind of bacterium converts milk into yogurt. Some bacteria cause diseases, such as pneumonia. Other bacteria make chemicals that help us fight disease-causing bacteria. Although bacteria and archaea are prokaryotes, differences in their characteristics allow them to live in very different kinds of environments.

Standards Check Describe one major difference between archaea and bacteria. 🐻 **7.1.a**

Figure 3 *Specimens of* E. coli *are shown on the point of a pin under a scanning electron microscope. These bacteria live in the intestines of animals and decompose undigested food.*

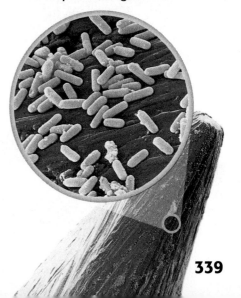

339

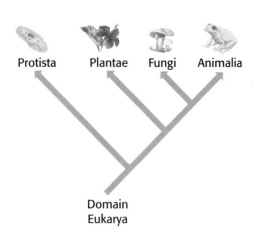

Protista   Plantae   Fungi   Animalia

Domain
Eukarya

Figure 4 *This branching diagram shows the four kingdoms in the domain Eukarya.*

Eukarya (yoo KAR ee uh) in a modern taxonomic system, a domain made up of all eukaryotes

Figure 5 *The slime mold on the left is a protist. The brightly colored fungus on the right is of the genus* Amanita *and is poisonous.*

Domain Eukarya

All organisms whose cells have a nucleus and membrane-bound organelles are called *eukaryotes*. Eukaryotes belong to the domain **Eukarya.** The four kingdoms within the domain Eukarya are Protista, Fungi, Plantae, and Animalia, as **Figure 4** shows.

Standards Check Based on the branching diagram, what are the the two kingdoms in Eukarya that evolved most recently? 🐻 **7.3.d**

Kingdom Protista

Members of the kingdom **Protista** commonly called *protists* (PROH tists), are single-celled or simple multicellular organisms. Scientists think that the first protists evolved from ancient bacteria about 2 billion years ago. Much later, ancient protists gave rise to fungi, plants, and animals. The kingdom Protista contains many kinds of organisms. Animal-like protists are called *protozoa*. Plantlike protists are called *algae*. Slime molds, such as the one shown in **Figure 5,** belong to the kingdom Protista.

Kingdom Fungi

Molds and mushrooms are examples of the complex, multicellular members of the kingdom **Fungi.** Unlike plants, fungi do not perform photosynthesis. Unlike animals, fungi do not eat food. Instead, fungi absorb nutrients from substances in their surroundings. They use digestive juices to break down the substances. **Figure 5** shows a very poisonous fungus. Never eat wild fungi.

Figure 6 *Giant sequoias can be found in California. Giant sequoias can measure 30 m around at the base and can grow to more than 91.5 m tall.*

Ring-Around-the-Sequoia

How many students would have to join hands to form a human chain around a giant sequoia that has a circumference of 30 m? Assume for this calculation that the average student can extend his or her arms about 1.3 m.

Kingdom Plantae

Although plants vary remarkably in size and form, most people easily recognize the members of the kingdom Plantae. **Plantae** consists of organisms that are eukaryotic, have cell walls, and make food through photosynthesis. For photosynthesis to occur, most plants need sunlight. Plants can therefore be found on land and in water that light can penetrate.

The food that plants make is important not only for the plants but also for all of the organisms that get nutrients from plants. Most life on Earth is dependent on plants. For example, some animals, fungi, protists, and bacteria consume plants. When these organisms digest the plant material, they get energy and nutrients made by the plants.

Plants also provide habitat for other organisms. The giant sequoias in **Figure 6** provide a home for birds, insects, and other animals.

Protista (proh TIST uh) a kingdom of mostly one-celled eukaryotic organisms that are different from plants, animals, bacteria, archaea, and fungi

Fungi (FUHN JIE) a kingdom made up of nongreen, eukaryotic organisms that have no means of movement, reproduce by using spores, and get food by breaking down substances in their surroundings and absorbing the nutrients

Plantae (PLAN tee) a kingdom made up of complex, multicellular organisms that are usually green, have cell walls made of cellulose, cannot move around, and use the sun's energy to make sugar by photosynthesis

Kingdom Animalia

Animalia (AN i MAY lee uh) a kingdom made up of complex, multicellular organisms that lack cell walls, can usually move around, and quickly respond to their environment

The kingdom **Animalia** contains complex, multicellular organisms that lack cell walls, are usually able to move around, and have specialized sense organs. These sense organs help most animals quickly respond to their environment. Organisms in the kingdom Animalia are commonly called *animals*. The bald eagle in **Figure 7** belongs to the kingdom Animalia.

Animals depend on the organisms from other kingdoms. For example, animals depend on plants for food. Animals also depend on bacteria and fungi to recycle the nutrients from dead organisms.

Figure 7 *The kingdom Animalia contains many different organisms, such as the bald eagle.*

Quick Lab

Fossils and Branching Diagrams

Try this activity to learn how you can study a fossil and include it in a branching diagram with modern organisms.

▶ **Try It!**

1. The image on the right is a photo of a fossil of an organism called an archaeopteryx.

2. Create a simple list of characteristics that describe the archaeopteryx.

3. Construct a branching diagram of the animal kingdom. Include fish, amphibians, reptiles, birds, and apes in the branching diagram. (Hint: Among these organisms, fish evolved earliest. Amphibians formed the next group, and they were followed by reptiles and then birds. Among these organisms, apes are the most recent group.)

4. Consider the characteristics of each group of organisms. Decide where the archaeopteryx would fit in your branching diagram, and add it to your diagram.

▶ **Think About It!**

5. Using your branching diagram, how can you tell that the archaeopteryx is extinct?

6. Which kinds of organisms are more recent than the archaeopteryx? Which kinds of organisms evolved before the archaeopteryx?

7.3.d
7.7.d

 15 min

Strange Organisms

Classifying organisms is often not easy. Like an animal, some plants can eat other organisms to obtain nutrition. Some protists can use photosynthesis as plants do and move around as animals do. The animal kingdom also includes some members that might surprise you, such as corals.

The red cup sponge in **Figure 8** is also an animal. Sponges are usually considered the simplest animals. They lack sense organs, and most of them cannot move. Scientists used to classify sponges as plants. But sponges cannot make their own food. They must eat other organisms to get nutrients, which is one reason that sponges are classified as animals.

Figure 8 *This red cup sponge is a simple animal.*

SECTION Review

7.1.a, 7.3.d

Summary

- Most biologists recognize three domains: Archaea, Bacteria, and Eukarya.

- As scientists discover new organisms, classification systems are changed to include the characteristics of those new organisms.

- Archaea can live in extreme environments. Bacteria live almost everywhere else. All prokaryotes are members of the domain Archaea or the domain Bacteria.

- Domain Eukarya is made up of four kingdoms: Protista, Fungi, Plantae, and Animalia. All members of Eukarya are eukaryotes.

Using Vocabulary

1. Write an original definition for *Archaea* and *Bacteria.*

Understanding Concepts

2. **Identifying** Describe one characteristic of the domain Eukarya and one characteristic of each kingdom in the domain Eukarya.

Critical Thinking

3. **Applying Concepts** What do all of the organisms from the three domains have in common?

4. **Making Inferences** A branching diagram shows an unusual group of organisms on a branch between birds and mammals. What could you tell about when this unusual group of organisms evolved?

5. **Applying Concepts** You have discovered a new prokaryote. It lives deep within the crust of Earth, which is an extreme environment that has little air or food. Into which domain would you classify this organism? Explain.

Math Skills

6. **Making Calculations** If a certain bacterium divides every 30 min, when will there be more than 1,000 bacteria?

Challenge

7. **Identifying Relationships** Very hot water gushes out of formations on the sea floor called black smokers. Scientists have discovered many new kinds of organisms around black smokers. Why are scientists using a classification system to group these organisms?

8. **Applying Concepts** To get nutrients, the Venus' flytrap uses photosynthesis and traps and digests insects. Its cells have cell walls. Into which kingdom would you place this organism? What makes this organism unusual in this kingdom?

Internet Resources

For a variety of links related to this chapter, go to www.scilinks.org

Topic: Kingdoms
SciLinks code: HY71397

Skills Practice Lab

Grouping Life-Forms by Their Characteristics

You are a crew member and a biologist on the USS *Adventure.* The USS *Adventure* has been on a 5-year mission to collect life-forms and fossils from outside the solar system. On the voyage back to Earth, your ship went through a meteor shower. The meteor shower damaged several of the rooms containing the alien life-forms and the fossils that you collected. Now, there are only two undamaged rooms in your starship for the life-forms. Assuming that life-forms with similar characteristics can live safely together, use observable characteristics to group the life-forms into these two rooms.

OBJECTIVES

Observe the characteristics of different life-forms.

Identify how life-forms can be grouped based on their characteristics.

Construct a branching diagram.

MATERIALS

• paper
• pencil

Procedure

1. Make a data table similar to the one below for all of the life-forms shown.

2. Fill in the columns about the shared derived characteristics of the life-forms based on your observations. (Remember that shared derived characteristics are characteristics that two or more life-forms share with their most recent common ancestor.) Use your observations to divide the life-forms and the remaining fossil into two main groups.

3. Fill in the last column of your table with the room assignments for each life-form.

4. Make a branching diagram based on the characteristics that you have recorded in the table. (Hint: Start with Life-form 1 at the base of the branching diagram. Because you have life-forms in two compartments, you are likely to have two branches splitting off from Life-form 1.) Also, include the fossil of Life-form 7 in the branching diagram.

7.3.d Students know how to construct a simple branching diagram to classify living groups of organisms by shared derived characteristics and how to expand the diagram to include fossil organisms.

Investigation and Experimentation

7.7.d Construct scale models, maps, and appropriately labeled diagrams to communicate scientific knowledge (e.g., motion of Earth's plates and cell structure).

Life-form Characteristics			
Life-form	**Number of body segments**	**Number of antennae**	**Room assignment**
1	DO NOT WRITE IN BOOK		
2			
3			

5 In deciding the order in which life-forms evolved, use the information about the number of body segments or the number of antennae. For example, life-forms that have many body segments may have evolved more recently than life-forms that have fewer body segments.

6 The USS *Adventure* makes one more stop on the way home. On planet X437, you discover another interesting life-form—the CC9, which is shown below. Based on your previous grouping of life-forms, decide if you can include CC9 in one of the rooms for the trip to Earth.

Analyze the Results

7 **Identifying Patterns** Describe the life-forms in room 1. How are they similar? How are they different?

8 **Identifying Patterns** Describe the life-forms in room 2. Are they similar to each other? How do they differ from the life-forms in room 1?

9 **Interpreting Information** To which life-forms is the fossil related? (Hint: Use your branching diagram.)

Draw Conclusions

10 **Applying Conclusions** In which room did you place life-form CC9? How did you decide?

11 **Making Inferences** What other characteristics could you use to make a branching diagram of these life-forms? Would the use of other information change the branching diagram? What difficulties can using other information cause for scientists?

Big Idea Question

12 **Identifying Patterns** How do you group living and extinct organisms? How do branching diagrams show evolutionary relationships?

Life-form 1

Life-form 2

Life-form 3

Life-form 4
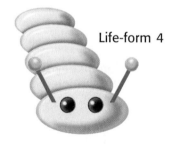

Life-form 5
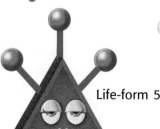

Life-form 6
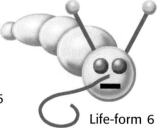

Fossil of life-form 7

CC9

Science Skills Activity

| Scientific Methods | **Research** | Data Analysis | Models, Maps & Diagrams |

Communicating Through Written Reports

Investigation and Experimentation
7.7.e Communicate the steps and results from an investigation in written reports and oral presentations.

▶ Tutorial

After completing an investigation, scientists record and communicate the steps they followed as well as the results of their investigation. Communicating this information can be in the form of a written report. Use the following instructions to write a report based on the steps and results of an investigation.

1 Gathering Information First, gather the information that you collected during your investigation.

2 Organizing Findings Then, organize your information. Your report should have the following parts:
- title
- introduction
- paragraph(s) on materials and methods used
- discussion of your findings and conclusions
- list of the sources of information used

3 Communicating Findings
- In the introductory paragraph, describe the question that you want to answer.
- In the materials and methods section, describe the steps you followed, the facts that you collected, and any observations that you made during the investigation.
- In the discussion section, explain what you learned from your research. Make sure to state whether or not you found an answer to your question.

4 Applying Concepts The style of writing in scientific reports is different from the writing in opinion columns in newspapers or mystery stories. Writing in science must be *objective.* Objective writing is writing that includes only facts. Inferences are only included if there is enough evidence. Review your report to make sure that your writing is objective.

▶ You Try It!

Procedure
Choose an extinct organism that interests you. Check with your teacher about your subject. Conduct research to find out about this organism. Write a report on your findings.

1 Designing Questions Think of a question that would help you learn about the fossils related to the organism you chose. For example, "Where and when did the Plesiosaur live?"

2 Conducting Research Use library resources and the Internet to find information about the organism you chose.

3 Communicating Findings Use the Tutorial to help you organize and communicate your findings.

Analysis

4 Applying Concepts Is your report objective? Explain your position.

5 Evaluating Sources All of your conclusions were based on the information that you found in your research. What did you assume about the information that you found? What kinds of problems may arise from using sources that may not be accurate?

Chapter Summary

The Big Idea
Organisms can be classified into groups based on their characteristics.

Section	Vocabulary

1 Sorting It All Out

Key Concept An eight-level classification system and branching diagrams are two basic tools that scientists use to study living and extinct organisms.

- Scientists use classification to study organisms and how organisms are related to each other.
- The eight levels of classification are the domain, kingdom, phylum, class, order, family, genus, and species.
- Each organism that has been described is given a scientific name.
- Branching diagrams show relatedness between living and extinct organisms over time.

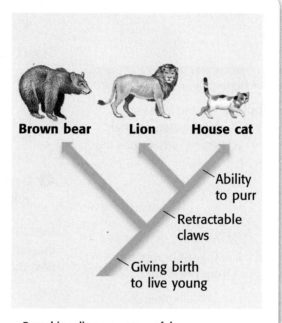

Brown bear   **Lion**   **House cat**

Ability to purr

Retractable claws

Giving birth to live young

Branching diagrams are useful when studying organisms.

classification p. 332
taxonomy p. 333

2 Domains and Kingdoms

Key Concept All organisms can be classified into three domains based on their shared derived characteristics.

- Classification systems change as greater numbers of different organisms are described.
- All prokaryotes are divided into one of two domains, domain Archaea or domain Bacteria.
- All eukaryotes are classified into the domain Eukarya, which is divided into four kingdoms.

These giant sequoias are in the domain Eukarya and the kingdom Plantae.

Archaea p. 339
Bacteria p. 339
Eukarya p. 340
Protista p. 340
Fungi p. 340
Plantae p. 341
Animalia p. 342

Organize

Booklet Review the FoldNote that you created at the beginning of the chapter. Add to or correct the FoldNote based on what you have learned.

Using Vocabulary

1 **Academic Vocabulary** In the sentence "Scientists classify organisms based on their shared derived characteristics," what does the word *derived* mean?
a. caused by
b. inherited from
c. rare
d. common

Complete each of the following sentences by choosing the correct term from the word bank.

Archaea	prokaryotes
eukaryotes	Animalia

2 Prokaryotes that live in extreme environments are in the domain ___.

3 Complex multicellular organisms that can usually move around and respond to their environment are in the kingdom ___.

4 Although ___ are very similar, they are divided into two domains in part because they can live in extremely different environments.

Understanding Concepts

Multiple Choice

5 How do scientists classify organisms?
a. by grouping the organisms by their characteristics
b. by giving the organisms many common names
c. by deciding whether the organisms are useful
d. by using only existing categories of classification

6 The scientific name for the European white water lily is *Nymphaea alba.* To which genus does this plant belong?
a. *Nymphaea*
b. *alba*
c. water lily
d. alba lily

Short Answer

7 **Identifying** Why is the use of scientific names important in biology?

8 **Evaluating** What kind of evidence is used by modern taxonomists to classify organisms based on evolutionary relationships?

9 **Demonstrating** Is a bacterium a type of eukaryote? Explain your answer.

INTERPRETING GRAPHICS Use the branching diagram of selected primates below to answer the next three questions.

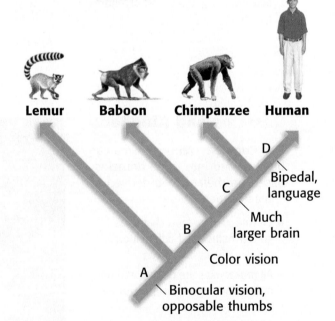

10 **Identifying** Which primate is the closest relative to the common ancestor of all primates?

11 **Evaluating** Which primate shares the most characteristics with humans?

12 **Demonstrating** Do both lemurs and humans have the characteristics listed at point D? Explain your answer.

Writing Skills

13 **Writing Persuasively**   In the past, scientists classified organisms as either plants or animals. Why doesn't that classification system work? Make sure to use examples to support your position.

Critical Thinking

14 **Concept Mapping**   Use the following terms to create a concept map: *domain, kingdom, fern, lizard, Animalia, Fungi, algae, Protista, Plantae,* and *mushroom.*

15 **Analyzing Methods**   Explain how the levels of classification depend on the similarities and differences between organisms.

16 **Identifying Relationships**   What characteristic do all of the members of the four kingdoms in the domain Eukarya share?

17 **Applying Concepts**   You have discovered the fossil of an organism that has a tail, gills, and legs. What steps would you take to figure out where this fossil would fit on a branching diagram that contains, fish, amphibians, reptiles, birds and mammals?

18 **Making Inferences**   Sometimes, the branches in a branching diagram stop at dead ends. These dead ends may not reach the top of the diagram. What can you tell about the organisms shown at the end of these branches? Explain.

19 **Identifying Relationships**   All organisms are made up of cells. Prokaryotes are made up of single cells but are divided into two domains. Describe a way in which you could determine the domain in which to classify a prokaryote.

20 **Expressing Opinions**   Sam has discovered a new organism that has some strange features. He has decided to create a new phylum for this organism. Do you think that this is the correct way to classify this organism? Explain your position.

INTERPRETING GRAPHICS   Use the photo below to answer the next three questions.

21 **Evaluating Data**   Describe two basic characteristics of the organism in the photo.

22 **Identifying Relationships**   Using the characteristics of the organism in the photo, can you decide whether this organism is a fish, a reptile, a bird, an animal, or a plant? Explain.

23 **Expressing Opinions**   What other kinds of information could help you decide how to classify the organism in the photo?

Math Skills

24 **Making Conversions**   Many prokaryotes live near deep-sea hydrothermal vents. The water coming out of the vents can be hotter than 536°F. Just a few meters away from the vent, the water temperature can be as cool as 35.6°F. Calculate the range of temperatures (in degrees Celsius), in which the prokaryotes live. (Hint: Convert both temperatures into degrees Celsius first.)

Challenge

25 **Identifying Relationships**   The kingdom Protista is made up of single-celled organisms and multicellular organisms. These organisms are classified into the kingdom Protista because they do not fit into the other kingdoms. Explain why this characteristic makes kingdom Protista unusual when compared to other kingdoms?

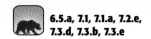
REVIEWING ACADEMIC VOCABULARY

1 In the sentence "The nucleus of a human cell is visible only with a microscope," what does the word *visible* mean?

  A hidden

  B observable

  C separable

  D driven

2 Which of the following words means "to build something by putting parts together"?

  A adapt

  B interpret

  C display

  D construct

3 In the sentence "The function of a branching diagram is to show how different kinds of organisms are related to each other," what does the word *function* mean?

  A a relationship between mathematical sets

  B a specialized activity of a tool or system

  C a characteristic that depends upon another

  D a social gathering or formal ceremony

4 Which of the following sets of words best completes the following sentence: The scientific name *Tyrannosaurus rex* ___ two Greek words that mean "tyrant lizard".

  A derives into

  B is derived with

  C is derived from

  D derives on

REVIEWING CONCEPTS

5 Classification is a tool that is used to study living and extinct organisms. Which of the following are levels in this system?

  A living and nonliving

  B families, genera, and species

  C endangered and not endangered

  D land, marine, and freshwater organisms

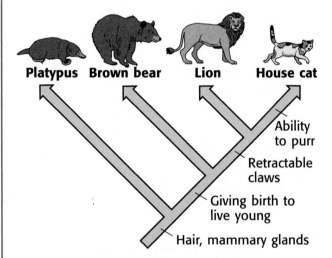

Platypus Brown bear Lion House cat

Ability to purr

Retractable claws

Giving birth to live young

Hair, mammary glands

6 The branching diagram above shows similarities and differences between four mammals. Which of the following mammals has retractable claws?

  A only the brown bear

  B only the house cat

  C the lion and the house cat

  D the platypus and the brown bear

7 A scientist discovers a fossil of a new mammal that was an immediate ancestor of the brown bear. How would this fossil be shown in a branching diagram?

  A It's name would be italicized.

  B It's name would be placed on a branch leading to the brown bear.

  C It's name would be placed at the tip of a new branch next to the brown bear.

  D It's name would appear at the base of a branching diagram showing all bears.

8 Scientists today use an eight-level classification system. Who developed the original system on which the current classification system is based?

A the Chicabo people

B Oliver Zompro

C Michael Fay

D Carolus Linnaeus

9 The fossil of an organism is found near a hot spring. This single-celled organism has a cell wall and no nucleus. Into which of the following groups would you classify this organism?

A domain Archaea

B kingdom Plantae

C kingdom Protista

D kingdom Fungi

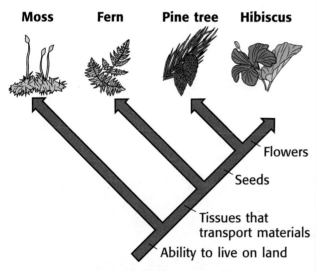

Moss Fern Pine tree Hibiscus

Flowers
Seeds
Tissues that transport materials
Ability to live on land

10 The branching diagram above shows the relationships between four groups of plants. According to the diagram, which group of plants is the oldest?

A hibiscus

B fern

C moss

D pine tree

11 Which of the following statements about cells is true?

A Some organisms have no cells.

B All cells make their own food.

C All cells function similarly.

D All cells have a nucleus.

12 Which of the following events is most likely to lead to the extinction of the largest number of species?

A a hurricane   C a flood

B an ice age   D a war

13 An algal cell's DNA is found

A in a loose loop within the cell.

B in long strands called *chromatin*.

C in the cytoplasm outside the nucleus.

D in the cell's endoplasmic reticulum.

14 Energy flows through the biosphere

A from decomposers to producers to consumers to sunlight.

B from sunlight to animals to producers.

C from sunlight through animals to plants.

D from sunlight through producers to consumers.

15 Darwin developed the following theory: Organisms that have heritable characteristics that are best suited to the organisms' environment survive and pass those characteristics on to their offspring more successfully than organisms that are not well suited to the environment do. What is this theory called?

A natural selection

B natural extinction

C genetic homogeneity

D uniformitarianism

Standards Assessment

Science in Action

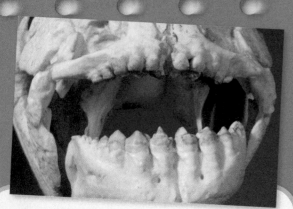

Weird Science

Fish That Eat Fruit

Have you ever thought about fish teeth? You probably know what shark teeth look like. So, you shouldn't be surprised that fish teeth are usually very different from your own teeth. But take a look at the fish shown above. This fish is *frugivorous* (froo JIV uh ruhs), which means that it eats fruit. Some frugivorous fishes live in the Amazon River in Brazil. Parts of the Amazon River basin flood for much of the year, which causes the water level to rise and spread under fruit trees. Fruit falls from the trees into the water, so these fishes have evolved to eat fruit. Eating fruit requires teeth that can bite and chew, just like human teeth. So, these fishes' teeth have evolved into a form that is similar to human teeth!

Math ACTIVITY

Suppose the water level in a river rose 8 m during a flood. At this time, only 4 m of a 16 m tall tree is above water. What was the original depth of the river before it was flooded? Record your work in your **Science Journal.**

Scientific Discoveries

A New Species of Black Coral

Milton Love from the University of California has recently discovered a new species of black coral. The black coral grows between 91 m deep (about 300 ft) and 221 m deep (about 725 ft) in the Channel Islands in California. Love named the coral *Antipathes dendochristos*. *Antipathes* is the genus name for black corals, which were once thought to help fight diseases (*anti* means "against" and *pathos* means "disease"). Love chose the specific name *dendochristos* (a Greek word for Christmas tree) because the live corals look like red or white decorated Christmas trees. Black corals are black only when they die and their black skeletons become exposed.

Language Arts ACTIVITY

Give the newly discovered species of black coral a nickname. Write a short essay in your **Science Journal** about why you chose that particular name for the coral.

Michael Fay

Crossing Africa Finding and classifying wild animals takes a great deal of perseverance. Just ask Michael Fay, who spent 15 months crossing 2,000 miles of uninhabited rain forest in the Congo River Basin of West Africa. He used video, photography, and old-fashioned note taking to record the types of animals and vegetation that he encountered along the way.

To find and classify wild animals, Fay often had to think like an animal. When coming across a group of monkeys swinging high above him in the emerald green canopy, Fay would greet the monkeys with his imitation of the crowned eagle's high-pitched, whistling cry. When the monkeys responded with their own distinctive call, Fay could identify exactly what species they were and would jot it down in one of his 87 waterproof notebooks. Fay also learned other tricks, such as staying downwind of an elephant to get as close to the elephant as possible. He could then identify its size, its age, and the length of its tusks.

Social Studies ACTIVITY

Many organizations around the world are committed to helping preserve biodiversity. Conduct some Internet and library research to find out about an organization that works to keep species safe from extinction. Record your work in your **Science Journal.** Then, create a poster that describes the organization and some of the species that the organization protects.

Internet Resources

- To learn more about careers in science, visit **www.scilinks.org** and enter the SciLinks code HY70225.

- To learn more about these Science in Action topics, visit **go.hrw.com** and type in the keyword HY7CLSF.

- Check out articles related to this chapter by visiting **go.hrw.com**. Just type in the keyword HY7CLSC.

TIMELINE

Structure and Function in Plants and Animals

Have you ever been to a botanical garden or zoo? If so, you have some idea of how many types of animals—from tiny insects to massive whales—are found on Earth. You may have noticed that an organism's shape, size, or appearance help it survive in the environment in which the organism lives. In this unit, you will learn about many types of plants and animals. This timeline shows some developments in the study of plants and animals.

1580

Prospero Alpini discovers that plants have both male structures and female structures.

1775

J. C. Fabricius develops a system for the classification of insects.

1960

Jane Goodall, an English zoologist, begins her research on chimpanzees in Tanzania.

1610
Galileo Galilei uses a compound micro-scope to study insect anatomy.

1761
The first veterinary school is founded in Lyons, France.

1763
Joseph Kolreuter studies orchid pollination and discovers that both parent plants con-tribute traits to the offspring.

1838
Matthias Schleiden discovers that all plant tissue is made up of cells.

1882
Research on the ship *The Albatross* helps increase our knowledge of marine life.

1935
Francis B. Sumner studies the protective coloration of fish.

1983
The U.S. Space Shuttle *Challenger* is launched. Sally Ride, the first American woman in space, is on board.

1987
The last wild Califor-nia condor is cap-tured in an effort to save the species from extinction.

1998
The collection of a flower of the species *Smithatris supranee-ana* leads to the discovery of a new genus of ginger.

Improving Comprehension

Graphic Organizers are important visual tools that can help you organize information and improve your reading comprehension. The Graphic Organizer below is called a *Venn diagram*. Instructions for creating other types of Graphic Organizers are located in the **Study Skills** section of the Appendix.

How to Make a Venn Diagram

1 Draw a diagram like the one shown below. Draw one circle for each topic. Make sure that each circle partially overlaps the other circles.

2 In each circle, write a topic that you want to compare with the topics in the other circles.

3 In the areas of the diagram where circles overlap, write the characteristics that the topics in the overlapping circles share.

4 In the areas of the diagram where circles do not overlap, write the characteristics that are unique to the topic of the particular circle.

When to Use a Venn Diagram

A Venn diagram is a useful tool for comparing two or three topics in science. A Venn diagram shows which characteristics the topics share and which characteristics are unique to each topic. Venn diagrams are ideal when you want to illustrate relationships in a pair or small group of topics. As you read, look for topics that have both shared and unique characteristics, and draw a Venn diagram that shows how the topics are related.

Seed Plants
- produce seeds
- gametophytes are dependent on sporophyte
- do not need water to reproduce sexually
- grouped into gymnosperms and angiosperms

- carry out photosynthesis
- reproduce sexually and asexually
- have a two-stage lifecycle
- have qualities that are useful for humans

Seedless Plants
- need water to reproduce sexually
- gametophytes live independently of sporophyte
- divided into two groups: vascular and nonvascular

You Try It!

This Reading Strategy can also be used within the chapter that you are about to read. Practice making your own *Venn diagram* as directed in the Reading Strategies for Section **2** and Section **3**. Record your work in your **Science Journal.**

Unpacking the Standards

The information below "unpacks" the standards by breaking them down into basic parts. The higher-level, academic vocabulary is highlighted and defined to help you understand the language of the standards. "What It Means" restates the standards as simply as possible.

California Standard	Academic Vocabulary	What It Means
7.1.b Students know the characteristics that distinguish plant cells from animal cells, including chloroplasts and cell walls.		Plant cells have some unique structures that make plant cells different from animal cells. These structures include chloroplasts and a cell wall.
7.1.d Students know that mitochondria **liberate** energy for the work that cells do and that chloroplasts capture sunlight **energy** for photosynthesis.	**liberate** (LIB uhr AYT) to release; to set free **energy** (EN uhr jee) the capacity to do work	Mitochondria release energy from sugar to power the cell's life processes. Chloroplasts use energy from the sun to produce sugars and oxygen.
7.2.a Students know the differences between the life **cycles** and reproduction **methods** of **sexual** and asexual organisms.	**cycle** (SIE kuhl) a repeating series of changes **method** (METH uhd) a way of doing something **sexual** (SEK shoo uhl) having to do with sex	You must know how the life cycles of living things that reproduce sexually differ from the life cycles of living things that reproduce asexually. You must also explain how these ways of reproducing differ.
7.5.a Students know plants and animals have levels of organization for **structure** and **function**, including cells, tissues, organs, organ systems, and the whole organism.	**structure** (STRUHK chuhr) the arrangement of the parts of a whole **function** (FUHNGK shuhn) use or purpose	Plants and animals are made of smaller parts which are organized by shape and purpose. These layers of organization include cells, tissues, organs, organ systems, and the whole organism.
7.5.f Students know the **structures** and **processes** by which flowering plants **generate** pollen, ovules, seeds, and fruit.	**process** (PRAH ses) a set of steps, events, or changes **generate** (JEN uhr AYT) to bring about; to produce	You must know the parts of flowering plants and the ways by which those parts make pollen, ovules, seeds, and fruit.

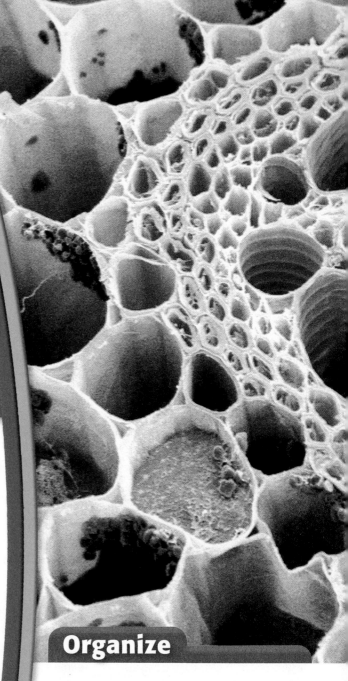

12

Introduction to Plants

The Big Idea

Plants have several common characteristics and can be classified by their structures.

 California Standards

Focus on Life Sciences
7.1 All living organisms are composed of cells, from just one to many trillions, whose details usually are visible only through a microscope. (Section 1)
7.2 A typical cell of any organism contains genetic instructions that specify its traits. Those traits may be modified by environmental influences. (Sections 2 and 3)
7.5 The anatomy and physiology of plants and animals illustrate the complementary nature of structure and function. (Sections 1, 2, 3, and 4)

Investigation and Experimentation
7.7 Scientific progress is made by asking meaningful questions and conducting careful investigations. (Science Skills Activity)

Math
7.1.1 Mathematical Reasoning

English–Language Arts
7.1.3 Reading
7.2.4 Writing

About the Photo

This picture looks alien, but it is very much of this Earth. This buttercup stem has been magnified so that individual cells can be seen. Some of the cells in this plant stem contain green chloroplasts, the organelles responsible for capturing sunlight for the process of photosynthesis.

Organize

Pyramid

Before you read the chapter, create the FoldNote entitled "Pyramid." Label the sides of the pyramid with "Nonvascular plants," "Seedless vascular plants," and "Seed plants." As you read the chapter, define each kind of plant, and write characteristics of each kind of plant on the appropriate side of the pyramid.

Instructions for creating FoldNotes are located in the Study Skills section on p. 579 of the Appendix.

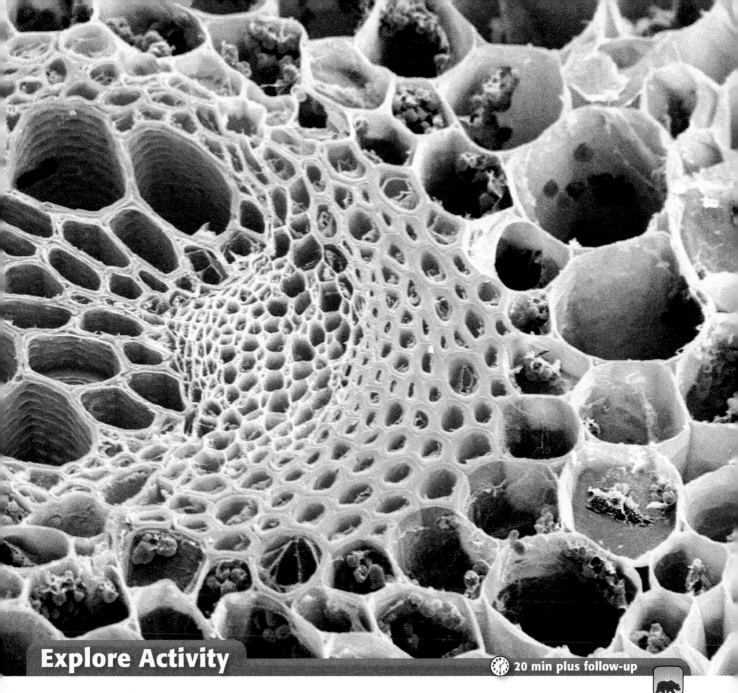

Explore Activity

20 min plus follow-up

Observing Plant Growth

When planting a garden, you bury seeds and water them. What happens to the seeds below the soil? How do seeds grow into plants?

Procedure

1. Fill a clear **2 L soda bottle** to within 8 cm of the top with **moist potting soil.** Your teacher will have already cut off the neck of the bottle.

2. Press **three or four bean seeds** into the soil and against the wall of the bottle. Add enough additional potting soil to cover the seeds.

3. Cover the sides of the bottle with **aluminum foil** to keep out light. Leave the top of the bottle uncovered.

4. Water the seeds with about **60 mL of water,** or water them until the soil is moist. Add more water when the soil dries out.   7.5.a 7.7.c

5. Place the bottle in an area that receives sunshine. Check on your seeds each day for 10 days, and record your observations.

Analysis

6. How many seeds grew?

7. How long did the seeds take to start growing?

8. From where did the seeds most likely get the energy to grow?

What Is a Plant?

Key Concept Most plants perform photosynthesis, reproduce, and share some physical characteristics.

What You Will Learn

● All plants share four main characteristics.

● Photosynthesis is a process that occurs in the chloroplasts of plant cells.

● Plant cells have some structures that animal cells do not have.

● Plants reproduce sexually and asexually.

Why It Matters

Plants supply most of the oxygen on Earth and use energy from the sun to make food.

Vocabulary

• nonvascular plant
• vascular plant
• gymnosperm
• angiosperm

READING STRATEGY

Brainstorming The main idea of this section is that all plants share certain characteristics and can be classified in groups. Brainstorm words and phrases related to the characteristics and classification of plants. Record your work in your **Science Journal.**

7.1.b Students know the characteristics that distinguish plant cells from animal cells, including chloroplasts and cell walls.

7.1.d Students know that mitochondria liberate energy for the work that cells do and that chloroplasts capture sunlight energy for photosynthesis.

7.5.a Students know plants and animals have levels of organization for structure and function, including cells, tissues, organs, organ systems, and the whole organism.

Figure 1 *Chlorophyll makes the leaves of this plant green. Chlorophyll allows plants to make their own food by capturing energy from sunlight.*

▶ Imagine spending a day without plants. It would be impossible to make bread and most other foods. Almost all food is made from plants or from animals that eat plants!

Plant Characteristics

Plants come in many different shapes and sizes. So, what do cactuses, water lilies, ferns, redwoods, and all other plants have in common? Almost all plants share certain characteristics.

Cuticles

Most plants live on land and need sunlight to live. But why don't plants dry out? Plants are protected by a cuticle. A *cuticle* is a waxy layer that coats most of the surfaces of plants that are exposed to air. The cuticle keeps plants from drying out. Plant cuticles vary in thickness depending on where the plants live. Plants that live in dry climates have thicker cuticles than plants that live in more humid climates do.

Photosynthesis

Look at **Figure 1.** Do you know why this plant is green? Plant cells contain chlorophyll. *Chlorophyll* is a green pigment that captures energy from sunlight. Chlorophyll is found in chloroplasts. Chloroplasts are organelles that are found only in plant cells and some protist cells. Animal cells do not have chloroplasts. Chloroplasts capture energy from sunlight to make food from carbon dioxide and water. This process is called *photosynthesis.* Because plants make their own food, they are called *producers.*

Standards Check List an organelle that only plant cells have, and describe its role in a plant cell. 🐻 **7.1.b, 7.1.d**

Figure 2 Some Structures of a Photosynthetic Plant Cell

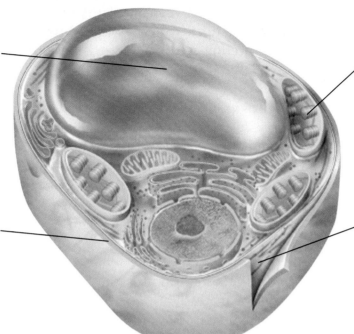

Large Central Vacuole A vacuole stores water, helps support the cell, and plays a role in many other cell functions.

Chloroplast Chloroplasts contain chlorophyll. Chlorophyll captures energy from the sun. Plants use this energy to make food.

Cell Wall The cell wall surrounds the cell membrane. The cell wall supports and protects the plant cell.

Cell Membrane The cell membrane surrounds a plant cell and lies beneath the cell wall.

Cell Walls

How do plants stay upright? They do not have skeletons like many animals do. Instead, plant cells are surrounded by a rigid cell wall. The cell wall lies outside the cell membrane, as **Figure 2** shows. Carbohydrates and other materials in the cell wall form a hard material. Cell walls support and protect the plant cell. Some plant cells also have a secondary cell wall that forms after the cell is mature. When this wall has formed, a plant cell cannot grow larger.

Reproduction

Plants have two stages in their life cycle—the sporophyte (SPOH ruh FIET) stage and the gametophyte (guh MEET uh FIET) stage. In the sporophyte stage, plants make spores. In a suitable environment, such as damp soil, some spores may grow. These new plants are called *gametophytes*.

During the gametophyte stage, female gametophytes produce eggs. Male gametophytes produce sperm. Eggs and sperm are sex cells. For a new plant to be produced, a sperm must fertilize an egg. This type of reproduction is called sexual reproduction. The fertilized egg will eventually grow into a sporophyte, and the cycle will begin again. During the sporophyte and gametophyte stages, the plant can be very different sizes. Most plants are also able to reproduce asexually.

Quick Lab

Cell Walls and Wilting

7.1.b

The vacuole and cell wall in plant cells work together to provide a plant with structure. Try this activity to find out how!

1. Take a **small piece of old celery,** and place it in a **beaker** with **colored water.**

2. Record the amount of water in the beaker.

3. Leave the setup overnight.

4. Describe any changes that occurred to the celery and to the volume of the water.

5. Describe how the structure of the plant cell is responsible for the change that you observed.

 15 min plus follow-up

Plant Classification

Plants can be classified into four groups. First, they are classified as nonvascular plants and vascular plants. Vascular plants are further divided into three groups—seedless plants, nonflowering seed plants, and flowering seed plants.

Nonvascular Plants

Mosses, liverworts, and hornworts are nonvascular plants. A **nonvascular plant** is a plant that does not have specialized tissues to move water and nutrients through the plant. Nonvascular plants depend on diffusion to move materials from one part of the plant to another. Diffusion is possible because nonvascular plants are small. If nonvascular plants were large, the cells of the plants would not get enough water and nutrients.

Vascular Plants

In the same way that the human body has special tissues to move materials through the body, so do many plants. A plant that has tissues to deliver water and nutrients from one part of the plant to another is called a **vascular plant.** These tissues are called *vascular tissues.* Vascular tissues can move water and nutrients to any part of a plant. So, vascular plants can be almost any size.

Vascular plants are divided into three groups—seedless plants and two types of seed plants. Seedless vascular plants include ferns, horsetails, and club mosses. Nonflowering seed plants are called **gymnosperms.** Flowering seed plants are called **angiosperms.** The four main groups of plants are shown in **Figure 3.**

Standards Check What is vascular tissue? 7.5.a

nonvascular plant (nahn VAHS kyuh luhr PLANT) a plant that lacks specialized conducting tissues and true roots, stems, and leaves

vascular plant (VAHS kyuh luhr PLANT) a plant that has specialized tissues that conduct materials from one part of the plant to another

gymnosperm (JIM noh SPUHRM) a woody, vascular seed plant whose seeds are not enclosed by an ovary or fruit
  Wordwise The root *gymn-* means "naked." The root *-sperm* means "seed."

angiosperm (AN jee oh SPUHRM) a flowering plant that produces seeds within a fruit
  Wordwise The root *angi-* means "vessel."

Figure 3 The Main Groups of Plants

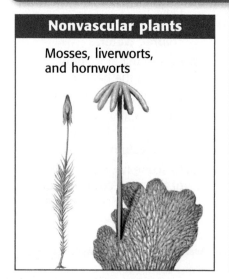

Nonvascular plants	Vascular plants		
Mosses, liverworts, and hornworts	Seedless plants	Seed plants	
	Ferns, horsetails, and club mosses	Nonflowering	Flowering
		Gymnosperms	Angiosperms

The Origin of Plants

Imagine that you traveled back in time about 440 million years. The Earth seems like a strange, bare, and unfriendly place. For one thing, no plants live on land. So, where did plants come from?

Look at **Figure 4.** The photo on the left shows a green alga. The photo on the right shows a fern. The green alga may look like a plant, such as a fern, but the green alga is not a plant.

Green algae lack structures that are present in some plants, such as specialized tissues. But green algae and plants have many similarities. Green algae cells and plant cells have the same kind of chlorophyll. They have similar cell walls. Green algae and plants make their own food through photosynthesis. Both store energy in the form of starch. Also, green algae have a two-stage life cycle. Because of these similarities, most scientists think that green algae and plants share a common ancestor.

Figure 4 *The similarities between a modern green alga (left) and plants, such as ferns (right), suggest that both may have originated from an ancient species of green algae.*

SECTION Review

 7.1.b, 7.1.d, 7.5.a

Summary

- All plants make their own food and have cuticles, cells walls, and a two-stage life cycle.

- Plants are first classified into two groups: nonvascular plants and vascular plants. Vascular plants are further divided into seedless plants, gymnosperms, and angiosperms.

- Similarities between green algae and plants suggest that they have a common ancestor.

Understanding Concepts

1. **Listing** What are four characteristics that all plants share?

2. **Comparing** What is the relationship between chlorophyll and chloroplasts?

3. **Analyzing** Describe the plant life cycle.

Critical Thinking

4. **Making Inferences** One difference between plant cells and animal cells is that animal cells lack cell walls. What is the function of the cell wall?

5. **Applying Concepts** Imagine an environment that is very dry and receives a lot of sunlight. Water is found deep below the soil. Which of the four groups of plants could survive in this environment? Explain your answer.

INTERPRETING GRAPHICS Use the diagram below to answer the next question.

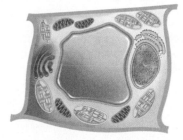

6. **Identifying Relationships** Which structures in the cell above are found only in plant cells? What do each of these structures do in the cell?

Internet Resources

For a variety of links related to this chapter, go to www.scilinks.org

Topic: Plant Characteristics; How Are Plants Classified?
SciLinks code: HY71158; HY70763

Seedless Plants

Key Concept Seedless plants do not produce seeds but are well adapted for reproduction and survival.

▶ When you think of plants, you probably think of plants, such as trees and flowers, that make seeds. But two groups of plants don't make seeds. The two groups of seedless plants are nonvascular plants and seedless vascular plants.

Nonvascular Plants

Mosses, liverworts, and hornworts do not have vascular tissue to transport water and nutrients. Each cell of the plant must get water from the environment or from a nearby cell. So, nonvascular plants usually live in places that are damp. Also, nonvascular plants are small. They grow on soil, the bark of trees, and rocks. Mosses, liverworts, and hornworts don't have true stems, roots, or leaves. They do, however, have structures that carry out the activities of stems, roots, and leaves.

Mosses

Large groups of mosses cover soil or rocks with a mat of tiny green plants. Mosses have leafy stalks and rhizoids. A **rhizoid** is a rootlike structure that holds nonvascular plants in place. Rhizoids help the plants get water and nutrients. As you can see in **Figure 1,** mosses have two stages in their life cycle. During the gametophyte stage, a sperm must travel through a thin film of water to fertilize an egg. This is sexual reproduction. Mosses can also reproduce asexually.

Figure 1 **Moss Life Cycle**

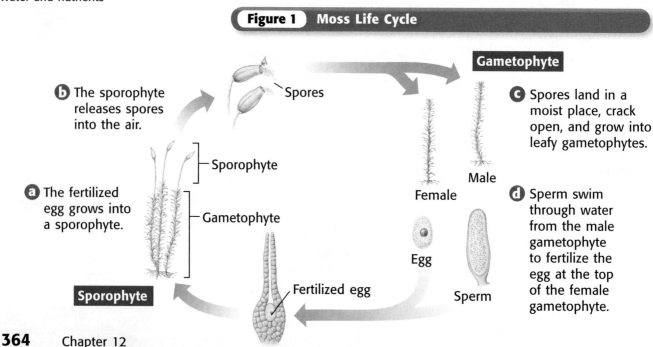

Gametophyte

ⓑ The sporophyte releases spores into the air.

Spores

ⓒ Spores land in a moist place, crack open, and grow into leafy gametophytes.

Sporophyte

ⓐ The fertilized egg grows into a sporophyte.

Gametophyte

Male

Female

ⓓ Sperm swim through water from the male gametophyte to fertilize the egg at the top of the female gametophyte.

Egg

Sporophyte

Fertilized egg

Sperm

Liverworts and Hornworts

Like mosses, liverworts and hornworts are small, nonvascular plants that usually live in damp places. The life cycles of liverworts and hornworts are similar to the life cycle of mosses. The gametophytes of liverworts can be leafy and mosslike or broad and flattened. Hornworts also have broad, flattened gametophytes. Both liverworts and hornworts have rhizoids.

The Importance of Nonvascular Plants

Nonvascular plants have an important role in the environment. They are usually the first plants to live in a new environment, such as newly exposed rock. When these nonvascular plants die, they decompose to help form a thin layer of soil. New plants can grow in this soil. More nonvascular plants may grow and hold the soil in place. This reduces soil erosion. Some animals eat nonvascular plants. Other animals use these plants for nesting material.

Peat mosses are important to humans. Peat mosses grow in bogs and other wet places. This peat can be dried and burned as a fuel. Peat mosses are also used in potting soil.

Seedless Vascular Plants

Seedless vascular plants include, ferns, horsetails, and club mosses. Ancient seedless vascular plants grew very tall. For example, club mosses grew to 40 m tall in ancient forests! Today, ferns, horsetails, and club mosses are usually much smaller. **Figure 2** shows modern club mosses.

Because they have vascular tissue, seedless vascular plants are often larger than nonvascular plants. Vascular tissue is specialized to transport water to all of the cells in a plant.

Standards Check How does vascular tissue help plants? **7.5.a**

7.2.a Students know the differences between the life cycles and reproduction methods of sexual and asexual organisms.

7.5.a Students know plants and animals have levels of organization for structure and function, including cells, tissues, organs, organ systems, and the whole organism.

Quick Lab

Moss Mass   7.2.a 7.7.c

1. Determine the mass of a small sample of **dry sphagnum moss.**

2. Observe what happens when you put a small piece of the moss in **water.** Predict what will happen if you put the entire sample in water.

3. Place the moss sample in a **large beaker of water** for 10 to 15 minutes.

4. Remove the wet moss from the beaker, and determine the mass of the moss.

5. How much mass did the moss gain? Compare your result with your prediction.

6. How is water important to the reproduction of moss?

🕐 **20 min**

Figure 2 *Club mosses are seedless vascular plants.*

Ferns

Ferns grow in many places, from the cold Arctic to warm, humid tropical forests. Many ferns are small plants. But some tropical tree ferns grow as tall as 24 m. Most ferns have a rhizome. A **rhizome** is an underground stem from which new leaves and roots grow. At first, fern leaves, or fronds, are tightly coiled. These fronds look like the end of a violin, or fiddle. So, they are called *fiddleheads*. You are probably most familiar with the leafy fern sporophyte. The fern gametophyte is a tiny plant about half the size of one of your fingernails. The fern gametophyte is green and flat. It is usually shaped like a tiny heart. The life cycle of ferns is shown in **Figure 3.** Ferns and other seedless vascular plants have two stages in their life cycle. Like mosses, ferns rely on water for sexual reproduction. Also, like mosses, ferns are also able to reproduce asexually.

rhizome (RIE ZOHM) a horizontal, underground stem that produces new leaves, shoots, and roots

Horsetails and Club Mosses

Modern horsetails can be as tall as 8 m. But many horsetails are smaller. They usually grow in wet, marshy places. Their stems are hollow and contain silica. The silica gives horsetails a gritty texture. In fact, early American pioneers used horsetails to scrub pots and pans. Club mosses grow in woodlands. Unlike mosses, club mosses have vascular tissue. Horsetails, club mosses, and ferns have similar life cycles.

Figure 3   **Fern Life Cycle**

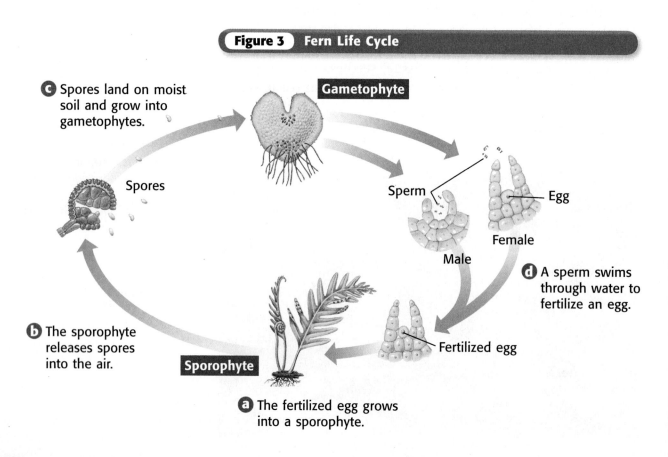

c Spores land on moist soil and grow into gametophytes.

Gametophyte

Spores

Sperm

Egg

Female

Male

d A sperm swims through water to fertilize an egg.

Fertilized egg

b The sporophyte releases spores into the air.

Sporophyte

a The fertilized egg grows into a sporophyte.

The Importance of Seedless Vascular Plants

Seedless vascular plants play important roles in the environment. Ferns, horsetails, and club mosses help form soil. They also help prevent soil erosion. In rocky areas, ferns can play a role in the formation of communities. After lichens and mosses create a layer of soil, ferns may take over. Ferns add to soil depth, which allows other plants to grow.

Ferns and some club mosses are popular houseplants. The fiddleheads of some ferns can be cooked and eaten. Young horsetail shoots and their roots are also edible. Horsetails are used in some dietary supplements, shampoos, and skin-care products.

Seedless vascular plants that lived and died about 300 million years ago are among the most important to humans living today. The remains of these ancient ferns, horsetails, and club mosses formed coal and oil. Coal and oil are fossil fuels that humans mine from Earth's crust. Coal and oil are called fossil fuels because they formed from plants that lived long ago. Humans rely on coal and oil for energy.

INTERNET ACTIVITY

Weird and Wonderful Plants

What is your favorite plant? What do you like about it most? Tell your classmates all about it. Go to **go.hrw.com**, and type in the keyword **HY7PL1W**.

SECTION Review

7.2.a, 7.5.a

Summary

- Nonvascular plants include mosses, liverworts, and hornworts.

- Seedless vascular plants include ferns, horsetails, and club mosses.

- Most plants have a two-stage life cycle and reproduce both sexually and asexually.

- The rhizoids and rhizomes of seedless plants prevent erosion by holding soil in place. The remains of seedless vascular plants that lived and died about 300 million years ago formed coal.

Understanding Concepts

1. **Listing** What are four important roles of seedless plants in the environment?

2. **Identifying** Describe six kinds of seedless plants.

3. **Analyzing** What is the relationship between coal and seedless vascular plants?

Critical Thinking

4. **Making Inferences** Imagine a very damp area. Mosses cover the rocks and trees in this area. Liverworts and hornworts are also very abundant. What might happen if the area dries out? Explain your answer.

5. **Applying Concepts** Modern ferns, horsetails, and club mosses are smaller than they were millions of years ago. Why might these plants be smaller?

6. **Making Comparisons** Compare the life cycle of mosses with the life cycle of ferns.

INTERPRETING GRAPHICS Use the image below to answer the next question.

7. **Identifying Relationships** Identify the structure shown above. What role does this structure play in reproduction?

Internet Resources

For a variety of links related to this chapter, go to www.scilinks.org
Topic: Seedless Plants
SciLinks code: HY71368

Seed Plants

Key Concept Seed plants produce seeds and are categorized as gymnosperms or angiosperms.

What You Will Learn

- Seed plants differ from seedless plants in three main ways.
- A seed is composed of a young plant, a food source, and an outer coating.
- Gymnosperms and angiosperms have different patterns of sexual reproduction.
- Gymnosperms and angiosperms are economically and environmentally important.

Why It Matters

Humans use seed plants as a source of food and as a source of clothing and construction materials.

Vocabulary

- pollen
- pollination

READING STRATEGY

Graphic Organizer In your **Science Journal,** create a Venn Diagram that compares various characteristics of the two groups of vascular plants that produce seeds.

pollen (PAHL uhn) the tiny granules that contain the male gametophytes of seed plants

Think about the seed plants that you use during the day. You likely use dozens of seed plants, from the food you eat to the paper you write on. The two groups of vascular plants that produce seeds are gymnosperms and angiosperms. Gymnosperms are trees and shrubs that do not have flowers or fruit. Angiosperms have flowers and seeds that are protected by fruit.

Characteristics of Seed Plants

Like seedless plants, seed plants have a life cycle that alternates between two stages. But seed plants, such as the plant in **Figure 1,** differ from seedless plants in the following ways:

- Seed plants produce seeds. Seeds nourish and protect young sporophytes.
- Unlike the gametophytes of seedless plants, the gametophytes of seed plants do not live independently of the sporophyte. The gametophytes of seed plants are tiny. The gametophytes form within the reproductive structures of the sporophyte.
- The sperm of seedless plants need water to swim to the eggs of female gametophytes. The sperm of seed plants do not need water to reach an egg. Sperm form inside tiny structures called **pollen.** Pollen can be transported by wind or by animals.

These three characteristics of seed plants allow them to live just about anywhere. For this reason, seed plants are the most common plants on Earth today.

Standards Check List three characteristics that seed plants share. 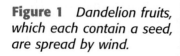 7.2.a, 7.5.f

Figure 1 *Dandelion fruits, which each contain a seed, are spread by wind.*

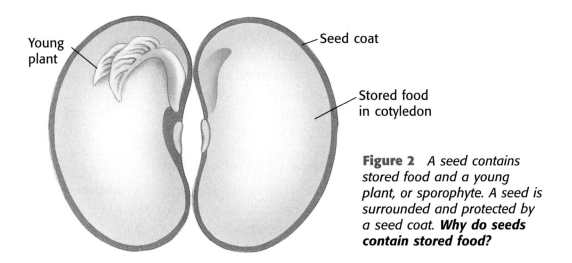

Young plant

Seed coat

Stored food in cotyledon

Figure 2 *A seed contains stored food and a young plant, or sporophyte. A seed is surrounded and protected by a seed coat.* **Why do seeds contain stored food?**

The Structure of Seeds

A seed forms after fertilization, when sperm and eggs are joined. A seed is made up of three parts, as **Figure 2** shows. The first part is a young plant, or the sporophyte. The second part is stored food. It is often found in the *cotyledons* (KAHT uh LEED uhnz), or the seed leaves of the young plant. Finally, a seed coat surrounds and protects the young plant.

Seed plants have some advantages over seedless plants. For example, when a seed begins to grow, the young plant uses the food stored in the seed. The spores of seedless plants don't have stored food to help a new plant grow. Another advantage of seed plants is that seeds can be spread by animals. The spores of seedless plants are usually spread by wind. Animals often spread seeds more efficiently than the wind spreads spores.

7.2.a Students know the differences between the life cycles and reproduction methods of sexual and asexual organisms.
7.5.f Students know the structures and processes by which flowering plants generate pollen, ovules, seeds, and fruit.

Standards Check After which process does a seed form? **7.2.a**

Quick Lab

Dissecting Seeds

7.5.f
7.7.c

1. Draw a **lima bean seed.** Then, soak the lima bean seed in **water** overnight.

2. Remove the seed from the water. Draw what you see.

3. The seed will likely look wrinkly. This is the seed coat. Use a **toothpick** to gently remove the seed coat from the lima bean seed.

4. Gently separate the halves of the lima bean seed. Draw and label what you see.

5. With gloves on, place a drop of **iodine** on one half of the lima bean. Describe what happens.

6. What structures did you see after you split the lima bean seed in half? How do these structures rely on one another?

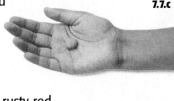

7. Iodine changes from a rusty red color to dark blue in the presence of starch. Explain what the iodine test indicated about the seed.

8. What part of the seed do you think provides the lima bean plant with the energy to grow?

 15 min

Gymnosperms

Seed plants that do not have flowers or fruit are called *gymnosperms*. Gymnosperm seeds are usually protected by a cone. The four groups of gymnosperms are conifers, ginkgoes, cycads, and gnetophytes (NEE toh FIETS). You can see some gymnosperms in **Figure 3.**

The Importance of Gymnosperms

Conifers are the most economically important gymnosperms. People use conifer wood for building materials and paper products. Pine trees produce a sticky fluid called *resin*. Resin is used to make soap, turpentine, paint, and ink. Some conifers produce an important anticancer drug. Some gnetophytes produce anti-allergy drugs. Conifers, cycads, and ginkgoes are popular in gardens and parks.

Figure 3 Examples of Gymnosperms

Conifers The conifers, such as this ponderosa pine, are the largest group of gymnosperms. There are about 630 species of conifers. Most conifers are evergreens that keep their needle-shaped leaves all year. Conifer seeds develop in cones.

Ginkgoes Today, there is only one living species of ginkgo, the ginkgo tree. Ginkgo seeds are not produced in cones. The seeds have fleshy seed coats and are attached directly to the branches of the tree.

Cycads The cycads were more common millions of years ago. Today, there are only about 140 species of cycads. These plants grow in the Tropics. Like conifer seeds, cycad seeds develop in cones.

Gnetophytes About 70 species of gnetophytes, such as this joint fir, exist today. Many gnetophytes are shrubs that grow in dry areas. The seeds of most gnetophytes develop in cones.

Figure 4 The Life Cycle of a Pine Tree

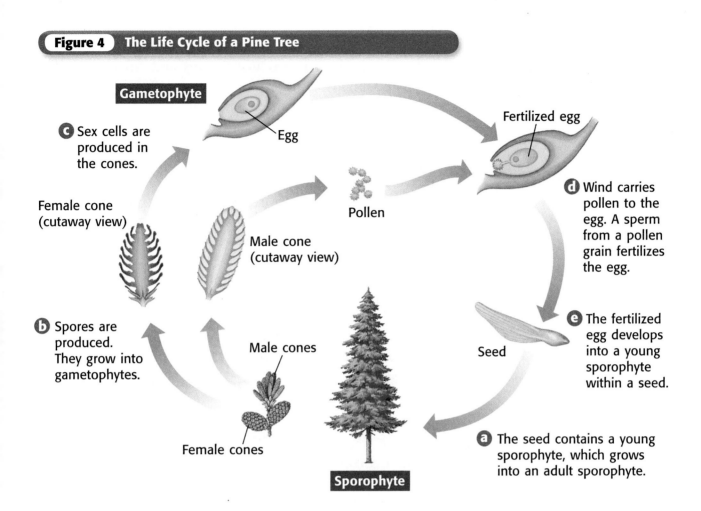

Gametophyte

Egg

c Sex cells are produced in the cones.

Female cone (cutaway view)

b Spores are produced. They grow into gametophytes.

Pollen

Male cone (cutaway view)

Male cones

Female cones

Fertilized egg

d Wind carries pollen to the egg. A sperm from a pollen grain fertilizes the egg.

Seed

e The fertilized egg develops into a young sporophyte within a seed.

a The seed contains a young sporophyte, which grows into an adult sporophyte.

Sporophyte

Life Cycle of Gymnosperms

The gymnosperms that are most familiar to you are probably the conifers. The word *conifer* comes from two words that mean "cone-bearing." Conifers have two kinds of cones—male cones and female cones. The spores from each kind of cone develop into tiny gametophytes.

The male gametophytes of gymnosperms are found in pollen. Pollen grains contain sperm. The female gametophytes produce eggs. Wind carries pollen from the male cones to the female cones. This transfer of pollen from the male to the female is called **pollination.** Pollination occurs during sexual reproduction.

Sperm from pollen fertilize the eggs of the female cone. A fertilized egg develops into a young sporophyte within the female cone. The sporophyte is surrounded by a seed. Eventually, the seed is released. Some cones release seeds right away. Other cones release seeds under special circumstances, such as after forest fires. If conditions are right, the seed will grow. The life cycle of a pine tree is shown in **Figure 4.**

Standards Check Describe the life cycle of gymnosperms. 7.2.a

pollination (PAWL uh NAY shuhn) the transfer of pollen from the male reproductive structures to the female structures of seed plants

Figure 5 *This bee is on its way to another squash flower, where it will leave some of the pollen it is carrying.*

Angiosperms

Vascular plants that produce flowers and fruits are called *angiosperms*. Angiosperms are the most abundant plants today. There are about 300,000 species of angiosperms. Angiosperms can be found in almost every land ecosystem.

Reproduction in Angiosperms

Flowers are the reproductive structures of angiosperms. Some angiosperms depend on the wind for pollination. But others have flowers that attract animals. As **Figure 5** shows, when animals visit different flowers, the animals may carry pollen from flower to flower.

Fruits surround seeds. Some fruits and seeds have structures that help the wind carry them short or long distances. Other fruits attract animals that eat the fruits. The animals discard the seeds away from the plant. Some fruits, such as burrs, are carried from place to place by sticking to the fur of animals.

Standards Check Why do angiosperms have flowers and fruits?
🐻 **7.5.f**

Two Kinds of Angiosperms

Most angiosperms are divided into two classes—monocots and eudicots. The two classes differ in the number of cotyledons, or seed leaves, their seeds have. Monocot seeds have one cotyledon. Grasses, orchids, onions, lilies, and palms are monocots. Eudicot seeds have two cotyledons. Eudicots include roses, cactuses, sunflowers, peanuts, and peas. Other differences between monocots and eudicots are shown in **Figure 6.**

Figure 6 **Two Classes of Angiosperms**

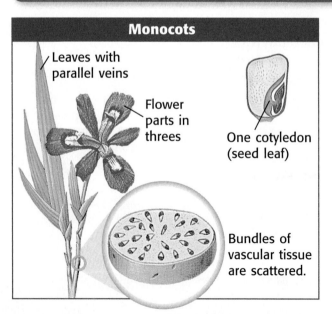

Monocots

Leaves with parallel veins

Flower parts in threes

One cotyledon (seed leaf)

Bundles of vascular tissue are scattered.

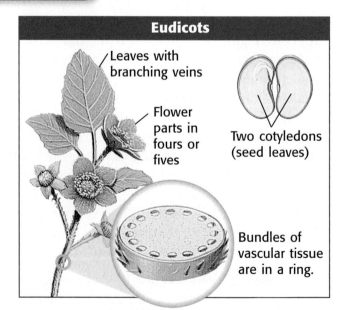

Eudicots

Leaves with branching veins

Flower parts in fours or fives

Two cotyledons (seed leaves)

Bundles of vascular tissue are in a ring.

The Importance of Angiosperms

Flowering plants provide many land animals with the food they need to survive. A field mouse that eats seeds and berries is using flowering plants directly as food. An owl that eats a field mouse is using flowering plants indirectly as food. Flowering plants are also a food source for the insects that pollinate them.

People use flowering plants in many ways. Major food crops, such as corn, wheat, and rice, are flowering plants. Some flowering plants, such as oak trees, are used for building materials. Flowering plants, such as cotton and flax, are used to make clothing and rope. Flowering plants are also used to make medicines, rubber, and perfume oils.

SECTION Review

7.2.a, 7.5.f

Summary

- Seeds nourish the young sporophyte of seed plants. Seed plant gametophytes rely on the sporophyte. Also, they do not need water for fertilization.

- Sexual reproduction occurs in gymnosperms when sperm from the male cone fertilizes the eggs of the female cone. The embryo develops within the female cone, which then releases seeds.

- Flowers are the reproductive structures of angiosperms. Wind and animals help angiosperms reproduce.

- Many organisms rely on seed plants for food. Humans have many uses for seed plants.

Understanding Concepts

1. **Describing** What are two advantages of seed plants?

2. **Comparing** How are the gametophytes of seed plants different from the gametophytes of seedless plants?

3. **Identifying** Describe the structure of seeds.

4. **Identifying** When does fertilization occur during the gymnosperm life cycle?

5. **Comparing** How are angiosperms and gymnosperms similar to one another?

Critical Thinking

6. **Making Inferences** How do angiosperms use flowers and fruits to reproduce?

7. **Applying Concepts** An angiosperm lives in a dense rain forest and close to the ground. It receives little wind. Several herbivores (animals that eat plants) live in this area of the rain forest. What are some ways the plant can ensure its seeds are carried throughout the forest?

INTERPRETING GRAPHICS Use the image below to answer the next question.

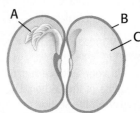

8. **Identifying Relationships** In the seed above, describe how part A relies on parts B and C for its survival.

Math Skills

9. **Making Calculations** About 330,000 species of plants have been discovered. Approximately 300,000 of those species are angiosperms. What percentage of plants are NOT angiosperms?

Internet Resources

For a variety of links related to this chapter, go to www.scilinks.org

Topic: Plants with Seeds;
Plants of California

SciLinks code: HY71168; HY7C03

Structures of Seed Plants

Key Concept Seed plants are made up of roots and shoots. Each part carries out functions for the seed plant.

What You Will Learn

- Seed plants have roots and shoots that allow for water and nutrient uptake and provide support.
- Leaves capture light energy for photosynthesis and provide a surface for gas exchange.
- Flowers are the reproductive structures for angiosperms.

Why It Matters

A seed plant's survival relies on both underground and above ground parts.

Vocabulary

- xylem
- stamen
- phloem
- pistil
- sepal
- ovary
- petal
- ovule

READING STRATEGY

Outlining In your **Science Journal**, create an outline of the section. Use the headings from the section in your outline.

xylem (ZIE luhm) the type of tissue in vascular plants that provides support and conducts water and nutrients from the roots

phloem (FLOH EM) the tissue that conducts food in vascular plants

Just like the human body, a plant has different parts that carry out many functions. Plants have roots, shoots, and reproductive structures. A plant's roots and shoots supply the plant with what it needs to survive. The roots are often found underground. The shoot includes stems and leaves. It is often found above ground.

The vascular tissues of the root and shoot are connected. There are two kinds of vascular tissue—xylem and phloem. **Xylem** is vascular tissue that transports water and minerals through the plant. Xylem moves materials from the roots to the shoots. **Phloem** is vascular tissue that transports food molecules to all parts of a plant. Xylem and phloem are found in all parts of vascular plants.

Roots

Most roots are underground, as **Figure 1** shows. Many people do not realize how extensive root systems can be. For example, a corn plant that is 2.5 m tall can have roots that grow 2.5 m deep and 1.2 m out and away from the stem!

Root Functions

The following are the three main functions of roots:

- Roots absorb water and dissolved minerals from the soil. The water and minerals are transported by the xylem to the shoots.
- Roots hold plants securely in the soil.
- Roots store surplus food made during photosynthesis. The food is produced in the leaves. Then, it is transported in the phloem to the roots. In the roots, the surplus food is usually stored as sugar or starch.

Onion **Dandelion** **Carrots**

Figure 1 *The roots of these plants absorb and store water and minerals.*

Root Structure

The structures of a root are shown in **Figure 2.** The layer of cells that covers the surface of roots is called the *epidermis.* Some cells of the epidermis extend from the root. These cells, or *root hairs,* increase the surface area of the root. This surface area helps the root absorb water and minerals. After water and minerals are absorbed by the epidermis, they diffuse into the center of the root, where the vascular tissue is located.

Roots grow longer at their tips. A group of cells called the *root cap* protects the tip of a root. The root cap produces a slimy substance. This substance makes it easier for the root to push through soil as it grows.

Root Systems

There are two kinds of root systems—taproot systems and fibrous root systems. A taproot system has one main root, or a taproot. The taproot grows downward. Many smaller roots branch from the taproot. Taproots can reach water deep underground. Eudicots and gymnosperms usually have taproot systems.

A fibrous root system has several roots that spread out from the base of a plant's stem. The roots are usually the same size. Fibrous roots usually get water from close to the soil surface. Monocots usually have fibrous roots.

Standards Check What are two types of root systems? **7.5.a**

Practice with Percentages

The table gives an estimate of the number of species in each plant group. What percentage of plant species do not produce seeds?

Plant Species	
Plant group	**Number of species**
Mosses, liverworts, and hornworts	16,000
Ferns, horsetails, and club mosses	12,200
Gymnosperms	840
Angiosperms	300,000

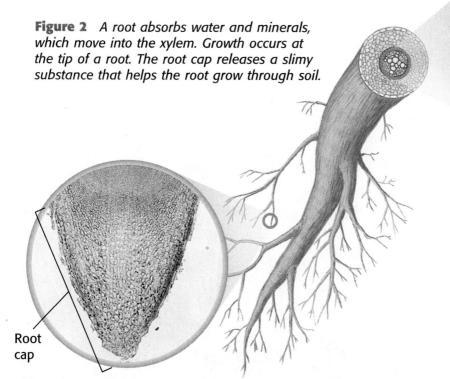

Figure 2 *A root absorbs water and minerals, which move into the xylem. Growth occurs at the tip of a root. The root cap releases a slimy substance that helps the root grow through soil.*

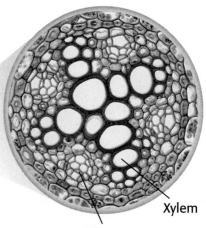

Xylem

Phloem

Root cap

7.5.a Students know plants and animals have levels of organization for structure and function, including cells, tissues, organs, organ systems, and the whole organism.

7.5.f Students know the structures and processes by which flowering plants generate pollen, ovules, seeds, and fruit.

Figure 3 *The stem, or trunk, of this valley oak keeps the tree upright, which helps leaves get sunlight for photosynthesis.*

Stems

Stems vary greatly in shape and size. Stems are usually located above ground. However, many plants have underground stems. The trunk of the valley oak in **Figure 3** is a stem.

Stem Functions

A stem connects a plant's roots to its leaves and reproductive structures. A stem also has the following functions:

- Stems support the plant body. Leaves are arranged along stems. This arrangement helps leaves get sunlight for photosynthesis. Stems hold up reproductive structures, like flowers, which helps pollinators, such as bees, find the flowers.
- Stems transport materials between the root system and the leaves and reproductive structures. Xylem carries water and dissolved minerals from the roots to the leaves and other shoot parts. Phloem carries the food made during photosynthesis to roots and other parts of the plant.
- Some stems store materials. For example, the stems of cactuses and some trees are adapted for water storage.

Herbaceous Stems

Many plants have stems that are soft, thin, and flexible. These stems are called *herbaceous stems* (huhr BAY shuhs STEMZ). Examples of plants that have herbaceous stems include wildflowers, such as clovers and poppies. Many crops, such as beans, tomatoes, and corn, have herbaceous stems. A cross section of an herbaceous stem is shown in **Figure 4.**

Standards Check What is an herbaceous stem? Give an example of a plant that has an herbaceous stem. 🐾 **7.5.a**

Figure 4 *Buttercups are just one plant that has herbaceous stems. Wildflowers and many vegetables have soft, thin, and flexible stems.*

Phloem

Xylem

Growth ring

Phloem

Xylem

Figure 5 *Some plants, such as these trees, have woody stems. Plants that have woody stems usually live for many years. People can use growth rings to estimate the age of a plant.*

Woody Stems

Trees and shrubs have rigid stems made of wood and bark. These stems are called *woody stems*. **Figure 5** shows a cross section of a woody stem. Trees or shrubs that live in areas with cold winters have a growing period during the spring and summer. These plants have a dormant period during the winter. At the beginning of each growing period, large xylem cells are produced. As fall approaches, the plants produce smaller xylem cells, which appear darker. In the fall and winter, the plants stop producing new cells. The cycle begins again the next spring. A ring of dark cells surrounding a ring of light cells makes up a growth ring.

Leaves

Leaves vary greatly in shape. They may be round, narrow, heart-shaped, or fan-shaped. Leaves also vary in size. The raffia palm has leaves that may be six times longer than you are tall. The leaves of duckweed, a tiny aquatic plant, are so small that several of the leaves can fit on your fingernail. **Figure 6** shows a poison ivy leaf. Leaf size, shape, and thickness can change based on the environment in which the plant lives.

Leaf Functions

The main function of leaves is to make food for the plant. Chloroplasts in the cells of leaves capture energy from sunlight. The leaves also absorb carbon dioxide from the air. The leaves use the captured energy to make food, or sugar, from carbon dioxide and water.

Figure 6 *The leaves of poison ivy are very distinctive. They make food to help the plant survive.*

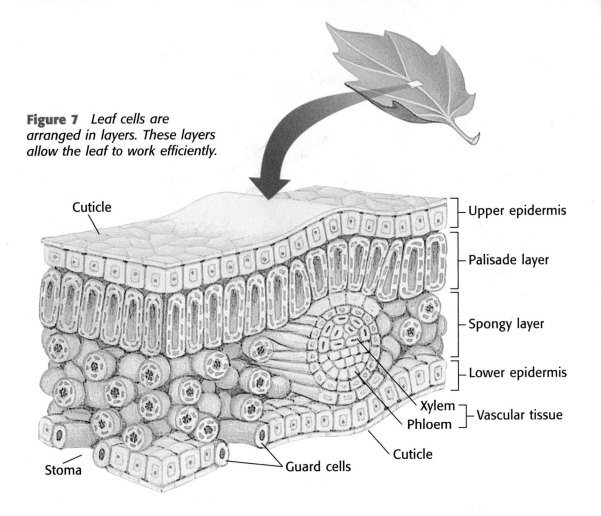

Figure 7 *Leaf cells are arranged in layers. These layers allow the leaf to work efficiently.*

Cuticle

Upper epidermis

Palisade layer

Spongy layer

Lower epidermis

Xylem
Phloem

Vascular tissue

Cuticle

Stoma

Guard cells

Leaf Structure

The structure of leaves, shown in **Figure 7,** is related to their main function—photosynthesis. A cuticle covers the outer surfaces of a leaf. The cuticle prevents the leaf from losing water. A single layer of cells, the epidermis, lies beneath the cuticle. Light passes through the epidermis. Tiny openings in the epidermis, called *stomata* (singular, *stoma*), let carbon dioxide enter the leaf. Guard cells open and close the stomata.

Most photosynthesis takes place in the middle of a leaf. This part of a leaf often has two layers. Cells in the upper layer, the palisade layer, contain many chloroplasts. Photosynthesis takes place in the chloroplasts. Carbon dioxide moves freely in the space between the cells of the second layer, the spongy layer. Xylem and phloem are also found in the spongy layer.

Leaf Adaptations

Some leaves have functions other than photosynthesis. For example, the leaves of many cactuses are modified as spines. These spines keep animals from eating the cactuses. The leaves of another plant, the sundew, are modified to catch insects. Sundews grow in soil that does not contain enough nitrogen to meet the plants' needs. By catching and digesting insects, a sundew is able to get the nitrogen that it needs to survive.

SCHOOL to HOME

Looking at Leaves

Leaves are many shapes and sizes. They are also arranged on a stem in many ways. Walk around your home. In your **Science Journal,** sketch the leaves of the plants you see. Notice the arrangement of the leaves on the stem, the shapes of the leaves, and the veins in the leaves. Use a ruler to measure the size of the leaves.

ACTIVITY

Flowers

Most people admire the beauty of flowers, but why do plants have flowers? Flowers are structures of sexual reproduction for flowering plants. Flowers come in many shapes, colors, and fragrances. Brightly colored and fragrant flowers usually rely on animals for pollination. Other flowers look and smell like rotting meat. These flowers attract flies. The flies pollinate the flowers. Plants that lack brightly colored flowers and fragrances, such as grasses, depend on the wind to spread pollen.

Many flowers also produce nectar. Nectar is a fluid that contains sugar. Nectar attracts birds and insects. These animals move from flower to flower and drink the nectar. As they do so, they often carry pollen to the flowers.

Sepals and Petals

Flowers may have the following basic parts: sepals, petals, stamens, and one or more pistils. Flowers that have all four basic parts are called *perfect flowers*. Flowers that have sepals, petals, and stamens are male flowers. And flowers that have sepals, petals, and one or more pistils are female flowers.

Sepals are modified leaves that make up the outermost ring of flower parts and protect the bud. Sepals are often green like other leaves. Sepals cover and protect the flower while it is a bud. As the blossom opens, the sepals fold back. Then, the petals can unfold and become visible. **Petals** are broad, flat, thin leaflike parts of a flower. Petals vary in color and shape. Petals attract insects or other animals to the flower. Animals help plants reproduce by carrying pollen from flower to flower.

sepal (SEE puhl) in a flower, one of the outermost rings of modified leaves that protect the flower bud

petal (PET uhl) one of the usually brightly colored leaf-shaped parts that make up one of the rings of a flower

Standards Check What is a perfect flower? 7.5.f

Quick Lab

How Do the Parts of a Plant Work Together?

1. Obtain a **potted plant** from your teacher.
2. Water the plant until the soil is damp to the touch.
3. Record the mass of the potted plant.
4. Place the plant in a **large, resealable bag.** Seal the bag.
5. Record the appearance of the plant and bag.
6. For the next week, record your observations of the plant without removing it from the plastic bag.

7. At the end of one week, remove the plant from the plastic bag. Record the final mass of the potted plant.

7.5.a
7.7.c

8. What changes occurred over the course of your observations?
9. Draw a picture of your plant. Label the different parts of the plant. How did these parts work together during the week that you observed the plant?
10. What do you think happened to make the mass of the plant change?

20 min plus follow-up

Figure 8 *The stamens, which produce pollen, and the pistil, which produces eggs, are surrounded by the petals and the sepals.*

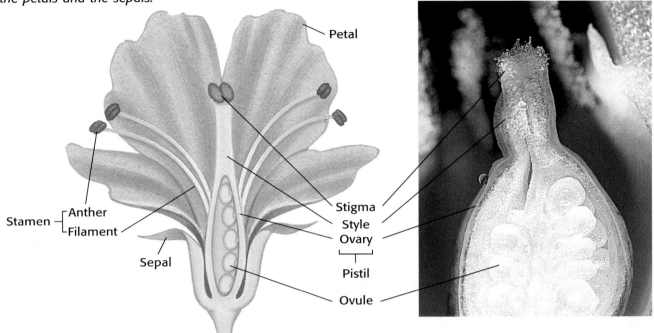

Petal

Stamen ⎧Anther
        ⎩Filament

Sepal

Stigma
Style
Ovary
⎭ Pistil

Ovule

Stamens and Pistils

As **Figure 8** shows, the stamens of flowers are usually found just above the petals. A **stamen** is the male reproductive structure of flowers. Each stamen has a thin stalk called a *filament*. The filament is topped by an anther. Anthers are saclike structures that produce pollen, the male gametophyte.

The center of most flowers contains one or more pistils. A **pistil** is the female reproductive structure of flowers. The tip of the pistil is called the *stigma*. Pollen grains collect on stigmas, which are often sticky or feathery. The long, slender part of the pistil is the style. The rounded base of a pistil that contains one or more ovules is called the **ovary**. Each **ovule** contains an egg. When the egg is fertilized, the ovule develops into a seed. The ovary develops into a fruit.

Standards Check Describe stamens and pistils. Which are the female parts of a flower? the male parts of a flower? 🐻 **7.5.f**

The Importance of Flowers

Flowers help plants reproduce. Humans also use flowers for many things. Roses and many other flowers are used for floral arrangements. Some flowers, such as artichokes, broccoli, and cauliflower, can be eaten. Other flowers, such as hibiscus and chamomile flowers, are used to make tea. Flowers used as spices include cloves and saffron. Flowers are also used in perfumes, lotions, and shampoos.

stamen (STAY muhn) the male reproductive structure of a flower that produces pollen and consists of an anther at the tip of a filament

pistil (PIS til) the female reproductive part of a flower that produces seeds and consists of an ovary, style, and stigma

ovary (OH vuh ree) in flowering plants, the lower part of a pistil that produces eggs in ovules

ovule (AHV yool) a structure in the ovary of a seed plant that contains an embryo sac and that develops into a seed after fertilization

Summary

- Roots supply plants with water and dissolved minerals. Roots support and anchor plants. Roots also store surplus food made during photosynthesis.

- Stems support the body of a plant. They allow transport of materials between the roots and shoots. Some stems store materials, such as water.

- A leaf has a thin epidermis on its upper and lower surfaces. The epidermis allows sunlight to pass through to the center of the leaf.

- Most photosynthesis takes place in the palisade layer of a leaf. The spongy layer of a leaf allows the movement of carbon dioxide and contains the xylem and phloem.

- Flowers are the reproductive structures of angiosperms. They may have four parts: sepals, petals, stamens, and one or more pistils.

- The pistil is usually located in the center of the flower. The ovary of a pistil contains ovules, which contain eggs. When the eggs are fertilized, ovules develop into seeds and the ovary becomes a fruit.

Using Vocabulary

1. Write an original definition for *xylem, phloem, stamen,* and *pistil.*

2. Use *sepal, petal, pistil,* and *ovary* in separate sentences.

Understanding Concepts

3. **Identifying**   Which flower structure produces pollen?

4. **Identifying**   What part of a leaf allows carbon dioxide to enter?

5. **Comparing**   Compare xylem and phloem.

6. **Describing**   Describe the internal structure of a leaf.

7. **Listing**   What are three functions of stems?

8. **Identifying**   Briefly describe the two types of stems.

Critical Thinking

9. **Making Inferences**   Describe two kinds of root systems. How does the structure of each system help the roots perform their three functions?

10. **Applying Concepts**   Pampas grass flowers are found at the top of tall stems, are light-colored, and are unscented. Explain how pampas grass flowers are most likely pollinated.

INTERPRETING GRAPHICS   Use the image below to answer the next question.

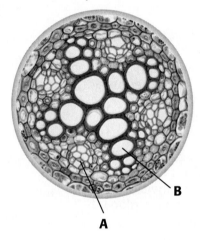

B

A

11. **Analyzing Processes**   Describe how parts A and B work together to keep a plant alive. What would happen if one part stopped functioning?

Challenge

12. **Making Inferences**   Flowers and some animals, especially insects, have influenced one another in the way they have evolved. Develop a hypothesis about how flowers may have changed because of their relationship with bees.

Internet Resources

For a variety of links related to this chapter, go to www.scilinks.org

Topic: Structure of Seed Plants

SciLinks code: HY71467

Model-Making Lab

Build a Flower

OBJECTIVES

Build a model of a flower.

Explain how the model represents an actual flower.

Describe the basic parts of a flower.

MATERIALS

- art materials, such as colored paper, pipe cleaners, beads, and yarn
- card, index, 3 × 5 in.
- glue
- recycled items, such as paper plates and cups, yogurt containers, wire, string, buttons, cardboard, and bottles
- scissors
- tape

SAFETY

Scientists often make models in the laboratory. Models help scientists understand processes and structures. Models are especially useful when scientists are trying to understand processes that are too small to be seen easily, such as pollination, or processes that are too large to be examined in a laboratory, such as the growth of a tree. Models also make it possible to examine the structures of objects, such as flowers.

In this activity, you will use your creativity and your understanding of the structure of a flower to make a model of a flower from recycled materials and art supplies. Remember, a perfect flower is a flower that has both male and female reproductive organs.

Procedure

1 Your teacher will assign to you one of the flowers in this lab. Draw and label the flower that you are assigned.

2 Decide which materials you will use to represent each flower part. Then, build a three-dimensional model of the flower. The model that you build should contain each of the parts present in your flower. Flowers may contain the following parts: stem, sepals, petals, stamens (anther and filament), and pistil (stigma, style, and ovary).

Perfect Flower

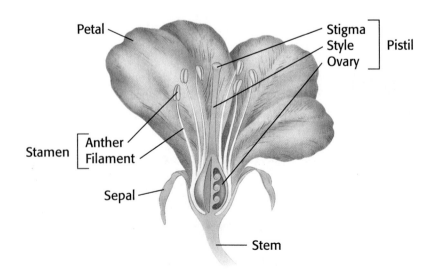

7.5.a Students know plants and animals have levels of organization for structure and function, including cells, tissues, organs, organ systems, and the whole organism.

7.5.f Students know the structures and processes by which flowering plants generate pollen, ovules, seeds, and fruit.

Investigation and Experimentation

7.7.d Construct scale models, maps, and appropriately labeled diagrams to communicate scientific knowledge (e.g., motion of Earth's plates and cell structure).

3 After you build your model, draw a key for your flower model on an index card. Label each of the structures represented on your flower.

Analyze the Results

4 **Organizing Data** List the structures of a flower, and explain the function of each part.

5 **Identifying Patterns** What is the outermost part of your flower? the innermost part of your flower?

6 **Analyzing Data** How are your flower model and an actual flower alike? How are they different?

Draw Conclusions

7 **Drawing Conclusions** How might your flower attract pollinators? What modifications could you make to your flower to attract a greater number of pollinators?

8 **Evaluating Models** Is your model an accurate representation of a flower? Why or why not?

9 **Making Predictions** Compare your flower model with the other two kinds of flowers. How do male and female flowers differ? Why might plants have male and female flowers instead of perfect flowers?

Big Idea Question

10 **Identifying Relationships** While plants share many characteristics, plants also differ in a variety of ways. For example, flowers are not the only structures that plants use for reproduction. Create a table that lists the different kinds of plants and lists their similarities and differences.

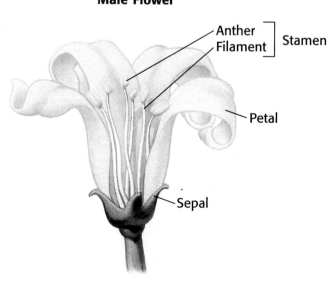

Male Flower

Anther ⎤ Stamen
Filament ⎦
Petal
Sepal

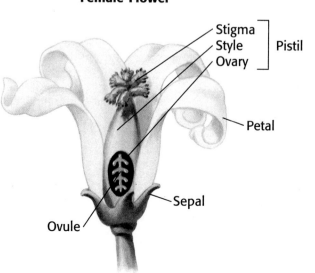

Female Flower

Stigma ⎤ Pistil
Style ⎥
Ovary ⎦
Petal
Sepal
Ovule

Science Skills Activity

Investigation and Experimentation
7.7.d Construct scale models, maps, and appropriately labeled diagrams to communicate scientific knowledge.

Constructing Scale Diagrams

▶ Tutorial

A scale diagram accurately represents the proportions of an object. A scale diagram must indicate the scale that was used to create the diagram. The scale explains how measurement is represented by each unit on the diagram. The following procedure explains how to construct scale diagrams.

Procedure

1 Determine the actual size of the object. You may be able to measure the object if it is big enough, or you may have to do research to find its size.

2 Determine the scale. Large objects, such as sequoia trees, may be represented by diagrams or models by using the following scale: 1 cm = 1 m. A model of a sequoia that is 75 m tall would be 7.5 cm tall.

3 Determine the scale. Small objects, such as cells, may be represented by diagrams or models that have the following scale: 1 cm = 5 µm. A model of a human red blood cell that has a diameter of 7 µm would have a diameter of 7 cm.

4 After you determine the scale, apply it consistently to every measurement you take of the object. A data table similar to **Table 1** may be helpful when creating your diagram or model.

Table 1	Scale Conversions of a Sequoia	
	Actual measurement	**Scale measurement**
Height of sequoia tree	75 m	7.5 cm
Diameter of sequoia trunk	11 m	1.1 cm
Height of first branch from ground	40 m	4.0 cm
Diameter of largest branch	2 m	0.2 cm

Scale: 1 cm = 1 m

▶ You Try It!

In this activity, you will construct a scale diagram of a leaf. The measurements for a lilac leaf are provided in **Table 2.**

Table 2	Scale Conversions of a Lilac Leaf	
Parts of lilac leaf cross section	**Actual measurement**	**Scale measurement**
Upper epidermis	24 µm	
Palisade layer	64 µm	
Spongy layer	124 µm	
Lower epidermis	20 µm	
Diameter of vein	40 µm	

Scale: 1 cm = 10 µm

Procedure

1 Complete **Table 2** to determine the measurements that you would use to construct a scale diagram of a lilac leaf.

2 Using your measurements and the cross section of a leaf in Section 4, create a scale diagram of a leaf cross section.

Analysis

3 **Analyzing** Why might the upper epidermis and lower epidermis be different sizes?

4 **Evaluating** Use **Table 2** to discuss other differences in the parts of the leaf. For example, what do you notice about the part of the leaf that performs photosynthesis? Is it larger than or smaller than the other parts of the leaf?

Chapter Summary

The Big Idea
Plants have several common characteristics and can be classified by their structures.

Section

Vocabulary

1 What Is a Plant?

Key Concept Most plants perform photosynthesis, reproduce, and share some physical characteristics.

- All plants share four main characteristics.
- Photosynthesis is a process that occurs in the chloroplasts of plant cells.
- Plants cells have some structures that animal cells do not have.
- Plants reproduce sexually and asexually.

A plant cell is different from an animal cell.

nonvascular plant p. 362

vascular plant p. 362

gymnosperm p. 362

angiosperm p. 362

2 Seedless Plants

Key Concept Seedless plants do not produce seeds but are well adapted for reproduction and survival.

- Nonvascular plants do not have specialized vascular tissues.
- Seedless vascular plants have specialized vascular tissues.
- Seedless plants reproduce sexually and asexually, but they need water to reproduce.
- Seedless plants have two stages in their life cycle.

Seedless plants have a two-stage life cycle.

rhizoid p. 364

rhizome p. 366

3 Seed Plants

Key Concept Seed plants produce seeds and are categorized as gymnosperms or angiosperms.

- Seed plants differ from seedless plants in three main ways.
- A seed is composed of a young plant, a food source, and an outer coating.
- Gymnosperms and angiosperms have different patterns of sexual reproduction.
- Gymnosperms and angiosperms are economically and environmentally important.

The structure of a seed protects a plant embryo.

pollen p. 368

pollination p. 371

4 Structures of Seed Plants

Key Concept Seed plants are made up of roots and shoots. Each part carries out functions for the seed plant.

- Seed plants have root and shoot systems that allow for water and nutrient uptake and provide support.
- Leaves capture sunlight energy for photosynthesis and provide a surface for gas exchange.
- Flowers are the reproductive structures for angiosperms.

Leaves are one specialized structure in a seed plant.

xylem p. 374

phloem p. 374

sepal p. 379

petal p. 379

stamen p. 380

pistil p. 380

ovary p. 380

ovule p. 380

Chapter Review

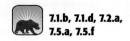

Organize

Pyramid Review the FoldNote that you created at the beginning of the chapter. Add to or correct the FoldNote based on what you have learned.

Using Vocabulary

1. **Academic Vocabulary** In the sentence "Most plants share some physical characteristics," what does the word *characteristics* mean?

Complete each of the following sentences by choosing the correct term from the word bank.

pistil	rhizoid
vascular plant	rhizome
xylem	phloem
pollen	stamen
nonvascular plant	

2. A ___ is the male part of a flower.

3. ___ is a specialized tissue that transports water and nutrients through a plant.

4. An underground stem that produces new leaves and roots is called a ___.

5. The male gametophytes of flowers are contained in structures called ___.

6. A ___ does not have specialized tissues for transporting water.

7. ___ is a specialized tissue that transports food through a plant.

Understanding Concepts

Multiple Choice

8. Which of the following statements about angiosperms is NOT true?
   a. Their seeds are protected by cones.
   b. They produce seeds.
   c. They provide animals with food.
   d. They have flowers.

9. Which of the following statements about roots is true?
   a. Roots supply water and nutrients.
   b. Roots anchor and support a plant.
   c. Roots store surplus food.
   d. All of the above

10. In which part of a leaf does most photosynthesis take place?
    a. palisade layer   c. xylem
    b. phloem   d. epidermis

Short Answer

11. **Listing** What are four ways in which plant cells differ from animal cells?

12. **Listing** What are the four main groups of plants?

13. **Identifying** What is the function of a chloroplast? How would life on Earth be different if plant cells did not have chloroplasts?

14. **Concluding** Why do scientists think green algae and plants have a common ancestor?

15. **Comparing** What are the differences between the sporophyte and gametophyte stages of the life cycle of moss?

16. **Evaluating** How are seedless plants, gymnosperms, and angiosperms important to the environment?

17. **Analyzing** What are two advantages that seeds have over spores?

INTERPRETING GRAPHICS Use the cross section of the woody stem below to answer the next question.

18. **Identifying** What is the age of the tree in the diagram?

INTERPRETING GRAPHICS Use the diagram below to answer the next three questions.

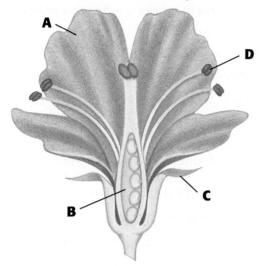

19 Identifying Which letter corresponds to the structure in which pollen is produced? What is the name of this structure?

20 Identifying Which letter corresponds to the structure that contains the ovules? What is the name of this structure?

21 Identifying Which letter corresponds to the structure that protects the flower bud? What is the name of this structure?

Writing Skills

22 Writing Persuasively Write a short essay that compares stems, leaves, and roots in terms of their structure and function in vascular plants.

Critical Thinking

23 Concept Mapping Use the following terms to create a concept map: *flowers, pollen, stamens, ovaries, pistils, stigmas, filaments, anthers, ovules, petals,* and *sepals.*

24 Making Comparisons Imagine that a seed and a spore are beginning to grow in a deep, dark crack in a rock. Which of the two is more likely to grow into an adult plant? Explain your answer.

25 Identifying Relationships Grass flowers do not have strong fragrances or bright colors. How might these characteristics be related to the way by which grass flowers are pollinated?

26 Analyzing Ideas Plants that are pollinated by wind produce more pollen than plants that are pollinated by animals do. Why might wind-pollinated plants produce more pollen?

27 Applying Concepts A scientist discovered a new plant. The plant has vascular tissue and produces seeds. It has brightly colored and strongly scented flowers. It also has sweet fruits. Based on this information, which of the four main types of plants did the scientist discover? How is the plant most likely pollinated? How does the plant most likely spread its seeds?

Math Skills

28 Solving Problems A peach tree produces 127 peaches. If 32% of the peach tree blossoms were fertilized, how many flowers were originally produced by the peach tree?

Challenge

29 Evaluating Data Choose three different kinds of plants. Prepare a table that illustrates the structures that the plants have in common and the structures that differ from plant to plant. Using this table, determine whether or not a mushroom is a plant. Explain your conclusion.

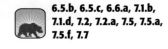
REVIEWING ACADEMIC VOCABULARY

1 **Which of the following words means "to change"?**

A eliminate

B replace

C explain

D modify

2 **In the sentence "The main function of a leaf is photosynthesis," what does the word *function* mean?**

A part

B system

C form

D use

3 **In the sentence "Molecules in the cell store energy and liberate it as the energy is needed for cells to do work," what does the word *liberate* mean?**

A absorb

B release

C capture

D expand

4 **Which of the following words is the closest in meaning to the word *illustrate*?**

A show

B legend

C sequence

D characteristic

REVIEWING CONCEPTS

5 **Which structures are used in the sexual reproduction of a conifer?**

A sexual and asexual spores

B herbaceous and woody stems

C male and female cones

D xylem and phloem tissues

6 **Mosses, hornworts, and liverworts are nonvascular plants. What do these plants lack that vascular plants have?**

A special tissues for making food

B special tissues for reproduction

C special tissues for taking in water and nutrients

D special tissues for moving water through the plant

7 **Which of the following questions can you answer by counting the growth rings on the tree trunk above?**

A What kind of a tree is it?

B How tall did the tree grow?

C How old is the tree?

D What caused the tree to die?

8 Which structures produce most of the food that a plant needs to survive?

A roots

B leaves

C stems

D flowers

9 What are seed plants that produce flowers or fruit called?

A angiosperms

B gymnosperms

C vascular plants

D conifers

10 Which of the following are structures found in a flower?

A xylem and phloem

B sepals and stamen

C chloroplasts and stomata

D fiddleheads and fronds

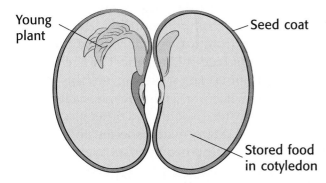

Young plant

Seed coat

Stored food in cotyledon

11 In the image above, what is the function of the seed coat?

A It produces the chloroplasts needed for photosynthesis.

B It eventually forms the adult plant.

C It contains stored food to nourish the young sporophyte.

D It protects the young plant while the seed is dormant.

REVIEWING PRIOR LEARNING

12 Which characteristics distinguish plant cells from animal cells?

A stamen and pistils

B nuclei and cytoplasm

C cell walls and chloroplasts

D pollination and photosynthesis

13 Which plant cell organelle captures and stores sunlight energy for photosynthesis?

A mitochondrion

B chloroplast

C chromosome

D lysosome

14 Which of the following organisms is the decomposer in the food web?

A fern

B vulture

C fungi

D squirrel

15 Which web shows how energy transfers between organisms on Earth?

A sun ⟶ plant ⟶ plant ⟶ animal

B sun ⟶ animal ⟶ animal ⟶ animal

C sun ⟶ plant ⟶ sun ⟶ animal

D sun ⟶ plant ⟶ animal ⟶ animal

16 What is a hypothesis?

A an explanation that can be tested

B a prediction that someone has made

C an experiment that can be performed

D a conclusion based on observation

Science in Action

Weird Science

The World's Oldest Known Tree

Long before Egyptians began building the pyramids at Giza, a seedling took root in the White Mountains in California. More than 4,000 years later, that bristlecone pine tree—known as the Methuselah (muh THOO zuh luh) Tree—is still alive.

The Methuselah Tree is a living history book. Its rings tell a story about volcanic eruptions, drought, and forest fires. A tree's growth appears as a series of rings or layers in the cross section of the tree's trunk. By studying these rings, scientists are able to learn about the changes in the climate that occurred during the life of the tree.

Social Studies ACTIVITY

Research the major events have happened in the lifetime of the Methuselah Tree. Make a timeline that shows these events. Include your work in your **Science Journal.**

Science, Technology, and Society

Plant Poachers

Imagine that you are walking through a swamp. The swamp is full of life. You are surrounded by trees, vines, and water lilies. You can hear frogs singing and mosquitoes buzzing. Then, you notice a ghost orchid hanging from a tree branch. The flower of this orchid looks like a ghost or like a white frog leaping. For some people, this orchid is worth stealing. These people, called *plant poachers,* steal orchids and other plants from the wild. Many plant species and natural areas are threatened by plant theft.

Math ACTIVITY

A plant poacher stole 100 plants from a nature preserve. The poacher planned to sell each plant for $50 but was caught and fined $300 for each stolen plant. What is the difference between the total fine and the total amount of money the plant poacher would have made by selling the plants? Record your work in your **Science Journal.**

Paul Cox

Ethnobotanist Paul Cox is an ethnobotanist. He travels to remote places to look for plants that can help treat diseases. He seeks the advice of native healers in his search. In Samoan cultures, the healer is one of the most valued members of the community. In 1984, Cox met a 78-year-old Samoan healer named Epenesa. Epenesa understood human anatomy, and she dispensed medicines with great accuracy.

After Cox spent months observing Epenesa, she gave him her treatment for yellow fever. Cox brought the yellow-fever remedy to the United States. In 1986, researchers at the National Cancer Institute found that the plant contains a virus-fighting chemical called *prostratin,* which may have potential as a treatment for AIDS.

When two of the Samoan healers that Cox observed died in 1993, generations of medical knowledge was lost with them. The healers' deaths show the urgency of recording this knowledge before all of the healers are gone. Cox and other ethnobotanists work hard to gather knowledge from healers before their knowledge is lost.

Language Arts ACTiViTY

Imagine that you are a healer. Write a letter to an ethnobotanist describing some of the plants you use to treat diseases. Record your work in your **Science Journal.**

Internet Resources

- To learn more about careers in science, visit **www.scilinks.org** and enter the SciLinks code HY70225.

- To learn more about these Science in Action topics, visit **go.hrw.com** and type in the keyword HY7PL1F.

- Check out articles related to this chapter by visiting **go.hrw.com.** Just type in the keyword HY7PL1C.

Improving Comprehension

Graphic Organizers are important visual tools that can help you organize information and improve your reading comprehension. The Graphic Organizer below is called an *idea wheel*. Instructions for creating other types of Graphic Organizers are located in the **Study Skills** section of the Appendix.

How to Make an Idea Wheel

1 Draw a circle. Draw a larger circle around the first circle. Divide the ring between the circles into sections by drawing lines from one circle to the other across the ring. Divide the ring into as many sections as you want.

2 Write a main idea or topic in the smaller circle. Label each section in the ring with a category or characteristic of the main idea.

3 In each section of the ring, include details that are unique to the topic.

When to Use an Idea Wheel

An idea wheel is an effective type of visual organization in which ideas in science can be divided into categories or parts. It is also a useful way to illustrate characteristics of a main idea or topic. As you read, look for topics that are divided into ideas or categories, that can be organized around an idea wheel.

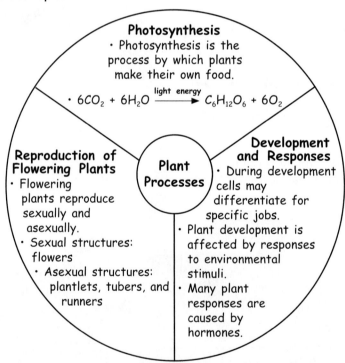

Photosynthesis
- Photosynthesis is the process by which plants make their own food.
- $6CO_2 + 6H_2O \xrightarrow{\text{light energy}} C_6H_{12}O_6 + 6O_2$

Plant Processes

Reproduction of Flowering Plants
- Flowering plants reproduce sexually and asexually.
- Sexual structures: flowers
- Asexual structures: plantlets, tubers, and runners

Development and Responses
- During development cells may differentiate for specific jobs.
- Plant development is affected by responses to environmental stimuli.
- Many plant responses are caused by hormones.

You Try It!

This Reading Strategy can also be used within the chapter that you are about to read. Practice making your own *idea wheel* as directed in the Reading Strategies for Section **2** and Section **3**. Record your work in your **Science Journal.**

Unpacking the Standards

The information below "unpacks" the standards by breaking them down into basic parts. The higher-level, academic vocabulary is highlighted and defined to help you understand the language of the standards. "What It Means" restates the standards as simply as possible.

California Standard	Academic Vocabulary	What It Means
7.1.b Students know the characteristics that distinguish plant cells from animal cells, including chloroplasts and cell walls.		Plant cells have some unique structures that make plant cells different from animal cells. These structures include chloroplasts and a cell wall.
7.1.d Students know that mitochondria **liberate** energy for the work that cells do and that chloroplasts capture sunlight **energy** for photosynthesis.	**liberate** (LIB uhr AYT) to release; to set free **energy** (EN uhr jee) the capacity to do work	Mitochondria release energy from sugar to power the cell's life processes. Chloroplasts use energy from the sun to produce sugars and oxygen.
7.1.f Students know that as multicellular organisms develop, their cells **differentiate.**	**differentiate** (DIF uhr EN shee AYT) to become specialized in structure and function	As a living thing that is made of more than one cell grows, the structure of its cells change so that the cells perform specific jobs.
7.2.a Students know the differences between the life **cycles** and reproduction **methods** of **sexual** and asexual organisms.	**cycle** (SIE kuhl) a repeating series of changes **method** (METH uhd) a way of doing something **sexual** (SEK shoo uhl) having to do with sex	You must know how the life cycles of living things that reproduce sexually differ from the life cycles of living things that reproduce asexually. You must also explain how these ways of reproducing differ.
7.5.a Students know plants and animals have levels of organization for **structure** and **function,** including cells, tissues, organs, organ systems, and the whole organism.	**structure** (STRUHK chuhr) the arrangement of the parts of a whole **function** (FUHNGK shuhn) use or purpose	Plants and animals are made of smaller parts which are organized by shape and purpose. These layers of organization include cells, tissues, organs, organ systems, and the whole organism.
7.5.f Students know the **structures** and **processes** by which flowering plants **generate** pollen, ovules, seeds, and fruit.	**process** (PRAH ses) a set of steps, events, or changes **generate** (JEN uhr AYT) to bring about; to produce	You must know the parts of flowering plants and the ways by which those parts make pollen, ovules, seeds, and fruit.

13

Plant Processes

The Big Idea

Like all living things, plants need nourishment, reproduce, and respond to stimuli.

 California Standards

Focus on Life Sciences

7.1 All living organisms are composed of cells, from just one to many trillions, whose details usually are visible only through a microscope. (Sections 1 and 3)

7.2 A typical cell of any organism contains genetic instructions that specify its traits. Those traits may be modified by environmental influences. (Section 2)

7.5 The anatomy and physiology of plants and animals illustrate the complementary nature of structure and function. (Sections 2 and 3)

Investigation and Experimentation

7.7 Scientific progress is made by asking meaningful questions and conducting careful investigations. (Science Skills Activity)

Math

7.1.1 Algebra and Functions
7.1.2 Mathematical Reasoning

English–Language Arts

7.1.3 Reading
7.2.4 Writing

About the Photo

The plant in this photo is a Venus' flytrap. Those red and green spiny pads are its leaves. Like other plants, Venus' flytraps depend on photosynthesis to get energy. Unlike most plants, the Venus' flytrap gets important nutrients, such as nitrogen, by capturing and digesting insects or other small animals.

Organize

Booklet

Before you read this chapter, create the FoldNote entitled "Booklet." On the front cover, title the booklet "Plant processes." Label the pages of the booklet with "Photosynthesis," "Flowering plants," "Sexual reproduction," "Asexual reproduction," "Plant development," and "Tropism." As you read the chapter, write what you learn about each topic on the appropriate page of the booklet.

Instructions for creating FoldNotes are located in the Study Skills section on p. 580 of the Appendix.

Explore Activity

🕐 **10 min plus follow-up**

7.1.f
7.5.a

Observing Structure and Function in Plants

If you plant seeds in such a way that their "tops" face different directions, will all of their stems grow upward? Do this activity to find the answer.

Procedure

1. Pack **slightly moistened paper towels** into a **clear, medium-sized plastic cup.**

2. Place **five or six corn seeds** between the side of the cup and the paper towels. Equally space the seeds around the cup. Point the tip of each seed in a different direction.

3. Use a **marker** to draw arrows on the outside of the cup to show the direction in which each seed tip is pointing.

4. Place the cup in a well-lit location for 1 week. Keep the seeds moist by adding **water** to the paper towels as needed.

5. After 1 week, observe the seeds. Record the direction in which each stem grew.

Analysis

6. In which direction did each of your shoots grow?

7. Why do you think that your stems grew in the direction that they did?

Plant Processes **395**

Photosynthesis

Key Concept Plants make food during photosynthesis and use the energy in the food during cellular respiration.

READING STRATEGY

Brainstorming The main idea of this section is that photosynthesis is a complicated but important process. Brainstorm words and phrases related to photosynthesis. Record your work in your **Science Journal.**

Plants do not have lungs. But like you, plants need air. Air contains oxygen, carbon dioxide, and other gases. Your body needs oxygen, and plants need oxygen. But what other gas is important to plants?

If you guessed *carbon dioxide,* you are correct. Plants use carbon dioxide for photosynthesis. **Photosynthesis** is the process by which plants make their own food. Plants capture energy from sunlight during photosynthesis. This energy is used to make the sugar glucose, $C_6H_{12}O_6$, from carbon dioxide, CO_2, and water, H_2O.

Capturing Light Energy

Plant cells have organelles called *chloroplasts* (KLAWR uh PLASTS), shown in **Figure 1.** Chloroplasts are the parts of plant cells that capture energy from sunlight for photosynthesis. Two membranes surround each chloroplast. Inside the chloroplast, another membrane forms stacks called *grana* (GRAY nuh). Grana contain **chlorophyll,** a green pigment that absorbs light energy. Because it reflects the green wavelengths of sunlight, chlorophyll looks green. Every green part of a plant looks green because of the presence of chloroplasts and the pigment chlorophyll.

Standards Check What organelle captures energy from sunlight? Is this organelle present in animal cells? 🐻 **7.1.b, 7.1.d**

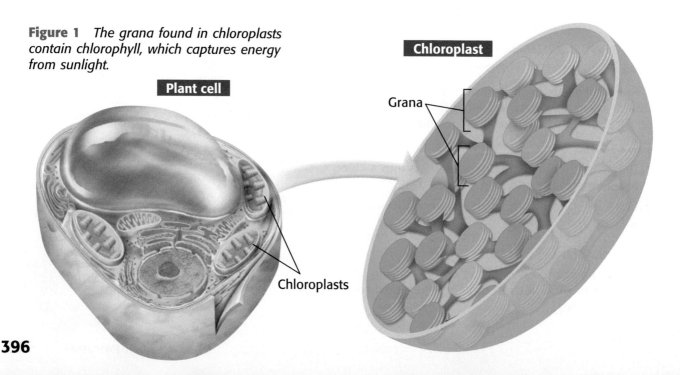

Figure 1 *The grana found in chloroplasts contain chlorophyll, which captures energy from sunlight.*

Plant cell

Chloroplast

Grana

Chloroplasts

Making Sugar

The light energy captured by chlorophyll is used to help form glucose molecules. Glucose is a simple sugar that plants use for food. In turn, plant cells give off oxygen gas, O_2. Photosynthesis is a complicated process made up of many steps. But it can be summarized by the following chemical equation:

$$6CO_2 + 6H_2O \xrightarrow{\text{light energy}} C_6H_{12}O_6 + 6O_2$$

Six molecules of carbon dioxide and six molecules of water are needed to form one molecule of glucose and six molecules of oxygen. **Figure 2** shows where plants get the materials for photosynthesis.

Getting Energy from Sugar

Glucose molecules store energy. Plant cells use this energy for their life processes. Mitochondria release the energy stored in glucose, which plant cells use to do work. To get energy, mitochondria in plant cells break down glucose and other food molecules in a process called **cellular respiration.** During this process, plant cells use oxygen and give off carbon dioxide and water. Excess glucose is converted into another sugar called *sucrose* or is stored as starch.

photosynthesis (FOHT oh SIN thuh sis) the process by which plants, algae, and some bacteria use sunlight, carbon dioxide, and water to make food

chlorophyll (KLAWR uh FIL) a green pigment that captures light energy for photosynthesis

cellular respiration (SEL yoo luhr RES puh RAY shuhn) the process by which cells use oxygen to produce energy from food

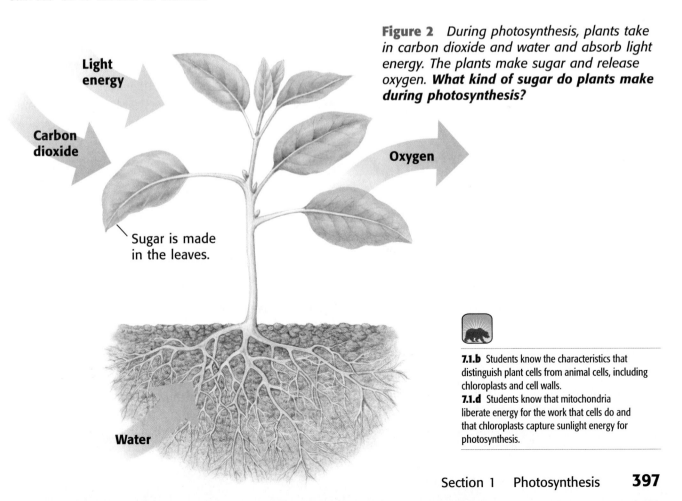

Figure 2 *During photosynthesis, plants take in carbon dioxide and water and absorb light energy. The plants make sugar and release oxygen.* **What kind of sugar do plants make during photosynthesis?**

Light energy

Carbon dioxide

Oxygen

Sugar is made in the leaves.

Water

7.1.b Students know the characteristics that distinguish plant cells from animal cells, including chloroplasts and cell walls.
7.1.d Students know that mitochondria liberate energy for the work that cells do and that chloroplasts capture sunlight energy for photosynthesis.

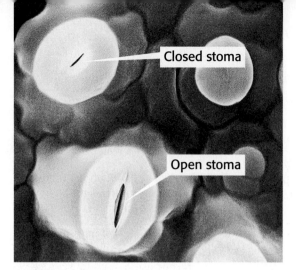

Closed stoma

Open stoma

Figure 3 *When light is available for photosynthesis, the stomata are usually open. At nighttime, the stomata close to conserve water.*

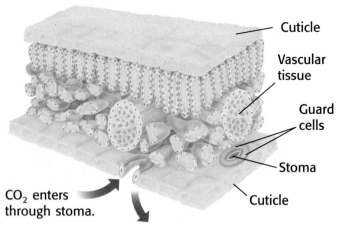

Cuticle

Vascular tissue

Guard cells

Stoma

Cuticle

CO_2 enters through stoma.

H_2O and O_2 exit through stoma.

stoma (STOH muh) one of many openings in a leaf or a stem of a plant that enable gas exchange to occur (plural, *stomata*)

transpiration (TRAN spuh RAY shuhn) the process by which plants release water vapor into the air through stomata

Gas Exchange

A waxy cuticle covers much of the above-ground outer surfaces of a plant. The cuticle protects the plant from water loss. How does a plant get carbon dioxide through this barrier? Carbon dioxide enters the plant's leaves through stomata (singular, *stoma*). A **stoma** is an opening in the epidermis and cuticle of a leaf. Each stoma is surrounded by two *guard cells*. The guard cells act like double doors by opening and closing the stoma. Stomata are shown in **Figure 3.**

When stomata are open, carbon dioxide enters the leaf. The oxygen produced during photosynthesis exits the leaf through the stomata. Water vapor also exits the leaf in this way. The loss of water through leaves is called **transpiration.** Most of the water absorbed by a plant's roots replaces the water lost during transpiration. Sometimes, the amount of water lost through a plant's leaves is greater than the amount of water absorbed by the plant's roots. As a result, the plant wilts.

Quick Lab

Measuring Gas Exchange in Plants

1. Obtain **4 jars** from your teacher. Label two of the jars with your last name and the letter *A*. Label the other 2 jars with your last name and the letter *B*.

2. Fill each jar with **bromothymol-blue (BTB) solution.**

3. Place a **small piece of elodea** in one of the jars labeled "A" and one of the jars labeled "B."

4. Carefully place the lids on the jars so that no air bubbles form.

5. Place the two jars labeled "A" in a dark place.

6. Place the two jars labeled "B" in a sunny place.

7.1.d
7.7.c

7. The next day, observe your jars. Record your observations.

8. When it turns yellow, BTB indicates the presence of carbon dioxide. Use this fact to explain what happened inside the jars.

9. What role did the jars without elodea play in this experiment?

 15 min plus follow-up

The Importance of Photosynthesis

Plants and other photosynthetic organisms, such as some bacteria and many protists, form the base of nearly all food chains on Earth. An example of one food chain is shown in **Figure 4.** During photosynthesis, plants store light energy as chemical energy. Some animals use this chemical energy when they eat plants. Other animals get energy from plants indirectly. These animals eat animals that eat plants. Most organisms could not survive without photosynthetic organisms.

Plants, animals, and most other organisms depend on cellular respiration to get energy. Cellular respiration requires oxygen. Oxygen is a byproduct of photosynthesis. So, photosynthesis provides the oxygen that animals and plants need for cellular respiration.

Standards Check What are two ways in which the products of photosynthesis are important? **7.1.d**

Figure 4 *Mice depend on plants for food. In turn, cats get energy from mice.*

SECTION Review

 7.1.b, 7.1.d

Summary

- Chloroplasts and mitochondria are important organelles in plant cells.

- During photosynthesis, plants use energy from sunlight, carbon dioxide, and water to make glucose and oxygen.

- Plants get energy from food by cellular respiration, which uses oxygen and releases carbon dioxide and water.

- Transpiration, or the loss of water through the leaves of plants, occurs when stomata are open.

Understanding Concepts

1. **Describing** What do chloroplasts and mitochondria do?

2. **Comparing** What is the relationship between cellular respiration and photosynthesis?

3. **Identifying** How do plants take in and give off gases?

Critical Thinking

INTERPRETING GRAPHICS Use the image below to answer the next question.

4. **Predicting Consequences** What would happen if the structure above was not present in plant cells?

5. **Predicting Consequences** Predict what might happen if plants and other photosynthetic organisms disappeared.

6. **Applying Concepts** Why are animals not able to perform photosynthesis? In what ways do animals depend on plants?

Math Skills

7. **Solving Problems** Plants use 6 carbon dioxide molecules and 6 water molecules to make 1 glucose molecule. How many carbon dioxide and water molecules are needed to make 12 glucose molecules?

Internet Resources

For a variety of links related to this chapter, go to www.scilinks.org
Topic: Photosynthesis
SciLinks code: HY71140

Reproduction of Flowering Plants

Key Concept Flowering plants reproduce sexually and asexually.

What You Will Learn

- After pollination, sexual reproduction in flowering plants occurs when an egg is fertilized by a sperm.
- Seeds form from fertilized ovules. The ovary of a flower becomes a fruit.
- In the proper conditions, seeds can sprout and develop into plants.
- Flowering plants can reproduce asexually.

Why It Matters

Flowering plants and their reproductive structures provide food for many organisms.

Vocabulary

- dormant

READING STRATEGY

Graphic Organizer In your **Science Journal,** create an Idea Wheel about the stages of sexual reproduction in a flowering plant.

▶ Imagine you are standing in a field of wildflowers. You're surrounded by bright colors and sweet fragrances. You can hear bees buzzing from flower to flower. Flowering plants are the largest and most diverse group of plants. Their success is partly due to their flowers. Flowers are structures for sexual reproduction. In sexual reproduction, an egg is fertilized by a sperm.

Fertilization

The fertilization of flowering plants takes place within the flower. *Pollination* occurs when pollen, which carries sperm, is moved from anthers to stigmas. Usually, wind or animals move pollen from one flower to another flower. After pollen lands on the stigma, a tube grows from each pollen grain. The tube grows through the style to an ovule. Ovules are found inside the ovary. Each ovule contains an egg. Sperm from the pollen grain move down the pollen tube and into an ovule. Fertilization occurs when a sperm fuses with the egg inside an ovule. **Figure 1** shows pollination and fertilization.

Standards Check Describe sexual reproduction in plants. 🐻 **7.2.a**

7.2.a Students know the differences between the life cycles and reproduction methods of sexual and asexual organisms.
7.5.f Students know the structures and processes by which flowering plants generate pollen, ovules, seeds, and fruit.

Figure 1 Pollination and Fertilization

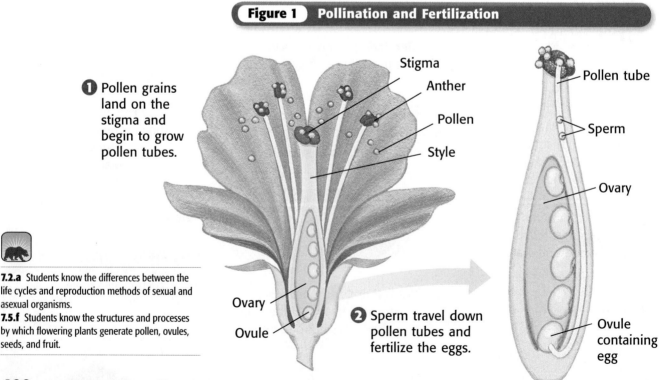

❶ Pollen grains land on the stigma and begin to grow pollen tubes.

Stigma
Anther
Pollen
Style
Ovary
Ovule

Pollen tube
Sperm
Ovary
Ovule containing egg

❷ Sperm travel down pollen tubes and fertilize the eggs.

Figure 2 Seed Production

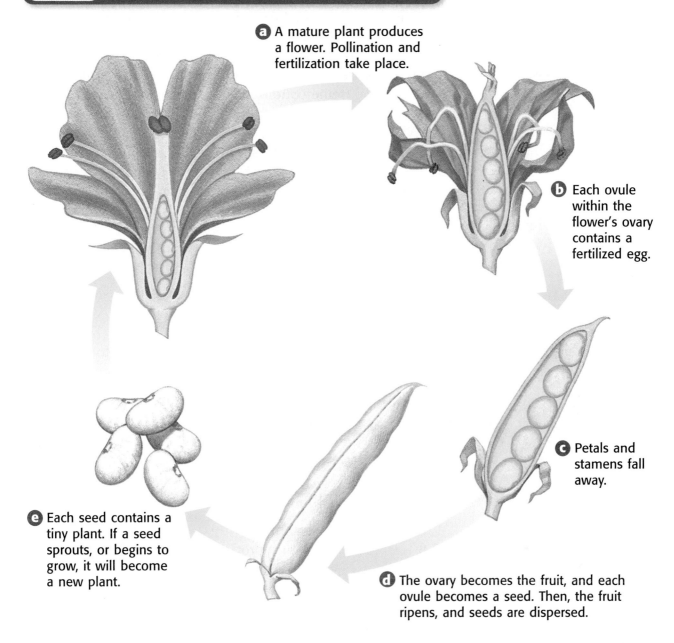

a A mature plant produces a flower. Pollination and fertilization take place.

b Each ovule within the flower's ovary contains a fertilized egg.

c Petals and stamens fall away.

d The ovary becomes the fruit, and each ovule becomes a seed. Then, the fruit ripens, and seeds are dispersed.

e Each seed contains a tiny plant. If a seed sprouts, or begins to grow, it will become a new plant.

From Flower to Fruit

After fertilization takes place, the ovule develops into a seed. The seed contains a tiny, undeveloped plant, called an *embryo*. The ovary surrounding the ovule becomes a fruit, as **Figure 2** shows.

As it swells and ripens, a fruit protects its developing seeds. **Figure 3** shows a common fruit. Fruits often help a plant spread its seeds. Many fruits are edible. Animals may eat these fruits. Then, the animals discard the seeds away from the parent plant. Fruits such as burrs are spread when they get caught in an animal's fur. And some fruits are carried by the wind.

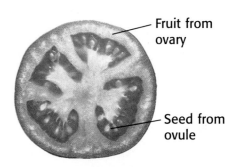

Fruit from ovary

Seed from ovule

Figure 3 *Tomatoes develop from a flower's ovary and ovules.*

Standards Check Where do seeds and fruit come from? 🐻 **7.5.f**

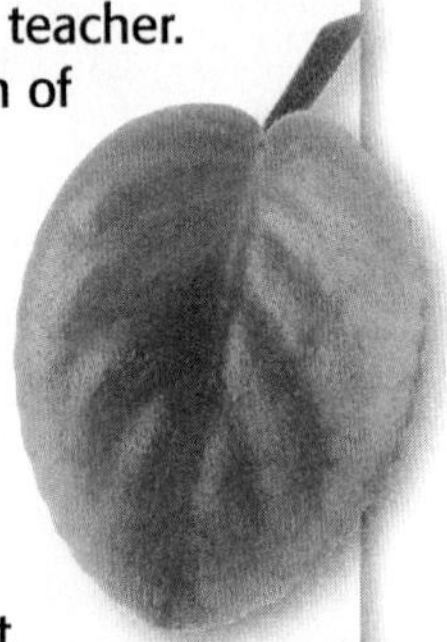

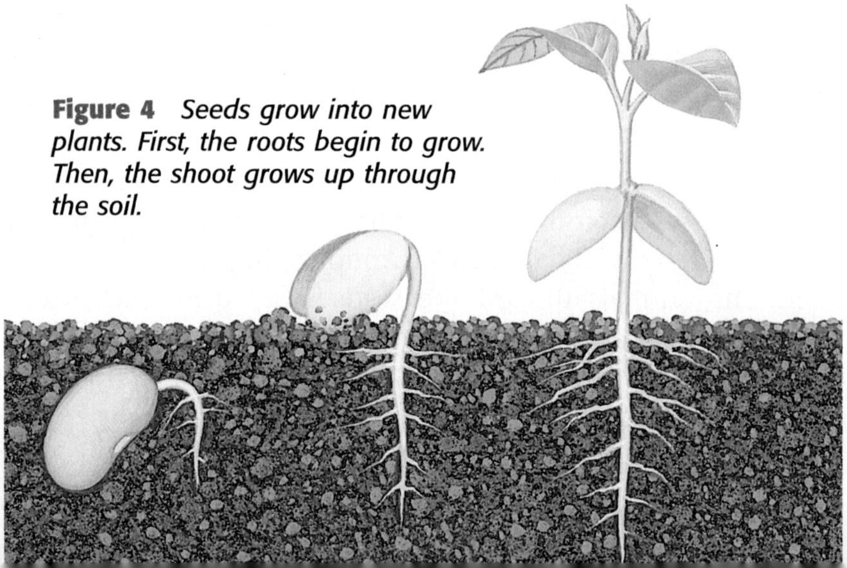

dormant (DAWR muhnt) describes the inactive state of a seed or other plant part when conditions are unfavorable to growth

From Seed to Plant

Once a seed is fully developed, the embryo inside the seed stops growing. If the conditions are not favorable for growth, the seed may become **dormant,** or inactive. Dormant seeds often survive long periods of drought or freezing temperatures. Some seeds need extreme conditions, such as cold winters or forest fires, to break their dormancy.

When seeds are dropped or planted in a suitable environment, the seeds sprout. To sprout, most seeds need water, air, and warm temperatures. Each plant species has an ideal temperature at which most of its seeds begin to grow. For many plants, the ideal temperature for growth is about 27°C (80.6°F). **Figure 4** shows the *germination,* or sprouting, of a bean seed.

Quick Lab

Plant Cuttings

7.2.a
7.7.c

1. Get an **African violet leaf** from your teacher. Create a sketch of the leaf.
2. Place the leaf in a **cup of soil** so that the tip of the leaf is above the soil.
3. Water the plant, and place it in a sunny location. Predict what will happen.
4. If the soil feels dry, water the plant as needed for three days. Record your observations.
5. On the fourth day, carefully take the leaf out of the soil. Use water to gently remove the soil from the leaf. Sketch the leaf.
6. How is the leaf different? What is happening to the leaf cells of this plant?

15 min plus follow-up

Other Methods of Reproduction

Flowering plants can also reproduce asexually. But they do not need flowers to do so. Instead, a new plant grows from one of the plant parts, such as a stem or root. The following are three examples of structures plants use to reproduce asexually:

- **Plantlets** Tiny plants grow along the edges of a plant's leaves. These plantlets fall off and grow on their own.
- **Tubers** Underground stems, or tubers, can produce new plants after a dormant season.
- **Runners** Above-ground stems from which new plants can grow are called *runners.*

Figure 5 shows examples of these three structures. A plant that results from sexual reproduction is genetically related to both parents. But a new plant that grows from the plantlet, tuber, or runner of another plant is genetically identical to that plant.

Standards Check **What are three structures that plants use to reproduce asexually? 7.2.a**

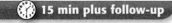

Figure 4 *Seeds grow into new plants. First, the roots begin to grow. Then, the shoot grows up through the soil.*

Figure 5 Three Structures for Asexual Reproduction

Kalanchoe plants produce **plantlets** along the edges of their leaves. The plantlets eventually fall off and root in the soil to grow on their own.

A potato is a **tuber,** or underground stem. The "eyes" of potatoes are buds that can grow into new plants.

The strawberry plant produces **runners,** or stems that grow horizontally along the ground. Buds along the runners take root and grow into new plants.

SECTION Review

7.2.a, 7.5.f

Summary

- In the sexual reproduction of flowering plants, a sperm fertilizes an egg.

- After fertilization, seeds and fruit form. The seeds may sprout into new plants.

- A dormant seed can survive drought and freezing temperatures. Some seeds need extreme conditions to break their dormancy.

- Some plants use plantlets, tubers, or runners to reproduce asexually.

Understanding Concepts

1 **Comparing** How are pollination and fertilization related?

2 **Identifying** Which part of a flower develops into a fruit? into a seed?

3 **Concluding** Why do some seeds become dormant?

4 **Describing** How do plants reproduce asexually?

Critical Thinking

5 **Identifying Relationships** When may asexual reproduction be important for the survival of some flowering plants?

6 **Analyzing Ideas** Sexual reproduction produces more genetic variety than asexual reproduction does. Why is variety important?

7 **Making Inferences** What do flowers and runners have in common? How do they differ?

Math Skills

8 **Using Equations** A seed sprouts when the temperature is 27°C. If the temperature starts at 20°C and rises 1.5°C each week, how many weeks will the seed take to sprout?

Challenge

9 **Predicting Consequences** How might the world be different if the ovaries of fertilized plants no longer developed into fruits?

Internet Resources

For a variety of links related to this chapter, go to www.scilinks.org
Topic: Reproduction of Plants
SciLinks code: HY71295

Plant Development and Responses

Key Concept Plants develop differently than animals do. Also, plants respond to stimuli in a variety of ways.

What You Will Learn

- Some plant cells are able to differentiate throughout the life of the plant.
- Hormones cause a plant to develop in response to certain stimuli.
- Plants may grow toward some stimuli and away from others.

Why It Matters

Environmental stimuli can affect the structures and functions in plants.

Vocabulary

- stimulus
- tropism

READING STRATEGY

Graphic Organizer In your **Science Journal,** create an Idea Wheel that describes plant tropisms.

stimulus (STIM yoo luhs) anything that causes a reaction or change in an organism or any part of an organism

▶ *Development* is the process by which an organism increases in ability or skill. Development is different from growth. *Growth* refers to an increase in size. During development, the cells of an organism become *differentiated*. In other words, each kind of cell is specialized to perform a specific function.

Plant Development

As a baby bird develops, its cells differentiate and become fixed in their development. So, the bird's cells lose the ability to differentiate into other kinds of cells. Most animal cells differentiate only once.

But some cells of some plants can differentiate many times as the plants develop. **Figure 1** shows an African violet leaf. Cells at the edge of this leaf are differentiating into root cells and stems cells. This process is one way some plants reproduce asexually. Many animals cannot reproduce asexually.

A plant's development can be affected by an environmental stimulus. A **stimulus** (plural, *stimuli*) is anything that causes a reaction or change in an organism. Plants do not see or react to stimuli, such as weather or light, in the same way that animals do. Many of a plant's responses to stimuli are caused by hormones. A *hormone* is a chemical that causes cells to react in certain ways. Hormones may cause certain plant cells to differentiate in response to stimuli.

Standards Check What happens when a cell differentiates? 7.1.f

Figure 1 *The cells in this African violet leaf are differentiating into stem cells and root cells.*

7.1.f Students know that as multicellular organisms develop, their cells differentiate.
7.5.a Students know plants and animals have levels of organization for structure and function, including cells, tissues, organs, organ systems, and the whole organism.

Plant Hormones

There are many groups of plant hormones. These hormones cause specific changes in plants.

Role of Hormones in Plants

Hormones play important roles in each stage of a plant's life cycle. Stimuli, such as the amount of light or water present in the environment or the temperature of the environment, change how much of a particular hormone is made in the cells of a plant. In turn, the concentrations of individual plant hormones change how and where a plant grows. For example, you may have noticed that plants grow toward light. The tendency of a plant to grow toward light is caused by a group of plant hormones called *auxins.* Auxins accumulate on the shaded side of a plant's stem, which makes the cells on that side *elongate,* or increase in length.

Use of Hormones in Agriculture

Some plant hormones are very useful in agriculture. A plant hormone called *ethylene* is used to ripen fruits, such as bananas and tomatoes, that are picked before they are ripe. Gibberellins are another group of plant hormones that are very useful in agriculture. The effect of gibberellins can be seen in **Figure 2.**

Figure 2 *A gibberellin was applied to the Thompson seedless grapes on the left. They are larger than the normal Thompson seedless grapes on the right.*

Quick Lab

7.5.a

Observing the Effects of Ethylene

In this experiment, you will use a ripe apple to observe how ethylene affects plants.

▶ Try It!

1. Place a **small plant** in a **large jar.** Tightly close the lid.
2. Place a **small plant** and an **apple** in a **second jar.** Tightly close the lid.
3. Observe the jars. Record your observations.
4. Place the jars in a well-lit place.
5. Observe the jars each day for a week. Record your observations.

▶ Think About It!

6. Describe any changes in the plants. Which plant changed the most?
7. A ripe apple releases ethylene gas. Using your observations, describe how ethylene may affect a plant?

 10 min/day for 6 days

Plant Tropisms

What happens when you get really cold? Do your teeth chatter? Do you shiver? What other reactions do you have to environmental stimuli? When it rains, you may go inside or get an umbrella. But, how do plants respond to stimuli?

Some plants respond to environmental stimuli by growing in particular directions. Growth in response to a stimulus is called a **tropism.** Tropisms are either positive or negative. Plant growth toward a stimulus is a positive tropism. Plant growth away from a stimulus is a negative tropism. Plant tropisms are caused by the concentrations of certain hormones in plants. These concentrations are affected by environmental stimuli.

Light

What happens if a houseplant is getting light from only one direction, such as through a window? The shoot tips probably bend toward the light. Bending toward the light is a positive tropism. A change in the direction of the growth of a plant in response to light is called *phototropism* (foh TAH troh PIZ uhm). The result of phototropism is shown in **Figure 3.** A shoot bends because cells on one side of the shoot grow longer than cells on the other side of the shoot. You read earlier that the plant hormone auxin plays a role in phototropism.

Standards Check What happens to the cells of a plant's shoots when the plant gets light from only one direction? 🐻7.5.a

tropism (TROH PIZ uhm) growth of all or part of an organism in response to an external stimulus, such as light

Wordwise The root *trop-* means "to turn." Other examples are *Tropics, phototropism,* and *gravitropism.*

Biographies of Biologists

How do biologists become famous? Write the biography of an interesting biologist. Go to **go.hrw.com,** and type in the keyword HY7PL2W.

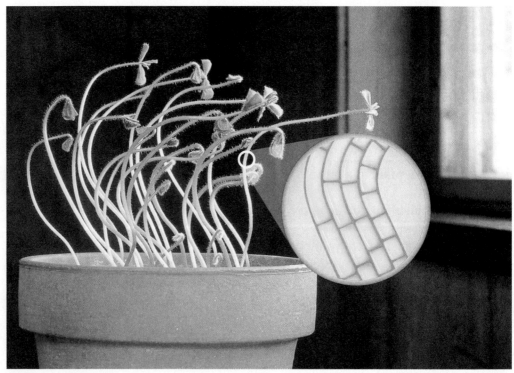

Figure 3 *The plant cells on the shaded side of the shoot grow longer than the cells on the other side. So, the shoot bends toward the light.*

Figure 4 Gravitropism

To grow away from the pull of gravity, this plant has grown upward.

This plant has recently been upside down.

Gravity

Gravity can also cause a change in the direction in which a plant is growing. This change is called *gravitropism* (GRAV i TROH PIZ uhm). The effect of gravitropism is demonstrated by the plants in **Figure 4.** A few days after a plant is placed on its side or turned upside down, the direction in which its roots and shoots are growing changes. Most shoot tips have negative gravitropism. They grow upward, away from the center of Earth. In contrast, most root tips have positive gravitropism. Roots grow downward, toward the center of Earth. Gravitropism is also known as *geotropism*.

Seasonal Responses

What would happen if a plant living in an area that has very cold winters flowered in December? Could the plant successfully produce seeds and fruits? Probably not. The plant's flowers would likely freeze and die. So, the flowers would never produce mature seeds.

Plants can respond to the change of seasons because they are affected by the change in the length of the day. For example, as fall and winter approach, the days get shorter, and the nights get longer. The opposite happens when spring and summer approach.

Standards Check Why must plants respond to seasonal changes?

Bending by Degrees
Suppose a plant has a positive phototropism and bends toward light at a rate of 0.3° per minute. In how many hours will the plant bend 90°? Record your work in your **Science Journal.**

7.1.f

Figure 5 Amount of Pigment Based on Season

Summer

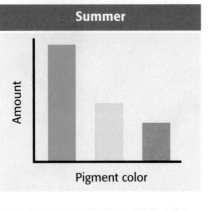

Amount

Pigment color

Fall

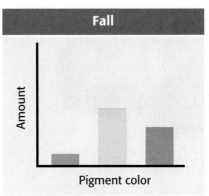

Amount

Pigment color

Earth's Orbit and the Seasons

The seasons are caused by Earth's tilt and Earth's orbit around the sun. Research how Earth's orbit determines the seasons. With a parent or guardian, make a model of the Earth's orbit around the sun to illustrate your findings.

Length of Day

The difference between the length of the nights and the length of the days is an important environmental stimulus for many plants. This stimulus can cause plants to begin reproducing. For example, some plants flower in fall or in winter. At this time, nights are long. These plants are called *short-day plants.* Poinsettias are short-day plants. Chrysanthemums are also short-day plants. Other plants flower in spring or early summer, when nights are short. These plants are called *long-day plants.* Clover, spinach, and lettuce are examples of long-day plants.

Seasons and Leaf Color

As **Figure 5** shows, the leaves of some trees may change color before the leaves fall off. As fall approaches, green chlorophyll breaks down. Then, orange or yellow pigments in the leaves are revealed. These pigments were always present in the leaves. But green chlorophyll hid the pigments. This change is most common in *deciduous trees* (dee SIJ oo uhs TREEZ). These trees lose all of their leaves at about the same time each year. Maple, oak, and elm trees are deciduous trees. The plant hormones auxin and ethylene are involved in this process.

Seasons and Leaf Loss

All trees lose their leaves. Some trees, such as pines, shed some of their leaves year-round so that some leaves are always on the tree. These trees are called *evergreen trees*. Evergreen trees have leaves that are often covered with a thick cuticle. This cuticle protects the leaves from cold and dry weather.

Deciduous trees lose all of their leaves at about the same time each year. In colder areas, deciduous trees usually lose their leaves before winter begins. In warmer climates that have wet and dry seasons, deciduous trees lose their leaves before the dry season. The loss of leaves helps plants survive low temperatures or long periods without rain.

SECTION Review

 7.1.f, 7.5.a

Summary

- Some plant cells are able to differentiate many times in the lifetime of the plant.

- There are many groups of plant hormones. Plant hormones can affect a plant's growth and development.

- A growth in response to a stimulus is called a tropism. Tropisms are positive or negative.

- Plants react to light, gravity, and the change of seasons.

- Short-day plants flower when nights are long. Long-day plants flower when nights are short.

Understanding Concepts

1. **Describing** How do light and gravity affect plants?

2. **Evaluating** Describe an advantage of having cells that can differentiate many times.

Critical Thinking

INTERPRETING GRAPHICS Use the image below to answer the next question.

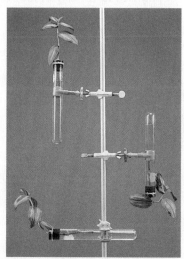

3. **Making Inferences** Describe the tropism that is shown in the picture above. What is causing the plants to grow this way?

4. **Making Inferences** Many evergreen trees live in areas with long, cold winters. Why do you think that these evergreen trees keep their leaves all year?

5. **Analyzing Ideas** Some short-day plants bloom during the winter. If cold weather reduces the chances that a plant will produce seeds, where do you think that these short-day plants are likely to be found?

Math Skills

6. **Using Equations** It must be dark for 70% of a 24 hour period before a certain plant will bloom. For how long will there be daylight on the day that this plant blooms?

Internet Resources

For a variety of links related to this chapter, go to www.scilinks.org

Topic: Plant Tropisms; Plant Growth

SciLinks code: HY71166; HY71159

Skills Practice Lab

Food Factory Waste

Plants use photosynthesis to make food. Photosynthesis produces oxygen gas. Humans and many other organisms cannot live without this oxygen. Oxygen is necessary for cellular respiration. In this activity, you will determine the rate of oxygen production for an elodea plant.

Procedure

1 Add 450 mL of baking soda and water solution to a beaker.

2 Put two or three sprigs of elodea in the beaker. The baking soda will produce the carbon dioxide which the elodea needs for photosynthesis.

3 Place the wide end of the funnel over the elodea. The small end of the funnel should be pointing up. The elodea and the funnel should be completely covered by the solution.

4 Fill a test tube with the remaining solution of baking soda and water. Place your thumb over the end of the test tube, and turn the test tube upside down. Make sure that no air enters the test tube. Hold the opening of the test tube under the solution. Place the test tube over the small end of the funnel. Try not to let any solution out of the test tube.

7.1.b Students know the characteristics that distinguish plant cells from animal cells, including chloroplasts and cell walls.
7.1.d Students know that mitochondria liberate energy for the work that cells do and that chloroplasts capture sunlight energy for photosynthesis.

Investigation and Experimentation
7.7.c Communicate the logical connection among hypotheses, science concepts, tests conducted, data collected, and conclusions drawn from the scientific evidence.

5 Place the beaker setup in a well-lit area.

6 Prepare a data table similar to the one below.

Amount of Gas Present in the Test Tube		
Days of exposure to light	Total amount of gas present (mm)	Amount of gas produced per day (mm)
0		
1		
2		
3		
4		
5		

DO NOT WRITE IN BOOK

7 If no air entered the test tube, record that 0 mm of gas was in the test tube before the plant was exposed to light. If air got into the tube while you were placing the tube, measure the height of the column of air in the test tube in millimeters. Measure the gas in the test tube from the middle of the curve on the bottom of the upside-down test tube to the level of the solution. Record this number in the first row.

8 As described in the previous step, measure the amount of gas in the test tube each day for the next 5 days. Record your measurements in the second column of your data table.

9 Calculate the amount of gas produced each day. Subtract the amount of gas present on the previous day from the amount of gas present on the current day. Record these amounts in the third column of your data table.

Analyze the Results

10 **Constructing Graphs** Make a graph similar to the one below. Based on your measurements, your graph should show the amount of gas produced versus time.

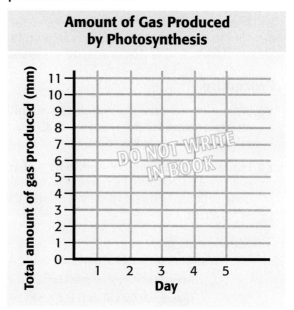

Amount of Gas Produced by Photosynthesis

11 **Describing Events** Use your graph to determine what happened to the amount of gas in the test tube.

Draw Conclusions

12 **Interpreting Information** Write the equation for photosynthesis. Then, relate each part of your experiment to a part of the equation.

Big Idea Question

13 **Defending Conclusions** Most plants perform photosynthesis to make food. In order to perform photosynthesis, plants need water. How does the cuticle covering the leaves of a pine tree help the tree perform photosynthesis in a cold and dry environment?

Science Skills Activity

Investigation and Experimentation

7.7.a Select and use appropriate tools and technology (including calculators, computers, balances, spring scales, microscopes, and binoculars) to perform tests, collect data, and display data.

Selecting Tools to Display Data

▶ Tutorial

Scientists ask many questions about the natural world. They conduct experiments to find answers. A scientist must choose the correct equipment and tools in order to perform the experiment and display the data gathered. It is very important to display data in a way that is easy to understand.

Procedure

1 Write a hypothesis. The hypothesis should offer an explanation for the question that you are asking. The hypothesis must also be testable.

2 List all of the equipment and tools that you will need to conduct the experiment, make observations, and record data. Perform the experiment.

> *Question: Will ice remain solid in a room-temperature environment?*
> *Hypothesis: Ice will melt in a room-temperature environment.*

Time Vs. Temperature	
Time (min)	**Temperature (°C)**
0	25
1	23
2	22
3	21.5
4	19

3 Examine the data that you collected. Numerical data can be displayed in tables and graphs, as the table above. Nonnumerical data, such as descriptions, can be displayed in maps, illustrations, and videos.

4 Use the format that you have chosen to display your data as clearly and accurately as possible. Be sure to include labels and units of measurement where necessary.

▶ You Try It!

Procedure

Imagine that you are examining the relationship between the surface area of a leaf and the rate at which photosynthesis occurs. Using three leaves from the same plant, you measured the amount of water each leaf loses through transpiration. Because each leaf is roughly the same size, you covered half of the surface of one leaf and a quarter of the surface of another leaf with white paper. Use the data listed below to answer the following questions.

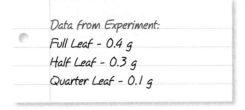

> *Data from Experiment:*
> *Full Leaf - 0.4 g*
> *Half Leaf - 0.3 g*
> *Quarter Leaf - 0.1 g*

Analysis

1 **Describing** Are these data numerical or non-numerical?

2 **Listing** What tools would you use to display these data? What technology could help you display these data?

3 **Modeling** Make a sketch of how you would display these data. Be sure to include all labels and units of measurement if necessary.

Chapter Summary

The Big Idea
Like all living things, plants need nourishment, reproduce, and respond to stimuli.

Section

Vocabulary

1 Photosynthesis

Key Concept Plants make food during photosynthesis and use energy in the food during cellular respiration.

- Chloroplasts capture sunlight energy for photosynthesis.
- Photosynthesis is the process by which most plants make food.
- Mitochondria release the energy that cells use to do work.
- Cellular respiration allows living things, including plants, to use the products of photosynthesis.

Gases produced during plant processes are exchanged through the leaves of plants.

photosynthesis p. 396
chlorophyll p. 396
cellular respiration p. 397
stoma p. 398
transpiration p. 398

2 Reproduction of Flowering Plants

Key Concept Flowering plants reproduce sexually and asexually.

- After pollination, sexual reproduction in flowering plants occurs when an egg is fertilized by a sperm.
- Seeds form from fertilized ovules. The ovary of a flower becomes a fruit.
- In the proper conditions, seeds can sprout and develop into plants.
- Flowering plants can reproduce asexually.

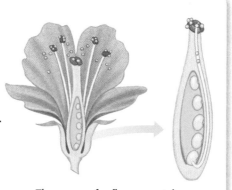

The ovary of a flower contains eggs that can be fertilized.

dormant p. 402

3 Plant Development and Responses

Key Concept Plants develop differently than animals do. Also, plants respond to stimuli in a variety of ways.

- Some plant cells are able to differentiate throughout the life of the plant.
- Hormones cause a plant to develop in response to certain stimuli.
- Plants may grow toward some stimuli and away from others.

This plant is growing toward light because of the plant hormone auxin.

stimulus p. 404
tropism p. 406

Chapter Review

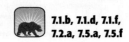

7.1.b, 7.1.d, 7.1.f,
7.2.a, 7.5.a, 7.5.f

Organize

Booklet Review the FoldNote that you created at the beginning of the chapter. Add to the Fold-Note or correct it based on what you have learned.

Using Vocabulary

1. **Academic Vocabulary** In the sentence "As multicellular organisms develop their cells differentiate," what does the word <u>differentiate</u> mean?
   a. migrate
   b. grow
   c. become different in structure and function
   d. change orientation and location in the organism

Complete each of the following sentences by choosing the correct term from the word bank.

stoma	photosynthesis
dormant	cellular respiration
tropism	chlorophyll
transpiration	

2. The loss of water from leaves is called ___.

3. A plant's response to light or gravity is called a ___.

4. ___ is a green pigment found in plant cells.

5. To get energy from the food made during photosynthesis, mitochondria in the cells of plants use the process of ___.

6. A ___ is an opening in the epidermis and cuticle of a leaf.

7. An inactive seed is ___.

8. ___ is the process by which plants make their own food.

Understanding Concepts

Multiple Choice

9. During gas exchange in plants,
   a. carbon dioxide exits the leaf while oxygen and water enter the leaf.
   b. oxygen and water exit the leaf while carbon dioxide enters the leaf.
   c. carbon dioxide and water enter the leaf while oxygen exits the leaf.
   d. carbon dioxide and oxygen enter the leaf while water exits the leaf.

10. Plants often respond to light from one direction by
    a. bending away from the light.
    b. bending toward the light.
    c. wilting.
    d. None of the above

11. Which of the following is NOT a structure that plants use to reproduce asexually?
    a. a runner
    b. a tuber
    c. a flower
    d. a plantlet

INTERPRETING GRAPHICS Use the image below to answer the next question.

12. What is the purpose of the structure shown above?
    a. reproduction
    b. water absorption
    c. food storage
    d. gas exchange

Short Answer

13 Comparing Describe the relationship between short-day plants and long-day plants.

14 Analyzing How do potted plants respond to gravity when they are placed on their sides?

15 Describing What happens during the pollination and fertilization of flowering plants?

16 Listing What three things do seeds need in order to sprout?

17 Describing How do fruits and seeds form from flowers?

18 Comparing Describe the relationship between photosynthesis and cellular respiration.

Writing Skills

19 Writing Persuasively Write a short essay that compares sexual and asexual reproduction in plants. Demonstrate which form of reproduction is the most advantageous.

Critical Thinking

20 Concept Mapping Use the following terms to create a concept map: *plants, cellular respiration, light energy, photosynthesis, chemical energy, carbon dioxide,* and *oxygen.*

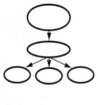

21 Analyzing Ideas Most plant shoots have positive phototropism. Plant roots have positive gravitropism. What are the benefits of each of these characteristics?

22 Applying Concepts Describe the advantages of a plant whose cells can differentiate more than one time, such as the cells of an African violet.

23 Making Inferences Imagine that someone discovers a new flowering plant. The plant has yellow flowers and underground stems. How could this plant reproduce asexually?

24 Predicting Consequences What would happen to a plant if its stem were the main surface for gas exchange?

INTERPRETING GRAPHICS Use the image below to answer the next question.

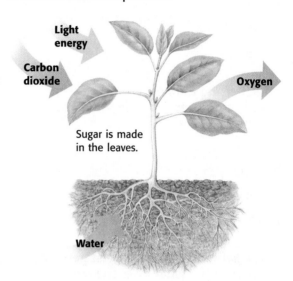

25 Identifying Relationships The blue arrows in the diagram above show gas exchange in the plant. How is the intake of carbon dioxide related to the release of oxygen?

Math Skills

26 Using Calculations Right before winter break, you accidentally knocked over a plant in the school greenhouse . The plant has a negative gravitropism, which means that the plant grows away from gravity. This plant grows away from gravity at a rate of 0.1° per hour. After how many days will the plant be growing perpendicular to the ground?

Challenge

27 Analyzing Relationships Animals depend on plants in many ways. But, plants also depend on animals. Describe how plants rely on animals. Be sure to include information about plant reproduction and food production.

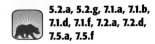
REVIEWING ACADEMIC VOCABULARY

1 Which of the following words is the closest in meaning to the word *energy*?

A work

B source

C increase

D power

2 Which of the following words means "to become specialized in structure or function"?

A separate

B classify

C differentiate

D merge

3 In the sentence "The biologist generated many results," what does the word *generated* mean?

A produced energy through a chemical process

B formed a geometrical figure on a curve

C brought into existence

D created offspring

4 Choose the appropriate form of the word *structure* for the following sentence: Plants are _____ to generate energy from sunlight.

A structured

B structural

C structure

D structurally

REVIEWING CONCEPTS

5 Why do most plants look green?

A The chlorophyll in plants captures green light for photosynthesis.

B The chlorophyll in plants reflects wavelengths of green light.

C The chloroplasts in plants are surrounded by two green membranes.

D The chloroplasts in plants make green sugar during photosynthesis.

6 When plants reproduce using plantlets, tubers, or runners, what is true of their offspring?

A They inherit characteristics from both parents.

B Their stems will grow horizontally along the ground.

C They are genetically identical to the parent plant.

D Their seeds will remain dormant through the winter.

7 In the image above, what does the blue arrow represent?

A Sugar is made in the leaves from light energy and CO_2.

B Oxygen is released from the plant as a waste product.

C The plant takes in water to help make glucose molecules.

D Carbon dioxide is absorbed through the plant's leaves.

8 **What must happen for sexual reproduction to occur in flowering plants?**

A Plantlets must fall from the parent.

B The fruit of the plant must be edible.

C An egg must be fertilized by a sperm.

D Pollen must be produced.

9 **Pollination occurs in angiosperms when**

A pollen moves from anthers to stigmas.

B the ovule develops into a seed.

C the ovary becomes the fruit.

D sperm moves down the pollen tube.

10 **A stoma is one of a plant's**

A systems.

B cells.

C tissues.

D organs.

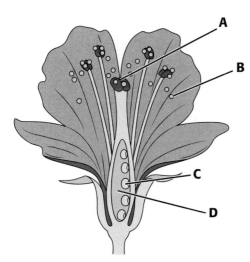

11 **At which point in the above diagram do you find the flower's ovary?**

A point A

B point B

C point C

D point D

12 **What structure in vascular plants carries food throughout the plant?**

A xylem

B cuticle

C phloem

D rhizome

13 **The chemical equation for cellular respiration is shown below.**

$$C_6H_{12}O_6 + 6O_2 \longrightarrow 6CO_2 + 6H_2O$$

What happens on the right side of the arrow?

A Sugar is produced.

B Carbon dioxide and water are produced.

C 6 carbon atoms combine with 6 oxygen atoms.

D Carbon dioxide and oxygen are produced.

14 **Two pea plants with purple flowers produce an offspring with white flowers. Which of the following is most likely true?**

A The trait for white flowers was passed through self-pollination.

B Both parents had dominant alleles for white flowers.

C The offspring of these parents was a first-generation pea plant.

D Both parents had recessive alleles for white flowers.

15 **Which of the following is a shared characteristic of all living things?**

A made of one or more cells

B are consumers in the ecosystem

C have nuclei which contain DNA

D perform sexual reproduction

Standards Assessment

Science in Action

Weird Science

What's That Smell?

Imagine that you are walking through a tropical rain forest. You're surrounded by green—green leaves, green vines, and green trees. You can hear monkeys and birds calling to one another. When you touch the plants nearby, they are wet from a recent rain shower. But what's that horrible smell? You don't see any rotting garbage, but you do see a huge flower spike. As you get closer, the smell gets stronger. Then, you realize the flower is what smells so bad! The flower is called a *corpse flower*. The corpse flower is just one plant that uses bad odors to attract pollinators.

Math ACTIVITY

A corpse flower sprouts and grows to a maximum height of 2.35 m in 28 days. In centimeters, what is the average growth of the corpse flower per day? Record the answer and your work in your **Science Journal.**

Nalini Nadkarni

Canopy Scientist As a child, Nalini Nadkarni loved to climb trees. She still does. Nadkarni is a biologist who studies the forest canopy. The canopy is the uppermost layer of the trees. It includes leaves, twigs, and branches and the air among them. Far above the ground, the canopy is home to plants, birds, insects, and other animals.

Canopy science was a new field of study when Nadkarni started her research 20 years ago. Because most canopies are tall, few scientists visited them. Most field biologists did their research with both feet planted firmly on the ground. Today, scientists know that the canopy is an important habitat for wildlife.

Nadkarni tells others about the importance of forests. As she puts it, "I can have a real impact in raising public awareness of the need to save forests." Nadkarni has invited artists and musicians to visit the canopy. "In my job, I try to understand the science of the canopy, but artists and musicians help capture the aesthetic value of the canopy."

Language Arts **ACTIVITY**

Imagine that you are a canopy scientist. Then, write a creative story about something that you would like to study in the canopy. Write your story in your **Science Journal.**

Internet Resources

- To learn more about careers in science, visit **www.scilinks.org** and enter the SciLinks code HY70225.

- To learn more about these Science in Action topics, visit **go.hrw.com** and type in the keyword HY7PL2F.

- Check out articles related to this chapter by visiting **go.hrw.com.** Just type in the keyword HY7PL2C.

Improving Comprehension

Graphic Organizers are important visual tools that can help you organize information and improve your reading comprehension. The Graphic Organizer below is called a *pyramid chart*. Instructions for creating other types of Graphic Organizers are located in the **Study Skills** section of the Appendix.

How to Make a Pyramid Chart

1 Draw a triangle that is divided into sections like the one shown below. Draw as many sections as you need to draw.

2 Draw a box to the left of the triangle, as shown in the example. Write the topic of your pyramid chart in the box.

3 In each section of your triangle, write information about the topic in the appropriate level of the pyramid.

When to Use a Pyramid Chart

A pyramid chart is used to organize information in a hierarchy of magnitude or detail. As the shape of the pyramid suggests, the pyramid's bottom level contains information that is largest in terms of magnitude and broadest, or least specific, in terms of detail. As you read about science, look for information that you can organize into a hierarchy.

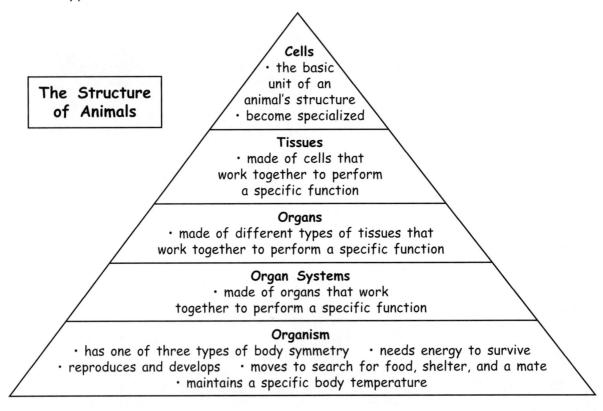

The Structure of Animals

Cells
- the basic unit of an animal's structure
- become specialized

Tissues
- made of cells that work together to perform a specific function

Organs
- made of different types of tissues that work together to perform a specific function

Organ Systems
- made of organs that work together to perform a specific function

Organism
- has one of three types of body symmetry
- needs energy to survive
- reproduces and develops
- moves to search for food, shelter, and a mate
- maintains a specific body temperature

You Try It!

This Reading Strategy can also be used within the chapter that you are about to read. Practice making your own *pyramid chart* as directed in the Reading Strategy for Section **2**. Record your work in your **Science Journal.**

Unpacking the Standards

The information below "unpacks" the standards by breaking them down into basic parts. The higher-level, academic vocabulary is highlighted and defined to help you understand the language of the standards. "What It Means" restates the standards as simply as possible.

California Standard	Academic Vocabulary	What It Means
7.2.a Students know the differences between the life **cycles** and reproduction **methods** of **sexual** and asexual organisms.	**cycle** (SIE kuhl) a repeating series of changes **method** (METH uhd) a way of doing something **sexual** (SEK shoo uhl) having to do with sex	You must know how the life cycles of living things that reproduce sexually differ from the life cycles of living things that reproduce asexually. You must also explain how these ways of reproducing differ.
7.5.a Students know plants and animals have levels of organization for **structure** and **function,** including cells, tissues, organs, organ systems, and the whole organism.	**structure** (STRUHK chuhr) the arrangement of the parts of a whole **function** (FUHNGK shuhn) use or purpose	Plants and animals are made of smaller parts which are organized by shape and purpose. These layers of organization include cells, tissues, organs, organ systems, and the whole organism.
7.5.b Students know organ systems **function** because of the **contributions** of **individual** organs, tissues, and cells. The failure of any part can **affect** the entire system.	**function** (FUHNGK shuhn) to work **contribution** (KAHN truh BYOO shuhn) a part given toward a whole **individual** (IN duh VIJ oo uhl) being a single, separate entity; particular **affect** (uh FEKT) to change; to have an effect on; to influence	An organ system is able to work because of the work that each of its smaller parts (organs, tissues, and cells) does. If any part of an organ system fails to work well, the entire system is changed.
7.5.c Students know how bones and muscles work together to provide a **structural framework** for movement.	**structural** (STRUHK chuhr uhl) having to do with the arrangement of the parts of a whole **framework** (FRAYM WUHRK) a basic structure that supports something	Bones and muscles work together to make a system of support that allows the body to move.
7.5.g Students know how to relate the **structures** of the eye and ear to their **functions.**		You must know how the shapes of the eye and the ear are related to the roles of these parts in the body.

The following identifies other standards that are covered in this chapter and where you can go to see them unpacked: **7.1.f** (Chapter 4)

Introduction to Animals

The Big Idea

Animals have many unique characteristics to perform their life functions.

California Standards

Focus on Life Sciences

7.1 All living organisms are composed of cells, from just one to many trillions, whose details usually are visible only through a microscope. (Sections 1, 3, and 4)

7.2 A typical cell of any organism contains genetic instructions that specify its traits. Those traits may be modified by environmental influences. (Sections 1, 3, and 4)

7.5 The anatomy and physiology of plants and animals illustrate the complementary nature of structure and function. (Sections 1, 2, 3, and 4)

Investigation and Experimentation

7.7 Scientific progress is made by asking meaningful questions and conducting careful investigations. (Science Skills Activity)

Math

7.1.2 Number Sense
7.4.2 Algebra and Functions

English–Language Arts

7.1.3 Reading
7.2.2 Writing

About the Photo

Many marine bird species are found on the California coast, including the booby. This bird can spot a fish in the water from as high as 15 m (50 ft). With the fish in sight, the booby power dives beak first and closes its wings only just before it hits the water. It may not resurface for several seconds.

Organize

Two-Panel Flip Chart

Before you read this chapter, create the FoldNote entitled "Two-Panel Flip Chart." Write "Invertebrates" on one flap of the two-Panel Flip chart and "Vertebrates" on the other flap. As you read the chapter, write the characteristics of invertebrates and vertebrates under the appropriate flaps.

Instructions for creating FoldNotes are located in the Study Skills section on p. 582 of the Appendix.

Explore Activity

⏱ 20 min

Observing Animal Characteristics

You don't have to travel far to see interesting animals. If you look closely, you can find many animals nearby. In this activity, you will observe the characteristics of two different animals. **Caution:** Always be careful around wild or unfamiliar animals, because they may bite or sting. Do not handle wild animals or any animals that are unfamiliar to you.

Procedure

1. Go outside, and find **two different kinds of animals** to observe.

2. Without disturbing the animals, watch them quietly for a few minutes from a distance. You may want to use **binoculars** or a **magnifying lens**.

3. Write down everything that you notice about each animal. Do you know what kind of animal each is? Where did you find them? What do they look like? What are they doing? You may want to draw a picture of them.

7.5.a
7.7.a

Analysis

4. Compare the two animals that you studied. Do they look alike? Identify their body parts.

5. How do the animals move? What structures are they using to help them move?

6. Can you tell what each animal eats? What characteristics of each animal help it find or catch food?

Introduction to Animals   **423**

What Is an Animal?

Key Concept Animals are made up of many cells. Animals consume other organisms to get the energy they need to grow, survive, and reproduce.

▶ What do you think of when you hear the word *animal*? You may think of your dog or cat. You may also think about giraffes or black bears. But would you think of a sponge? Some natural sponges that people use when showering are the remains of an animal. Animals come in many shapes and sizes. Some have four legs and fur, but most do not. Some are too small to be seen without a microscope, and others are bigger than a school bus.

Animal Characteristics

Sponges, worms, penguins, and lions are all animals. But until about 200 years ago, most people thought sponges were plants. And worms don't look like penguins or lions. Some different kinds of organisms are shown in **Figure 1.** The feather star has many flexible arms that it uses to trap food. The coral has a rigid skeleton that is attached to a hard surface. Fish move their bodies to swim from place to place. So, are all of these organisms animals? And what determines whether an organism is an animal, a plant, or something else? There is no simple answer. But all animals share characteristics that set them apart from all other organisms.

Figure 1 *Most of the organisms in this picture are animals.*

Feather star

Fish

Coral

Multicellular Makeup

Like all organisms, animals are made up of cells. Unlike plant cells, animal cells do not have cell walls. Animal cells are surrounded by only cell membranes. All animals are made up of many cells and are therefore *multicellular* organisms. In animals, all of the cells work together to perform the life functions of the animal.

Organization in Animals

Animals have different levels of structural organization in their bodies. Each cell in a multicellular organism does not perform every life function of the organism. Instead, a specific kind of cell can specialize to perform a specific function. For example, muscle cells in an animal help the animal move. Groups of the same kinds of cells that work together form *tissues*. For example, muscle cells form muscle tissue.

When different kinds of tissues work together to perform a specific function for the organism, these tissues form an *organ*. The heart, lungs, and kidneys are organs. When a group of organs work together to perform a specific function, the organs form an *organ system*. Each organ system has a unique job that is important to the survival of the whole organism. The failure of any organ system may lead to the death of the organism. The shark shown in **Figure 2** has organ systems that allow the shark to digest food, pump blood, and sense the environment.

Standards Check What would happen to the shark if its heart failed? **7.5.b**

7.1.f Students know that as multicellular organisms develop, their cells differentiate.

7.2.a Students know the differences between the life cycles and reproduction methods of sexual and asexual organisms.

7.5.a Students know plants and animals have levels of organization for structure and function, including cells, tissues, organs, organ systems, and the whole organism.

7.5.b Students know organ systems function because of the contributions of individual organs, tissues, and cells. The failure of any part can affect the entire system.

7.5.c Students know how bones and muscles work together to provide a structural framework for movement.

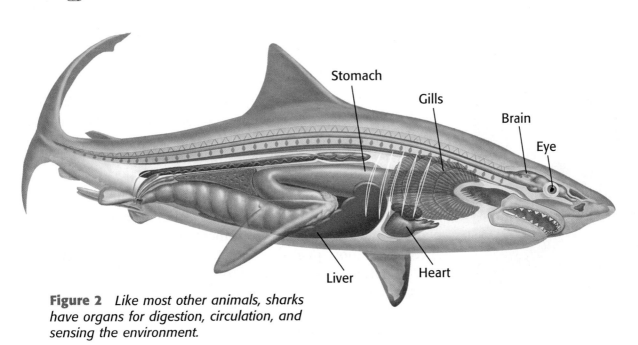

Figure 2 *Like most other animals, sharks have organs for digestion, circulation, and sensing the environment.*

Figure 3 Symmetry in Animal Body Plans

This tortoise has **bilateral symmetry.** The two sides of its body mirror each other. On each side of its body, the tortoise has one eye, one ear, and two legs.

This sea star has **radial symmetry.** Its body is organized around the center, like spokes on a wheel.

This sponge is **asymmetrical.** You cannot draw a straight line to divide its body into two or more equal parts. Its body is not organized around a center.

coelom (SEE luhm) a body cavity that contains the internal organs

consumer (kuhn SOOM uhr) an organism that eats other organisms or organic matter

Body Plans

Animal bodies have two basic types of *symmetry*. Symmetry can be bilateral (bievLAT uhr uhl) or radial (RAY dee uhl). Animals that have no symmetry are asymmetrical (AY suh ME tri kuhl). Most animals have bilateral symmetry. **Figure 3** shows an example of each type of symmetry.

Another basic characteristic of a body plan is whether or not it has a *coelom*. A **coelom** is a body cavity that surrounds and protects many organs, such as the heart. Many animals have coeloms.

Getting Energy

All organisms need energy to survive. Plants can make their own food to get the energy that they need to live. Unlike plants however, animals cannot make their own food. Animals get energy by consuming other organisms or parts and products of other organisms. Therefore, animals are *consumers*. A **consumer** is an organism that feeds on other organisms to meet its energy needs. One way in which animals differ from plants is that animals are consumers. Although there are a few exceptions, most plants do not feed on other organisms.

Animals eat many kinds of foods. As **Figure 4** shows, pandas eat bamboo. Spiders eat other animals. Mosquitoes drink blood. Butterflies drink nectar from flowers. Also, some animals eat more than one kind of food. For example, the black bear eats both fruits and other animals.

Figure 4 *Pandas eat about 13.6 kg of bamboo every day.*

Reproduction

Animals make more animals like themselves through reproduction. Some animals reproduce asexually. In *asexual reproduction,* a parent has offspring that are genetically identical to the parent. For example, hydras can reproduce by budding. In *budding,* part of an organism develops into a new organism. As the new organism develops, it breaks off from the parent. Another kind of asexual reproduction is called *fragmentation.* In fragmentation, parts of an organism break off and then develop into new individuals.

Most animals reproduce sexually. In *sexual reproduction,* offspring are formed when sex cells from two parents combine. The female parent produces sex cells called *eggs.* The male parent produces sex cells called *sperm.* When an egg's nucleus and a sperm's nucleus join in a process called *fertilization,* the first cell of a new organism is formed.

<u>Wordwise</u> **asexual reproduction**
The prefix *a-* means "not."

differentiation (DIF uhr EN shee AY shuhn) the process in which the structure and function of the parts of an organism change to enable specialization of those parts

Development

A fertilized egg cell divides into many cells to form an *embryo* (EM bree OH). An embryo is one of the early stages of development of an organism, such as the mouse embryo shown in **Figure 5.**

As a multicellular organism develops, its cells become specialized through *differentiation.* **Differentiation** is the process by which cells that will perform different functions develop different structures. For example, some nerve cells grow very long, to carry electrical signals from your spine to your feet.

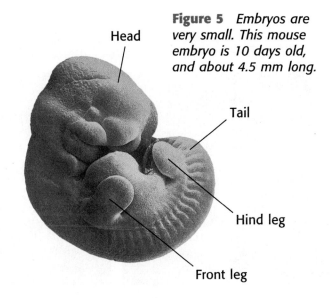

Head

Tail

Hind leg

Front leg

Figure 5 *Embryos are very small. This mouse embryo is 10 days old, and about 4.5 mm long.*

Standards Check What happens during differentiation? **7.1.f**

Quick Lab

Differentiating Blood Cells

1. Examine the **slide of the red bone marrow smear.**

2. Notice the different kinds of blood cells in the smear. Sketch a red blood cell and a white blood cell.

3. All blood cells differentiate from the same kind of cell called a blood stem cell. Examine the sketch of a *blood stem cell* made by your teacher.

4. Make a **flip book animation** that shows how one of the blood cells that you sketched developed from the blood stem cell.

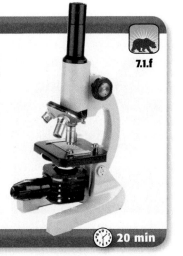

7.1.f

⏱ **20 min**

Movement

Nearly all animals move to search for food, shelter, or mates. **Figure 6** shows some of the different ways in which animals move. Some animals can move from place to place only at certain stages of their life. For example, a young sea anemone finds its food as it drifts in ocean currents. When a sea anemone is older, it will swim to the ocean floor and attach itself there. As an adult, a sea anemone cannot move around and must wait for food to come within reach of its tentacles, as **Figure 6** shows.

Most movement in animals is possible because of muscle cells. By contracting and relaxing, groups of muscle cells work together to help an animal move. For example, a parrot flies because the muscles that are attached to its breast bone and bones in its wings contract and relax.

Standards Check How do muscle cells allow a parrot to fly?
7.5.a, 7.5.c

Figure 6 **How Animals Move**

Anemone catching food

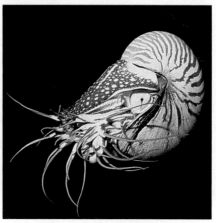

Nautilus swimming

Fish swimming

Caterpillar crawling

Moth flying

Parrot flying

Gibbon walking

Maintaining Body Temperature

To function well, all animals need to maintain their bodies within a specific range of temperatures. Birds and mammals maintain their own body temperatures by using some of the energy released by chemical reactions. These kinds of animals are called *endotherms* (EN doh THURMZ).

Animals that rely on their environment to maintain their body temperature are called *ectotherms* (EK toh THURMZ). Some ectotherms have developed different behaviors to control their body temperatures. For example, some lizards sit in the sun to warm themselves in the morning before they hunt. When the weather gets too hot, the lizard may burrow underground to stay cool.

SCHOOL to HOME

Exploring Your Home

With an adult, list all of the animals that you find around your home. Do you have pets? Are there any spiders in spider webs outside? Can you see any animals from your window? When you have finished writing your list, make a poster about the animals you found.

ACTIVITY

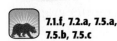

SECTION Review

7.1.f, 7.2.a, 7.5.a, 7.5.b, 7.5.c

Summary

- All animals are multicellular organisms. Specialized cells in animals are organized into tissues, organs, and organ systems.

- Most animals have bilateral symmetry or radial symmetry. Some are asymmetrical.

- Animals consume other organisms to get energy.

- Animals reproduce asexually or sexually.

- As an embryo develops, its cells differentiate.

- Animals move in many ways.

- Animals that maintain their own body temperature are endotherms. Animals that rely on their environment to maintain their body temperature are ectotherms.

Using Vocabulary

1. Write an original definition for *embryo* and *consumer*.

Understanding Concepts

2. **Identifying** What is differentiation?

3. **Describing** Starting at the level of the cell, describe the levels of structural organization in animals.

Critical Thinking

4. **Making Comparisons** What are the two main kinds of reproduction in animals? How do the kinds of reproduction differ?

5. **Identifying Relationships** A fish tank contains water, chemicals, fish, snails, algae, and gravel. Which of these items are alive? Which of these items are animals? Why are some of the living organisms not classified as animals?

6. **Making Inferences** Could a parrot fly if it did not have muscle cells? Explain.

INTERPRETING GRAPHICS The graph shows body temperatures of organism A and organism B and shows the ground temperature. Use the graph below to answer the next two questions.

Body and Ground Temperatures

7. **Evaluating Data** How do the body temperatures of the two organisms change as the ground temperature changes?

8. **Making Inferences** Which organism is probably an ectotherm? Which organism is probably an endotherm? Explain.

Internet Resources

For a variety of links related to this chapter, go to www.scilinks.org

Topic: Animals of California
SciLinks code: HY7C02

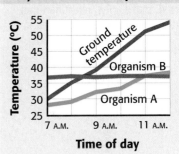

The Animal Kingdom

Key Concept Animals are a diverse group of organisms that have adaptations to live in water and on land.

▶ Both eagles and butterflies have wings. Are eagles and butterflies closely related because they both have wings? The answer is no. Butterflies are insects, and eagles are birds. Insects, birds, and other animals show great diversity in body structure and function, as well as in how and where they live.

Animal Diversity

Scientists have named more than 1 million species of animals. Many species that exist have not yet been discovered and named. Some scientists estimate that more than 3 million species of animals live on Earth. Some of these animals are becoming extinct before they have been discovered or described.

Animals that have been discovered and described have been placed into groups. Placing animals into groups makes it easier to study all of the different kinds of animals. The pie graph in **Figure 1** shows the proportions of the main groups of animals in the animal kingdom.

Figure 1 *Each slice in this pie graph shows what proportion of the animal kingdom is made up by a particular group of animals.* **Which group is the largest?**

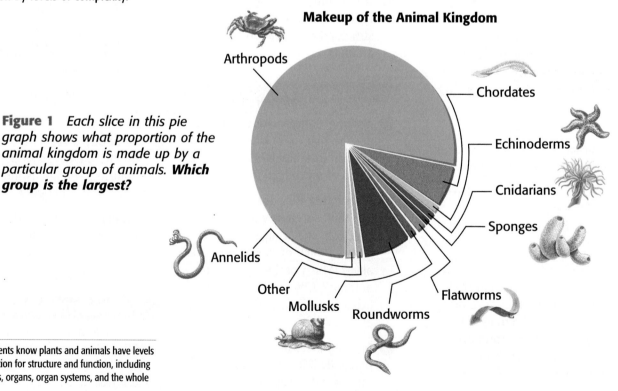

Makeup of the Animal Kingdom

Arthropods · Chordates · Echinoderms · Cnidarians · Sponges · Flatworms · Roundworms · Mollusks · Other · Annelids

7.5.a Students know plants and animals have levels of organization for structure and function, including cells, tissues, organs, organ systems, and the whole organism.

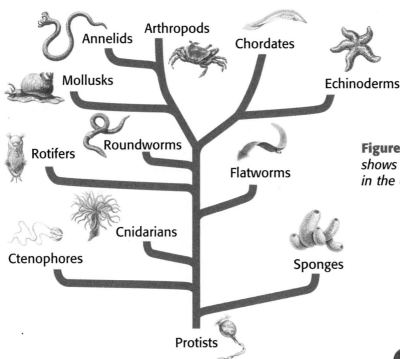

Annelids

Arthropods

Chordates

Mollusks

Echinoderms

Rotifers

Roundworms

Flatworms

Cnidarians

Ctenophores

Sponges

Protists

Figure 2 *This diagram shows the major groups in the animal kingdom.*

Classification

Scientists organize animals into groups based on the animals' characteristics and evolutionary relationships. In the past, scientists grouped animals based on only structural characteristics, such as symmetry. Today, scientists also use DNA to place animals into groups. **Figure 2** shows groups of animals and how they are related to each other. All animals, except for most of the members of chordates, are known as *invertebrates*.

Invertebrate Characteristics

Most of the animals on Earth are invertebrates. An **invertebrate** is an animal that does not have a backbone. In fact, invertebrates do not have any bones. Insects, snails, jellyfish, and worms are all examples of invertebrates. Invertebrates can be found living in every environment on Earth. Sponges are some of the simplest invertebrates.

Sponges

Most sponges live in the ocean. Sponges have an asymmetrical body plan. A sponge is a mass of specialized cells that is held together by a jelly-like material. Tiny, glassy structures in the sponge also provide support. The body of a sponge has many tubes and thousands of small holes or *pores*. A sponge sweeps water through the pores into the tubes. In the tubes, specialized cells filter and digest food particles from the water. Sponges reproduce asexually by fragmentation and sexually.

Standards Check Describe the body of a sponge. 🐻 **7.5.a**

invertebrate (in VUHR tuh brit) an animal that does not have a backbone

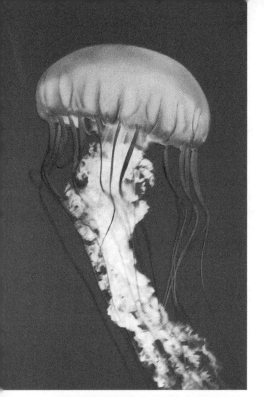

Figure 3 *This jellyfish has a medusa body form. It floats in ocean currents and traps prey with its tentacles.*

Cnidarians

Cnidarians are also invertebrates, but they are more complex than sponges. Most cnidarians (ni DER ee uhnz) live in the ocean. The three major classes of cnidarians are hydrozoans (HIE droh ZOH uhnz), jellyfish, and sea anemones and corals.

Cnidarians have one of two radially symmetrical body plans—the *medusa* or the *polyp* form. The medusa is a cup or bell-shaped body that has tentacles extending from it. The jellyfish **Figure 3** shows, has the medusa body form. Sea anemones and corals have medusa body forms when they are young, or *larvae*. As adults, sea anemones and corals have polyp body forms. Polyps attach to hard surfaces at the base of the cup. The tentacles of the animal then extend into the water. Specialized stinging cells, called *cnidocytes* (NEE doh siets), are located on the tentacles. Cnidocytes are used to stun and capture prey. Many cnidarians reproduce by sexual reproduction. Some cnidarians can also reproduce by budding or fragmentation.

Standards Check Describe two cnidarian body plans. 7.5.a

Flatworms

Flatworms are the simplest worms. Many flatworms live in water, while some live in damp soils. Other flatworms are parasites. A parasite is an organism that invades and feeds on the body of another organism. For example, tapeworms are parasites that live in the intestines of humans.

Flatworms have more-complex bodies than sponges or cnidarians do. Flatworms have flat bodies that are bilaterally symmetrical. The flatworm, as **Figure 4** shows, has a clearly defined head with eyespots, which are sensitive to light. Flatworms reproduce both sexually and by fragmentation.

Roundworms

Unlike flatworms, roundworms have a coelom and are cylindrical, like spaghetti. Roundworms also have bilateral symmetry. Most roundworms are little more than 2 cm long. They live in freshwater habitats, in damp soils, and as parasites in the tissues and body fluids of other animals. Some roundworms eat tiny organisms. Other roundworms break down dead organisms and make soils more fertile.

exoskeleton (EKS oh SKEL uh tuhn) a hard, external, supporting structure
Wordwise The prefix *exo-* means "outside" or "external." Another example is *exotic*.

Figure 4 *This flatworm has a head with eyespots and sensory lobes. This kind of flatworm is often about 15 mm long.*

— Eyespot

Sensory lobe

Mollusks

Snails, slugs, clams, oysters, squids, and octopuses are mollusks. Although most mollusks live in the ocean, some live in fresh water. Others live on land. Mollusks have a specialized tissue called a *mantle*. The mantle secretes the shell of snails, clams, and oysters. Mollusks also have a muscular foot. Snails use the foot to move. In squids, such as the one in **Figure 5,** and in octopuses, the foot has evolved into tentacles. Squids and octopuses use their tentacles to capture prey, such as fish. Mollusks that do not have tentacles feed differently. Clams and oysters filter food from the water. Snails and slugs feed on plants and break down dead organisms. Mollusks reproduce sexually.

Figure 5 *The squid is a mollusk that moves by forcing water out of its mantle.*

Annelids

Annelids live in the ocean and on land. Annelids have round, bilaterally symmetrical bodies. Because annelids are made up of repeating compartments, or segments, annelids are also called *segmented worms*. Leeches are annelids that suck blood. Earthworms, such as the worm in **Figure 6,** break down dead organisms as they burrow through soil. Marine annelids eat mollusks and small animals. Each annelid has both male and female sex organs. But individuals cannot fertilize themselves. Individuals fertilize each other to reproduce sexually.

Arthropods

Arthropods are the most diverse group in the animal kingdom. Arthropods have bilaterally symmetry and a strong, external armor called an **exoskeleton.** The exoskeleton provides defense against predators. The exoskeleton also prevents the animal from drying out in the air and in the sun. Insects, such as the bumblebee in **Figure 7,** are a familiar group of arthropods that live on land. Insects' bodies are clearly divided into a head, thorax, and abdomen. Millipedes, centipedes, and arachnids, such as spiders, and scorpions are also arthropods. Arthropods that live in the water include crab and shrimp. Most arthropods are either males or females and reproduce sexually.

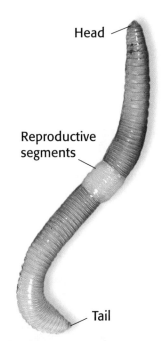

Head

Reproductive segments

Tail

Figure 6 *Except for the head, tail, and reproductive segments, all of the segments of this common garden earthworm are identical.*

Figure 7 *The bumblebee has two antennae, two wings, six legs, a head, a thorax, and an abdomen.*

Figure 8 *Sea urchins are common in kelp forests along the coast of California.*

Echinoderms

Echinoderms (ee KIE noh DUHRMZ) are invertebrates that live in the ocean and include sea stars, sea urchins, and sand dollars. The name *echinoderm* means "spiny skinned." Echinoderms, such as the sea urchins in **Figure 8,** have an exoskeleton covered in bumps and spines. Echinoderms have bilateral symmetry as larvae but have radial symmetry as adults. They also have a unique system of canals filled with water called the *water vascular system* (WAWT uhr VAS kuh luhr SIS tuhm). The water vascular system uses water pumps to help the animals move, eat, breathe, and sense the environment. Most echinoderms feed by scavenging and filtering food out of the water. However, many sea stars prey on mollusks, such as clams.

Echinoderms usually reproduce sexually. For fertilization to take place, males release sperm into the water and females release eggs into the water. Larvae are formed when the sperm fertilizes the eggs. Some sea stars can regenerate a whole individual from an arm that is cut off. This is a form of asexual reproduction.

Vertebrate Characteristics

Vertebrates belong to the phylum Chordata. Members of this phylum are called *chordates* (KAWR DAYTS). Lancelets (LANS lits), such as the one shown in **Figure 9,** and tunicates (TOO ni kits) are also chordates. All chordates share some characteristics, such as a *notochord*, during their life cycle. The notochord is a stiff but flexible rod that supports the body of the animal.

As a vertebrate develops, the notochord is replaced by a backbone. **Vertebrates** are animals that have backbones. The backbone is a strong but flexible column of individual bony units called *vertebrae* (VUHR tuh BRAY). The backbone is a part of the endoskeleton of a vertebrate. An **endoskeleton** is an internal skeleton that supports the body of the animal and provides a place for muscles to attach. Muscles that are attached to the endoskeleton allow the animal to move.

Less than 5% of the known animal species are vertebrates. Vertebrates are divided into five main groups: fishes, amphibians, reptiles, birds, and mammals. Vertebrates can live in water and on land. Some vertebrates feed on only plants or on only animals. Some feed on both plants and animals. Vertebrates are either male or female and reproduce mainly by sexual reproduction.

vertebrate (VUHR tuh brit) an animal that has a backbone

endoskeleton (EN doh SKEL uh tuhn) an internal skeleton made of bone and cartilage

Figure 9 *Lancelets are one of the few marine organisms grouped as chordates. A lancelet has a notochord but does not have a backbone.*

Standards Check How do lancelets differ from vertebrates? 7.5.a

Fish

More than half of the species of vertebrates are fish. The oldest recognizable vertebrates that appeared nearly 500 million years ago were small, odd-looking fish without jaws. Today, there are two small groups of jawless fishes. All other fishes can be divided into two main groups: the *cartilaginous fish* and the *bony fish.* Cartilaginous fish have a skeleton made of a flexible tissue called *cartilage.* This group includes sharks and stingrays. All other fish have a bony skeleton. Bony fish, such as the Garibaldi in **Figure 10,** are found in marine and freshwater environments around the world.

Figure 10 *This Garibaldi, is a bony fish that is commonly found in the kelp forests along the coast of California.*

Amphibians

Most modern amphibians live near fresh water because their eggs and larvae need water to survive. Salamanders, frogs, toads, and caecilians are amphibians. Adult frogs, such as the frog shown in **Figure 11,** and toads do not have tails. Frogs and toads have long hind legs used for hopping and swimming. Adult salamanders have tails, and most have legs equal in size to the tail. Like frogs, some salamanders live completely in the water. However, others spend their lives on land and return to water only to reproduce. Caecilians are tropical amphibians that live under logs and in burrows. All amphibians have thin skins that must be moist. Most amphibians have an aquatic larval stage in their life cycle. In the larval stage, a frog is called a tadpole.

Figure 11 *The Pacific Tree frog can be found in western North America, including California.* **By studying this photo, can you tell which part of its life cycle this frog has reached?**

Reptiles

Reptiles live nearly anywhere on land because they do not need water to lay their eggs. Reptile eggs are protected from drying out by membranes and a shell. Some reptiles, such as turtles, alligators, and snakes can also live in water. Some reptiles feed on plants. Other reptiles feed on insects and other arthropods. Some reptiles, such as the snake in **Figure 12,** eat other vertebrates. Reptiles mainly reproduce sexually.

Figure 12 *Both the caiman and the snake are reptiles. The caiman and the snake share many characteristics, such as tails and scaly skins.*

Birds

Some birds live on land. Others live in the water. Birds such as the pelican in **Figure 13** live on land and on the water. Birds share many characteristics with reptiles, such as similar structures in their feet. But birds also have unique characteristics. For example, birds are the only living animals that have feathers. Feathers are important for maintaining body temperature. Feathers also help shape the body and the wings for flying. Some birds, such as the penguin, no longer use their wings to fly. The penguin uses its wings to swim. Birds such as the ostrich and emu do not fly but have unique characteristics that help them run. All birds reproduce by sexual reproduction.

Standards Check List two reasons that feathers are important? 📖 **7.5.a**

Mammals

All of the approximately 5,000 species of mammals share certain characteristics. For example, all mammals have hair, and all female mammals can produce milk for their young. Some members of the three main groups of mammals are shown in **Figure 14.** The echidna is a monotreme. Monotremes lay eggs that have shells. Kangaroos and opossums are marsupials or "pouched mammals." Marsupials give birth to embryos. The embryos continue to develop in their mother's pouch. The sea otter is a placental mammal, which means that is has a placenta in its uterus. The *placenta* is an organ through which nutrients and wastes are exchanged between the mother and developing offspring. All mammals reproduce by sexual reproduction.

Figure 13 *The California brown pelican can live on land and on water. Pelicans feed on fish.*

Figure 14 **Examples of Three Kinds of Mammals**

Echidna (monotreme)

Kangaroo (marsupial)

Sea Otter (placental mammal)

Summary

- The animal kingdom can be divided into two main groups: invertebrates and vertebrates. Invertebrates do not have backbones. Vertebrates have backbones.

- Sponges, cnidarians, flatworms, roundworms, mollusks, annelids, arthropods, and echinoderms are groups of invertebrates.

- Fish, amphibians, reptiles, birds, and mammals are groups of vertebrates.

- Invertebrate bodies can be asymmetrical, radially symmetrical, or bilaterally symmetrical. Some invertebrates have different body symmetries at different stages in their life cycle.

- Most vertebrate bodies have bilateral symmetry.

- Many invertebrates reproduce by asexual reproduction and sexual reproduction. Most vertebrates reproduce only by sexual reproduction.

Using Vocabulary

1. Write an original definition for *exoskeleton*.

2. Use the following terms in the same sentence: *invertebrate and vertebrate*, and *placenta*.

Understanding Concepts

3. **Describing** Describe the kinds of cnidarian body forms and cnidarian stinging cells.

4. **Identifying** Name two characteristics that are found in mollusks.

5. **Comparing** What are two main differences between a sponge and a roundworm?

6. **Identifying** Identify one similarity and one difference between vertebrates and other chordates.

7. **Classifying** Into what group would you classify a female organism that is covered in fur and that provides milk for its young?

Critical Thinking

8. **Applying Concepts** Explain why adult amphibians have to live near water or in a very wet habitat.

INTERPRETING GRAPHICS Use the two diagrams below to answer the next two questions.

9. **Making Comparisons** What kind of skeleton does the organism in (a) have? What kind of skeleton does the organism in (b) have?

10. **Identifying Relationships** Could you classify these two organisms as an invertebrate or a vertebrate based on only the kind of the skeleton they have? Explain.

Math Skills

11. **Making Calculations** A bird that weighs 15 g eats 10 times its weight in food in a week. Calculate how much food the bird eats in a day.

Challenge

12. **Analyzing Relationships** What is the relationship between the kind of eggs reptiles produce and where reptiles can live?

Internet Resources

For a variety of links related to this chapter, go to www.scilinks.org

Topic: Vertebrates and Invertebrates
SciLinks code: HY71603

Invertebrates

Key Concept Invertebrates do not have backbones, but they do have other structures to perform their life functions.

What You Will Learn

- Invertebrates have many specialized structures that perform specialized functions.
- Organ systems perform basic life functions in some invertebrates.
- Invertebrates have many methods for reproduction and development.

Why It Matters

Studying the characteristics of invertebrates will help you understand how the same life function may be performed in different ways.

Vocabulary

- segment
- open circulatory system
- closed circulatory system
- metamorphosis

READING STRATEGY

Outlining In your **Science Journal,** create an outline of the section. Use the headings from the section in your outline.

▶ Humans and snakes have them, but octopuses and butterflies don't. What are they? Backbones! Most animals do not have backbones. These animals are called *invertebrates*.

Invertebrate Characteristics

Invertebrates can be found in nearly every environment on Earth. Invertebrates also have many different shapes and sizes. For example, grasshoppers, clams, earthworms, and jellyfish are all invertebrates. Some invertebrates have heads, and others do not. Some invertebrates eat food through their mouths. Others absorb food particles through their tissues.

The structures of invertebrates show how well adapted invertebrates are to their environment. For example, insects have different kinds of wings that help them fly. Some invertebrates have legs that help them burrow through the ground. Others have strong bodies that help them swim. But all invertebrates are similar because they do not have backbones.

Body Symmetry

Invertebrate bodies have one of two kinds of symmetry or no symmetry at all. Sponges have irregular shapes and are therefore asymmetrical. Jellyfish have radial symmetry. In animals that have radial symmetry, many lines can be drawn through the center of the body. Each line divides the animal into opposite, or mirror images. Animals that have radial symmetry have only a top and a bottom.

Most invertebrates have "two sides," or bilateral symmetry. A body with bilateral symmetry can be divided into two parts by one vertical line. A line through the middle of the body divides the body into nearly equal right and left halves. Animals with bilateral symmetry have a top and bottom, as well as a front end and a back end. The development of a head is only seen in organisms with bilateral symmetry, such as in the sea hare seen in **Figure 1.**

Standards Check Would you expect an animal with radial symmetry to have a head? Explain. 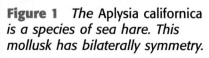 **7.5.a**

Figure 1 *The* Aplysia californica *is a species of sea hare. This mollusk has bilaterally symmetry.*

Figure 2 **Segmentation in Invertebrate Bodies**

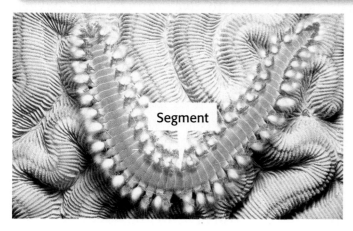

Segment

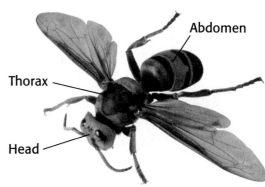

Abdomen

Thorax

Head

Segmentation

The bodies of many animals are divided into sections or **segments.** The body of the marine worm shown in **Figure 2** has many nearly equal segments. The body of the insect shown in **Figure 2** has three unequal segments. The insect has a head, a thorax, and an abdomen. Segmentation in the body has many advantages. For example, each segment in an earthworm has a set of muscles that help the earthworm push through soil.

Support of the Body

Invertebrate bodies need support and protection. **Figure 3** shows three invertebrates that have different kinds of support. The body of a sponge is supported by a jelly-like material and tiny, glassy structures. Other invertebrates have tough outer coverings. For example, round worms have thick skins, and lobsters have exoskeletons. These coverings are also important because muscles that are attached to these coverings contract and relax to help invertebrates move.

Standards Check Why are outer coverings important for movement in animals? **7.5.a**

segment (SEG muhnt) any part of a larger structure, such as the body of an organism, that is set off by natural or arbitrary boundaries

7.2.a Students know the differences between the life cycles and reproduction methods of sexual and asexual organisms.
7.5.a Students know plants and animals have levels of organization for structure and function, including cells, tissues, organs, organ systems, and the whole organism.
7.5.b Students know organ systems function because of the contributions of individual organs, tissues, and cells. The failure of any part can affect the entire system.
7.5.g Students know how to relate the structures of the eye and ear to their functions.

Figure 3 **Support in Invertebrate Bodies**

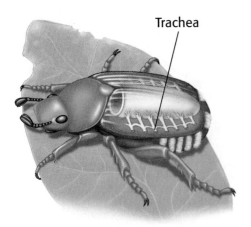

Trachea

Figure 4 *This beetle moves air into its body and out of its body through small holes along the sides of its body.*

Human Metamorphosis
How would you help a friend who turned into a larva? Using pictures, describe the changes that your friend would go through. Go to **go.hrw.com,** and type in the keyword HY7INVW.

Respiratory and Circulatory Systems

All animals need oxygen to live. Animals take oxygen into their bodies and release carbon dioxide from their bodies through respiration. Respiration is performed by the *respiratory system* (RES puhr uh TAWR ee SIS tuhm). In lobsters, gills are the main organs that perform respiration. In insects, such as the beetle in **Figure 4,** a network of tubes inside the body, called *tracheae* (TRAY kee EE), performs respiration.

Oxygen, carbon dioxide, and nutrients must be moved or circulated throughout the body. The *circulatory system* transports many substances in a fluid called *blood*. Most mollusks have an **open circulatory system.** In open circulatory systems, blood moves through open spaces in the body. Invertebrates, such as annelids, have a **closed circulatory system.** In closed circulatory systems, blood moves through tubes that form a closed loop.

Standards Check What would happen to an insect if its tracheae became clogged? 🐻 **7.5.b**

Digestive and Excretory Systems

Animals obtain the energy they need by digesting food. Digestion is performed by the *digestive system*. Food is digested as it is consumed and broken down. Any remaining material is expelled from the body. Invertebrates have relatively simple digestive systems. The mouth and anus form two ends of a tube called a *digestive tract*. The snail shown in **Figure 5** has a stomach and other specialized areas along the digestive tract.

As cells in the body use up nutrients, wastes are formed. The *excretory system* (EKS kruh TAWR ee SIS tuhm) eliminates these wastes from cells with any excess water. In many invertebrates, the digestive tract also eliminates this kind of waste. Other invertebrates have separate excretory systems. These systems have specialized organs to eliminate excess water and waste from cells.

Figure 5 *The digestive system in the snail is made up of a digestive tract that has four parts: a mouth, a stomach, an intestine, and an anus.*

Stomach

Anus

Intestine

Mouth

Figure 6 Examples of Invertebrate Nervous Systems

Hydra

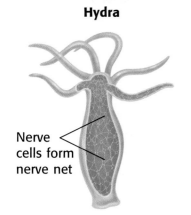

Nerve cells form nerve net

Flatworm

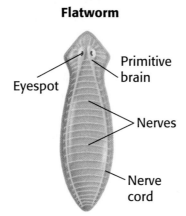

Eyespot

Primitive brain

Nerves

Nerve cord

Grasshopper

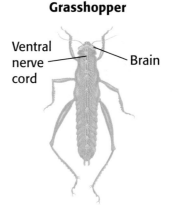

Ventral nerve cord

Brain

Nervous Systems

The *nervous system* is specialized for receiving and sending electrical signals that control all of the functions of the body. **Figure 6** shows examples of the nervous systems of three invertebrates. Many nervous systems have a specialized area called the *brain*. The brain acts as the control center. Nervous systems also have specialized areas called *sense organs*. Sense organs collect information, such as sound and light, from outside and inside the body. For example, eyes are organs that sense light. When light enters the eye, signals are sent to the brain. The brain interprets the signals as an image.

open circulatory system
(OH puhn SUHR kyuh luh TAWR ee SIS tuhm) a circulatory system in which the circulatory fluid is not contained entirely within vessels

closed circulatory system
(KLOHZD SUHR kyuh luh TAWR ee SIS tuhm) a circulatory system in which the heart circulates blood through a network of vessels that form a closed loop

Quick Lab

Seeing Like an Insect

Insects have a compound eye made up of repeating units. Each unit has its own lens.

▶ Try It!

1. Use a **ruler** to draw a grid with dimensions of about 10 cm × 10 cm on a **sheet of tracing paper.** The grid lines should be separated by 0.5 cm.
2. Place the **grid** over a **black-and-white image.** Secure the grid with **tape.**
3. Note the relative amount of black ink that shows through in each box.
4. Use a **black marker** to fill in the grid boxes that are on top of an area that is mostly black. Don't fill in the grid boxes that are above squares that are mostly white.

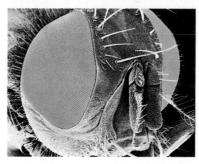

7.5.g

▶ Think About It!

5. Remove your grid, and examine it from across the room. Describe what you see?
6. What part of the activity mimicked the repeating units in the eye of an insect?
7. How might the curve of the insect eye further change how an insect sees images?

🕐 20 min

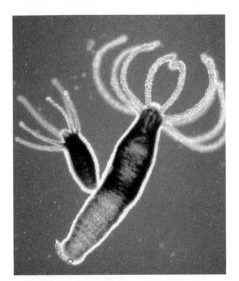

Figure 7 *Hydra reproduce by asexual reproduction. The offspring look similar to and are genetically identical to the parent.*

metamorphosis (met uh MAWR fuh sis) a process in the lifecycle of many animals during which a rapid change from the immature organism to the adult takes place

Reproduction and Development

Many invertebrates reproduce asexually. One kind of asexual reproduction is called *budding*. Budding happens when a part of the parent organism develops into a new organism. The new organism then pinches off from the parent and lives independently. The hydra, shown in **Figure 7,** reproduces by budding. The new hydra is genetically identical to its parent. Fragmentation is a second kind of asexual reproduction. In fragmentation, parts of an organism break off and then develop into a new individual that is identical to the original organism. Certain organisms, such as flatworms called *planaria,* reproduce by fragmentation.

Complete Metamorphosis

Many insects reproduce sexually and lay eggs. As an insect hatches from an egg and develops, the insect changes form through a process called **metamorphosis.** Most insects go through a complex change called *complete metamorphosis*. As shown in **Figure 8,** complete metamorphosis has four main stages: egg, larva, pupa (PYOO puh), and adult. Butterflies, beetles, flies, bees, wasps, and ants go through this change.

Standards Check Compare the life cycle of a hydra with the life cycle of a butterfly. **7.2.a**

Figure 8 The Stages of Complete Metamorphosis

e The adult butterfly pumps blood-like fluid into its wings until they are full-sized. The butterfly is now ready to fly.

d Adult body parts replace the larval body parts. The **adult** splits its chrysalis and emerges.

c After its final molt, the caterpillar makes a chrysalis and becomes a **pupa.** The pupal stage may last a few days or several months. During this stage, the insect is inactive.

a An adult lays **eggs.** An embryo forms inside each egg.

b A **larva** hatches from the egg. Butterfly and moth larvae are called *caterpillars*. The caterpillar eats leaves and grows rapidly. As the caterpillar grows, it sheds its outer layer several times. This process is called *molting*.

Incomplete Metamorphosis

Grasshoppers and cockroaches are two kinds of insects that go through *incomplete metamorphosis.* Incomplete metamorphosis is less complicated than complete metamorphosis. As shown in **Figure 9,** incomplete metamorphosis has three main stages: egg, nymph, and adult. Some nymphs shed their exoskeleton several times in a process called *molting.* An insect in the nymph stage looks very much like an adult insect. But a nymph does not have wings and is smaller than an adult. Through molting, the nymph develops into an adult.

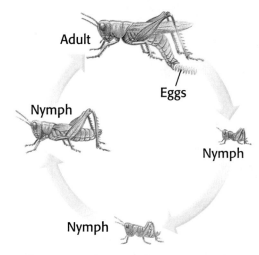

Figure 9 *The grasshopper nymphs look like smaller versions of the adult.*

SECTION Review

 7.2.a, 7.5.a, 7.5.b, 7.5.g

Summary

- Invertebrate bodies are asymmetrical, have radial symmetry, or bilateral symmetry.
- The bodies of many invertebrates are divided into segments.
- Invertebrates have protective outer coverings that provide support and serve as a place for muscles to attach.
- Invertebrates may have many basic organ systems, such as a respiratory system, a circulatory system, a digestive system, an excretory system, a nervous system, and a reproductive system.
- Invertebrates reproduce asexually and sexually. Invertebrates develop from embryos into larvae and from larvae into adults.

Understanding Concepts

1. **Describing** Explain why respiration is important. Be sure to include an example of an invertebrate respiratory system.

2. **Comparing** How is the support in the body of a sponge different from the support in the body of an insect?

3. **Identifying** How do invertebrates remove wastes that are produced by cells in their bodies?

4. **Comparing** In the life cycle of a grasshopper, what are two main differences between nymphs and adults?

5. **Inferring** If an animal has a head, which kind of body symmetry would you expect the animal to have?

Critical Thinking

6. **Analyzing Processes** Describe metamorphosis in the life cycle of a butterfly and in the life cycle of a grasshopper.

7. **Making Comparisons** Compare an open circulatory system and a closed circulatory system.

8. **Expressing Opinions** Why are earthworms in a different group than roundworms? Explain.

9. **Applying Concepts** Why can't insects see in complete darkness?

Math Skills

10. **Making Calculations** A sea urchin lost 12 of its 178 spines in a storm. What percentage of its spines does the sea urchin still have?

Challenge

11. **Applying Concepts** If the head of an insect became stuck underwater, would the insect drown? Explain your answer.

12. **Making Inferences** What other body part do invertebrates that have ears or noses have?

Internet Resources

For a variety of links related to this chapter, go to www.scilinks.org
Topic: Sponges; Echinoderms
SciLinks code: HY71443; HY70458

Vertebrates

Key Concept All vertebrates have a backbone, which supports other specialized body structures and functions.

▶ You may have seen a dinosaur skeleton at a museum. You have probably also seen many fish. Have you ever thought about what these animals might have in common with each other? These animals have backbones, which makes them vertebrates.

Vertebrate Characteristics

Vertebrates live in the oceans, in freshwater, and on land. Vertebrates swim, crawl, burrow, hop, run, and fly. Like many invertebrates, vertebrates have organ systems to perform their life functions. However, vertebrates also have features that other organisms do not have. For example, only vertebrates have a backbone, which is part of a skeleton that is made of bone. Bone is a special type of very hard tissue that is found only in vertebrates.

Vertebrates also have a well-developed head that is protected by a skull. The skull is made of either cartilage or bone. **Cartilage** is a flexible material made of cells and proteins. The skeletons of all embryos are made of cartilage. But as most vertebrates grow, the cartilage is replaced by the much harder bone.

Body Symmetry

All vertebrates, such as the frog in **Figure 1,** are bilaterally symmetrical. In vertebrates, the head is distinct from the rest of the body. A bilaterally symmetrical body has at least four main parts. For example, the upper body surface, or back, is the *dorsal* side. The lower surface or belly is the *ventral* side. The head is in the front, or *anterior* of the body. The tail is in the back, or *posterior* of the body.

Figure 1 *This frog has bilateral symmetry.*

Figure 2 **Body Coverings in Vertebrates**

Scales   Feathers   Fur   Skin

Body Coverings

The body of a vertebrate is covered by skin. One function of skin is to protect the body from the external environment. The skin of vertebrates varies in structure. For example, reptiles, such as the chameleon in **Figure 2,** and most fish are covered in small, thin plates called *scales*. However, fish scales have a different structure than reptile scales do. The scales of fish are also covered in a slippery fluid called *mucus* (MYOO kuhs), while the scales of reptiles are dry. The skin of amphibians is also covered in mucus and functions in part as a respiratory organ. Feathers on birds and the hair and fur on mammals help keep the organisms' body temperatures stable. Some body coverings display colors and patterns that allow vertebrates to hide from predators.

cartilage (KAHRT uhl ij) a flexible and strong connective tissue

Support of the Body

The body of a vertebrate is supported by an endoskeleton. **Figure 3** shows the endoskeleton of a bird. The three main parts of an endoskeleton are the skull, the backbone, and the limb bones. The skull surrounds and protects the brain of the vertebrate. The backbone is made up of many vertebrae. Vertebrae surround and protect the spinal cord. Limb bones, such as leg bones, are an important part of movement in vertebrates. Bones provide a place for muscles to attach. As muscles contract and relax, the bones move. For example, in arms and in legs, pairs of muscles work together to move the limb. Vertebrates need large bones and muscles for support and movement on land.

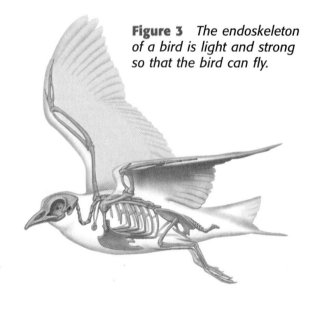

Figure 3 *The endoskeleton of a bird is light and strong so that the bird can fly.*

Standards Check Describe the three main parts of an endoskeleton. 🐻 **7.5.c**

Figure 4 Respiratory Systems in Vertebrates

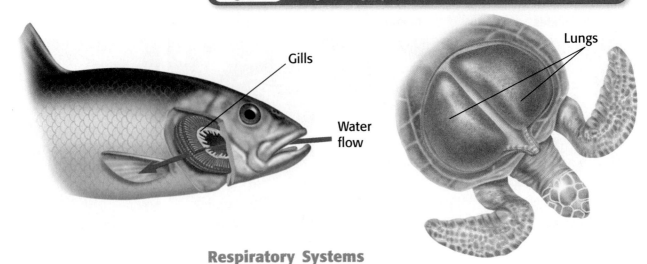

Gills

Water flow

Lungs

Respiratory Systems

Like invertebrates, vertebrates have a respiratory system to perform respiration. **Figure 4** shows the two kinds of respiratory systems in vertebrates. The main respiratory organs in vertebrates are either lungs or gills. These organs have many blood vessels that provide the organs with a steady blood supply. In fish, water flows into the mouth and over the gills. Oxygen from the water moves across the gills and into the bloodstream. At the same time, carbon dioxide moves from the bloodstream, across the gills, and into the water.

In vertebrates that live on land, respiratory organs must be protected from drying out. Therefore, the main respiratory organs are inside the body. Lungs are sacs that are kept moist by the body's fluids. The internal surface of the lungs is made up of small pockets that increase the area available for the exchange of oxygen and carbon dioxide.

Circulatory Systems

Vertebrates have a closed circulatory system made up of blood, vessels, and a pump. Blood is pushed through the vessels by a pump, or *heart*. Vessels that carry blood away from the heart are called *arteries*. Vessels that carry blood to the heart are called *veins*. Arteries are connected to veins by a network of *capillaries*. Capillaries are the smallest blood vessels in the body. **Figure 5** shows the circulatory system of a frog.

In land vertebrates, the heart first pumps the blood to the lungs or gills. In lungs or gills, oxygen moves into the blood. At the same time, carbon dioxide moves out of the body from the blood. Then, the oxygen-rich blood returns to the heart and is pumped to the rest of the body. The circulatory system also transports nutrients and other substances around the body.

Standards Check Describe how the circulatory system and the respiratory system in a vertebrate work together. **7.5.b**

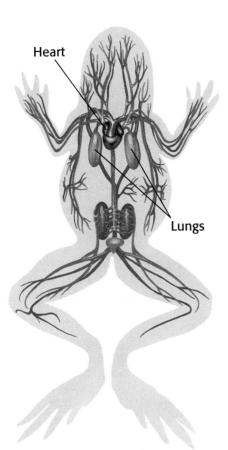

Heart

Lungs

Figure 5 *The frog has a closed circulatory system. The arteries are shown in red, and the veins are shown in blue.*

Digestive and Excretory Systems

Vertebrates have digestive systems to break down food. The digestive system is made up of a long tube called the *digestive tract*. Some vertebrates, such as fish and snakes, swallow their food whole. Other vertebrates crush or chew their food before swallowing. Food passes from the mouth to the stomach. Acids and other chemicals in the stomach turn the food into a kind of soup. This soup then moves into the next part of the digestive tract, an organ called the **small intestine.** Blood vessels in the small intestine absorb nutrients. Then, the materials move into an organ called the **large intestine.** The large intestine absorbs excess water and converts undigested material into feces.

Some cell activities result in the formation of nitrogen compounds, such as ammonia. Ammonia diffuses into the blood and is removed from the body by the excretory system. In mammals, the liver converts ammonia into urea. Then, the *kidneys* filter urea from the blood. Urea is then combined with excess water to form urine, which is expelled from the body.

Nervous Systems

In the nervous system of a vertebrate, the brain is part of the spinal cord. The brain is an organ that serves as the main control center of the body. Nerves from the spinal cord branch throughout the body. Nerves carry impulses between the brain and the body. For example, when a sound reaches the ear, the ear sends an impulse through *sensory nerves* and the spinal cord, to the brain. To make the body react, the brain interprets the impulses and sends command impulses throughout the body through *motor nerves.*

The brain of a fish is much smaller than the brain of a dog, as **Figure 6** shows. Animals that have larger brains depend more on learning than on instinct. Learning is a behavior that changes the reaction of an animal based on new experiences.

Standards Check Describe what happens when a sound reaches the ear. 7.5.g

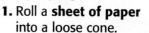

Quick Lab

Amplifying Sound

1. Roll a **sheet of paper** into a loose cone.
2. Wrap the smaller open end of the cone around the stem of a **funnel.** Use **tape** to secure the shape of the cone.
3. Place the funnel over an ear.
4. Move the cone towards a faint sound and then away from the sound. How does the sound change?
5. Make a new cone with several sheets of paper. Repeat step 4. How does the size of the cone affect what you hear?

🕐 15 min

small intestine
(SMAWL in TES tuhn) the organ between the stomach and the large intestine where most of the breakdown of food happens and most of the nutrients from food are absorbed

large intestine (LAHRJ in TES tuhn) the wider and shorter portion of the intestine that removes water from mostly digested food and that turns the waste into semisolid feces, or stool

Figure 6 Nervous Systems in Vertebrates

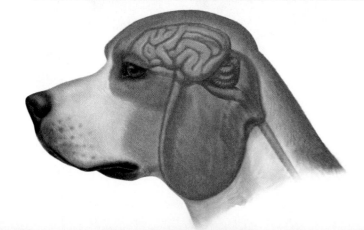
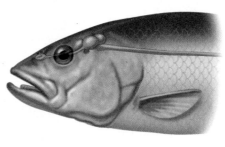

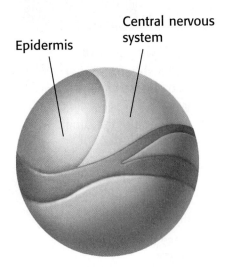

Figure 7 *Parts of a frog embryo are beginning to differentiate into the kind of cells they will become.*

Epidermis

Central nervous system

Reproduction and Development

Most vertebrates reproduce by sexual reproduction. Fertilization happens when the nucleus of a sperm cell fuses with the nucleus of an egg cell. A fertilized egg cell divides many times as it becomes a multicellular embryo. As the embryo develops, its cells differentiate. Differentiation is the process in which cells become specialized. For example, cells that will perform different functions, such as skin cells and blood cells, will develop different structures. **Figure 7** shows the differentiation of some tissues of a frog embryo.

In most fish and amphibians, larvae hatch in the water and live on their own. These larvae behave similarly to adults. However, larvae cannot reproduce. Eventually, the larvae metamorphose into adults.

Reptiles, birds, and mammals do not have a larval stage in their lifecycle. The eggs of reptiles, birds, and mammals are protected by special membranes. The eggs of reptiles, birds, and some mammals also have a shell. Eggs that have shells are laid on land. Most mammals do not lay eggs, and the embryo develops in the female until the offspring is born. **Figure 8** shows the embryos of vertebrates during early stages of their development. Embryos of different species are similar to each other at early stages of development. Embryos begin to look more like the adults of their own species as they develop. Offspring of reptiles, birds, and mammals look similar to adults when they are born. These offspring gradually develop into adults.

Standards Check Why do cells in a developing embryo undergo differentiation? 🐻 **7.1.f**

Figure 8 **The Embryos of Different Vertebrates**

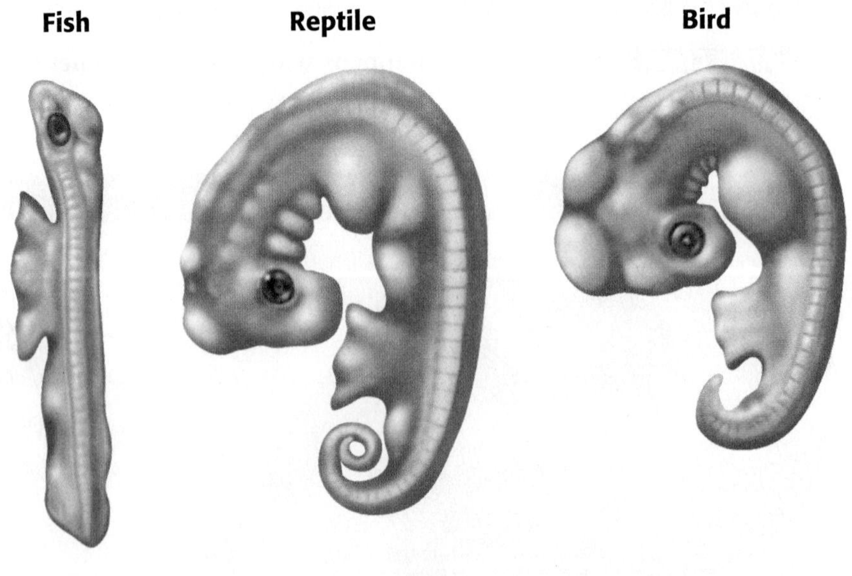

Fish   **Reptile**   **Bird**

Parental Care

Some vertebrates do not care for their young. The female simply lays the eggs and leaves. These animals lay hundreds of eggs, so at least a few offspring will survive. Many fish species and reptile species guard the nest until the eggs hatch. Afterward, the offspring are left on their own. Birds and mammals are very different. Birds and mammals have only a few offspring at a time. Therefore, birds and mammals spend a lot of time and energy feeding and protecting their offspring. The fish shown in **Figure 9** is unusual because it cares for its offspring after they hatch. The parent fish holds its offspring in its mouth to protect them as they develop. Parental care increases the chances of offspring surviving.

Figure 9 *This fish will hold its offspring in its mouth to protect them from predators.*

SECTION Review

7.1.f, 7.2.a, 7.5.a,
7.5.b, 7.5.c, 7.5.g

Summary

- Skin protects the body from the environment. Skin of vertebrates may be covered in scales, feathers, or fur.

- Most vertebrates have an endoskeleton made of bone. The endoskeleton provides support, protection, and a place for muscles to attach.

- Major organs systems of vertebrates are the respiratory system, circulatory system, digestive system, excretory system, nervous system, and reproductive system.

- Cells of embryos differentiate and specialize as the embryo develops.

- The amount of parental care given to offspring varies among species of vertebrates.

Understanding Concepts

1. **Demonstrating** How do different kinds of cells develop in an embryo?

2. **Describing** Describe the structure of the backbone and what it provides the vertebrate body.

3. **Identifying** What kind of circulatory system do vertebrates have?

INTERPRETING GRAPHICS Use the graph below to answer the next two questions.

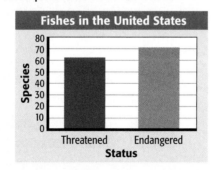

Fishes in the United States

4. **Evaluating** How many fish species in the United States are endangered?

5. **Calculating** What is the total number of endangered and threatened fish species in the United States?

Critical Thinking

6. **Making Comparisons** How does gas exchange in gills differ from gas exchange in lungs?

7. **Applying Concepts** What is an advantage and a disadvantage of depositing a large number of eggs?

8. **Applying Concepts** How does an egg become fertilized? Is this sexual or asexual reproduction? Explain your answer.

Challenge

9. **Making Inferences** What factors might limit the maximum body size to which land vertebrates can grow?

10. **Applying Concepts** Why might large ears be better able to hear a sound than small ears?

Internet Resources

For a variety of links related to this chapter, go to www.scilinks.org

Topic: Vertebrates
SciLinks code: HY71602

Skills Practice Lab

OBJECTIVES

Determine the density of three kinds of animal bones.

Compare the bone of a mammal, a fish, and a bird.

Identify the relationship between the structure of the bone and the function of the bone.

MATERIALS

- balance, laboratory
- beef bone
- chicken bone
- fish bone
- graduated cylinder, large
- string
- wire

SAFETY

7.5.a Students know plants and animals have levels of organization for structure and function, including cells, tissues, organs, organ systems, and the whole organism.
7.5.c Students know how bones and muscles work together to provide a structural framework for movement.

Investigation and Experimentation
7.7.a Select and use appropriate tools and technology (including calculators, computers, balances, spring scales, microscopes, and binoculars) to perform tests, collect data, and display data.

Structure and Function of Bone

The structure of each body part of an organism is related to the function of that body part. For example, animals depend on specialized body parts for movement. Animals contract and relax muscles that are attached to bones in order to move. Some animals have legs, wings, or fins to move around. In vertebrates, most movement is the result of bones and muscles working together. Bones that support a lot of weight are thick and heavy, such as in elephants. Bones that do not support a lot of weight are light, such as in the wings of birds.

You have already learned that the bones of vertebrates have many similarities. In this activity, you will compare the bones of a mammal, a bird, and a fish. Through this activity, you will learn how differences in the structure of different bones relates to the function of these bones.

Ask a Question

1 Lets ask, "Are the bones of animals that walk more dense than the bones of animals that swim or of animals that fly?"

Form a Testable Hypothesis

2 To change the question into a testable hypothesis, you may come up with the following: "There are no differences in density between the bones of animals that walk, swim, or fly."

Procedure

3 Create a table like the one below to record the measurements for each kind of bone.

Bone Measurements			
Kind of bone	Mass of bone (g)	Volume of bone (cm³)	Density of bone (g/cm³)
Mammal bone			
Chicken bone		DO NOT WRITE IN BOOK	
Fish bone			

4 Use a balance to determine the mass of a mammal bone. Record this value in your table.

5 Fill a graduated cylinder about 3/4 full with water. Note the water level in the cylinder. (Note: 1 mL = 1 cm³)

6 Tie a string around the beef bone. Gently lower it into the cylinder. When the bone is completely submerged, note the new water level.

7 Determine the volume of the bone, by subtracting the initial water level in the graduated cylinder from the water level when the bone was submerged. Record you finding in your table.

8 Calculate the density of this bone by dividing the bone's mass by its volume. Record this value in grams per centimeter cubed (g/cm³) in your table.

9 Repeat steps 4–8 using a chicken bone and a fish bone. If a bone floats, you will need to hold it under the surface of the water by using a length of wire.

Analyze the Results

10 **Analyzing Results** Which bones sank? Which bones floated?

11 **Evaluating Results** Which bone was the most dense? Which bone was the least dense?

Draw Conclusions

12 **Drawing Conclusions** Did you prove or disprove the hypothesis?

13 **Applying Results** What can you assume about the muscles that are needed to move these bones?

14 **Making Inferences** What other factors may affect the characteristics of the muscles required to move these bones?

15 **Making Inferences** How is the density of the different bones related to how the organisms move? How is the density of the different bones related to where the organism lives?

16 **Applying Conclusions** If an organism that was the size of a whale lived on land, what kind of bones would the organism have? What kind of muscles would the animal need to move those bones?

Big Idea Question

17 **Identifying Relationships** Describe how the structure of a bone is related to a life function of the animal. Make sure to include examples in your answer.

Science Skills Activity

| Scientific Methods | Research | Data Analysis | Models, Maps & Diagrams |

Investigation and Experimentation

7.7.d Construct scale models, maps, and appropriately labeled diagrams to communicate scientific knowledge (e.g., motion of Earth's plates and cell structure).

Constructing Distribution Maps

▶ Tutorial

Procedure

Use the following instructions to construct the distribution map of a specific population of organisms.

1 Organizing A labelled grid has been placed on top of a map. Use **Table 1** to write the number of goats that were found at each intersection.

Analysis

2 Evaluating Draw a line around the intersections that have at least one goat.

3 Evaluating In another color, draw a second line around the intersections that have at least 10 goats.

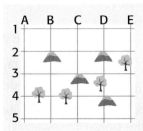

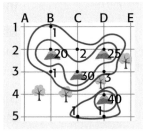

Table 1	Distribution of Mountain Goats
Intersection	**Population Size**
1B	1
2B	20
2C	2
2D	25
3B	1
3C	30
3D	3
4D	40
5C	1
5D	1

▶ You Try It!

Procedure

Use the map and the data table below to construct a distribution map of a population of rare red beetles.

1 Organizing Redraw the map shown here. Use **Table 2** to write the number of beetles that are found at each intersection.

Analysis

2 Evaluating Draw a line around the intersections that have at least one beetle. In another color, draw a second line around the intersections that have at least 10 beetles.

3 Inferring Use the map to identify where the beetle is found. How might this information be helpful if the beetle were becoming extinct?

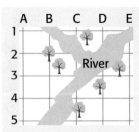

Table 2	Distribution of Red Beetles
Intersection	**Population Size**
2A	1
2B	30
3B	5
3D	20
3E	3
4B	40
4C	30
4D	4

Chapter Summary

go.hrw.com
SUPER SUMMARY
KEYWORD: HY7AMLS

The Big Idea Animals have many unique characteristics to perform their life functions.

Section	Vocabulary

1 What Is an Animal?

Key Concept Animals are made up of many cells. Animals consume other organisms to get the energy they need to grow, survive, and reproduce.

- Animals are multicellular organisms.
- Animals have specialized cells, tissues, organs, and organ systems.
- Animals have seven basic characteristics.

coelom p. 426
consumer p. 426
differentiation p. 427

2 The Animal Kingdom

Key Concept Animals are a diverse group of organisms that have adaptations to live in water and on land.

- The animal kingdom is made up of many different kinds of animals.
- Animals can be divided into two main groups: invertebrates and vertebrates.
- Each group of animals has unique characteristics.

invertebrate p. 431
exoskeleton p. 433
vertebrate p. 434
endoskeleton p. 434

3 Invertebrates

Key Concept Invertebrates do not have backbones, but they do have other structures to perform their life functions.

- Invertebrates have many specialized structures that perform specialized functions.
- Organ systems perform basic life functions in some invertebrates.
- Invertebrates have many methods for reproduction and development.

segment p. 439
open circulatory system p. 440
closed circulatory system p. 440
metamorphosis p. 442

4 Vertebrates

Key Concept All vertebrates have a backbone, which supports other specialized body structures and functions.

- Vertebrates have an endoskeleton that provides support and protection.
- Vertebrates have organ systems that perform life functions.
- Nearly all vertebrates reproduce by only sexual reproduction.

cartilage p. 444
small intestine p. 447
large intestine p. 447

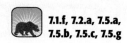
Organize

Two-Panel Flip Chart Review the FoldNote that you created at the beginning of the chapter. Add to or correct the FoldNote based on what you have learned.

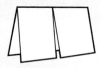

Using Vocabulary

1 Academic Vocabulary Which word best completes the following sentence: "Through ___ the cells in a developing embryo specialize to develop into different kinds of cells."

For each pair of terms, explain how the meanings of the terms differ.

2 *endoskeleton* and *exoskeleton*

3 *invertebrate* and *vertebrate*

4 *asexual reproduction* and *sexual reproduction*

Understanding Concepts

Multiple Choice

5 The sea urchin's body is organized around the organism's center, like the spokes on a wheel. What kind of symmetry does the sea urchin have?
a. bilateral
b. radial
c. asymmetrical
d. unilateral

6 Members of which of the following groups of invertebrates have segmented bodies?
a. mollusks
b. sea anemones
c. roundworms
d. arthropods

7 What would happen if the gills of a fish stopped working?
a. The fish would probably die.
b. The fish would make its own oxygen.
c. The fish would make more carbon dioxide.
d. The fish would not be able to maintain its body temperature.

8 Which of the following is NOT a function of the endoskeleton?
a. The endoskeleton provides a place for muscles to attach.
b. The endoskeleton supports the body from the outside of the body.
c. The endoskeleton supports the body from the inside of the body.
d. The endoskeleton protects the organs of the body.

Short Answer

9 Listing List the seven basic characteristics of animals.

10 Inferring Some insects develop from nymphs into adults. What kind of metamorphosis do these insects undergo? Explain.

11 Comparing How does fragmentation in sponges differ from reproduction in reptiles?

12 Listing What are the levels of structural organization in the body of a shark?

INTERPRETING GRAPHICS The picture below shows a member of the animal kingdom. Use the picture to answer the next three questions.

13 Identifying Name the body segments labeled a, b, and c.

14 Identifying To which segment are the legs of this animal attached?

15 Analyzing Into which group you would classify this animal? Explain.

Writing Skills

16 **Explaining Ideas** What is the relationship between bones and muscles? Describe how these two kinds of structures help vertebrates move around.

Critical Thinking

17 **Concept Mapping** Use the following terms to create a concept map: *vertebrates, bilateral symmetry, fish, sponge, radial symmetry, sea urchin, sexual reproduction, asymmetrical, asexual reproduction,* and *invertebrates*.

18 **Identifying Relationships** Why are vertebrates classified as chordates?

19 **Making Comparisons** Describe three groups of mammals and how they differ.

20 **Predicting Consequences** If differentiation in an embryo is stopped, predict what is likely to happen to the embryo. Explain.

21 **Analyzing Methods** Could you identfy the entire life cycle of an animal by studying only the adult forms of that animal? Explain.

22 **Analyzing Relationships** How do the eyes of a dog help the dog fetch a ball?

23 **Predicting Consequences** Cats are endotherms, and geckos are ectotherms. Describe what would happen to a cat and a gecko if they were caught in a snowstorm.

24 **Making Inferences** A bird may have only two or three offspring at a time. A sea turtle may lay 100 eggs at a time. Which of these two organisms is more likely to provide its offspring with more parental care?

25 **Making Comparisons** Compare the circulatory system in an insect with a fish.

INTERPRETING GRAPHICS The graph below shows the kinds of amphibians that are threatened or endangered in the United States. Use the graph to answer the next two questions.

Threatened and Endangered Amphibian Species in the United States

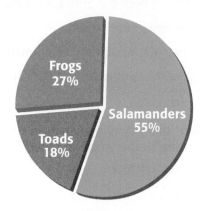

26 **Making Conversions** If the total number of threatened and endangered amphibian species in the United States is 22, how many more species of salamanders are threatened or endangered than species of frogs and toads?

27 **Making Inferences** What do you expect to happen to the percentage of toads in the pie graph as endangered toad species become extinct?

Math Skills

28 **Making Calculations** All of the females in a boar population produce exactly 10 offspring during their lifetime. What percentage of each female's offspring must survive so that the number of individuals in the population remains constant?

Challenge

29 **Making Inferences** On land, only animals that have endoskeletons become very large. Why are vertebrates on land larger than invertebrates on land?

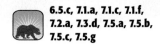
REVIEWING ACADEMIC VOCABULARY

1 In the sentence "As multicellular organisms develop, their cells differentiate into specialized cells," what does the word *differentiate* mean?

  A to see or show the difference between

  B to multiply more rapidly

  C to calculate a mathematical function

  D to become specialized for specific functions

2 Which of the following words is closest in meaning to the word *methods*?

  A ways   **C** orders

  B actions   **D** sets

3 In the sentence "The failure of an organ can affect the entire organ system," what does the word *affect* mean?

  A move emotionally

  B act upon or have an effect upon

  C infect or damage with disease

  D assume a particular form

4 Which of the following words means "a structure for supporting something"?

  A construction

  B house

  C framework

  D plane

5 Choose the appropriate form of the word for the following sentence: Organ systems are made up of ___ cells, tissues, and organs.

  A individually

  B individuate

  C individual

  D individualize

REVIEWING CONCEPTS

6 Which of the following is a method of asexual reproduction?

  A monotreme   **C** segmentation

  B budding   **D** metamorphosis

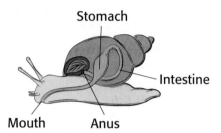

Stomach — Intestine — Mouth — Anus

7 In the image of the snail above, which organ system is shown?

  A the respiratory system

  B the nervous system

  C the circulatory system

  D the digestive system

8 How do the eyes of a dragonfly help the dragonfly catch its prey?

  A Specialized cells in the eyes send signals to the bones in the dragonfly's wings.

  B The brain interprets the signals sent by the dragonfly's eyes as images to identify the location of the prey.

  C The dragonfly's eyes have receptors on their surface to locate the prey.

  D The nerve cells in the dragonfly's eyes interpret the location of the prey.

9 Which of the following is a difference between invertebrates and vertebrates?

  A Vertebrates have exoskeletons, and invertebrates have endoskeletons.

  B Invertebrates reproduce only asexually, and vertebrates reproduce only sexually.

  C Vertebrates have a backbone, while invertebrates do not.

  D Invertebrates have bilateral symmetry, while vertebrates have radial symmetry.

10 What type of body symmetry does a sea urchin have?

A radial   C bilateral

B skeletal   D asymetrical

11 Which of the following statements about vertebrate embryos is true?

A As embryos develop, their cells become specialized to perform different functions.

B All vertebrate embryos develop fins before becoming adults.

C Cell differentiation occurs only after the birth of a vertebrate.

D Even as embryos, vertebrates look much like the adults of the species.

12 Most vertebrates reproduce sexually. When does fertilization occur in sexual reproduction?

A when a male animal releases sperm and a female animal releases eggs

B when part of an organism breaks off and begins to grow independently

C when the cells of the embryo begin to differentiate and become specialized

D when the nucleus of a sperm cell fuses with the nucleus of an egg cell

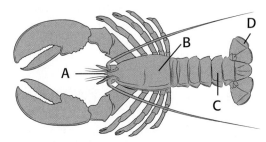

13 In the diagram of a lobster shown above, which segment of the lobster's body is labeled B?

A the thorax

B the abdomen

C the head

D the nerves

14 What does the statement "All animals are eukaryotes," mean?

A It means that all animals live on land.

B It means that all of the DNA of an animal is located in the nuclei of the cells of the animal.

C It means that all animals have closed circulatory systems.

D It means that all animal bodies have coeloms.

15 Which of the following is an example of similar cell function in different animals?

A The wings of a bat and the flippers of a dolphin look similar.

B Animals have a variety of coverings, including skin, scales, and fur.

C Sea anemone larvae have medusa body forms but are polyps as adults.

D Nerve cells carry impulses throughout the body in both a tortoise and a chicken.

16 What role does an earthworm play in the transfer of energy in the food web of an ecosystem?

A decomposer

B consumer

C producer

D scavenger

17 What characteristics might a fossil that was classified into the animal kingdom have?

A The fossilized organism had bones.

B The fossilized organism had structures identified as cell walls.

C The fossil is of a single-celled organism.

D The fossilized organism had root structures.

Standards Assessment

Science in Action

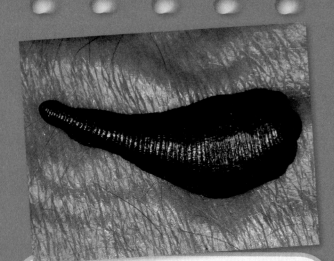

Science, Technology, and Society

Leeches to the Rescue

Bloodsucking leeches may sound scary, but they could save your toes! Leeches are used in operations to reattach lost limbs, fingers, or toes. During these operations, doctors can reconnect arteries, but not small veins, which are more delicate. As a result, blood flow in the limb, finger, or toe is impaired. The tissues may become swollen with blood. If this happens, the tissues of the reattached parts die. But if leeches suck the extra blood from the reattached part, the tissues can remain healthy until the veins grow back.

Math ACTiViTY

Measure the widest and narrowest parts of the leech in the photo. Calculate how many times larger the wide part is than the narrow part. Which end of the leech do you think is the head? Why do you think so? Record your work in your **Science Journal**.

Weird Science

Sounds of the Lyrebird

Imagine that you are hiking in an Australian forest. You hear many different bird calls, beaks snapping, and wings rustling. There must be many species of birds around, right? Not if a lyrebird is nearby—all of those sounds could be coming from just one bird! The lyrebird imitates the songs of other birds. In fact, lyrebirds can imitate almost any sound they hear. Many Australians have heard lyrebirds singing the sounds of chainsaws, car engines, and dog barks. According to stories, a lyrebird once confused timber-mill workers when it sang the sound of the mill's whistle and caused the workers to quit for the day.

Language Arts ACTiViTY

A lyrebird's ability to imitate noises could lead to a lot of humorous confusion for people who hear its songs. Think about how lyrebirds could mimic human-made sounds and cause confusion for the people nearby. Then, write a short story in your **Science Journal** about the situation.

George Matsumoto

Marine Biologist Dr. George Matsumoto is a marine biologist at the Monterey Bay Aquarium in California. A seventh-grade snorkeling class first sparked his interest in ocean research. Since then, he has studied the oceans by snorkeling, scuba diving, using research vessels, using remotely operated vehicles (ROVs), and using deep-sea submersibles. On the Johnson Sea Link submersible, he traveled to 1,000 m (3,281 ft) below sea level!

Marine biology is a field in which there are many strange and wonderful creatures. Matsumoto focuses on marine invertebrates, particularly the delicate animals called comb jellies. Comb jellies are also called *ctenophores* (TEN uh FAWRZ), which means "comb-bearers." Ctenophores have eight rows of cilia that look like the rows of a comb. These cilia help ctenophores move through the water. Some ctenophores glow when they are disturbed. By studying ctenophores and similar marine invertebrates, Matsumoto and other marine scientists can learn about the ecology of ocean communities.

Social Studies AcTiViTy

One kind of ctenophore from the United States took over both the Black Sea and the Sea of Azov by eating small fish. This left little food for bigger fish and thus changed the ecosystem and ruined the fisheries. Write a paragraph in your **Science Journal** about how Matsumoto's work as a marine biologist could help solve problems like this one.

Internet Resources

- To learn more about careers in science, visit **www.scilinks.org** and enter the SciLinks code HY70225.

- To learn more about these Science in Action topics, visit **go.hrw.com** and type in the keyword HY7AMLF.

- Check out articles related to this chapter by visiting **go.hrw.com**. Just type in the keyword HY7AMLC.

Human Body Systems

Like a finely tuned machine, your body is made up of many systems that work together. Your lungs take in oxygen. Your brain reacts to things you see, hear, and smell and sends signals through your nervous system that cause you to react to those things. Your digestive system converts the food you eat into energy that the cells of your body can use. And those are just a few things that your body can do!

In this unit, you will study the systems of your body. You'll discover how the parts of your body work together.

Around 3000 BCE

Ancient Egyptian doctors are the first to study the human body scientifically.

1824

Jean Louis Prevost and Jean Batiste Dumas prove that sperm is essential for fertilization.

1766

Albrecht von Haller determines that nerves control muscle movement and that all nerves are connected to the spinal cord or to the brain.

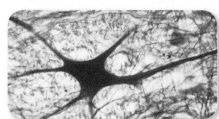

1940

During World War II in Italy, Rita Levi-Montalcini is forced to leave her work at a medical school laboratory because she is Jewish. She sets up a laboratory in her bedroom and studies the development of the nervous system.

Around 500 BCE

Indian surgeon Susrata performs operations to remove cataracts.

1492

Christopher Columbus lands in the West Indies.

1543

Andreas Vesalius publishes the first complete description of the structure of the human body.

1616

William Harvey discovers that blood circulates and that the heart acts as a pump.

1893

Daniel Hale Williams, an African American surgeon, becomes the first person to repair a tear in the pericardium, the sac around the heart.

1922

Frederick Banting, Charles Best, and John McLeod discover insulin.

1930

Karl Landsteiner receives a Nobel Prize for his discovery of the four human blood types.

1982

Dr. William DeVries implants an artificial heart in Barney Clark.

1998

The first successful hand transplant is performed in France.

2001

Drs. Laman A. Gray, Jr. and Robert D. Dowling at Jewish Hospital in Louisville, Kentucky, implant the first self-contained mechanical human heart.

Improving Comprehension

Graphic Organizers are important visual tools that can help you organize information and improve your reading comprehension. The Graphic Organizer below is called a *comparison table*. Instructions for creating other types of Graphic Organizers are located in the **Study Skills** section of the Appendix.

How to Make a Comparison Table

1. Draw a table like the one shown below. Draw as many columns and rows as you want to draw.

2. In the top row, write the topics that you want to compare.

3. In the left column, write the general characteristics that you want to compare. As you read the chapter, fill in the characteristics for each topic in the appropriate boxes.

When to Use a Comparison Table

A comparison table is useful when you want to compare the characteristics of two or more topics in science. Organizing information in a table helps you compare several topics at one time. In a table, all topics are described in terms of the same list of characteristics, which helps you make a thorough comparison. As you read, look for topics whose characteristics you may want to compare in a table.

	Skeletal System	Muscular System
Parts	• bones, cartilage, connective tissue	• muscles
Structure	• Bone is made of connective tissue and minerals. • Compact bone is rigid and dense bone tissue. • Spongy bone is bone tissue that has open spaces.	• Smooth muscle is in the digestive tract and in the walls of blood vessels. • Cardiac muscle is in the heart. • Skeletal muscle is attached to bones.
Function	• Some bones protect organs. • Bones store minerals that help nerves and muscles function. • Bones provide the body with structure. • Some bones make blood cells.	• Muscles let a person move. • Voluntary action is action that can be controlled. (skeletal) • Involuntary action is action that cannot be controlled. (smooth, cardiac, or skeletal) • Muscles often work in pairs.

You Try It!

This Reading Strategy can also be used within the chapter that you are about to read. Practice making your own *comparison table* as directed in the Reading Strategies for Section ❶ and Section ❷. Record your work in your **Science Journal.**

Unpacking the Standards

The information below "unpacks" the standards by breaking them down into basic parts. The higher-level, academic vocabulary is highlighted and defined to help you understand the language of the standards. "What It Means" restates the standards as simply as possible.

California Standard	Academic Vocabulary	What It Means
7.5.a Students know plants and animals have levels of organization for **structure** and **function,** including cells, tissues, organs, organ systems, and the whole organism.	**structure** (STRUHK chuhr) the arrangement of the parts of a whole **function** (FUHNGK shuhn) use or purpose	Plants and animals are made of smaller parts which are organized by shape and purpose. These layers of organization include cells, tissues, organs, organ systems, and the whole organism.
7.5.b Students know organ systems **function** because of the **contributions** of **individual** organs, tissues, and cells. The failure of any part can **affect** the entire system.	**function** (FUHNGK shuhn) to work **contribution** (KAHN truh BYOO shuhn) a part given toward a whole **individual** (IN duh VIJ oo uhl) being a single, separate entity; particular **affect** (uh FEKT) to change; to have an effect on; to influence	An organ system is able to work because of the work that each of its smaller parts (organs, tissues, and cells) does. If any part of an organ system fails to work well, the entire system is changed.
7.5.c Students know how bones and muscles work together to provide a **structural framework** for movement.	**structural** (STRUHK chuhr uhl) having to do with the arrangement of the parts of a whole **framework** (FRAYM WUHRK) a basic structure that supports something	Bones and muscles work together to make a system of support that allows the body to move.
7.6.h Students know how to compare joints in the body (wrist, shoulder, thigh) with **structures** used in machines and simple **devices** (hinge, ball-and-socket, and sliding joints).	**device** (di VIES) a piece of equipment made for a specific use	You must be able to compare places in the body where two or more bones meet, such as wrists, shoulders, and thighs, with structures used in simple machines, such as hinge, ball-and-socket, and sliding joints.
7.6.i Students know how levers **confer** mechanical advantage and how the application of this **principle** applies to the musculoskeletal system.	**confer** (kuhn FUHR) to give **principle** (PRIN suh puhl) basic law, rule, or belief	You must know how levers can reduce the amount of force required to perform a task or can increase the speed of a motion. You must also know how levers are part of the muscular and skeletal systems of the human body.

The following identifies other standards that are covered in this chapter and where you can go to see them unpacked: **7.1.f** (Chapter 18)

15

Body Organization and Structure

The Big Idea

The human body is composed of major systems that have differing functions, but all of the systems work together to maintain homeostasis.

California Standards

Focus on Life Sciences
7.1 All living organisms are composed of cells, from just one to many trillions, whose details usually are visible only through a microscope. (Sections 1 and 2)
7.5 The anatomy and physiology of plants and animals illustrate the complementary nature of structure and function. (Sections 1, 2, and 3)
7.6 Physical principles underlie biological structures and functions. (Sections 2 and 3)

Investigation and Experimentation
7.7 Scientific progress is made by asking meaningful questions and conducting careful investigations. (Science Skills Activity)

Math
7.1.1 Algebra and Functions

English–Language Arts
7.1.3 Reading
7.2.5 Writing

About the Photo

Lance Armstrong has won the Tour de France seven times. These victories are especially remarkable because he was diagnosed with cancer in 1996. But with medicine to treat the cancer and hard work, he grew strong enough to win one of the toughest racing events.

Organize

Table Fold

Before you read this chapter, create the FoldNote entitled "Table Fold." Label the columns of the table with "Example," and "Function." Label the rows with "Levels of organization," "Joints," and "Levers." As you read the chapter, write an example and the function of each example under the appropriate column.

Instructions for creating FoldNotes are located in the Study Skills section on p. 582 of the Appendix.

Explore Activity

25 min

How Do Your Legs Bend?

Use simple materials to model a joint in the body. Then, observe how muscles and bones work together.

Procedure

1. Make a T-shaped figure by **using two pieces of crayon.** Wrap the entire T-shaped figure with **masking tape.**

2. Shape **modeling clay** into a socket in which the short end of the T-shaped figure will be able to move freely. The socket is the base of your model.

3. Insert **two half-opened paper clips** into opposite sides of the base.

4. Tie **two pieces of twine** to the tip of the long end of the T-shaped figure. Thread one piece of twine through each of the paper clips.

5. Insert the short end of the T-shaped figure into the socket. Pull one piece of twine and then the other. Repeat this motion.

7.5.c
7.6.h
7.7.d

Analysis

6. What happens when you pull each piece of twine?

7. Does the twine represent muscle or bone?

8. Does the T shape represent muscle or bone?

9. How do muscles and bones work together to produce movement?

10. You have just created a model of a hinge joint. Your knee is one example of a hinge joint. Describe the motion permitted by a hinge joint.

465

Body Organization

Key Concept The human body functions because of the contributions of cells, tissues, organs, and organ systems.

Your body contains approximately 100 trillion cells and more than 100 kinds of cells. How do all of those cells work together? The body has different levels of organization: cells, tissues, organs, organ systems, and the whole organism. **Figure 1** shows four kinds of tissues. Tissues are one level of organization in the human body.

A Stable Internal Environment

Elements in each level of organization, whether in the cell, tissue, or organ level, work with other parts of the body to maintain a stable environment. *Homeostasis* is the maintenance of a stable environment inside the body. For example, the temperature outside your body changes, but your internal temperature remains close to 37°C. When homeostasis is not maintained, most cells do not function properly and may die.

Cells, Tissues, and Organs

Your cells must do many jobs to maintain homeostasis. But each of your cells does not have to do all jobs. Just as each person on a soccer team has a role during a game, each cell in your body plays a part in maintaining homeostasis.

Figure 1 Four Kinds of Tissue

Epithelial tissue covers and protects underlying tissue. When you look at the surface of your skin, you see epithelial tissue. The cells form a continuous sheet.

Nervous tissue sends electrical signals through the body. It is found in the brain, nerves, and sense organs.

Figure 2 Examples of Differentiated Body Cells

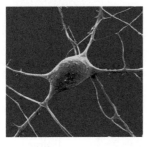

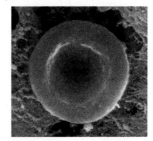

Muscle cells have proteins that are specialized for contraction.

Neurons are nerve cells. Most neurons are long and thin.

Red blood cells have no nucleus but contain a special pigment that picks up oxygen.

Epithelial cells have many jobs. They are found in skin and the linings of your organs.

Cells Form Tissues

Most cells in your body are *differentiated*. A differentiated cell is a cell that has unique structures that are specialized to perform specific functions in the body. **Figure 2** shows four kinds of differentiated cells. The function of each cell is related to the cell's structure. For example, the muscle cell has special proteins that allow the cell to shorten in length. This structure of the muscle cell allows the cell to contract. Thus, many muscle cells working together can cause an organism to move.

Your cells are organized into groups. A group of similar cells working together forms a **tissue.** Your body has four main kinds of tissue. The four kinds of tissue are shown in **Figure 1.**

Standards Check What is a differentiated cell? **7.1.f**

tissue (TISH oo) a group of similar cells that perform a common function

7.1.f Students know that as multicellular organisms develop, their cells differentiate.
7.5.a Students know plants and animals have levels of organization for structure and function, including cells, tissues, organs, organ systems, and the whole organism.
7.5.b Students know organ systems function because of the contributions of individual organs, tissues, and cells. The failure of any part can affect the entire system.

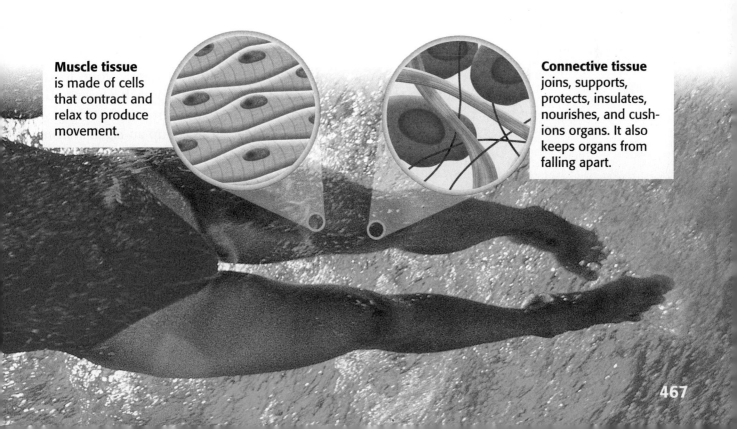

Muscle tissue is made of cells that contract and relax to produce movement.

Connective tissue joins, supports, protects, insulates, nourishes, and cushions organs. It also keeps organs from falling apart.

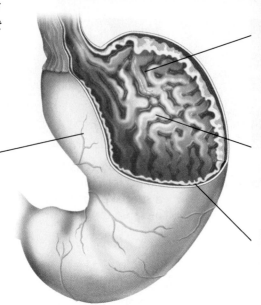

Figure 3 *The stomach is an organ. The four kinds of tissue work together so that the stomach can carry out digestion.*

Nervous tissue in the stomach helps coordinate the movements of the stomach. Nervous tissue also helps regulate the production of the acids that aid in digestion.

Blood is a **connective tissue** found in the wall of the stomach.

Epithelial tissue lines the stomach and forms a protective lining against the acid environment of the stomach.

Layers of **muscle tissue** mix the stomach contents and move them toward the small intestine.

Tissues Form Organs

One kind of tissue alone cannot do all of the things that several kinds of tissue working together can do. Two or more tissues working together form an **organ.** The stomach, shown in **Figure 3,** uses the four kinds of tissue to carry out digestion. Another organ, the heart, is made of muscle tissue, connective tissue, and epithelial tissue (EP i THEE lee uhl TISH oo).

Organs, such as the heart, can perform jobs that the tissues, which make up the organ, cannot perform on their own. The heart pumps blood throughout the body. None of the tissues that make up the heart could perform this job alone.

organ (AWR guhn) a collection of tissues that carry out a specialized function of the body

Organs Form Organ Systems

Your stomach does a lot to help you digest your food. But the stomach does not do it all. Your stomach works with other organs, such as the small and large intestines, to digest your food. Organs that work together make up an *organ system.* Your stomach is part of the digestive system. In another organ system called the nervous system, the brain, spinal cord, nerves, sense organs, and receptors work together. Each organ helps the nervous system control body movements.

Organ systems also perform jobs that organs alone cannot perform. In an organ system, each organ is specialized to perform part of the organ system's job. Each human organ system has a unique function. The human body's 11 organ systems are shown in **Figure 4.**

Standards Check Describe how the stomach functions as part of an organ system. ▨ **7.5.a**

Figure 4 **Organ Systems**

Integumentary System
Your skin, hair, and nails protect the tissue that lies beneath them.

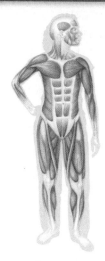

Muscular System Your muscular system works with the skeletal system to help you move.

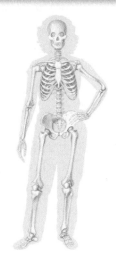

Skeletal System Your bones provide a frame to support and protect your body parts.

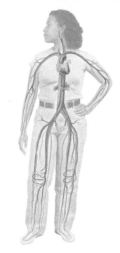

Cardiovascular System Your heart pumps blood through all of your blood vessels.

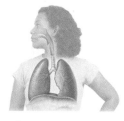

Respiratory System Your lungs absorb oxygen and release carbon dioxide.

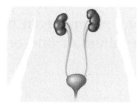

Urinary System Your urinary system removes wastes from the blood and regulates your body's fluids.

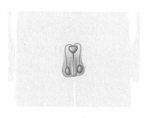

Male Reproductive System The male reproductive system produces and delivers sperm.

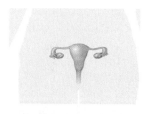

Female Reproductive System The female reproductive system produces eggs and nourishes and protects the fetus.

Nervous System Your nervous system receives and sends electrical messages throughout your body.

Digestive System Your digestive system breaks down the food you eat into nutrients that your body can absorb.

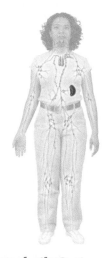

Lymphatic System The lymphatic system returns leaked fluids to blood vessels and helps get rid of bacteria and viruses.

Endocrine System Your glands send out chemical messages. Ovaries and testes are part of this system.

Organ Systems Working Together

Your body's major organ systems work together to maintain homeostasis. For example, the cardiovascular system, which includes the heart, blood, and blood vessels, works with the respiratory system, which includes the lungs. The cardiovascular system picks up oxygen from the lungs and carries the oxygen to cells in the body. These cells produce carbon dioxide, which is returned to the respiratory system by the cardiovascular system. Then, the respiratory system expels the carbon dioxide.

Standards Check How does the cardiovascular system work with the respiratory system in the human body? **7.5.b**

Interdependence of Organ Systems

Some organs perform jobs that are important to more than one organ system. For example, the pancreas is an organ that produces fluids for digestion. But the pancreas is also part of the endocrine system. If the pancreas became damaged, the damage would affect both the digestive and endocrine systems. Therefore, the failure of one organ may affect more than one organ system. The failure of one organ may even affect the entire organism.

Quick Lab

Modeling the Stomach

Creating a model of the stomach can help you understand how this organ functions. The model will also help you understand how each tissue contributes to the function of the organ.

7.5.a
7.5.b
7.7.d

▶ Try It!

1. Collect some **art supplies** from your teacher.
2. Use the diagram of the stomach in **Figure 3** to decide which material to use for each type of tissue.
3. Make a table that lists each material and what each material represents in the model.
4. Make a sketch of your model, and label the different tissues. Then, construct a model of a stomach.

▶ Think About It!

5. Describe the role of each tissue that makes up the stomach.
6. How do the materials in your model represent the role of each tissue?
7. Change your model so that it does not have any muscle tissue. Describe what happened.
8. What can the stomach do that the tissues alone cannot do?

 25 min

When Systems Fail

To maintain homeostasis, the body's organ systems must function properly and work together. When one part of an organ system fails to perform its roles in the body, the entire organism is affected and may die. The entire organism is affected because all of the processes needed for life are divided between the body's organ systems. Each organ system is specialized and thus performs a certain job. For example, the cardiovascular system transports nutrients and other substances throughout the entire body. Without the cardiovascular system, cells, tissues, and organs would not get the nutrients they need to function. No other organ system is able to do this job.

INTERNET ACTIVITY

Humans in Space
What are the effects of zero gravity and space travel on the human body systems? Go to **go.hrw.com,** and type in the keyword HY7BD1W to find out!

SECTION Review

7.1.f, 7.5.a, 7.5.b

Summary

- A human has many levels of organization.

- Most human cells are differentiated in structure for specific functions, or jobs, within the body.

- A group of cells that work together is a tissue. Tissues form organs. Organs that work together form organ systems.

- There are four kinds of tissue in the human body.

- There are 11 organ systems in the human body.

- Organ systems work together to help the body maintain homeostasis.

Using Vocabulary

1. Use *homeostasis, tissue,* and *organ* in the same sentence.

Understanding Concepts

2. **Analyzing** How are tissues, organs, and organ systems related?

3. **Listing** Name the 11 organ systems.

4. **Concluding** Are the organs in an organ system able to do the same jobs as the organ system? Explain.

5. **Describing** What happens when a cell becomes differentiated?

6. **Evaluating** How are organ systems related to one another?

Critical Thinking

7. **Applying Concepts** Tanya went to a restaurant and ate a hamburger. Describe how Tanya used five organ systems to eat and digest her hamburger.

8. **Predicting Consequences** Predict what might happen if the human body did not have specialized cells, tissues, organs, and organ systems to maintain homeostasis.

Math Skills

9. **Making Calculations** The human skeleton has 206 bones. The human skull has 22 bones. What percentage of human bones are skull bones?

Challenge

10. **Making Inferences** What would happen if the muscle tissue in your body suddenly stopped working? Which organ systems would be affected? How would each system be affected?

Internet Resources

For a variety of links related to this chapter, go to www.scilinks.org
Topic: Tissues and Organs; Body Systems
SciLinks code: HY71530; HY70184

The Skeletal System

Key Concept The skeletal system is an organ system. The functions of the skeletal system include support, protection, movement, and the production of blood cells.

What You Will Learn

● The skeletal system includes bones, cartilage, and connective tissue.

● Bones have four important functions in the body. Bones are structured to perform these functions.

● Three human body joints are gliding, ball and socket, and hinge.

Why It Matters

The functions of the skeletal system play a role in maintaining the body's homeostasis.

Vocabulary

• skeletal system
• joint

READING STRATEGY

Graphic Organizer In your **Science Journal,** make a Comparison Table that compares various types of joints.

▶ You may think that your bones are dry and brittle. But they are alive and active. Bones, cartilage, and the connective tissue that holds bones together make up your **skeletal system.**

Bones

The adult human skeleton, shown in **Figure 1,** has 206 bones. Bones help support and protect parts of your body. They work with your muscles so that you can move. Bones also help your body maintain homeostasis by storing minerals and making blood cells. The skeletal system has the following functions:

● Some bones protect organs. For example, your heart and lungs are protected by the ribs.

● Bones store minerals that help your nerves and muscles function properly. Long bones store fat that can be used as energy.

● Skeletal muscles pull on bones to produce movement. Without bones, you would not be able to sit, stand, or run.

● Some of your bones make blood cells. *Marrow* is a special material found in these bones. Marrow makes blood cells.

Figure 1 *The human skeleton is made of many bones. These bones serve many important functions in the body including the production of blood cells, protection, and support.*

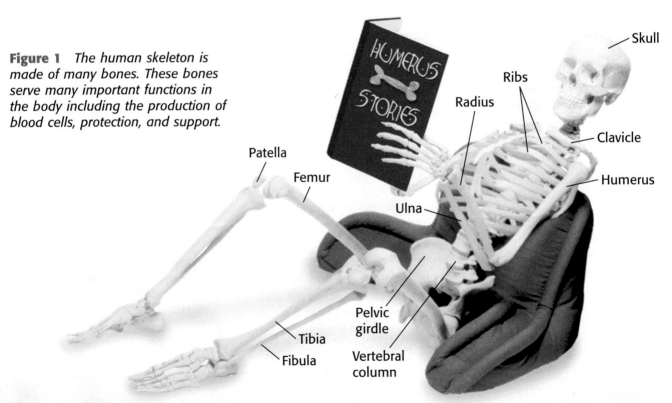

Skull

Ribs

Radius

Clavicle

Humerus

Patella

Femur

Ulna

Tibia

Pelvic girdle

Fibula

Vertebral column

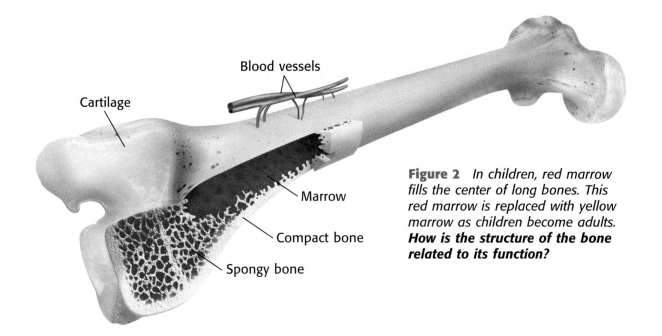

Cartilage

Blood vessels

Marrow

Compact bone

Spongy bone

Figure 2 *In children, red marrow fills the center of long bones. This red marrow is replaced with yellow marrow as children become adults.* **How is the structure of the bone related to its function?**

Bone Structure

A bone may seem lifeless. But a bone is a living organ that is made of several different tissues. Bone is made of connective tissue and minerals. These minerals are deposited by living cells called *osteoblasts* (AHS tee oh BLASTS).

If you look inside a bone, you will notice two kinds of bone tissue. If the bone tissue does not have any visible open spaces, it is called *compact bone.* Compact bone is rigid and dense. Tiny canals within compact bone contain small blood vessels. Bone tissue that has many open spaces is called *spongy bone.* Spongy bone provides most of the strength and support for a bone because it is able to absorb shock easily.

As you read earlier, some bones contain a tissue called marrow. There are two types of marrow. Red marrow produces both red and white blood cells. Yellow marrow, which is found in the central cavity of long bones, stores fat. **Figure 2** shows a cross section of a long bone.

Standards Check How does the structure of bones provide support?
🐻 **7.5.c**

Bone Growth

Do you know that most of your skeleton used to be soft and rubbery? Most bones start out as a flexible tissue called *cartilage.* When you were born, you did not have much true bone. But as you grew, most of the cartilage was replaced by bone. During childhood, most bones still have growth plates of cartilage. These growth plates provide a place for bones to continue to grow.

Feel the end of your nose. Or bend the top of your ear. These areas are two places where cartilage is never replaced by bone. These areas stay flexible.

skeletal system (SKEL i tuhl SIS tuhm) the organ system whose primary function is to support and protect the body and to allow the body to move

7.5.a Students know plants and animals have levels of organization for structure and function, including cells, tissues, organs, organ systems, and the whole organism.
7.5.c Students know how bones and muscles work together to provide a structural framework for movement.
7.6.h Students know how to compare joints in the body (wrist, shoulder, thigh) with structures used in machines and simple devices (hinge, ball-and-socket, and sliding joints).

Figure 3   Three Joints in the Human Body

Gliding Joint   Gliding joints allow bones in the wrist to glide over one another and give some flexibility to the area.

Ball-and-Socket Joint   In the same way that a video-game joystick lets you move your character around, the shoulder lets your arm move freely in all directions.

Hinge Joint   In the same way that a hinge allows a door to open and close, the knee enables you to flex and extend your lower leg.

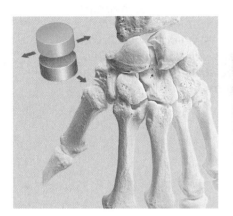

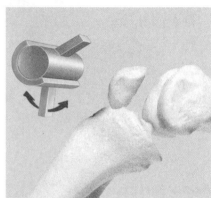

joint (JOYNT) a place where two or more bones meet

Joints

A place where two or more bones meet is called a **joint.** Your joints allow your body to move when your muscles contract. Some joints, such as fixed joints, allow little or no movement. Many of the joints in the skull are fixed joints. Other joints, such as your shoulder, allow a lot of movement. Joints can be classified based on how the bones in a joint move. Three joints are shown in **Figure 3.**

Your shoulder is a ball-and-socket joint. Ball-and-socket joints are similar to video-game joysticks. A ball-and-socket joint allows a bone to move up, down, forward, backward, and in a complete circle. A hinge joint allows less movement. The hinge joint that joins your thigh and lower leg allows the knee to bend in one direction. This joint is similar to some door hinges. Gliding joints, also called sliding joints, allow the bones in the wrist and the bones in the foot to glide over one another.

Standards Check   How is a door hinge similar to the joint in your knee?   7.6.h

The Structure of Joints

Joints are often placed under a great deal of stress. But joints can withstand a lot of wear and tear because of their structure. Joints are held together by *ligaments* (LIG uh muhnts). Ligaments are strong elastic bands of connective tissue. They connect the bones in a joint. Also, cartilage covers the ends of many bones. Cartilage helps cushion the area in a joint where bones meet.

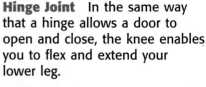

Quick Lab

Pickled Bones

7.5.a
7.7.c

1. Place a **clean chicken bone** in a **jar of vinegar.**

2. After 1 week, remove the bone and rinse it with **water.**

3. Describe the changes that you can see or feel.

4. How has the bone's strength changed?

5. What did the vinegar remove?

6. How would this change in the bone's structure change the bone's function in the chicken's body?

 15 min

Skeletal System Injuries and Diseases

Sometimes, parts of the skeletal system are injured. As **Figure 4** shows, bones may be fractured, or broken. Joints can also be injured. A dislocated joint is a joint in which one or more bones have been moved out of place. Another joint injury, called a *sprain,* happens if a ligament is stretched too far or torn.

There are also diseases of the skeletal system. *Osteoporosis* (AHS tee OH puh ROH sis) is a disease in which the bones become less dense. Bones become weak and break more easily. Age and poor eating habits can make it more likely for people to develop osteoporosis. Other bone diseases affect the marrow or make bones soft. A disease that affects the joints is called *arthritis* (ahr THRIET is). Arthritis is painful. Joints may swell or stiffen. As they get older, some people are more likely to have some types of arthritis.

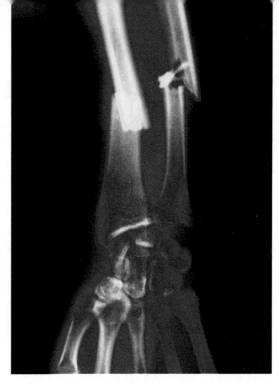

Figure 4 *This X ray shows that the two bones of the forearm have been fractured, or broken.*

SECTION Review

7.5.a, 7.5.c, 7.6.h

Summary

- The skeletal system includes bones, cartilage, and the connective tissue that connects bones.
- Bones protect the body, store minerals, allow movement, and make blood cells.
- A joint is a place where two or more bones meet.
- Skeletal system injuries include fractures, dislocations, and sprains. Skeletal system diseases include osteoporosis and arthritis.

Understanding Concepts

1. **Listing** What parts make up the skeletal system?

2. **Describing** What are four functions of bones?

3. **Summarizing** Name three joints, and describe the range of motion they allow.

Critical Thinking

INTERPRETING GRAPHICS Use the image below to answer the next question.

4. **Identifying Relationships** How is the object related to your skeletal system?

5. **Identifying Relationships** How do bones provide a structure for muscles to move?

6. **Predicting Consequences** What might happen if children's bones didn't have growth plates made of cartilage?

Math Skills

7. **Using Equations** A broken bone usually heals in about six weeks. A mild sprain takes one-third as long to heal. How many days does a mild sprain take to heal?

Internet Resources

For a variety of links related to this chapter, go to www.scilinks.org

Topic: Skeletal System
SciLinks code: HY71399

The Muscular System

Key Concept The muscular system is an organ system. The skeletal and muscular systems work together to provide a structural framework for movement.

▶ Your heart is a muscle. Muscles make you breathe. And muscles hold you upright. If all of your muscles rested at the same time, you would collapse. The **muscular system** is made up of the muscles that let you move.

Kinds of Muscle

Figure 1 shows the three kinds of muscle in your body. *Smooth muscle* is found in the digestive tract and in the walls of blood vessels. *Cardiac muscle* is found only in your heart. *Skeletal muscle* is attached to your bones and helps you move. Skeletal muscle also helps protect your inner organs.

Muscle action can be voluntary or involuntary. Muscle action that is under your control is *voluntary*. Muscle action that is not under your control is *involuntary*. Smooth muscle and cardiac muscle are involuntary muscles. Skeletal muscles can be both voluntary and involuntary muscles. For example, you can blink your eyes anytime you want to. But your eyes will also blink automatically.

Figure 1 Three Kinds of Muscle

Skeletal muscle enables bones to move.

Smooth muscle moves food through the digestive system.

Cardiac muscle pumps blood around the body.

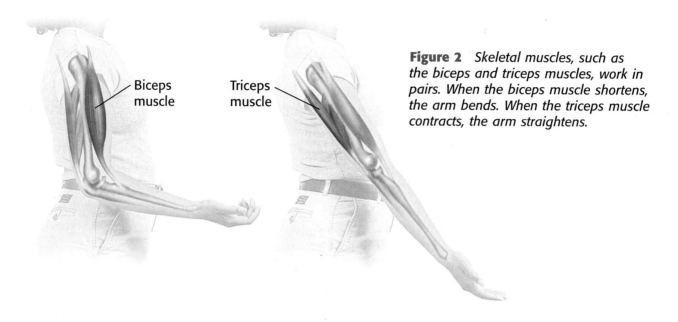

Figure 2 *Skeletal muscles, such as the biceps and triceps muscles, work in pairs. When the biceps muscle shortens, the arm bends. When the triceps muscle contracts, the arm straightens.*

Biceps muscle

Triceps muscle

Movement

Skeletal muscles are responsible for hundreds of movements. You can see many of these movements by watching a dancer or even someone smiling or frowning. When you want to move, signals travel from your brain to your skeletal muscle cells. The muscle cells then contract, or get shorter. Mitochondria in muscle cells provide energy for the cells to contract.

muscular system (MUHS kyoo luhr SIS tuhm) the organ system whose primary function is movement and flexibility

Muscles Attach to Bones

Strands of tough connective tissue connect your skeletal muscles to your bones. These strands of tissue are called *tendons.* When a muscle that connects two bones gets shorter, the bones are pulled closer to each other. For example, tendons attach the biceps muscle to a bone in your shoulder and to a bone in your forearm. When the biceps muscle shortens, your forearm bends toward your shoulder. The combination of skeletal muscles and bones working together is sometimes called the *musculoskeletal system.*

Muscles Work in Pairs

Your skeletal muscles often work in pairs to produce smooth, controlled motions. Usually, one muscle in the pair bends part of the body. The other muscle straightens part of the body. A muscle that bends part of your body is called a *flexor.* A muscle that straightens part of your body is an *extensor.* As shown in **Figure 2,** the biceps muscle of the arm is a flexor. The triceps muscle of the arm is an extensor.

Standards Check Describe how skeletal muscles work in pairs.
 7.5.c

7.5.a Students know plants and animals have levels of organization for structure and function, including cells, tissues, organs, organ systems, and the whole organism.
7.5.c Students know how bones and muscles work together to provide a structural framework for movement.
7.6.i Students know how levers confer mechanical advantage and how the application of this principle applies to the musculoskeletal system.

Levers in the Human Body

lever (LEV uhr) a simple machine that consists of a bar that pivots at a fixed point called a *fulcrum*

mechanical advantage (muh KAN i kuhl ad VANT ij) a number that tells you how many times a machine multiplies force

The action of a muscle pulling on a bone often works like a type of simple machine called a lever. A **lever** is a rigid bar that pivots at a fixed point known as a *fulcrum*. Any force applied to the lever is called the *effort force*. A force that resists the motion of the lever, such as the downward force exerted by a weight on the bar, is called the *load*. **Figure 3** shows the action of three types of levers in the human body. In your body, the rigid bar is a bone. The effort force is supplied by muscles. And the fulcrum at which the bone pivots, is a joint.

Levers increase the amount of work that can be done by the effort force applied to a load. This increase in work is called **mechanical advantage.**

Figure 3   Levers in the Human Body

⇨ Load   ⇨ Effort   ▲ Fulcrum

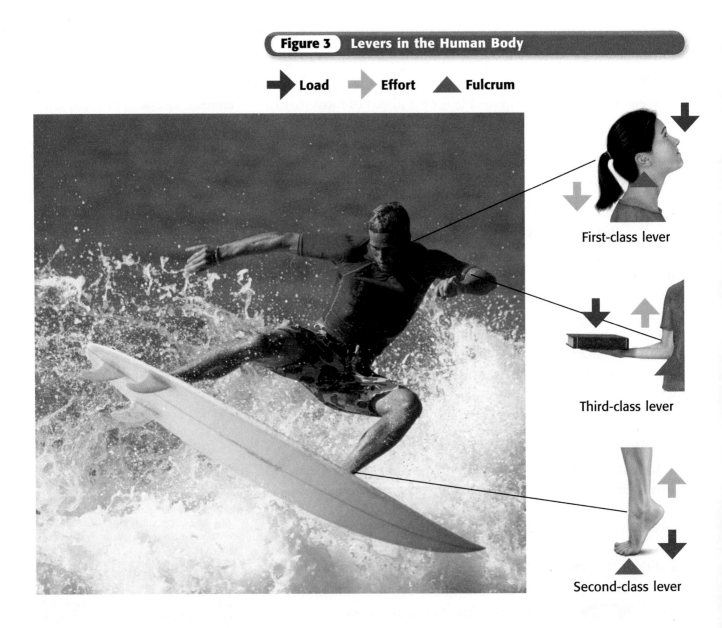

First-class lever

Third-class lever

Second-class lever

Three Classes of Levers

As **Figure 3** shows, there are three classes of levers. First-class and second-class levers increase the amount of force applied to a load. Third-class levers increase the speed of the motion. The class of a lever is determined by the location of the fulcrum, load, and effort force.

In a *first-class lever,* the fulcrum is between the effort force and the load. First-class levers work like a car jack or seesaw. To lift a load, a downward effort force must be applied to the other end of the lever. There are few first-class levers in the body. The joint in your neck acts as the fulcrum in a first-class lever that lifts your head. The effort force is supplied by the muscles at the back of your neck.

In a *second-class lever,* the load is between the fulcrum and the effort force. Second-class levers allow you to use less effort force than the force exerted by the load. Second-class levers work like a shovel. There are also few second-class levers in the body. The action of rising onto your toes represents the action of a second-class lever.

The effort force in a *third-class lever* is between the fulcrum and the load. Third-class levers increase the distance through which the load is moved. Third-class levers work like a dolly that is used to carry heavy boxes. Most movable joints in the human body work like third-class levers. You use a third-class lever to lift your textbook. Your elbow is the fulcrum, and the biceps muscle in your upper arm provides the effort force.

Standards Check **Give an example of a lever in the body.** 🐻 7.6.i

Mechanical Advantage

Force is measured using the SI unit called a newton (N). Use the equation below to answer the questions that follow.

mechanical advantage = force applied to load ÷ effort force

If a second-class lever in your body has a mechanical advantage of 8. What is the effort force applied to a load of 40 N? Where is this lever in your body?

Quick Lab

How Do Levers Work?

You can use simple materials to model how levers in the human body work.

1. Draw a table like the one below.

Class of lever	Sketch of model	Human body sketch
First		
Second		
Third		

DO NOT WRITE IN BOOK

2. Use a **meterstick, small wooden block,** and **100 g weight,** to build a lever from each class. Refer to **Figure 3** as needed.

7.6.i

3. Sketch each of your models in your table.

4. Which part of the human body moves like each class of lever? Sketch this body part in the table that you created.

5. How does the location of the fulcrum change the action of the lever?

6. What advantage does each class of lever provide?

🕐 25 min

Figure 4 *This girl (left) is strengthening her heart and improving her endurance by doing aerobic exercise. This boy (right) is doing resistance exercise to build strong muscles.*

Use It or Lose It

What happens when someone wears a cast for a broken arm? Skeletal muscles around the broken bone become smaller and weaker. The muscles weaken because they are not exercised. Exercised muscles are stronger and larger. Strong muscles can help other organs, too. For example, contracting muscles squeeze blood vessels. These muscle contractions help move blood back to the heart.

Certain exercises can give muscles more strength and endurance. More endurance lets muscles work longer without getting tired. Two kinds of exercise can increase muscle strength and endurance. They are resistance exercise and aerobic exercise. You can see an example of each kind in **Figure 4.**

Standards Check How can exercise benefit organ systems? 🐻 **7.5.a**

Resistance Exercise

Resistance exercise is a great way to strengthen skeletal muscles. During resistance exercise, people work against the resistance, or weight, of an object. Some resistance exercises, such as curl-ups, use your own weight for resistance.

Aerobic Exercise

Steady, moderately intense activity is called *aerobic exercise*. Jogging, cycling, skating, swimming, and walking are aerobic exercises. This kind of exercise can increase muscle strength. However, aerobic exercise mostly strengthens the heart and increases endurance.

Any exercise program should be started slowly. Starting slowly will help prevent you from getting hurt. You should also warm up for exercise by stretching.

SCHOOL to HOME

Power in Pairs

Ask a parent or guardian to sit in a chair and to place a hand palm up under the edge of a table. Tell your parent to apply gentle upward pressure. Feel the front and back of your parent's upper arm. Next, ask your parent to push down on top of the table. Feel your parent's arm again. What did you notice about the muscles in your parent's arm when he or she was pressing up? pushing down?

ACTIVITY

Wordwise **aerobic**
The root *aero-* means "air."

Muscle Injury

A *strain* is an injury in which a muscle or tendon is over-stretched or torn. Strains often happen because a muscle has not been warmed up by stretching or it has been overworked. If a tendon is injured, the body cannot repair it before the next exercise session. So, the tendon becomes inflamed. This condition is called *tendinitis*. Often, a long rest is needed for it to heal.

Some people try to make their muscles stronger by taking drugs called *anabolic steroids* (an uh BAHL ik STER OYDZ). Anabolic steroids cause long-term health problems. They can damage the heart, liver, and kidneys. If taken before the skeleton is mature, anabolic steroids can cause bones to stop growing.

SECTION Review

 7.5.a, 7.5.c, 7.6.i

Summary

- The three kinds of muscle tissue are smooth muscle, cardiac muscle, and skeletal muscle.

- Skeletal muscles work in pairs. Skeletal muscles contract to move bones.

- Muscles and bones work together to form levers.

- There are three classes of levers in the human body. Levers work to provide some advantage to body movements.

- First- and second-class levers increase the amount of force applied to a load. Third-class levers increase the speed of the motion.

- Strains are injuries that affect muscles and tendons. Tendinitis affects tendons.

Using Vocabulary

1. Write an original definition for *muscular system*.

Understanding Concepts

2. **Comparing** Describe three kinds of muscle.

3. **Listing** Name two kinds of exercise.

4. **Summarizing** What is a lever?

5. **Analyzing** What are the roles of bones and muscles in levers?

Critical Thinking

6. **Applying Concepts** Describe the muscle action needed to pick up a book. Include flexors and extensors in your description. Also, include a description of the kind of lever action used.

7. **Analyzing Ideas** What is the difference between a voluntary muscle action and an involuntary muscle action? Do bones and muscles work together differently in voluntary muscle actions when compared to involuntary muscle actions?

INTERPRETING GRAPHICS Use the image below to answer the next question.

8. **Identifying Relationships** Describe how the muscles and bones in this soccer player are working together to move the soccer ball. How are levers involved in this action?

Math Skills

9. **Using Equations** If Trey can do one curl-up every 2.5 s, about how long will it take him to do 35 curl-ups?

Internet Resources

For a variety of links related to this chapter, go to www.scilinks.org
Topic: Muscular System
SciLinks code: HY71008

Skills Practice Lab

Levers and Mechanical Advantage

Your skeleton contains many joints, such as the knee and elbow. These joints act as first-class, second-class, or third-class levers. The three classes of levers are shown below. Most of the levers in the human body act as third-class levers. As you have learned, some levers provide a *mechanical advantage*. Levers always reduce the effort force required to move a load, right? Actually, that is not always true. Sometimes, the advantage of the lever does not reduce the amount of force needed to move a load. In fact, a lever may require additional force to move a load. But levers can offer another kind of advantage. Perform this lab to find out the other advantages of levers.

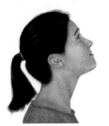  

First-class lever   Second-class lever   Third-class lever

Procedure

1 Copy the data table below onto a sheet of paper.

Levers Data Table			
	Trial 1	Trial 2	Trial 3
30 cm			
15 cm			
3 cm			

DO NOT WRITE IN BOOK

2 Open three paper clips to form a right-angle bend in each paper clip.

3 Tape one paper clip to the surface of a ruler at the 30 cm mark. Make sure that the loop of the paper clip is upright.

④ Tape a second paper clip to the ruler at the 15 cm mark. Tape the third paper clip at the 3 cm mark.

⑤ Tape the end of the ruler to a table. Make sure that you tape the end closest to the 3 cm mark. Attach the ruler so that it forms a joint with the table.

⑥ Attach the spring scale to the paper clip positioned at the 30 cm mark. Using the spring scale, lift the ruler from the table. In your data table, record the amount of force needed to lift the ruler. Repeat this step two more times.

⑦ Attach the spring scale to the paper clip positioned at the 15 cm mark. Using the spring scale, lift the ruler from the table. In your data table, record the amount of force needed to lift the ruler. Repeat this step two more times.

⑧ Attach the spring scale to the paper clip positioned at the 3 cm mark. Using the spring scale, lift the ruler from the table. In your data table, record the amount of force needed to lift the ruler. Repeat this step two more times.

Analyze the Results

⑨ **Recognizing Patterns** The tape that attached the ruler to the table represented your elbow. The table represented your upper arm. What part of your body did the ruler represent?

⑩ **Analyzing Data** Which paper clip position, 30 cm, 15 cm, or 3 cm, required the greatest force to raise the ruler?

⑪ **Analyzing Data** When you performed step 7, which paper clip position on the ruler moved the farthest distance?

Draw Conclusions

⑫ **Making Predictions** If each paper clip represented the point at which your muscle attaches to your lower arm bones, which paper clip position would require you to do the least amount of work when lifting an object?

⑬ **Applying Concepts** In your elbow joint, the muscle that does the kind of lifting modeled in this lab is attached close to the joint. In fact, in the model used, the muscle would be attached to the bone at the 3 cm mark. Does this placement provide the best mechanical advantage for lifting your arm? Explain your answer.

Big Idea Question

⑭ **Making Predictions** If the lever action of a joint does not reduce the amount of force needed to lift a load, what other advantage might be provided by this joint? Use the model to determine the advantage of this joint when comparing the joint with the other kinds of joints.

Science Skills Activity

Investigation and Experimentation

7.7.c Communicate the logical connection among hypotheses, science concepts, tests conducted, data collected, and conclusions drawn from the scientific evidence.

Modifying a Hypothesis

▶ Tutorial

When you perform a scientific investigation, you often start with a question and then develop a hypothesis. A hypothesis is a possible answer to the question. A hypothesis must be testable. The next step in an investigation is to test your hypothesis. Often, in the course of your experiment, you will gather data that will require you to modify your original hypothesis. In this tutorial, you will learn how to modify a hypothesis. Read the question and hypothesis below.

> Question: How do your muscles move your bones?
> Hypothesis: One muscle is responsible for moving each bone.

Procedure

1 Design a Test for the Hypothesis In this investigation, you might use rulers or sticks to model bones and rubber bands to model muscles. You will be testing if it is possible for one muscle to move one bone.

2 Identify the Expected Outcome If your hypothesis is correct, what results do you expect? In this investigation, if your hypothesis is correct, you will be able to move each bone model with a single rubber band.

3 Analyze the Actual Outcome In your experiment, the results show that it is not possible to move the bone model with a single rubber band. You notice that the bones will not move predictably or smoothly.

4 Form a New Hypothesis In what way do the observations that you made agree with or disagree with your original hypothesis? In this example, your observations disagree with your hypothesis. One muscle did not move the bone. The hypothesis must be modified. See the modified hypothesis below.

> Question: How do your muscles move your bones?
> Hypothesis: Muscle pairs work together to move each bone.

▶ You Try It!

Your body tissues contain water. In fact, the human body is made up of about 75% water. Imagine that you are part of a research team working to answer this question: Does water help the body maintain a constant temperature? You have decided to focus your research on whether or not water helps the body maintain a constant temperature. Your hypothesis is the following: Water does not help the body maintain a constant temperature.

Procedure

1 Complete steps 1 and 2 from the tutorial above.

Analysis

2 Applying Concepts If you were to test your hypothesis, the results would disagree with the expected results. You would conclude that the temperature of objects that are surrounded by water or objects that are mostly made of water would remain fairly constant. Based on this information, modify the original hypothesis.

3 Analyzing Methods Will you need to change the original experiment to test the new hypothesis? Why or why not?

4 Expressing Opinions Why is it important that scientists modify their hypotheses?

Chapter Summary

The Big Idea The human body is composed of major systems that have differing functions, but all of the systems work together to maintain homeostasis.

Section

Vocabulary

1 Body Organization

Key Concept The human body functions because of the contributions of cells, tissues, organs, and organ systems.

- The levels of organization in the human body include cells, tissues, organs, organ systems, and the organism.
- Human cells are differentiated to perform specific jobs in the body.
- There are 11 human organ systems.
- Organ systems work together to maintain homeostasis. The failure of one organ system affects the entire body.

The muscular system is just one of 11 organ systems.

tissue p. 467
organ p. 468

2 The Skeletal System

Key Concept The skeletal system is an organ system. The functions of the skeletal system include support, protection, movement, and the production of blood cells.

- The skeletal system includes bones, cartilage, and connective tissue.
- Bones have four important functions in the body. Bones are structured to perform these functions.
- Three human body joints are gliding, ball and socket, and hinge.

Bones are one kind of organ in the skeletal system.

skeletal system p. 472
joint p. 474

3 The Muscular System

Key Concept The muscular system is an organ system. The skeletal and muscular systems work together to provide a structural framework for movement.

- There are three kinds of muscle tissue: cardiac, smooth, and skeletal.
- Bones and muscles work together to form levers, which increase the mechanical advantage of most movements.
- The two kinds of exercise include resistance exercise and aerobic exercise.

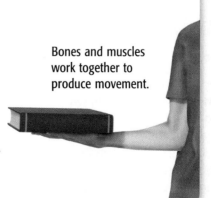

Bones and muscles work together to produce movement.

muscular system p. 476
lever p. 478
mechanical advantage p. 478

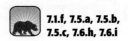
Organize

Table Fold Review the FoldNote that you created at the beginning of the chapter. Add to or correct the FoldNote based on what you have learned.

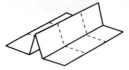

Using Vocabulary

① **Academic Vocabulary** In the sentence "Levers confer a mechanical advantage," what does the word *confer* mean?
a. decrease
b. cancel out
c. give
d. complete

Complete each of the following sentences by choosing the correct term from the word bank.

homeostasis	organ
joint	skeletal system
tissue	muscular system

② A(n) ___ is a place where two or more bones meet.

③ ___ is the maintenance of a stable internal environment.

④ A(n) ___ is made up of two or more tissues working together.

⑤ The ___ supports and protects the body, stores minerals, and allows movement.

Understanding Concepts

Multiple Choice

⑥ Which of the following lists of the levels of organization shows the way in which the body is organized?
a. cells, organs, organ systems, tissues
b. tissues, cells, organs, organ systems
c. cells, tissues, organs, organ systems
d. cells, tissues, organ systems, organs

⑦ Which muscle tissue can be both voluntary and involuntary?
a. smooth muscle
b. cardiac muscle
c. skeletal muscle
d. All of the above

⑧ Which of the following statements about muscles is true?
a. They work in pairs.
b. They can be voluntary or involuntary.
c. They become stronger if exercised.
d. All of the above

Short Answer

⑨ **Analyzing** Describe the skeletal system, and list four functions of bones.

⑩ **Summarizing** Give an example of how organ systems work together.

⑪ **Listing** Name three injuries and two diseases that affect the skeletal system.

⑫ **Comparing** How are aerobic exercise and resistance exercise related?

⑬ **Evaluating** What is the role of joints in the human body?

INTERPRETING GRAPHICS Use the image below to answer the next two questions.

⑭ **Describing** How are this boy's muscles and bones working together to produce movement?

⑮ **Classifying** In the image, what class of levers is at work?

16 Communicating Concepts Create a brochure that describes the relationship between human body levers and joints. Include information about the relationship of muscles and bones to these concepts.

Critical Thinking

17 Concept Mapping Use the following terms to create a concept map: *tissues, muscle tissue, connective tissue, cells, organ systems, organs, epithelial tissue,* and *nervous tissue.*

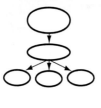

18 Making Comparisons Compare the shapes of the bones of the human skull with the shapes of the bones of the human leg. How do the shapes differ? Why are the shapes important?

INTERPRETING GRAPHICS Use the image below to answer the next three questions.

19 Identifying Relationships What class of levers is shown in the image?

20 Analyzing Processes How does this human body lever work?

21 Making Inferences How would the motion shown in the image be different if the lever was replaced by a second-class lever?

22 Making Inferences How does your muscular system rely on the health and functions of your skeletal system?

23 Making Inferences Imagine that you are building a robot. Your robot will have a skeleton that is similar to a human skeleton. If the robot needs to be able to move a limb in all directions, what kind of joint would be needed? Explain your answer.

24 Analyzing Ideas Human bones are dense and are often filled with marrow. But many bones of birds are hollow. Why might birds have hollow bones?

25 Identifying Relationships Why might some muscles fail to work properly if a bone is broken?

26 Analyzing Ideas Why are red blood cells called differentiated cells? What happens to a cell when it becomes differentiated?

Math Skills

INTERPRETING GRAPHICS Use the table below to answer the next question.

Number of Sit-ups Vs. Time			
	30 s	**60 s**	**120 s**
Martin	10	20	35
Midori	9	19	38
Maria	11	18	36

27 Analyzing Data Use the data in the table above to create a graph. Be sure to include all of the appropriate labels.

Challenge

28 Identifying Relationships Describe how the muscular and skeletal organ systems maintain homeostasis. What would happen if the skeletal system no longer functioned properly?

Standards Assessment

5.1.h, 5.2.a, 5.2.b, 5.2.c,
7.1.f, 7.5, 7.5.a, 7.5.b, 7.5.c,
7.6, 7.6.h, 7.6.i

REVIEWING ACADEMIC VOCABULARY

1 In the sentence "Human body systems have a complementary relationship," what does the word *complementary* mean?

A supporting each other

B competing against each other

C unrelated to each other

D replacing each other

2 Which of the following sets of words is closest in meaning to the word *underlie*?

A to form the foundation of

B to take the place of

C to take care of

D to stand in the way of

3 In the sentence "Each major system of the body serves a different function," what does the word *function* mean?

A position

B purpose

C variable

D gathering

4 Which of the following words is the closest in meaning to the word *principle*?

A idea

B rule

C hypothesis

D situation

5 In the sentence "As multicellular organisms develop, their cells differentiate," what does the word *differentiate* mean?

A to show the differences between

B to merge two different things

C to recognize a difference between

D to become different from each other

REVIEWING CONCEPTS

6 Which kind of joint allows the most movement in different directions?

A gliding joint

B hinge joint

C ball-and-socket joint

D sliding joint

7 How are tissue and organs related in the body?

A Organs are surrounded by tissue.

B Organs are made up of tissue.

C Tissue contains one or more organs.

D Tissue and organs work independently.

8 The body's cells, tissues, and organs work together to maintain homeostasis. What is the goal of homeostasis?

A to keep the body physically active

B to keep the body free of disease

C to maintain a stable internal environment

D to remove and replace dead tissue

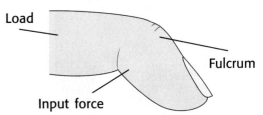

Load

Fulcrum

Input force

9 What kind of lever is shown in the illustration above?

A a first-class lever

B a second-class lever

C a third-class lever

D a fourth-class lever

10 Which of the following must occur for the forearm to move toward the shoulder?

A The forearm muscle must contract.

B The shoulder muscle must contract.

C The triceps muscle must contract.

D The biceps muscle must contract.

11 Which of the following helps cushion the area in a joint where bones meet?

A cartilage

B muscle tissue

C blood vessels

D marrow

12 How is the structure of muscle cells different from that of other cells?

A Muscle cells are organized into groups that work together.

B Muscle cells contain a special pigment that picks up oxygen.

C Muscle cells are shaped for the transfer of electrical impulses.

D Muscle cells contain special proteins that allow them to contract.

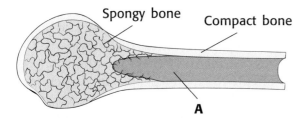

13 What does point A represent in the diagram above?

A osteoblasts

B marrow

C cartilage

D blood vessels

14 The human body is composed of just a few elements. Which element is most abundant in the body?

A carbon

B oxygen

C hydrogen

D nitrogen

15 Which organ system is responsible for transporting oxygen to each cell?

A the digestive system

B the nervous system

C the circulatory system

D the endocrine system

16 How do the heart and lungs work together to replace oxygen in the blood?

A Blood enters the lungs, where it is filled with oxygen, and then the blood is sent to the heart.

B Blood fills with oxygen in the heart, and then the lungs remove carbon dioxide.

C The heart pumps blood into the lungs, where it is then filled with oxygen.

D The heart removes carbon dioxide from the blood, and then the lungs fill it with oxygen.

17 What is the first step in the process of digestion?

A passing food into the small intestine

B chewing food in the mouth

C breaking down food in the stomach

D absorbing molecules of food into the blood

Standards Assessment

Science
in Action

Scientific Discoveries

Engineering Inspired by Nature

What can a cockroach contribute to engineering and science? The answer is nothing, right? Well, that's wrong! Cockroaches, as well as many other organisms, provide models for scientists and engineers. These scientists synthesize new materials that have structures and functions related to materials found in nature. For example, researchers in the California Institute for Quantitative Biomedical Research (QB3) have developed a new prosthesis. Instead of replacing a leg or arm, this prosthesis provides vision and is based on the structure of human eyes. This prosthesis could bring vision to many.

Math ACTiViTY

One out of every 4,000 people loses the ability to see because special cells in the eye stop functioning properly. In a city that has a population of 750,000, how many people are blind in this way? Record your work in your **Science Journal.**

Science, Technology, and Society

Beating the Odds

Sometimes, people are born without limbs or lose limbs in accidents. Many of these people have prostheses (prahs THEE SEEZ), or human-made replacements for the body parts. Until recently, many of these prostheses made it difficult for many people to participate in physical activities, such as sports. But new designs have led to lighter, more comfortable prostheses that move the way that a human limb does. These new designs have allowed athletes that have physical disabilities to compete at higher levels.

Social Studies ACTiViTY

Research the use of prostheses throughout history. Create a timeline showing major advances in prosthesis use and design.

Zahra Beheshti

Physical Therapist A physical therapist is a licensed professional who helps people recover from injuries by using hands-on treatment instead of medicines. Dr. Zahra Beheshti is a physical therapist at the Princeton Physical Therapy Center in New Jersey. She often helps athletes who suffer from sports injuries.

After an injury, a person may go through a process called *rehabilitation* to regain the use of the injured body part. The most common mistake made by athletes is that they play sports before completely recovering from injuries. Dr. Beheshti explains, "Going back to their usual pre-injury routine could result in another injury."

Dr. Beheshti also teaches patients about preventing future sports injuries. "Most injuries happen when an individual engages in strenuous activities without a proper warm-up or cool-down period." Being a physical therapist is rewarding work. Dr. Beheshti says, "I get a lot of satisfaction when treating patients and seeing them regain their function and independence and return to their normal life."

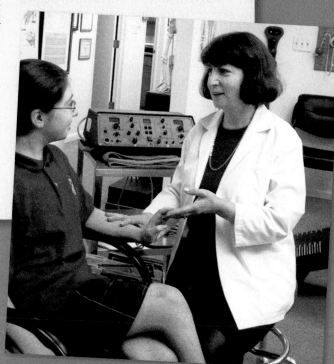

Language Arts ACTIVITY

Interview a physical therapist who works in or near your community. Write a newspaper article about the therapist that you interview in your **Science Journal.**

Internet Resources

- To learn more about careers in science, visit **www.scilinks.org** and enter the SciLinks code HY70225.

- To learn more about these Science in Action topics, visit **go.hrw.com** and type in the keyword HY7BD1F.

- Check out articles related to this chapter by visiting **go.hrw.com.** Just type in the keyword HY7BD1C.

Improving Comprehension

Graphic Organizers are important visual tools that can help you organize information and improve your reading comprehension. The Graphic Organizer below is called a *Venn diagram*. Instructions for creating other types of Graphic Organizers are located in the **Study Skills** section of the Appendix.

How to Make a Venn Diagram

1. Draw a diagram like the one shown below. Draw one circle for each topic. Make sure that each circle partially overlaps the other circles.

2. In each circle, write a topic that you want to compare with the topics in the other circles.

3. In the areas of the diagram where circles overlap, write the characteristics that the topics in the overlapping circles share.

4. In the areas of the diagram where circles do not overlap, write the characteristics that are unique to the topic of the particular circle.

When to Use a Venn Diagram

A Venn diagram is a useful tool for comparing two or three topics in science. A Venn diagram shows which characteristics the topics share and which characteristics are unique to each topic. Venn diagrams are ideal when you want to illustrate relationships in a pair or small group of topics. As you read, look for topics that have both shared and unique characteristics, and draw a Venn diagram that shows how the topics are related.

Cardiovascular System
- supplies nutrients to cells and removes wastes
- is made up of heart, blood, and blood vessels
- carries heat and hormones throughout the body

- is an organ system
- is necessary for cellular gas exchange
- is essential to the proper functioning of the entire organism

Respiratory System
- is responsible for taking in oxygen and releasing carbon dioxide
- includes the nose, mouth, pharynx, larynx, trachea, lungs, bronchi, diaphragm, and mouth
- makes breathing possible

You Try It!

This Reading Strategy can also be used within the chapter that you are about to read. Practice making your own *Venn diagram* as directed in the Reading Strategy for Section 1. Record your work in your **Science Journal.**

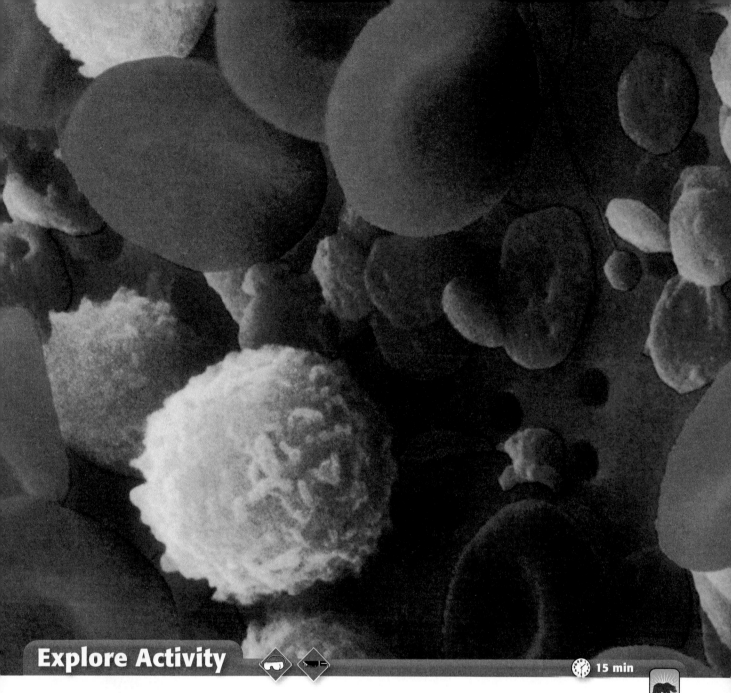

Explore Activity

Modeling a Valve

In this activity, you will create a model of a valve that allows material to flow in only one direction. Similar valves in the heart and in certain large blood vessels prevent blood from flowing in the wrong direction.

Procedure

1. Roll a **sheet of paper** into a cone, and secure it with a piece of **tape**. The diameter of the wide part of the cone should be 7 cm. Use **scissors** to create several slits that extend outward from the point of the cone so that you make a series of paper flaps.

2. Insert the point of the cone into one end of a **cardboard tube.** Secure the tube in place with tape. Place a **bowl** beneath the open end of the tube.

3. Hold the tube with the cone positioned at the top. Pour a **handful of marbles** into the tube.

4. Turn the tube upside down so that the cone is at the bottom. Pour the marbles into the tube.

Analysis

5. How did the paper cone affect the movement of the marbles?

6. Describe how this model valve works.

7. Why do you think valves are needed in the heart?

7.6.j
7.7.d

⏱ 15 min

The Cardiovascular System

Key Concept The cardiovascular system circulates blood, gases, and nutrients throughout your body.

What You Will Learn

- The cardiovascular system is made up of the heart, three types of blood vessels, and blood.
- Contractions of the heart pump blood throughout the entire body.
- Cardiovascular problems include atherosclerosis, high blood pressure, strokes, heart attacks, and heart failure.

Why It Matters

Learning about the cardiovascular system helps you understand how organ systems in the human body work together.

Vocabulary

- cardiovascular system
- artery
- capillary
- vein
- pulmonary circulation
- systemic circulation

READING STRATEGY

Graphic Organizer In your **Science Journal,** create a Venn Diagram that compares systemic circulation and pulmonary circulation.

cardiovascular system
(KAR dee OH VAS kyoo luhr SIS tuhm) a collection of organs that transport blood throughout the body

7.5.a Students know plants and animals have levels of organization for structure and function, including cells, tissues, organs, organ systems, and the whole organism.
7.5.b Students know organ systems function because of the contributions of individual organs, tissues, and cells. The failure of any part can affect the entire system.
7.6.j Students know that contractions of the heart generate blood pressure and that heart valves prevent backflow of blood in the circulatory system.

▶ When you hear the word *heart,* what do you think of first? Many people think of love. But the heart is much more than a symbol of love. Your heart is an amazing pump.

The heart is an organ that is part of your cardiovascular system. The word *cardio* means "heart," and the word *vascular* means "blood vessel." The blood vessels—arteries, capillaries, and veins—carry blood pumped by the heart. The cardiovascular system is sometimes called the *circulatory system* because it circulates materials around the body.

Your Cardiovascular System

Your heart, blood, and blood vessels make up your **cardiovascular system.** Your *heart* is an organ made mostly of cardiac muscle tissue. When the heart *contracts,* or squeezes, pressure is created. This pressure moves blood throughout your body. **Figure 1** shows your heart, major arteries, and major veins.

The cardiovascular system helps maintain *homeostasis,* a state of stable internal conditions. The cardiovascular system supplies oxygen and nutrients to cells and removes wastes from cells. It also carries heat and chemical signals called *hormones* throughout the body.

Standards Check What are the main parts of the cardiovascular system? 7.5.a

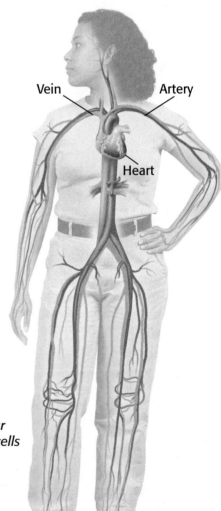

Figure 1 *The cardiovascular system carries blood to the cells in your body.*

The Heart

Your heart is a muscular organ that is about the size of your fist. It is almost in the center of your chest. Like hearts of all mammals, your heart has a left side and a right side that are separated by a thick wall. The right side of the heart pumps oxygen-poor blood to the lungs. The left side pumps oxygen-rich blood to the body. As you can see in **Figure 2,** each side has an upper chamber and a lower chamber. Each upper chamber is called an *atrium* (plural, *atria*). Each lower chamber is called a *ventricle*.

Flaplike structures called *valves* are found between the atria and ventricles. Valves are also found where some large blood vessels attach to the heart. As blood moves through the heart, the valves close and produce the "lub-dub, lub-dub" sound of a beating heart. Valves prevent blood from going backward. **Figure 3** shows the flow of blood through the heart.

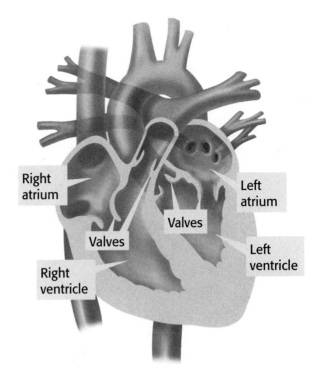

Figure 2 *The heart pumps blood through blood vessels. The vessels carrying oxygen-rich blood are shown in red. The vessels carrying oxygen-poor blood are shown in blue.*

Figure 3 **The Flow of Blood Through the Heart**

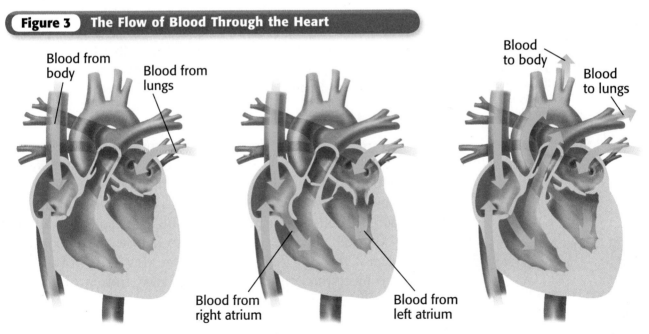

❶ Blood enters the atria first. The left atrium receives oxygen-rich blood from the lungs. The right atrium receives oxygen-poor blood from the body.

❷ When the atria contract, blood moves into the ventricles.

❸ While the atria relax, the ventricles contract and push blood out of the heart. Blood from the right ventricle goes to the lungs. Blood from the left ventricle goes to the rest of the body.

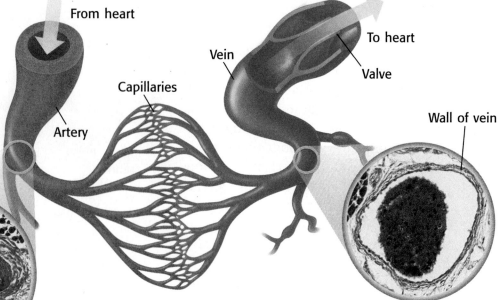

Figure 4 *Large arteries branch into smaller arteries, which branch into capillaries. Capillaries join small veins, which join to form large veins.*

From heart

To heart

Vein

Valve

Capillaries

Artery

Wall of vein

Wall of artery

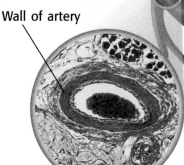

Blood Vessels

Blood travels throughout your body in hollow tubes called *blood vessels*. The three types of blood vessels—arteries, capillaries, and veins—are shown in **Figure 4.**

Arteries

A blood vessel that carries blood away from the heart is an **artery.** Arteries have thick walls, which contain a layer of smooth muscle. Each heartbeat pumps blood into your arteries at high pressure. Artery walls stretch and are usually strong enough to stand the pressure. Your *pulse* is caused by the rhythmic contractions of the heart pumping blood into arteries.

Capillaries

Nutrients, oxygen, and other substances must leave blood and get to your body's cells. Carbon dioxide and other wastes leave body cells and are carried away by blood. A **capillary** is a tiny blood vessel that allows exchanges between body cells and blood. The exchanges can take place because capillary walls are only one cell thick. Capillaries are so narrow that blood cells must pass through them in single file. Most cells in the body are no more than three or four cells away from a capillary.

Veins

After leaving capillaries, blood enters veins. A **vein** is a blood vessel that carries blood back to the heart. As blood travels through veins, valves found in large veins keep the blood from flowing backward. When skeletal muscles contract, they squeeze nearby veins and help push blood toward the heart.

Standards Check How do the three types of blood vessels work together? 🐻 **7.5.a**

artery (ART uhr ee) a blood vessel that carries blood away from the heart to the body's organs

capillary (CAP uh LEYR ee) a tiny blood vessel that allows an exchange between blood and cells in tissue

vein (VAYN) in biology, a vessel that carries blood to the heart

William Harvey Biography
Why is William Harvey famous? Write about the life and work of William Harvey in your **Science Journal**. Go to **go.hrw.com,** and type in the keyword HY7BD2W.

Two Types of Circulation

Where does blood get the oxygen to deliver to your body? From your lungs! Your heart contracts and pumps blood to the lungs. Here, carbon dioxide leaves the blood and oxygen enters the blood. The oxygen-rich blood then flows back to the heart. This circulation of blood between your heart and lungs is called **pulmonary circulation.**

The oxygen-rich blood returning to the heart from the lungs is then pumped to the rest of the body. The circulation of blood between the heart and the rest of the body is called **systemic circulation.** Both types of circulation are shown in **Figure 5.**

pulmonary circulation
(PUL muh NER ee SUHR kyoo LAY shuhn) the flow of blood from the heart to the lungs and back to the heart through the pulmonary arteries, capillaries, and veins

systemic circulation
(sis TEM ik SUHR kyoo LAY shuhn) the flow of blood from the heart to all parts of the body and back to the heart

Figure 5 The Flow of Blood Through the Body

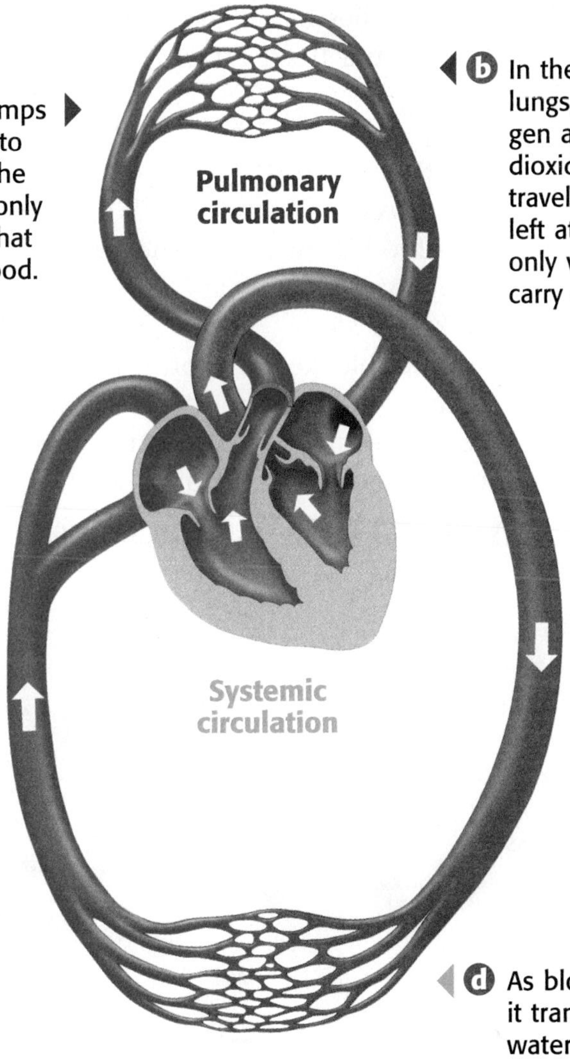

a The right ventricle pumps oxygen-poor blood into arteries that lead to the lungs. These are the only arteries in the body that carry oxygen-poor blood.

Pulmonary circulation

b In the capillaries of the lungs, blood takes up oxygen and releases carbon dioxide. Oxygen-rich blood travels through veins to the left atrium. These are the only veins in the body that carry oxygen-rich blood.

c The heart pumps oxygen-rich blood from the left ventricle into arteries and then into capillaries.

Systemic circulation

e Oxygen-poor blood travels back to the heart and is delivered into the right atrium by two large veins.

d As blood travels through capillaries, it transports oxygen, nutrients, and water to the cells of the body. At the same time, waste materials and carbon dioxide are carried away.

Cardiovascular Problems

More than just your heart and blood vessels are at risk if you have cardiovascular problems. Your whole body may be harmed. Cardiovascular problems can be caused by smoking, high levels of cholesterol in the blood, stress, physical inactivity, or heredity. Eating a healthy diet and getting plenty of exercise can lower the risk of having cardiovascular problems.

Atherosclerosis

Heart diseases are the leading cause of death in the United States. One major cause of heart diseases is a cardiovascular disease called *atherosclerosis* (ATH uhr OH skluh ROH sis). Atherosclerosis happens when cholesterol (kuh LES tuhr AWL) and other lipids build up inside blood vessels. This buildup causes the blood vessels to become narrower and less elastic. **Figure 6** shows a blocked pathway through an artery. When an artery that supplies blood to the heart becomes blocked, the person may have a heart attack.

High Blood Pressure

Atherosclerosis may be caused in part by hypertension. *Hypertension* is abnormally high blood pressure. The higher the blood pressure is, the greater the risk of cardiovascular problems is. For example, high blood pressure can cause a stroke. A *stroke* happens when a blood vessel in the brain becomes blocked or ruptures. As a result, that part of the brain receives no oxygen. Without oxygen, brain cells die. High blood pressure can also cause other cardiovascular problems, such as heart attacks and heart failure.

Standards Check How can high blood pressure lead to a stroke?
7.5.b, 7.6.j

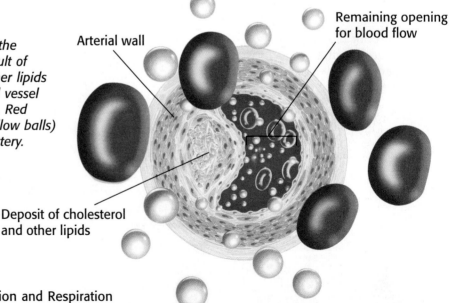

Figure 6 *This illustration shows the narrowing of an artery as the result of lipid deposits. Cholesterol and other lipids (yellow) build up inside the blood vessel walls and block the flow of blood. Red blood cells and lipid particles (yellow balls) are shown moving through the artery.*

Remaining opening for blood flow

Arterial wall

Deposit of cholesterol and other lipids

Heart Attacks and Heart Failure

A *heart attack* happens when heart muscle cells do not get enough blood. The heart muscle is damaged. As shown in **Figure 7,** arteries that deliver oxygen to the heart may be blocked. Without oxygen, heart muscle cells may be damaged. If enough heart muscle cells are damaged, the heart may stop.

Heart failure happens when the heart is too weak to pump enough blood to meet the body's needs. Organs, such as the brain, lungs, and kidneys, may be damaged by lack of oxygen and nutrients or by the buildup of fluids or wastes.

Standards Check What is heart failure? 🐻**7.5.b**

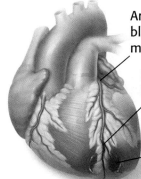

Artery delivering blood to heart muscle

Location of blocked artery

Area of heart damaged by lack of oxygen to heart muscle

Figure 7 *A heart attack happens when an artery to the heart is blocked.*

SECTION Review

🐻 7.5.a, 7.5.b, 7.6.j

- Parts of the cardiovascular system include the heart, three types of blood vessels, and blood.

- Contractions of the heart pump blood throughout the body. Valves ensure that blood flows in only one direction.

- The three types of blood vessels are arteries, veins, and capillaries.

- Oxygen-poor blood flows from the heart through the lungs, where it picks up oxygen. Oxygen-rich blood flows from the heart to the rest of the body.

- Cardiovascular problems include atherosclerosis, hypertension, strokes, heart attacks, and heart failure.

Understanding Concepts

1 **Modeling** Describe the pathway of blood flow. Begin and end in the left atrium.

2 **Describing** Describe the functions of the five parts of the cardiovascular system.

3 **Comparing** Compare a heart attack and heart failure.

4 **Analyzing** What is the function of valves?

Critical Thinking

5 **Identifying Relationships** How is the structure of capillaries related to their function?

6 **Making Inferences** One of aspirin's effects is that it prevents substances in blood from being too "sticky." Why might doctors prescribe aspirin for patients who have had a heart attack?

7 **Analyzing Ideas** Veins and arteries are everywhere in your body. When a pulse is taken, it is usually taken at an artery in the neck or wrist. Explain why.

8 **Identifying Relationships** How are heart contractions and blood pressure related?

Math Skills

9 **Making Conversions** An adult male's heart pumps about 2.8 million liters of blood per year. If his heart beats 70 times per minute, how much blood does his heart pump with each beat?

Challenge

10 **Predicting Consequences** Cardiac bypass surgery allows surgeons to remove unhealthy blood vessels near the heart. They are replaced with healthy blood vessels from other places in the patient's body. Why might a patient need this type of surgery?

Internet Resources

For a variety of links related to this chapter, go to www.scilinks.org

Topic: The Cardiovascular System; Cardiovascular Problems

SciLinks code: HY70221; HY70220

Blood

Key Concept Blood transports many things through the body, including oxygen, nutrients, wastes, heat, immune system cells, and hormones.

▶ Blood is the carrier for the cardiovascular system. It moves through miles of blood vessels to reach the cells in your body. So, you must have a lot of blood, right? Not really. An adult human body has about 5 L of blood. Your body most likely has a little less than that. All the blood in your body would not fill two 3 L soda bottles.

Components of Blood

Your cardiovascular system is made up of your heart, your blood vessels, and blood. **Blood** is a connective tissue made up of plasma, red blood cells, platelets, and white blood cells. Blood carries important materials to all parts of your body.

Plasma

The fluid part of the blood is called plasma (PLAZ muh). *Plasma* is a mixture of water, minerals, nutrients, sugars, proteins, and other substances. Red blood cells, white blood cells, and platelets are found in plasma.

Red Blood Cells

Most blood cells are *red blood cells,* or RBCs. RBCs, such as the ones shown in **Figure 1,** supply oxygen for every living cell in your body. Cells need this gas to carry out their functions. Each RBC has hemoglobin (HEE moh GLOH bin). *Hemoglobin* is an oxygen-carrying protein. Hemoglobin attaches to the oxygen you inhale. RBCs can then move oxygen throughout the body. Hemoglobin also gives RBCs their red color.

Standards Check Describe the function of red blood cells. **7.5.a**

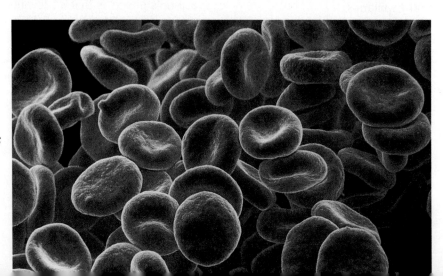

Figure 1 *Red blood cells are made in the bone marrow of certain bones. As red blood cells mature, they lose their nucleus and their DNA.*

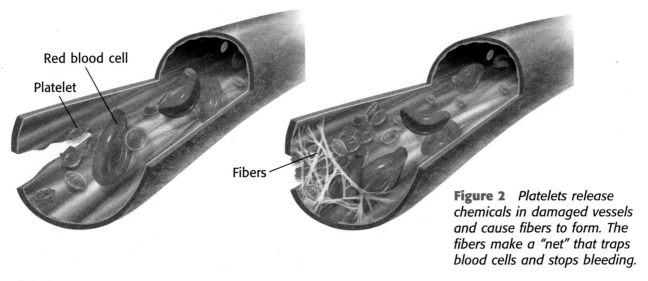

Red blood cell

Platelet

Fibers

Figure 2 *Platelets release chemicals in damaged vessels and cause fibers to form. The fibers make a "net" that traps blood cells and stops bleeding.*

Platelets

Drifting among the blood cells are tiny particles called platelets. *Platelets* are pieces of larger cells found in bone marrow. These larger cells remain in the bone marrow, but pieces are pinched off. Then, these pieces enter the bloodstream as platelets. Platelets last for only 5 to 10 days, but they are an important part of blood. When you cut or scrape your skin, you bleed because blood vessels have been opened. As soon as bleeding starts, platelets begin to clump together in the damaged area. They form a plug that helps reduce blood loss, as shown in **Figure 2.** Platelets also release chemicals that react with proteins in plasma. The reaction causes tiny fibers to form. The fibers help make a blood clot.

blood (BLUHD) the fluid that carries gases, nutrients, and wastes through the body and that is made up of platelets, white blood cells, red blood cells, and plasma

White Blood Cells

Sometimes *pathogens* (PATH uh juhnz)—bacteria, viruses, and other microscopic particles that can make you sick— enter your body. When they do, they often meet *white blood cells,* or WBCs. WBCs, shown in **Figure 3,** help keep you healthy by destroying pathogens. WBCs also help clean wounds.

WBCs fight pathogens in several ways. Some WBCs squeeze out of blood vessels and move around in tissues, searching for pathogens. When they find a pathogen, they destroy it. Other WBCs release antibodies. *Antibodies* are chemicals that identify or destroy pathogens. WBCs also keep you healthy by destroying body cells that have died or been damaged. Most WBCs are made in bone marrow. Some WBCs mature in the lymphatic system.

Standards Check What functions do WBCs perform? 7.5.a

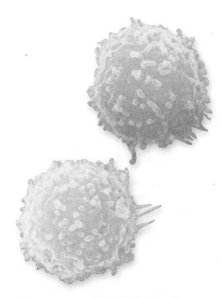

Figure 3 *White blood cells defend the body against pathogens. These white blood cells have been colored yellow to make their shape easier to see.*

Body Temperature Regulation

Your blood does more than carry oxygen and nutrients to your cells. It also helps regulate your body temperature. When you are hot, your blood vessels enlarge. Blood flow to the skin is increased. Heat can then be released into the environment to cool your body. When you are cold, the blood vessels to the skin narrow. Blood flow to the skin is decreased. So, less heat is lost to the environment through your skin.

Blood Pressure

Every time your heart contracts, blood is pushed out of the heart and into your arteries. The force of the blood on the inside walls of arteries is called **blood pressure.**

Blood pressure is expressed in millimeters of mercury (mm Hg). For example, a blood pressure of 110 mm Hg means that the pressure on the artery walls can push a column of mercury to a height of 110 mm.

Blood pressure is usually given as two numbers, such as 110/70 mm Hg. Systolic (sis TAHL ik) pressure is the first number. *Systolic pressure* is the pressure inside large arteries when the ventricles contract. The surge of blood causes the arteries to bulge and produce a pulse. The second number, *diastolic* (DIE uh STAHL ik) *pressure,* is the pressure inside arteries when the ventricles relax. For adults, a blood pressure of 120/80 mm Hg or below is considered healthy. High blood pressure can cause heart or kidney damage.

Standards Check In what unit is blood pressure normally expressed? 🐻 **7.6.j**

blood pressure (BLUDH PRESH uhr) the force that blood exerts on the walls of the arteries

Wordwise The root *press-* means "to press."

Quick Lab

Modeling Blood Pressure

In this activity, you will demonstrate systolic and diastolic blood pressure. You will use a pipet bulb to represent the heart.

1. Fill a **pipet bulb** with **water.** Stretch the mouth of a **long balloon** around the end of the pipet bulb. Secure with **tape.**

2. Carefully squeeze the pipet bulb in one hand. Describe the pressure in the balloon.

3. Release your squeeze on the pipet bulb. Describe the pressure in the balloon now.

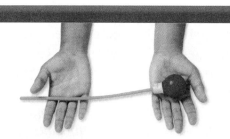

7.6.j
7.7.d

4. If the pipet bulb represents the heart, what does the balloon represent?

5. Which state, bulb squeezed or not squeezed, is similar to systolic pressure? Explain.

6. What is your blood pressure if your diastolic pressure is 60 mm Hg and your systolic pressure is 95 mm Hg?

 10 min

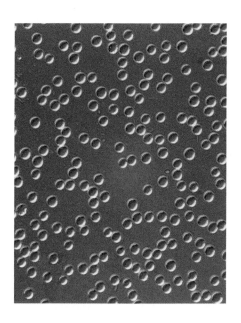
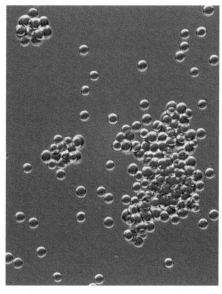

Figure 4 *The slide on the left shows a mixture of blood from two people with the same blood type. The slide on the right shows a mixture of blood from two people with different blood types.* **What is happening in the slides?**

Blood Types

Your blood type refers to the kinds of molecules you have on the surface of your RBCs. These surface molecules are called *antigens* (AN tuh juhnz). Different blood types have different antigens on their RBCs. Different blood types may also have different antibodies in the plasma. As shown in **Figure 4,** these antibodies react to antigens of other blood types as if the antigens were pathogens.

ABO System

The ABO system is one way of classifying blood based on the kinds of antigens on the surface. Every person has one of four blood types: A, B, AB, or O. Type A blood has A antigens; type B has B antigens; and type AB has both A and B antigens. Type O blood has neither A nor B antigens.

Each blood type may also have different antibodies, as shown in **Figure 5.** For example, type A blood has antibodies that react to type B blood. If a person with type A blood is injected with type B blood, the type B antibodies attach themselves to the type B RBCs. These RBCs begin to clump together, and the clumps may block blood vessels. A reaction to the wrong blood type may be fatal.

Rh System

Another antigen that may be on the surface of RBCs is the Rh antigen. A person with the Rh antigen is considered Rh-positive (Rh$^+$). A person without the Rh antigen is Rh-negative (Rh$^-$). If an Rh$^-$ person receives a blood transfusion of Rh$^+$ blood, antibodies may react and cause the blood to clump.

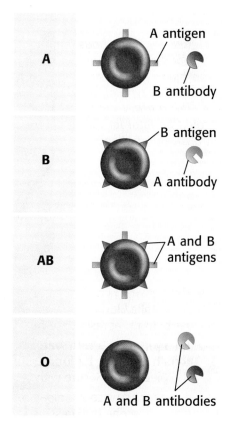

Figure 5 *This figure shows which antigens and antibodies may be present in each blood type.*

Calculating Heartbeats

A person's heart averages about 70 beats per minute.

1. Calculate how many times a heart beats in one day.
2. If a person lives for 75 years, how many times will his or her heart beat?
3. If an athlete's heart beats 50 times per minute, how many fewer times than an average heart will his or her heart beat in 30 days?

Transfusions and Blood Types

Sometimes, a person must be given a blood transfusion. A *transfusion* is the injection of blood or blood components into a person to replace blood that has been lost because of surgery or an injury. Blood loss may lead to shock. *Shock* happens when a person's cells do not get enough blood. Without blood, cells do not get the oxygen and nutrients that they need, and wastes build up. Cell death may occur. Significant cell death may be fatal to the person.

Blood used in transfusions must be carefully handled. **Figure 6** shows bags of blood that may be given in a transfusion. The blood type is clearly marked. Because the ABO blood types have different antigen-antibody reactions, a person receiving blood cannot receive blood from just anyone. **Table 1** shows blood-transfusion possibilities.

Standards Check   Why is shock dangerous to a person?   🐻 **7.5.b**

Figure 6 *These bags of blood clearly show the blood type. Giving the wrong type of blood during a transfusion could be fatal for the transfusion patient.*

Table 1	Blood Transfusion Possibilities	
Type	**Can receive**	**Can donate to**
A	A, O	A, AB
B	B, O	B, AB
AB	A, B, AB, O	AB
O	O	A, B, AB, O

Blood Disorders

Two of the most common blood disorders are hemophilia and leukemia. A person with *hemophilia* (HEE moh FIL ee uh) is missing a protein that helps blood clot. Blood clots form in a healthy person when blood vessels have been damaged or opened. A person with hemophilia does not form blood clots normally. Even a small cut may lead to significant blood loss. *Leukemia* is a type of cancer that affects blood cells. A person with leukemia may not be able to make enough healthy WBCs and RBCs. Doctors may treat leukemia with bone-marrow transfusions. Bone marrow is often taken from the hip bones of donors, as indicated by the purple dots in **Figure 7.**

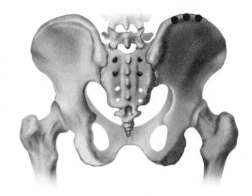

Figure 7 *Bone marrow must be collected from a donor before it can be given to a patient through a bone-marrow transfusion.*

SECTION Review

7.5.a, 7.5.b, 7.6.j

Summary

- The four main components of blood are plasma, red blood cells, platelets, and white blood cells.

- Blood carries oxygen and nutrients to cells, helps protect against disease, and helps regulate body temperature.

- Blood pressure is the force that blood exerts on the inside walls of arteries. It is often expressed in the unit of millimeters of mercury.

- Every person has one of four ABO blood types.

- Losing blood, mixing blood types, and blood disorders can be fatal.

Using Vocabulary

1. Write an original definition for *blood* and *blood pressure.*

Understanding Concepts

2. **Applying** A person with type B blood can donate blood to people with which type(s) of blood?

3. **Describing** Describe the functions of the four main components of blood.

4. **Concluding** Why is it important for a doctor to know a patient's blood type?

5. **Identifying** What causes blood pressure?

Critical Thinking

6. **Identifying Relationships** How does the body use blood and blood vessels to help maintain proper body temperature?

7. **Predicting Consequences** Some blood diseases affect the ability of red blood cells to deliver oxygen to cells of the body. What might happen to a person with such a disease?

INTERPRETING GRAPHICS The photomicrograph shows a WBC attacking pathogens. Use the image below to answer the next question.

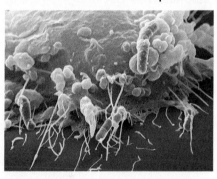

8. **Analyzing Relationships** Explain the function of blood that is being demonstrated in the image.

Math Skills

9. **Making Calculations** What percentage of normal (120 mm Hg) is a systolic pressure of 174 mm Hg?

Internet Resources

For a variety of links related to this chapter, go to www.scilinks.org

Topic: Blood; Blood Donations
SciLinks code: HY70175; HY70178

The Respiratory System

Key Concept The respiratory system is responsible for taking in oxygen and releasing carbon dioxide.

Breathing—you do it all the time. You're doing it right now. But you hardly ever think about it, unless you suddenly can't breathe.

Then, it becomes very clear that you have to breathe in order to live. But why is breathing important? Your body needs oxygen in order to get energy from the foods you eat. Breathing makes this process possible.

Respiration and the Respiratory System

The words *breathing* and *respiration* are often used to mean the same thing. However, breathing is only one part of respiration. **Respiration** is the process by which a body gains and uses oxygen and gets rid of carbon dioxide and water. Respiration is divided into two parts. The first part is breathing, which involves inhaling and exhaling. The second part is cellular respiration, which involves chemical reactions that release energy from food.

Breathing is made possible by your respiratory system. The **respiratory system** is the group of organs that take in oxygen and get rid of carbon dioxide. The nose, throat, lungs, and passageways that lead to the lungs make up the respiratory system. **Figure 1** shows the parts of the respiratory system.

respiration (RES puh RAY shuhn) in biology, the exchange of oxygen and carbon dioxide between living cells and their environment; includes breathing and cellular respiration

respiratory system (RES puhr uh TAWR ee SIS tuhm) a collection of organs whose primary function is to take in oxygen and expel carbon dioxide

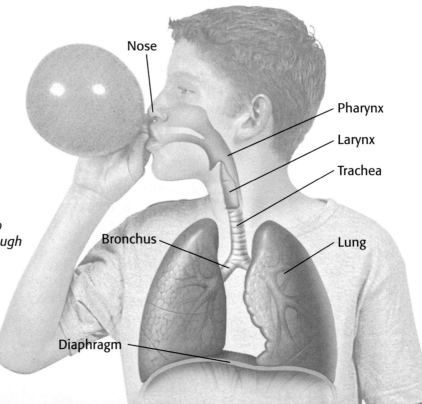

Figure 1 *Air moves into and out of the body through the respiratory system.*

Nose

Pharynx

Larynx

Trachea

Bronchus

Lung

Diaphragm

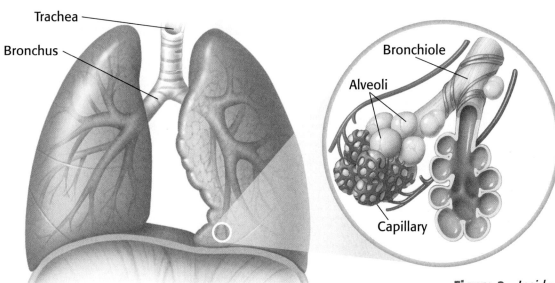

Trachea

Bronchus

Bronchiole

Alveoli

Capillary

Figure 2 *Inside your lungs, the bronchi branch into bronchioles. The bronchioles lead to tiny sacs called* alveoli.

Nose, Pharynx, and Larynx

Your *nose* is the main passageway into and out of the respiratory system. Air can be breathed in through and out of the nose. Air can also enter and leave through the mouth.

From the nose, air flows through the **pharynx,** or throat. Food and drink also move through the pharynx on the way to the stomach. The pharynx branches into two tubes. One tube, the *esophagus,* leads to the stomach. The other tube leads to the lungs. The larynx sits at the beginning of this tube.

The **larynx** is the part of the throat that contains the vocal cords. The *vocal cords* are a pair of elastic bands that stretch across the larynx. Muscles connected to the larynx control how much the vocal cords are stretched. When air flows between the vocal cords, the cords vibrate. These vibrations make sound.

Trachea

The larynx guards the entrance to a large tube called the **trachea,** or windpipe. Your body has two large, spongelike lungs. The trachea, shown in **Figure 2,** is the passageway for air traveling from the larynx toward the lungs.

Bronchi and Alveoli

The trachea splits into two branches called **bronchi** (singular, *bronchus*). One bronchus connects to each lung. Each bronchus branches into smaller and smaller tubes. They eventually form a smaller series of airways called *bronchioles* (BRAHNG kee OHLZ). In the lungs, each bronchiole branches to form tiny sacs that are called **alveoli** (singular, *alveolus*).

Standards Check Describe the structure and function of the pharynx and larynx. **7.5.a**

pharynx (FAR ingks) the passage from the mouth to the larynx and esophagus

larynx (LAR ingks) the area of the throat that contains the vocal cords and produces vocal sounds

trachea (TRAY kee uh) the tube that connects the larynx to the lungs

bronchus (BRAHNG kuhs) one of the two tubes that connect the lungs with the trachea

alveolus (al VEE uh luhs) any of the tiny air sacs of the lungs where oxygen and carbon dioxide are exchanged

7.5.a Students know plants and animals have levels of organization for structure and function, including cells, tissues, organs, organ systems, and the whole organism.
7.5.b Students know organ systems function because of the contributions of individual organs, tissues, and cells. The failure of any part can affect the entire system.

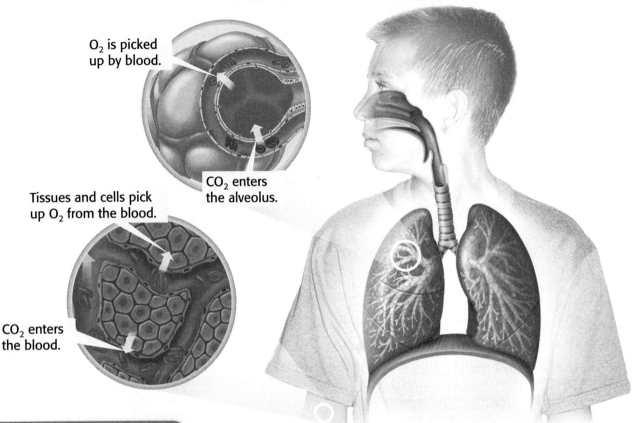

Figure 3 The Role of Blood in Respiration

O$_2$ is picked up by blood.

CO$_2$ enters the alveolus.

Tissues and cells pick up O$_2$ from the blood.

CO$_2$ enters the blood.

Quick Lab

Replicate Respiration

7.5.a

1. Use **scissors** to cut the bottom off an empty **1 liter soda bottle**.

2. Stretch a **latex glove** over the open bottom of the bottle. Secure with **tape**.

3. Insert a **balloon** into the top of the bottle. Pull the lip of the balloon to fit over the mouth of the bottle. Secure with tape.

4. Pull on the fingers of the glove. What happens to the balloon?

5. How does this activity relate to respiration and the diaphragm?

 15 min

Breathing

When you breathe, air is sucked into or pushed out of your lungs. However, your lungs have no muscles of their own. Instead, breathing is done by the diaphragm (DIE uh FRAM) and rib muscles. The *diaphragm* is a dome-shaped muscle beneath the lungs. When the diaphragm contracts and moves down, you inhale. The chest cavity's volume gets larger. At the same time, some of your rib muscles contract and lift your rib cage. As a result, your chest cavity gets bigger and a vacuum is created. Air is sucked in. Exhaling is this process in reverse.

Breathing and Cellular Respiration

In *cellular respiration,* oxygen is used by cells to release energy stored in molecules of the sugar glucose. Where does the oxygen come from? When you inhale, you take in oxygen gas. This gas moves into red blood cells and is carried to tissue cells. The oxygen then moves out of the red blood cells and into each cell. Cells use the oxygen to release energy. During this process, carbon dioxide (CO$_2$) and water are made. Carbon dioxide is exhaled from the lungs. **Figure 3** shows how breathing and blood circulation are related.

Respiratory Disorders

Millions of people suffer from respiratory disorders. These disorders include asthma, emphysema, and severe acute respiratory syndrome (SARS). Asthma causes the bronchioles to narrow. A person who has asthma has trouble breathing. An asthma attack may be triggered by irritants such as dust or pollen. Emphysema happens when the alveoli have been damaged. **Figure 4** shows a lung damaged by emphysema. SARS is caused by a virus. A person who has SARS may have a fever and difficulty breathing.

People who have respiratory disorders have trouble getting the oxygen they need. Cells need oxygen for cellular respiration. They can't efficiently free energy stored in glucose without oxygen. If a person's cells are not able to free this energy, the person may feel tired all the time. People with respiratory disorders may also have problems getting rid of carbon dioxide. It may build up inside the body to a toxic level.

Standards Check How does asthma affect bronchioles? 7.5.b

Figure 4 *The photo at the top shows a healthy lung. The photo at the bottom shows the lung of a person who had emphysema.*

SECTION Review

7.5.a, 7.5.b

Summary

- Air enters through the nose or mouth, then travels to the pharynx, larynx, trachea, and bronchi. The bronchi branch into bronchioles, which branch into alveoli.

- Breathing involves lungs, muscles in the rib cage, and the diaphragm.

- Oxygen enters the blood through the alveoli in the lungs. Carbon dioxide leaves the blood and is exhaled.

- Respiratory disorders include asthma, emphysema, and SARS.

Understanding Concepts

1. **Describing** Describe the causes of SARS, emphysema, and some asthma attacks.

2. **Summarizing** How does breathing happen?

3. **Applying** Describe how your cardiovascular and respiratory systems work together.

Critical Thinking

4. **Predicting Consequences** If a respiratory disorder causes lungs to fill with fluid, how could this affect a person's health?

5. **Interpreting Statistics** About 6.3 million children in the United States have asthma. About 4 million of them had an asthma attack last year. What do these statistics tell you about the relationship between asthma and asthma attacks?

Math Skills

6. **Making Calculations** Usable lung capacity is about 6 L. A person can exhale about 3.6 L. What percentage of the lung capacity cannot be exhaled?

Challenge

7. **Identifying Relationships** Emphysema often occurs in people who smoke cigarettes. How could smoking damage alveoli? How could emphysema affect the rest of the body?

Internet Resources

For a variety of links related to this chapter, go to www.scilinks.org
Topic: The Respiratory System; Respiratory Disorders
SciLinks code: HY71307; HY71306

Skills Practice Lab

Carbon Dioxide in Respiration

Carbon dioxide is important to both plants and animals. Plants take in carbon dioxide during photosynthesis and give off oxygen as a byproduct of the process. Animals—including you—take in oxygen during cellular respiration and give off carbon dioxide as a byproduct of the process.

Procedure

1 Find a partner. Put on your gloves, safety goggles, and apron.

2 Use the graduated cylinder to pour 100 mL of water into a 250 mL flask.

3 Repeat step 2 so that you have two flasks, each containing 100 mL of water.

4 Using an eyedropper, carefully place four drops of phenol red indicator solution into the water of the first flask. The water should turn orange.

5 Place a plastic drinking straw into the solution of phenol red and water. Drape a paper towel over the flask to prevent splashing.

6 Make sure your lab partner has the stopwatch ready. You will soon exhale into the straw. Your lab partner should begin keeping time as soon as you start to exhale through the straw.

7.5.a Students know plants and animals have levels of organization for structure and function, including cells, tissues, organs, organ systems, and the whole organism.
7.5.b Students know organ systems function because of the contributions of individual organs, tissues, and cells. The failure of any part can affect the entire system.

Investigation and Experimentation
7.7.c Communicate the logical connection among hypotheses, science concepts, tests conducted, data collected, and conclusions drawn from the scientific evidence.

7 Breathe normally, but exhale into the straw in the solution. **Caution:** Do not inhale through the straw. Do not drink the solution, and do not share a straw with anyone. Have your lab partner time how long the solution takes to change color. Record the time.

8 Do jumping jacks or sit-ups for 3 min, and repeat steps 4–7 using the second flask.

Analyze the Results

9 **Describing Events** Describe what happened to the indicator solution.

10 **Organizing Data** Make a table with three columns. Title the columns "Student name," "Time without exercise," and "Time with exercise." Write your data in the appropriate columns. Collect data from your classmates, and add the data to your table.

11 **Examining Data** Look at the data in the first column. What was the longest length of time it took to see a color change? What was the shortest? How do you account for the difference? Repeat for the second column.

12 **Examining Data** Did exercising make a difference in the time it took for the solution to change color? Why or why not?

13 **Constructing Graphs** Make a bar graph that compares your data from the first column with the data of your classmates.

Draw Conclusions

14 **Interpreting Information** Do you think that there is a relationship between the length of time the solution takes to change color and the person's physical characteristics, such as which gender the tester is or whether the tester has an athletic build? Explain.

Big Idea Question

15 **Making Predictions** Which individual organs in the body contribute to getting rid of waste products, such as carbon dioxide? What would happen if these organs failed and excess carbon dioxide could not be removed from the body?

Science Skills Activity

Investigation and Experimentation
7.7.b Use a variety of print and electronic resources (including the World Wide Web) to collect information and evidence as part of a research project.

Evaluating Resources for Research

▶ Tutorial

Before writing a paper, you must gather information. This process can leave you with stacks of books and thousands of Internet sites. Reading all of these sources would take a very long time. How do you know which sources will have the most relevant information? The procedure below can help you determine the best sources for your research.

Procedure

1 Select the keywords of your topic. Keywords should be specific.

2 Create a research map similar to the one below.

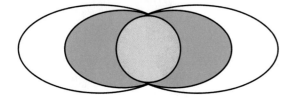

3 Put your keywords in the center circle. Think of broader topics, and place those in the areas outside the center circle. The example below shows a research map on the topic of whale sharks.

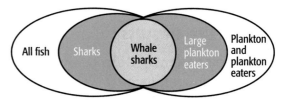

All fish | Sharks | Whale sharks | Large plankton eaters | Plankton and plankton eaters

4 List the sources where you may find information about each of your topics including books, CD-ROMs, science magazines, and Web sites.

5 List places where you may find these sources, including computers and libraries.

6 Begin your search with the sources that seem most relevant or have the most information.

7 Scan the books or online articles. Check or print out sources that have good information. Read what you have gathered.

▶ You Try It!

Collect information for a research project on the topic of emphysema. Emphysema is a respiratory disorder that happens when alveoli in the lungs have been damaged. Emphysema is often associated with smoking cigarettes.

Procedure

1 **Constructing Maps** Create a research map to identify your keywords and the broader topics that may be helpful when finding sources.

2 **Organizing Data** Use the topics on your research map to find at least eight sources of information. List your sources by type. For example, all of the textbook sources can be listed together.

Analysis

3 **Evaluating Data** Which of your sources have the most relevant information? Choose the three best sources. Explain why these sources are the most relevant to your research.

4 **Identifying Patterns** You may find sources with information that is out of date or unscientific. These sources should be dismissed. How will you determine which sources are legitimate and which are not?

5 **Evaluating Methods** Why do you think it is important to map specific keywords and broader topics? What might happen if you researched only specific topics? What might happen if you researched only broad topics?

Chapter Summary

The Big Idea The human body has organ systems that transport gases, nutrients, and wastes.

Section

Vocabulary

1 The Cardiovascular System

Key Concept The cardiovascular system circulates blood, gases, and nutrients throughout your body.

- The cardiovascular system is made up of the heart, three types of blood vessels, and blood.
- Contractions of the heart pump blood throughout the entire body.
- Cardiovascular problems include atherosclerosis, high blood pressure, strokes, heart attacks, and heart failure.

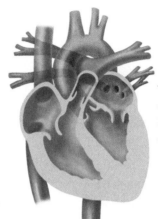

The heart is an organ that pumps blood to all parts of the body.

cardiovascular system p. 496

artery p. 498

capillary p. 498

vein p. 498

pulmonary circulation p. 499

systemic circulation p. 499

2 Blood

Key Concept Blood transports many things through the body, including oxygen, nutrients, wastes, heat, immune system cells, and hormones.

- Blood is a tissue that is made up of red blood cells, white blood cells, platelets, and plasma.
- Blood pressure is the force exerted by blood on the inside walls of arteries.
- The loss of blood, mixing blood types, or blood disorders can be fatal.

A

B

AB

O

Each blood type has specific antigens and antibodies.

blood p. 502

blood pressure p. 504

3 The Respiratory System

Key Concept The respiratory system is responsible for taking in oxygen and releasing carbon dioxide.

- The respiratory system includes the diaphragm, lungs, bronchi, trachea, larynx, pharynx, and nose.
- The respiratory system and the cardiovascular system work together to supply oxygen and remove carbon dioxide.
- Respiratory disorders include asthma, emphysema, and SARS.

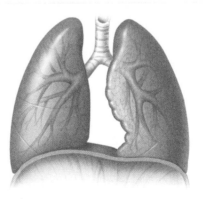

The bronchi branch into bronchioles inside the lungs.

respiration p. 508

respiratory system p. 508

pharynx p. 509

larynx p. 509

trachea p. 509

bronchus p. 509

alveolus p. 509

7.5.a, 7.5.b, 7.6.j

Organize

Four-Corner Fold Review the FoldNote that you created at the beginning of the chapter. Add to or correct the FoldNote based on what you have learned.

Using Vocabulary

1 **Academic Vocabulary** In the sentence "The function of RBCs is to transport oxygen throughout the body," what does the word *function* mean?

Complete each of the following sentences by choosing the correct term from the word bank.

red blood cells	veins
white blood cells	arteries
pulmonary circulation	blood pressure
alveoli	bronchi

2 ___ deliver oxygen to the cells of the body.

3 ___ are blood vessels that carry blood away from the heart.

4 The force that blood exerts on the walls of the arteries is called ___.

Understanding Concepts

Multiple Choice

5 ___ create blood pressure.
a. Heart contractions
b. Arteries
c. Valves
d. Atria

6 The parts of the heart that prevent blood from flowing backward are
a. ventricles.   c. atria.
b. capillaries.   d. valves.

7 Alveoli are surrounded by
a. veins.   c. capillaries.
b. muscles.   d. cholesterol.

8 Air moves into the lungs when the diaphragm muscle
a. contracts and moves down.
b. contracts and moves up.
c. relaxes and moves down.
d. relaxes and moves up.

Short Answer

9 **Comparing** Compare pulmonary circulation and systemic circulation.

10 **Applying** Braden's blood pressure is 110/65. What do the two numbers mean?

11 **Listing** List examples of one organ, one tissue, and two types of cells in the cardiovascular system.

INTERPRETING GRAPHICS The diagram shows how the human heart would look in cross section. Use the diagram below to answer the next three questions.

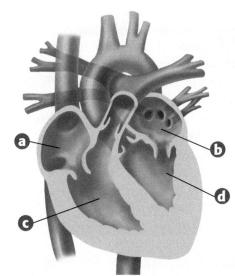

12 **Identifying** Which letter identifies the chamber that receives blood from systemic circulation? What is this chamber's name?

13 **Identifying** Which letter identifies the chamber that receives blood from the lungs? What is this chamber's name?

14 **Identifying** Which letter identifies the chamber that pumps blood to the lungs? What is this chamber's name?

15 Summarizing Briefly describe the path that oxygen follows in your respiratory system and your cardiovascular system.

Writing Skills

16 Writing Persuasively The blood used for blood transfusions comes from donations to blood banks. Write a paragraph persuading your friends and family members to donate blood. Use your understanding of the importance of blood transfusions in your answer.

Critical Thinking

17 Concept Mapping Use the following terms to create a concept map: *blood, oxygen, alveoli, capillaries,* and *carbon dioxide.*

18 Identifying Relationships How are the functions of red blood cells and white blood cells different?

19 Predicting Consequences What would happen if all of the red blood cells in your blood disappeared?

20 Applying Concepts When a person is not feeling well, a doctor may examine samples of the person's blood to see how many white blood cells are present. Why would this information be useful?

INTERPRETING GRAPHICS Use the image below to answer the next question.

21 Making Comparisons How is the heart similar to the revolving doors in the image?

22 Making Comparisons What organs are affected by heart attacks and strokes? How could this affect the organism?

INTERPRETING GRAPHICS Use the image below to answer the next question.

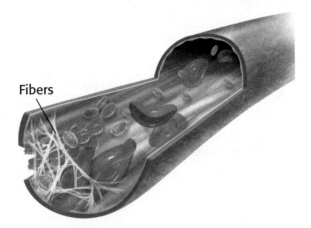

Fibers

23 Making Inferences The image shows platelets and fibers forming a blood clot to seal a broken blood vessel. A person with hemophilia cannot form blood clots normally. What do you think happens when a person with hemophilia gets a cut?

Math Skills

24 Making Conversions After a person donates blood, the blood is stored in 1 pt bags until it is needed for a transfusion. A healthy person has about 5 million RBCs in each cubic millimeter (1 mm^3) of blood.
  a. How many RBCs are in 1 mL of blood? (One milliliter is equal to 1 cm^3 and to 1,000 mm^3.)
  b. How many RBCs are there in 1 pt? (One pint is equal to 473 mL.)

Challenge

25 Applying Concepts Blood types are most often reported using both the ABO system and the Rh system. For example, a person with type A blood that is Rh$^+$ will have A$^+$ blood. What blood type does a person with B antigens, A antibodies, and Rh antigens have?

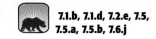
REVIEWING ACADEMIC VOCABULARY

1 Choose the appropriate form of the word *illustrate* for the following sentence: The complementary nature of structure and function is ___ by the anatomy of plants and animals.

A illustrate

B illustrated

C illustration

D illustrating

2 Which of the following words means "the arrangement of the parts of the whole"?

A process

B system

C function

D structure

3 Which of the following words is the closest in meaning to the word *generate*?

A produce

B find

C filter

D destroy

4 Which of the following words means "a part given to the whole"?

A distribution

B contribution

C execution

D retribution

REVIEWING CONCEPTS

5 Which of the following actions pumps blood through the body?

A the expansion of the heart

B the expansion of blood vessels

C the contractions of the heart

D the contractions of the blood vessels

6 Which type of blood vessel allows for the exchange of gases between the blood and body cells?

A capillaries   C ventricles

B arteries   D veins

7 Which of the following is a direct cause of a stroke?

A Cholesterol builds up in an artery and blocks blood flow through it.

B A blood vessel ruptures in the brain, so oxygen flow is cut off.

C The heart cannot pump enough blood to meet the body's needs.

D A blood vessel collapses, so the flow of oxygen to the heart is cut off.

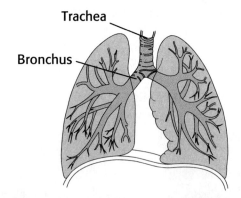

8 The diagram above shows parts of the respiratory system. What label could be added to the diagram?

A Capillaries   C Pharynx

B Larynx   D Bronchioles

9 Which of the following occurs when the body becomes too warm and tries to cool itself?

A Blood vessels in the skin enlarge.

B Blood vessels in the skin contract.

C The heart pumps blood more slowly.

D The heart pumps blood more quickly.

10 What is systolic blood pressure?

A The pressure inside capillaries when the heart contracts.

B The pressure inside arteries when the heart relaxes.

C The pressure inside veins when the heart contracts.

D The pressure inside arteries when the heart contracts.

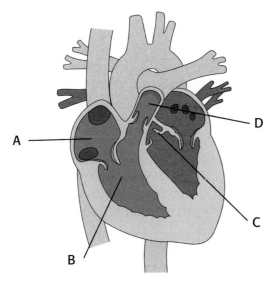

11 Which part of the diagram above shows an atrium?

A part A   **C** part C

B part B   **D** part D

REVIEWING PRIOR LEARNING

12 Why do cells need oxygen?

A Oxygen is used during the process of fermentation.

B Oxygen is used during the process of cell division.

C Oxygen is used during the process of cellular respiration.

D Oxygen is used during the process of meiosis.

13 What is the result of cellular respiration?

A Energy is produced from radiant sunlight and carbon dioxide.

B Energy is produced from sugar molecules and oxygen.

C Sunlight is converted into sugar molecules and oxygen.

D Sunlight is converted into water molecules.

14 A white blood cell is not likely to have a

A mitochondrion.

B cell membrane.

C nucleus.

D chloroplast.

15 Which of the following is the genetic material for a cell?

A ribosome

B DNA

C endoplasmic reticulum

D nucleolus

Science in Action

Science, Technology, and Society

California Marathons

Some of the world's most popular marathons are held every year in California cities, such as San Diego and San Francisco. A marathon is a 26.2 mi race. The majority of runners take more than four hours to complete a marathon. To compete in a marathon, a runner must have respiratory and circulatory systems that are in top form. Long-distance running requires a lot of oxygen and glucose. Oxygen is taken into the lungs through breathing. Glucose is acquired through the foods we eat. Oxygen and glucose are both carried by blood to muscles. Muscle cells use oxygen to convert glucose into usable energy.

Language Arts ACTIVITY

Think of all the activities you perform that require your respiratory and circulatory systems to function well. In your **Science Journal**, write a list of some ways you can keep these organ systems healthy.

Weird Science

Circular Breathing and the Didgeridoo

Do you play a musical instrument such as a clarinet, flute, or tuba? How long can you blow into it before you have to take a breath? Can you blow into it for one minute? Two minutes? What happens when you stop to breathe? The Aboriginal people of Australia have a musical instrument called the *didgeridoo* (DIJ uh ree DOO). Didgeridoo players can play for hours without stopping to take a breath. They use a technique called *circular breathing* that lets them inhale through the nose and exhale air stored in their mouths at the same time. With a little practice, maybe you can do it, too.

Social Studies ACTIVITY

Select a country that is in Africa or Asia. Research that country's traditional musical instruments or singing style. Write a description in your **Science Journal** that describes the instruments or singing style of that country. How do they differ from those of the United States? Illustrate your report.

Anthony Roberts, Jr.

Leader in Training Anthony Roberts, Jr., has asthma. When he was in the fifth grade, his school counselor told him about a summer camp—The Boggy Creek Gang Camp—that was just being built. His counselor said that the camp was designed to serve kids who have asthma or other disabilities and diseases, such as AIDS, cancer, diabetes, epilepsy, hemophilia, heart disease, kidney disease, rheumatic diseases, and sickle cell anemia. These kids might have difficulties at a traditional summer camp. Anthony jumped at the chance to go. Anthony grew too old to be a camper, but he was too young to be a regular counselor. Instead he became a *Leader in Training* (LIT). Some camps have LIT programs that help young people make the transition from camper to counselor.

For Anthony, the chance to be an LIT fit perfectly with his love of camping and with his desire to work with kids with disabilities. Anthony remembers the fun he had and wants to help other kids have the same summer fun he did.

Math ACTIVITY

Research how many children under 17 years of age in the United States have asthma. In your **Science Journal,** make a bar graph that shows how the number of children who have asthma has changed since 1981. What does this graph tell you about rates of asthma among children in the United States?

Internet Resources

- To learn more about careers in science, visit **www.scilinks.org** and enter the SciLinks code **HY70225.**

- To learn more about these Science in Action topics, visit **go.hrw.com** and type in the keyword **HY7BD2F.**

- Check out articles related to this chapter by visiting **go.hrw.com.** Just type in the keyword **HY7BD2C.**

Improving Comprehension

Graphic Organizers are important visual tools that can help you organize information and improve your reading comprehension. The Graphic Organizer below is called a *process chart*. Instructions for creating other types of Graphic Organizers are located in the **Study Skills** section of the Appendix.

How to Make a Process Chart

1 Draw a box. In the box, write the first step of a process, chain of events, or cycle.

2 Under the box, draw another box, and draw an arrow to connect the two boxes. In the second box, write the next step of the process or the next event in the timeline.

3 Continue adding boxes until each step of the process, chain of events, or cycle is written in a box. For cycles only, draw an arrow to connect the last box and the first box.

When to Use a Process Chart

Science is full of processes. A process chart shows the steps that a process takes to get from one point to another point. Timelines, chains of events, and cycles are examples of the kinds of information that can be organized well in a process chart. As you read, look for information that is described in steps or in a sequence, and draw a process chart that shows the progression of the steps or sequence.

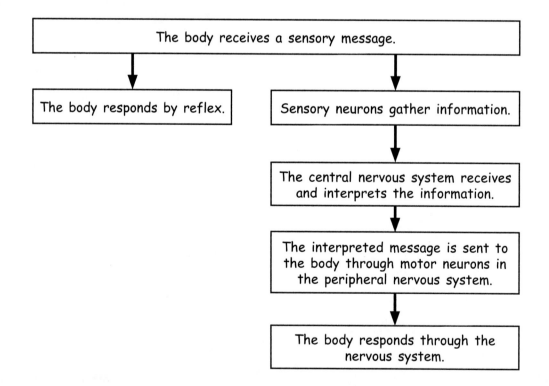

You Try It!

This Reading Strategy can also be used within the chapter that you are about to read. Practice making your own *process chart* as directed in the Reading Strategy for Section **2**. Record your work in your **Science Journal.**

Unpacking the Standards

The information below "unpacks" the standards by breaking them down into basic parts. The higher-level, academic vocabulary is highlighted and defined to help you understand the language of the standards. "What It Means" restates the standards as simply as possible.

California Standard	Academic Vocabulary	What It Means
7.5.a Students know plants and animals have levels of organization for **structure** and **function,** including cells, tissues, organs, organ systems, and the whole organism.	**structure** (STRUHK chuhr) the arrangement of the parts of a whole **function** (FUHNGK shuhn) use or purpose	Plants and animals are made of smaller parts which are organized by shape and purpose. These layers of organization include cells, tissues, organs, organ systems, and the whole organism.
7.5.b Students know organ systems **function** because of the **contributions** of **individual** organs, tissues, and cells. The failure of any part can **affect** the entire system.	**function** (FUHNGK shuhn) to work **contribution** (KAHN truh BYOO shuhn) a part given toward a whole **individual** (IN duh VIJ oo uhl) being a single, separate entity; particular **affect** (uh FEKT) to change; to have an effect on; to influence	An organ system is able to work because of the work that each of its smaller parts (organs, tissues, and cells) does. If any part of an organ system fails to work well, the entire system is changed.
7.5.g Students know how to relate the **structures** of the eye and ear to their **functions.**		You must know how the shapes of the eye and the ear are related to the roles of these parts in the body.
7.6.b Students know that for an object to be seen, light emitted by or scattered from it must be **detected** by the eye.	**detect** (dee TEKT) to notice	For you to see an object, the light that is given off by an object or that bounces off an object must enter your eye.

17

Communication and Control

The Big Idea

The human body has organ systems that respond to its internal and external environments.

California Standards

Focus on Life Sciences
7.5 The anatomy and physiology of plants and animals illustrate the complementary nature of structure and function. (Sections 1 and 2)
7.6 Physical principles underlie biological structures and functions. (Section 2)

Investigation and Experimentation
7.7 Scientific progress is made by asking meaningful questions and conducting careful investigations. (Science Skills Activity)

Math
7.1.1 Algebra and Functions
7.2.1, 7.2.8 Mathematical Reasoning

English–Language Arts
7.1.3 Reading
7.2.5 Writing

About the Photo

This picture may look like it shows a flower garden or a coral reef. But it really shows something much closer to home. It shows the human tongue (magnified thousands of times, of course). Both the large red bumps and the smaller pink bumps are papillae (puh PIL ee), which contain the taste buds. You use taste and other senses to gather information about your surroundings.

Organize

Double Door

Before you read this chapter, create the FoldNote entitled "Double Door." Write "The nervous system" on one flap of the double door and "Sensing the environment" on the other flap. As you read the chapter, compare the two topics, and write characteristics of each topic on the inside of the appropriate flap.

Instructions for creating FoldNotes are located in the Study Skills section on p. 579 of the Appendix.

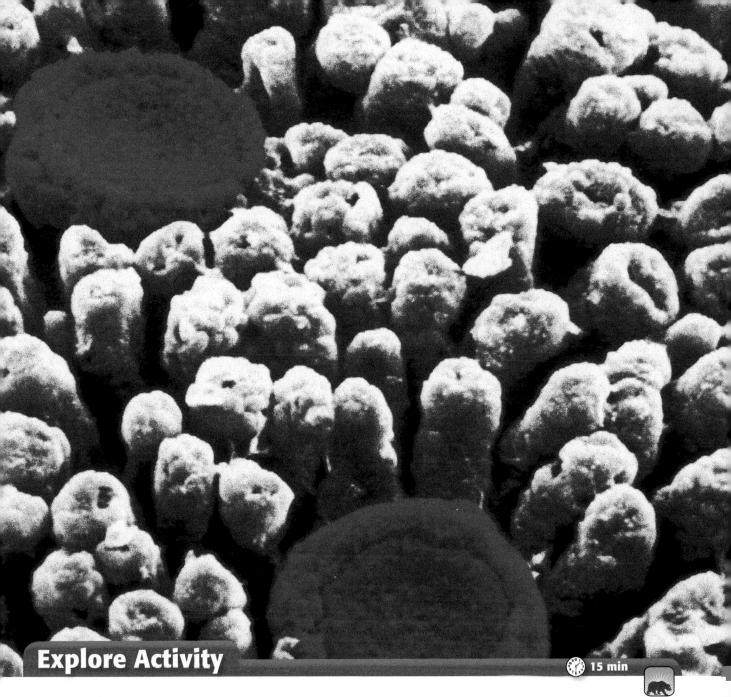

Explore Activity

 15 min

Measuring Reaction Time

If you want to catch an object, your brain sends a message to the muscles in your arm. In this exercise, you will see how long sending that message takes.

Procedure

1. Sit in a **chair** with one of your arms in a "handshake" position. A partner should stand facing you and should hold a **meterstick** vertically. Position the stick to fall between your thumb and fingers.

2. Tell your partner to let go of the meterstick without warning you. Catch the stick between your thumb and fingers. Your partner should catch the meterstick if it tips over.

3. Record the number of centimeters that the stick dropped before you caught it. That distance represents your reaction time.

4. Repeat steps 1–3 three times. Calculate the average distance.

5. Repeat steps 1–4 with your other hand.

6. Trade places with your partner, and repeat steps 1–5.

7.5.b

Analysis

7. Compare your results with your partner's. Why may one person react more quickly than another?

8. In this activity, how are your muscles and your brain working together? Be specific.

The Nervous System

Key Concept   Your nervous system is an organ system that gathers, interprets, and responds to sensory information.

What You Will Learn

- The central nervous system processes and responds to all messages coming from the peripheral nervous system.
- The somatic nervous system controls voluntary movements. The autonomic nervous system controls functions that are involuntary.
- The brain is made of many parts that function together as the control center of the nervous system.

Why It Matters

Without a nervous system, you would not be able to sense or respond to your environment.

Vocabulary

- central nervous system
- peripheral nervous system
- neuron
- nerve
- brain

READING STRATEGY

Clarifying Concepts   Take turns reading this section out loud with a partner. Stop to discuss ideas that seem confusing.

▶ What is one thing that you have done today that did NOT involve your nervous system? This is a trick question! In fact, your nervous system controls almost everything that you do.

Two Systems Within a System

The nervous system acts as the body's central command post. It has two basic functions. First, it gathers and interprets information. This information comes from inside your body and from the world outside your body. Then, the nervous system responds to that information as needed.

The nervous system has two parts: the central nervous system and the peripheral nervous system. The **central nervous system** (CNS) is the brain and spinal cord. The CNS processes and responds to all messages coming from the peripheral nervous system. The **peripheral nervous system** (PNS) includes all of the parts of the nervous system except for the brain and the spinal cord. The PNS connects all parts of the body to the CNS. The PNS uses specialized structures called *nerves* to carry information between your body and your CNS. **Figure 1** shows the major divisions of the nervous system.

Standards Check   Describe the difference between the function of the CNS and the function of the PNS. **7.5.a**

7.5.a Students know plants and animals have levels of organization for structure and function, including cells, tissues, organs, organ systems, and the whole organism.
7.5.b Students know organ systems function because of the contributions of individual organs, tissues, and cells. The failure of any part can affect the entire system.

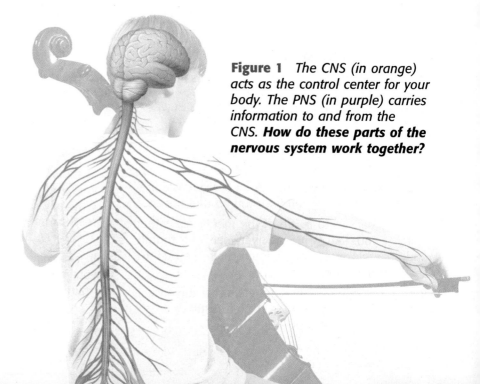

Figure 1   *The CNS (in orange) acts as the control center for your body. The PNS (in purple) carries information to and from the CNS.* **How do these parts of the nervous system work together?**

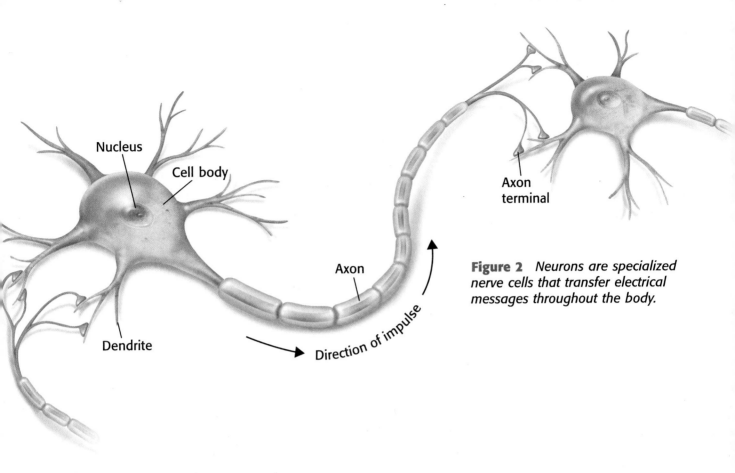

Figure 2 *Neurons are specialized nerve cells that transfer electrical messages throughout the body.*

Labels: Nucleus, Cell body, Axon terminal, Axon, Dendrite, Direction of impulse

The Peripheral Nervous System

Messages about your environment travel through the nervous system along neurons. A **neuron** is a nerve cell that is specialized to transfer messages in the form of fast-moving electrical energy. These electrical messages are called *impulses*. Impulses may travel as fast as 150 m/s or as slow as 0.2 m/s. **Figure 2** shows a typical neuron transferring an impulse.

Neuron Structure

In many ways, a neuron is similar to other cells. A neuron has a large region called the *cell body*. The cell body has a nucleus and cell organelles. But neurons also have special structures called *dendrites* and *axons*. Dendrites are usually short, branched extensions of the cell. A neuron receives information from other cells through its dendrites. A neuron may have many dendrites, which allows it to receive impulses from thousands of other cells.

Impulses are carried away from the cell body by axons. Axons are elongated extensions of a neuron. They can be very short or quite long. Some long axons extend almost 1 m from your lower back to your toes. The end of an axon often has branches that allow information to pass to other cells. The tip of each branch is called an *axon terminal.*

Standards Check In your own words, describe the structure of a neuron. 🐻 7.5.a

central nervous system
(SEN trahl NUHR vuhs SIS tuhm) the brain and the spinal cord

peripheral nervous system
(puh RIF uhr uhl NUHR vuhs SIS tuhm) all of the parts of the nervous system except for the brain and the spinal cord

Wordwise The root *peri-* means "around" or "near." The root *pher-* means "to bear" or "to go."

neuron (NOO RAHN) a nerve cell that is specialized to receive and conduct electrical impulses

Sensory Neurons: Collecting Information

Remember that neurons are a type of nerve cell that carries impulses. Some neurons are *sensory neurons*. These neurons gather information about what is happening in and around your body. They have specialized nerve endings called *receptors*. Receptors detect changes inside and outside the body. For example, receptors in your eyes detect light. Sensory neurons then send this information to the CNS for processing.

Motor Neurons: Delivering Orders

Neurons that send impulses from the brain and spinal cord to other systems are called *motor neurons*. When muscles get impulses from motor neurons, the muscles respond by contracting. For example, motor neurons cause muscles around your eyes to contract when you are in bright light. These muscles make you squint so that less light enters your eyes. Motor neurons also send messages to glands, such as sweat glands. These messages tell sweat glands when to make sweat.

Nerves

The central nervous system is connected to the rest of your body by nerves. A **nerve** is a collection of axons bundled together with blood vessels and connective tissue. Nerves are found everywhere in your PNS. Most nerves have axons of both sensory neurons and motor neurons. Axons are parts of nerves, but nerves are more than simply axons. **Figure 3** shows the structure of a nerve. The axon in this nerve transmits information from the spinal cord to muscle fibers.

Standards Check What would happen if your nerves stopped working? 🐾 **7.5.b**

nerve (NUHRV) a collection of nerve fibers through which impulses travel between the central nervous system and other parts of the body

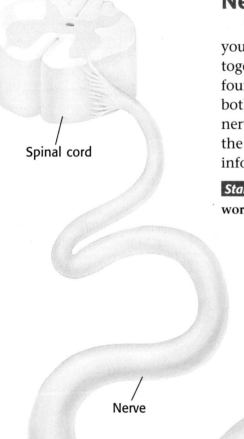

Spinal cord

Nerve

Muscle fiber

Axon terminal

Axon

Figure 3 *A message from the brain travels down the spinal cord and then along the axon of a motor neuron inside a nerve to the muscle. The message makes the muscle contract.*

Somatic and Autonomic Nervous Systems

Remember, the peripheral nervous system (PNS) connects the central nervous system (CNS) to the rest of the body. And the PNS includes two main kinds of neurons: sensory neurons and motor neurons. You know that sensory neurons collect information from your senses and send that information to the CNS. You also know that motor neurons carry out the CNS's responses to that sensory information. The PNS has two types of motor neurons to carry out these responses: somatic neurons and autonomic neurons.

Somatic Nervous System

Most of the neurons that are part of the *somatic nervous system* are under your conscious control. These neurons stimulate skeletal muscles. So, the neurons control voluntary movements, such as writing, talking, smiling, or jumping.

Autonomic Nervous System

Autonomic neurons do not need your conscious control. These neurons are part of the autonomic nervous system. The *autonomic nervous system* controls body functions that you do not think about, such as digestion and heart rate (the number of times that your heart beats per minute).

The main job of the autonomic nervous system is to keep all of the body's functions in balance. Depending on the situation, the autonomic nervous system can speed up or slow down these functions. The autonomic nervous system has two divisions: the *sympathetic nervous system* and the *parasympathetic nervous system*. These two divisions work together to maintain a stable internal state, called *homeostasis*. **Table 1** shows some effects of these divisions.

Time to Travel

To calculate how long an impulse takes to travel a certain distance, you can use the following equation:

$$time = \frac{distance}{speed}$$

If an impulse travels 100 m/s, about how long will it take the impulse to travel 10 m? Record your work in your **Science Journal.**

Table 1	Effects of the Autonomic Nervous System on the Body	
Organ	**Effect of sympathetic division**	**Effect of parasympathetic division**
Eyes	dilates (enlarges) pupils; making seeing objects easier	constricts pupils; makes vision normal
Heart	increases heart rate; increases blood flow	slows heart rate; slows blood flow
Lungs	dilates (enlarges) bronchioles; increases oxygen in blood	constricts bronchioles
Blood vessels	constricts blood vessels; increases blood pressure	has little or no effect
Intestines	slows digestion; reduces blood flow to stomach and intestines	returns digestion to normal

The Central Nervous System

The central nervous system receives information from the sensory neurons. Then, the CNS responds by sending messages to the body through motor neurons in the PNS.

The Brain

brain (BRAYN) the organ that is the main control center of the nervous system

The largest organ in the nervous system is the brain. The **brain** is the main control center of the nervous system. Many processes that the brain controls happen automatically. These processes are *involuntary*. For example, you could not stop digesting food even if you tried. On the other hand, some actions controlled by your brain are *voluntary*. When you want to move your arm, your brain sends signals along motor neurons to muscles in your arm. Then, the muscles contract, and your arm moves. The brain has three main parts: the cerebrum (suh REE bruhm), the cerebellum (SER uh BEL uhm), and the medulla (mi DUHL uh). Each part has its own job.

Standards Check What is the brain's function in the nervous system? Describe what the brain controls. 7.5.a

The Cerebrum

The largest part of your brain is called the *cerebrum*. It looks like a mushroom cap. This dome-shaped area is where you think and where most memories are stored. The cerebrum controls voluntary movements. It also allows you to sense touch, light, sound, odors, taste, pain, heat, and cold.

The cerebrum is made up of two halves, called *hemispheres*. The left hemisphere directs the right side of the body, and the right hemisphere directs the left side of the body. **Figure 4** shows some of the activities that each hemisphere controls. However, most brain activities use both hemispheres.

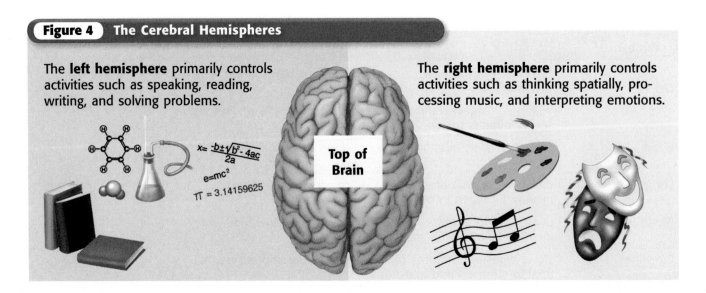

Figure 4   The Cerebral Hemispheres

The **left hemisphere** primarily controls activities such as speaking, reading, writing, and solving problems.

The **right hemisphere** primarily controls activities such as thinking spatially, processing music, and interpreting emotions.

$$x = \frac{-b \pm \sqrt{b^2 - 4ac}}{2a}$$

$$e = mc^2$$

$$\pi = 3.14159625$$

Top of Brain

The Cerebellum

The second-largest part of your brain is the *cerebellum*. It lies beneath the back of the cerebrum. The cerebellum processes sensory information from your body, such as from skeletal muscles and joints. This information allows the brain to keep track of the body's position. Look at the girl in **Figure 5.** If she begins to lose her balance, her cerebellum sends impulses telling skeletal muscles to contract. Those muscles shift her weight and keep her from losing her balance.

The Medulla

The *medulla* is the part of your brain that connects to your spinal cord. The medulla is about 3 cm long, and you can not live without it. The medulla controls involuntary processes, such as involuntary breathing and the regulation of blood pressure and heart rate.

Your medulla constantly receives sensory impulses from receptors in your blood vessels. It uses this information to regulate your blood pressure. If your blood pressure gets too low, the medulla sends out impulses that tell blood vessels to tighten up. As a result, blood pressure rises. The medulla also sends impulses to the heart to make the heart beat faster or slower. **Figure 6** shows the locations of the three main parts of the brain and some of the functions of each part.

Standards Check Explain why the medulla is important. 🐻 **7.5.b**

Figure 5 *Your cerebellum causes skeletal muscles to make adjustments so that you will stay upright.*

Figure 6 Areas of the Brain at Work

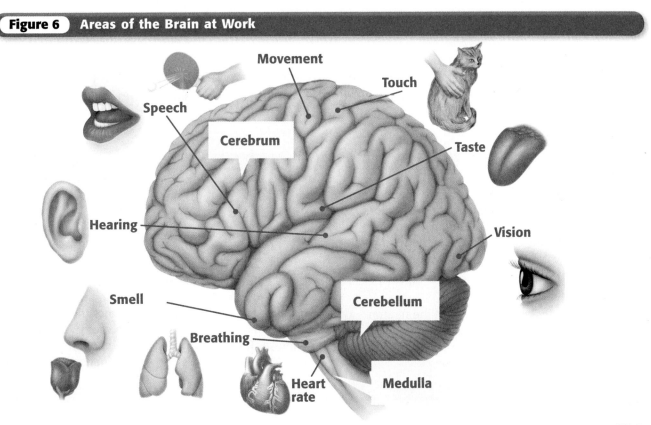

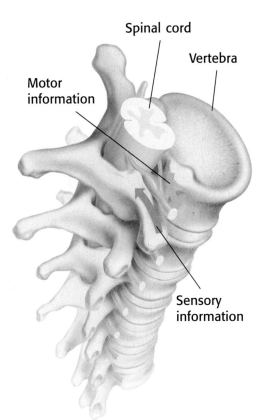

Motor
information

Spinal cord

Vertebra

Sensory
information

Figure 7 *The spinal cord carries information to and from the brain. Vertebrae protect the spinal cord.*

The Spinal Cord

Your spinal cord, which is part of your central nervous system, is about as big around as your thumb. The spinal cord is made of neurons and bundles of axons that pass impulses to and from the brain. As shown in **Figure 7,** the spinal cord is surrounded by protective bones called *vertebrae* (VUHR tuh BRAY).

The axons in your spinal cord allow your brain to communicate with your PNS. The axons of sensory neurons in your skin and muscles carry impulses to your spinal cord. The spinal cord relays these impulses to your brain. The brain interprets these impulses as pain, temperature, or other sensations. Then, the brain responds to the situation. Impulses moving from the brain down the spinal cord are relayed to motor neurons. The axons of motor neurons carry the impulses to muscles and glands all over your body.

Standards Check Describe the path of an impulse from the skin to the brain and the path of the response. **7.5.a**

Spinal Cord Injury

A spinal cord injury may block all information to and from the brain. Sensory information coming from below the injury may not get to the brain. For example, a spinal cord injury may block all sensory impulses from the feet and legs. People who have such an injury can not sense pain, touch, or temperature with their feet. And motor commands from the brain to the injured area may not reach the peripheral nerves. So, the person may not be able to move his or her legs.

Each year, thousands of people are paralyzed by spinal cord injuries. Among young people, spinal cord injuries are sometimes related to sports or other activities. These injuries may be prevented by wearing proper safety equipment.

Quick Lab

Building a Neuron

1. Your teacher will provide **at least four colors of modeling clay.** Build a model of a neuron by using various colors of clay for the various parts of the neuron.

2. Use **tape** to attach your model to a **piece of plain white paper.**

3. On the paper, label each part of the neuron. Draw an arrow from the label to the part.

7.5.a
7.7.d

4. Use a **colored pencil, marker,** or **crayon** to draw arrows showing the path of an impulse traveling in your neuron. Tell whether the impulse is a sensory impulse or a motor impulse. Then, describe what will happen when the impulse reaches its destination.

 20 min

Summary

- The central nervous system (CNS) is the brain and the spinal cord.

- The peripheral nervous system (PNS) is all of the parts of the nervous system except for the brain and spinal cord.

- Nerves in the peripheral nervous system are bundles of axons, blood vessels, and connective tissue.

- Sensory neurons have receptors that detect information about the body and its environment. Motor neurons carry messages from the brain and spinal cord to other parts of the body.

- The PNS has two types of motor neurons: somatic neurons and autonomic neurons.

- The cerebrum is the largest part of the brain and controls thinking, sensing, and voluntary movement.

- The cerebellum is the part of the brain that keeps track of the body's position and that helps maintain balance.

- The medulla controls involuntary processes, such as breathing and the regulation of heart rate, blood pressure, and body temperature.

Using Vocabulary

1. Write an original definition for *neuron* and *nerve*.

2. Use *brain* and *peripheral nervous system* in the same sentence.

Understanding Concepts

3. **Describing** What is one function of each of the three main parts of the brain?

4. **Comparing** How are the somatic nervous system and the autonomic nervous system related?

5. **Analyzing** What is the relationship between the peripheral nervous system and the central nervous system?

6. **Evaluating** Explain how a severe injury to the spinal cord can affect other parts of the body.

Critical Thinking

7. **Applying Concepts** Some medications slow a person's nervous system. These drugs are often labeled "May cause drowsiness." Explain why a person needs to know about this side effect.

8. **Predicting Consequences** Explain how your life would change if your autonomic nervous system suddenly stopped working.

9. **Making Inferences** Briefly explain why the nervous system is made up of many smaller parts that have specialized functions.

INTERPRETING GRAPHICS Use the figure below to answer the next two questions.

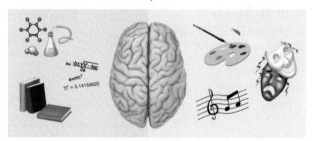

10. **Identifying Relationships** Which hemisphere of the brain recognizes and processes words, numbers, and letters? faces, places, and objects?

11. **Analyzing Processes** For a person whose left hemisphere is primarily in control, would it be easier to learn to play a new computer game by reading the rules and following instructions or by watching a friend play and imitating his actions?

Challenge

12. **Analyzing Relationships** The nervous system is one of eleven systems of the human body. Describe how the other body systems depend on the nervous system to function. How does the nervous system depend on the other body systems?

Sensing the Environment

Key Concept   Your organ systems have specialized structures and functions to sense and gather information.

You feel a tap on your shoulder. Who tapped you? You turn to look, hoping to see a friend. Your senses are on the job! The tap produces impulses in sensory receptors on your shoulder. These impulses travel to your brain.

Once the impulses reach your brain, they create an awareness called a *sensation.* In this case, the sensation is that of being touched on your shoulder. But you still do not know who tapped you. So, you turn around. The sensory receptors in your eyes send impulses to your brain. Now, your brain recognizes your best friend.

Sense of Touch

When you shake hands or feel a breeze, the sensation that you experience is touch. Touch arises from the stimulation of sensory receptors in the skin. Skin is part of the integumentary system. The **integumentary system** is an organ system that protects the body from damage. This system includes hair, skin, and nails. As **Figure 1** shows, skin is not only protective. It also has many kinds of sensory receptors. Each kind of receptor responds mainly to one kind of stimulus. For example, *thermoreceptors* respond to temperature change. Each kind of receptor produces a specific sensation of touch, such as pressure, temperature, pain, or vibration.

Standards Check   What sensations can your skin detect? 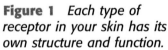 **7.5.a**

Figure 1   *Each type of receptor in your skin has its own structure and function.*

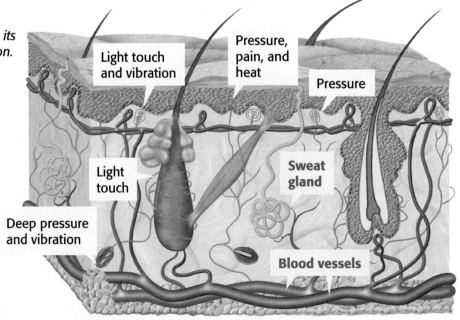

Light touch and vibration

Pressure, pain, and heat

Pressure

Light touch

Sweat gland

Deep pressure and vibration

Blood vessels

Responding to Sensory Messages

When you step on something sharp, as the man in **Figure 2** did, pain receptors in your foot or toe send impulses to your spinal cord. Almost immediately, a message to move your foot travels back to the muscles in your leg and foot. Without thinking, you quickly lift your foot. This immediate, involuntary action is called a **reflex.** Your brain is not telling your leg to move. In fact, by the time that the message reaches your brain, your leg and foot have already moved. If you had to wait for your brain to act, your toes could get seriously hurt!

Standards Check Why are reflexes important? 🐻 **7.5.b**

Feedback Mechanisms

Most of the time, the brain processes information from skin receptors. For example, on a hot day, heat receptors in your skin detect an increase in your temperature. The receptors send impulses to the brain. Your brain responds by sending messages that cause your sweat glands to make sweat. As sweat evaporates, it cools your body. Your brain also tells the blood vessels in your skin to dilate (open wider). Blood flow increases. Thermal energy from the blood in your skin moves to your surroundings. This process also cools your body. As your body cools, it sends messages to your brain. The brain responds by sending messages that cause sweat glands to reduce their activity and blood vessels to constrict.

This cooling process is one of your body's feedback mechanisms. A **feedback mechanism** is a cycle of events in which information from one step controls or affects a previous step. The temperature-regulating feedback mechanism helps keep your body temperature within safe limits. This cooling mechanism works like a thermostat on an air conditioner. Once a room reaches a certain temperature, the thermostat sends a message that causes the air conditioner to stop blowing cold air.

integumentary system
(in TEG yoo MEN tuhr ee SIS tuhm) the organ system that forms a protective covering on the outside of the body

reflex (REE FLEKS) an involuntary and almost immediate movement in response to a stimulus

feedback mechanism (FEED BAK MEK uh NIZ uhm) a cycle of events in which information from one step controls or affects a previous step

Figure 2 *A reflex, such as lifting your foot when you step on something sharp, is one way in which your nervous system responds to your environment.*

Sense of Sight

Cameras capture images of objects that reflect visible light. Sight is the sense that allows you to see the size, shape, motion, and color of objects around you. You see an object when your eyes, like a camera, receive visible light that is scattered, reflected, or emitted by the object. Once your eyes detect the light, your brain can form visual images. Your eyes are complex sensory organs, as **Figure 3** shows. A clear membrane called the *cornea* covers the front of the eye. The cornea protects the eye but allows light to enter. Light from an object enters the front of your eye through an opening called the **pupil.** Then, the light travels through the lens to the back of the eye. There, the light strikes the **retina,** a layer of light-sensitive cells.

The retina is packed with retinal cells called *photoreceptors*. A photoreceptor is a special neuron that responds to light energy by causing other cells in the retina to create electric impulses. The brain perceives these impulses as light. The retina has two kinds of photoreceptors: rods and cones. Rods are very sensitive to dim light. They are important for night vision. Impulses from rods are interpreted as black-and-white images. Cones are very sensitive to bright light. Impulses from cones allow you to see fine details and colors. Impulses from the rods and cones travel along axons. The impulses leave the back of each eye through an optic nerve. The optic nerve carries the impulses to your brain, where the impulses are interpreted.

Standards Check Explain what happens when light enters the eye.
7.6.b

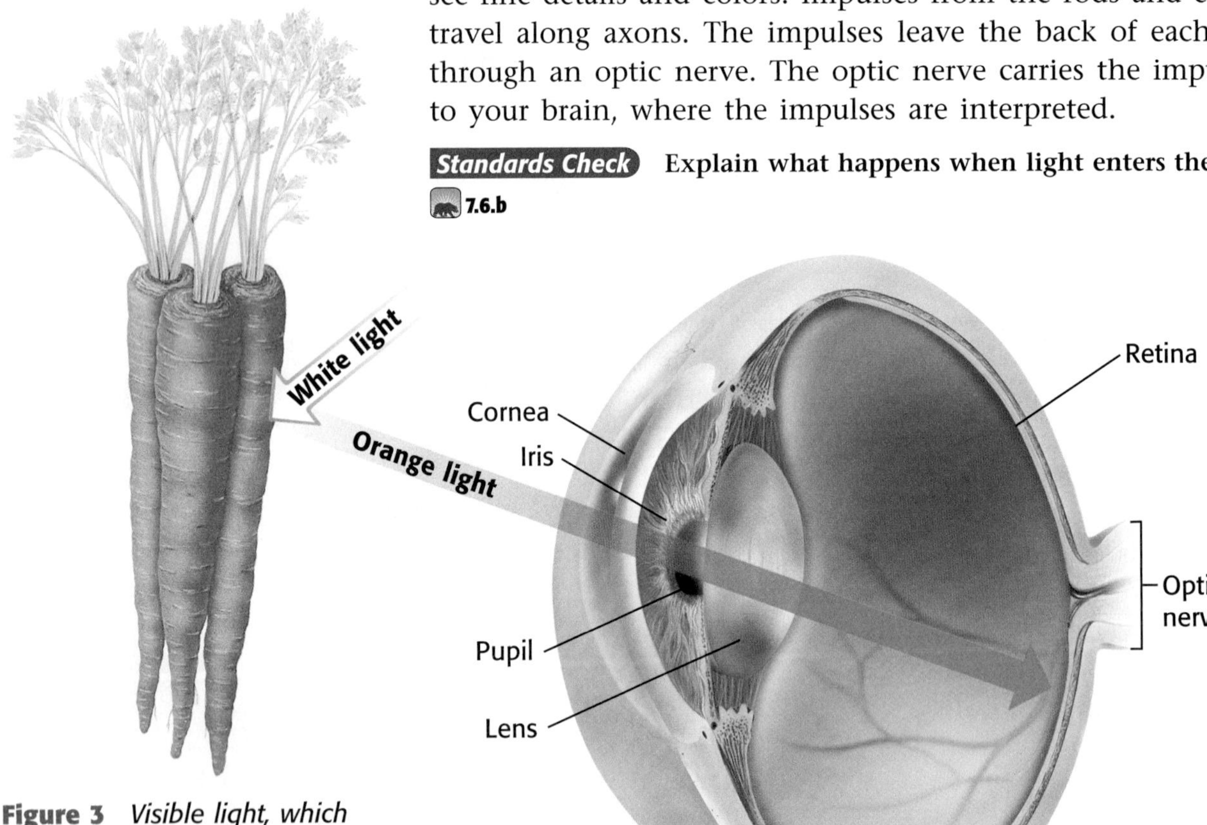

pupil (PYOO puhl) the opening that is located in the center of the iris of the eye and that controls the amount of light that enters the eye

retina (RET 'n uh) the light-sensitive inner layer of the eye, which receives images formed by the lens and transmits them through the optic nerve to the brain

White light

Orange light

Cornea
Iris
Pupil
Lens

Retina

Optic nerve

Figure 3 *Visible light, which is made of many colors of light, hits the carrots. Carrots look orange because they reflect orange light to your eyes.*

Reacting to Light

Your pupil looks like a black dot in the center of your eye. In fact, it is an opening that lets light enter the eye. The pupil is surrounded by the **iris,** a ring of muscle. The iris controls the amount of light entering the eye and gives the eye its color. In bright light, the iris contracts, which makes the pupil smaller in diameter. A smaller pupil reduces the amount of light entering the eye and passing onto the retina. In dim light, the iris relaxes, which dilates the pupil to let in more light.

Standards Check How does your iris react to bright light? 🐘 **7.5.g**

Focusing the Light

Light travels in straight lines until it passes through the cornea and the lens. The *lens* is an oval-shaped piece of clear, curved material behind the iris. The lens refracts, or bends light. Muscles in the eye change the shape of the lens in order to focus light onto the retina. When you look at objects that are close to the eye, the lens becomes more curved. When you look at objects that are far away, the lens gets flatter.

Figure 4 shows some common vision problems. In some eyes, the lens focuses the light in front of the retina, which results in nearsightedness. If the lens focuses the light just behind the retina, the result is farsightedness. Glasses, contact lenses, or surgery can usually correct these vision problems.

Brain Brochure

How does the brain keep track of various activities? Develop a brochure that discusses the structure and function of the human brain. Go to **go.hrw.com,** and type in the keyword HY7BD4W.

iris (IE ris) the colored, circular part of the eye

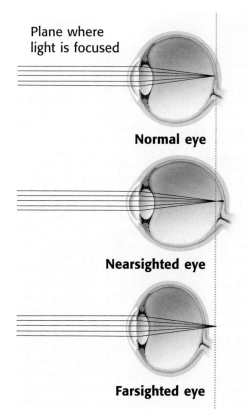

Plane where light is focused

Normal eye

Nearsighted eye

Farsighted eye

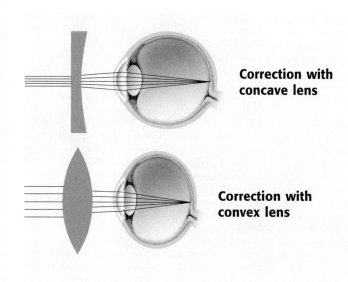

Figure 4 *A concave lens bends light rays outward to correct nearsightedness. A convex lens bends light rays inward to correct farsightedness.*

Correction with concave lens

Correction with convex lens

Sense of Hearing

Sound is produced when something, such as a drum, vibrates. Vibrations push on nearby air particles, which push on other air particles. The vibrations create waves of sound energy. Hearing is the sense that allows you to experience sound energy.

Ears are organs that are specialized for hearing. Each ear has an outer, middle, and inner portion, as shown in **Figure 5.** The outer ear consists of the ear canal. The middle ear includes the *tympanic membrane,* or eardrum. The middle ear also includes the three ear bones: the hammer, anvil, and stirrup. The inner ear includes the cochlea and the auditory nerve.

Sound waves reaching the outer ear are funneled into the middle ear. There, the waves make the eardrum vibrate. The eardrum is a thin membrane separating the outer ear from the middle ear. The vibrating eardrum makes three small bones in the middle ear vibrate. One of these bones, the stirrup, vibrates against the **cochlea,** a fluid-filled organ of the inner ear. Inside the cochlea, vibrations make waves that are just like the waves you make by tapping on a glass of water. Neurons in the cochlea respond to the waves by creating electric impulses. These impulses travel along the *cochlear nerve,* or auditory nerve, to the area of the brain where sound is interpreted.

cochlea (KAHK lee uh) a coiled tube that is found in the inner ear and that is essential to hearing

Figure 5 *A sound wave travels into the outer ear. The wave becomes bone vibrations in the middle ear, liquid vibrations in the inner ear, and finally, nerve impulses that travel to the brain.*

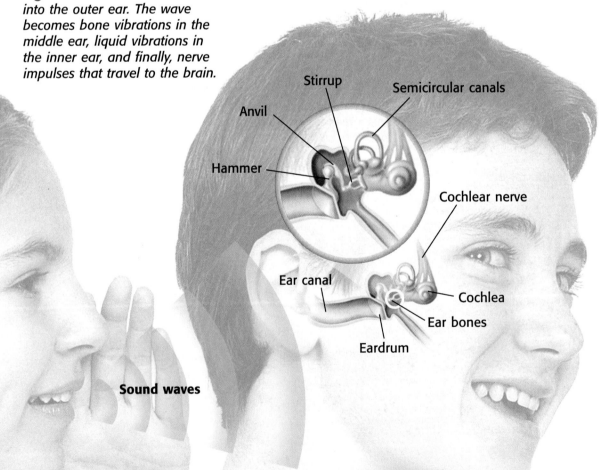

Stirrup
Anvil
Semicircular canals
Hammer
Cochlear nerve
Ear canal
Cochlea
Ear bones
Eardrum
Sound waves

Quick Lab

What Does the Ear Drum Do?

In this activity, you will use simple materials to model the human ear. This model will help you understand how the ear functions.

7.5.g
7.7.d

▶ Try It!

1. Stretch a **piece of plastic wrap** over one end of a **cardboard tube.** Secure the edges of the plastic with a **rubber band.**

2. Use a **piece of paper** to make a cone. Tape the cone together so that it does not unroll.

3. Place the small end of the cone into the open end of the cardboard tube.

4. Use **modeling clay** to place an **index card** vertically on the table.

5. Point a **flashlight** at the plastic wrap–covered end of the tube so that the light reflects onto the index card.

▶ Think About It!

6. Shout, sing, and talk into the open end of the cone. Record your observations.

7. Draw the model that you created. Label the part of the human ear that the model represents and describe the function of that part.

8. Why did the light vibrate?

9. How are the parts of the ear specialized to perform their jobs?

30 min

The External Ear and Sound

You have just read that the human ear is structured to efficiently transfer sound waves into electric impulses. But how is sound gathered and delivered to the ear? The external ear, the part of the ear that you can see, gathers sound waves. It also directs those sound waves into your ear canal. The external ear of a human is fixed in place, but many animals can adjust the position of their external ears to listen to faint sounds. Being able to change the position of the external ear also helps some animals, such as rabbits, determine the direction from which a sound is coming.

Standards Check Describe the role that the external ear plays in hearing. 7.5.g

Keeping Your Balance

Your ears enable you not only to hear but also to maintain your balance. The *semicircular canals,* special fluid-filled canals in your inner ear, are filled with hair cells. These hair cells respond to changes in the position of your head with respect to gravity. The hair cells help your brain determine the orientation and position of your head.

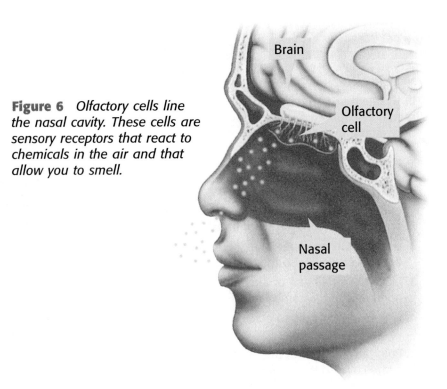

Figure 6 *Olfactory cells line the nasal cavity. These cells are sensory receptors that react to chemicals in the air and that allow you to smell.*

Brain

Olfactory cell

Nasal passage

Disorders of the Senses

With a parent or guardian, research a disorder of one of the five senses discussed in this section. What causes this disorder? What technology is used to help people who are affected by this disorder? Create a poster that illustrates your research.

Sense of Taste

Taste is the sense that allows you to detect chemicals and to distinguish flavors. Your tongue is covered with tiny bumps called *papillae* (puh PIL ee). Most papillae contain taste buds. Taste buds contain clusters of *taste cells,* the receptors for taste. Taste cells respond to dissolved-food molecules. Taste cells react to five basic tastes: sweetness (sugar), sourness (lemon), saltiness (salt), savoriness (meats and cheeses), and bitterness (some medicines). When the brain combines information from all of the taste buds, you taste a "combination" flavor.

Sense of Smell

As you can see in **Figure 6,** receptors for smell are located on *olfactory* cells in the upper part of your nasal cavity. An olfactory cell is a nerve cell that responds to chemical molecules in the air. You smell something when the receptors react to molecules that have been inhaled. The molecules dissolve in the moist lining of the nasal cavity and trigger an impulse. Olfactory cells send those impulses to the brain, which interprets the impulses as odors.

Taste buds and olfactory cells both detect dissolved molecules. Your brain combines information from both senses to give you sensations of flavor.

Standards Check How do your taste cells and olfactory cells communicate with your nervous system? 7.5.a

Summary

- Touch allows you to respond to temperature, pressure, pain, and vibration on the skin.
- Reflexes and feedback mechanisms help you respond to your environment.
- Sight allows you to respond to light energy. The eye has specialized structures to respond to light.
- Hearing allows you to respond to sound energy. The ear has specialized structures to respond to the information in sound waves.
- Taste allows you to distinguish flavors.
- Smell allows you to perceive various odors.

Using Vocabulary

1 Write an original definition for *reflex* and *feedback mechanism*.

2 Use *retina* and *cochlea* in separate sentences.

Understanding Concepts

3 **Listing** What are three sensations that receptors in the skin detect?

4 **Comparing** Explain how light and sight are related.

5 **Describing** How do your senses of hearing, taste, and smell work?

6 **Concluding** Why are bright colors difficult to see in a room lit by candles?

7 **Comparing** How is your sense of taste similar to your sense of smell, and how do these senses work together?

8 **Describing** How does the feedback mechanism that regulates body temperature work?

Critical Thinking

9 **Making Inferences** Why is it important for the human body to have reflexes?

10 **Applying Concepts** Rods help you detect objects and shapes in dim light. Explain why it is important for human eyes to have both rods and cones.

11 **Analyzing Relationships** How do the parts of the ear work together to convert sound waves into nerve impulses?

INTERPRETING GRAPHICS Use the images below to answer the next question.

12 **Analyzing Relationships** Describe the similarities between an eye and a camera lens.

Math Skills

13 **Solving Problems** Suppose a nerve impulse must travel 0.90 m from your toe to your central nervous system. If the impulse travels at 150 m/s, calculate how long it will take the impulse to arrive. If the impulse travels at 0.2 m/s, how long will it take the impulse to arrive?

Challenge

14 **Analyzing Relationships** How do your eyes and ears work together to help you move around a room? (Hint: What functions, other than hearing, do the ears have?)

Internet Resources

For a variety of links related to this chapter, go to www.scilinks.org
Topic: The Senses; The Eye
SciLinks code: HY71378; HY70560

Skills Practice Lab

Dissecting a Cow's Eye

Eyes are sensory organs that detect light. Like a camera, eyes are composed of various parts that each have a specific function. By examining the shape, appearance, and arrangement of the parts of an eye, you can learn more about how the eye works.

Procedure

1 Put on safety goggles, gloves, and a lab apron. **Caution:** Be extremely careful when using sharp and pointed instruments, such as scalpels.

2 Place your cow's eye into a dissecting tray. Observe the outer structure of the eye. Make a sketch of what you see. Use the image below to label the following parts on your sketch: optic nerve, cornea, pupil, iris, and muscles.

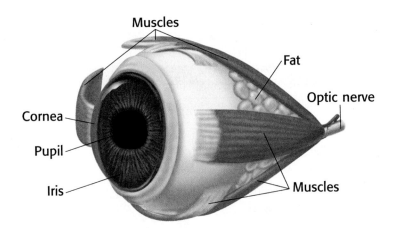

3 Make a small slit in the cornea to drain the clear liquid stored under this thick covering. This liquid is called *vitreous humor*. The vitreous humor helps the eye maintain its shape and hold the retina in place.

4 Use your scalpel and scissors to divide the eye in half so that the front half includes the cornea, pupil, and iris. Although a sharp scalpel can slice into the eye, dissecting scissors will help you cut through this tough tissue in a straight line. As you cut through the eye, more vitreous humor may come out of the eye.

7.5.g Students know how to relate the structures of the eye and ear to their functions.

Investigation and Experimentation
7.7.a Select and use appropriate tools and technology (including calculators, computers, balances, spring scales, microscopes, and binoculars) to perform tests, collect data, and display data.

5 Sketch the eye again. Use the image on the previous page to label the following parts: lens, retina, pupil, cornea, and optic nerve.

6 Examine the front half of the eye. Use your scalpel or scissors to cut out the cornea along its rim. Note the thickness of the cow's cornea.

7 The removal of the cornea reveals the muscular iris and the pupil opening. You should be able to pull out the iris in one piece. Describe the appearance of the cornea and pupil.

8 Remove the lens. Use a paper towel to gently dry this part of the eye. Use the lens to read a portion of a newspaper. How does the lens change the appearance of the newspaper?

9 Examine the other half of the eye. Note the thin sheet of tissue. This is the retina. Find where the nerve fibers of the retina join together. Identify where these fibers exit the eye.

Analyze the Results

10 **Analyzing Data**   Why is the eye filled with vitreous humor?

11 **Classifying**   Is the pupil a physical structure of the eye? Explain your answer. How does the actual structure of the pupil complement its function?

12 **Explaining Events**   An eye lens focuses light as the light enters the eye. Does the lens of an eye work only when an animal is alive? How can you tell?

Draw Conclusions

13 **Applying Conclusions**   Describe the path of light as light travels into and through the eye.

14 **Drawing Conclusions**   How is an eye similar to a camera? What structures of an eye are similar to the shutter and film in a camera?

Big Idea Question

15 **Interpreting Information**   How do the parts of the eye that you have labeled in your two sketches work together to sense and communicate the surroundings?

Science Skills Activity

| Scientific Methods | Research | Data Analysis | Models, Maps & Diagrams |

Selecting Tools to Perform Tests

▶ Tutorial

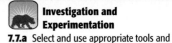

Investigation and Experimentation

7.7.a Select and use appropriate tools and technology (including calculators, computers, balances, spring scales, microscopes, and binoculars) to perform tests, collect data, and display data.

Scientists ask many questions about the natural world. They conduct experiments to find answers to these questions. A scientist must choose the correct equipment and tools in order to perform the experiment and communicate the results. It is very important to select the appropriate tools before beginning the experiment so that data is not lost.

Procedure

1 Write a hypothesis. The hypothesis should offer an explanation for the question that you are asking. The hypothesis must also be testable. If it is not testable, rewrite the hypothesis.

> *Question: How do eyes respond when the intensity of light changes?*
> *Hypothesis: The iris of an eye will open in dim light and close in bright light.*

2 List the possible variables in your experiment. Select only one variable to test in your experiment.

> *Variables:*
> *– intensity of light*
> *– time*
> *– amount of sleep of test subjects*

3 List the materials that you will need to perform the experiment. This list should also include equipment that you need for safety.

> *Materials:*
> *– flashlight*
> *– black paper*
> *– test subjects*

4 Determine the scientific equipment and tools that you will need to perform the tests involved in your experiment. For example, metric rulers are used to measure the dimensions of objects. Scales are used to measure the mass of objects. Cameras capture many important details of an experimental setup.

> *Scientific Equipment and Tools:*
> *– digital camera*
> *– metric ruler*

▶ You Try It!

You are a member of a research team that is trying to determine how external temperature affects the sensitivity of skin. Therefore, you need to find an answer to the following question: Does the temperature of the environment change the way that skin perceives sensation?

Procedure

1 Use the steps above to plan an experiment and to select the appropriate tools and equipment to perform your tests.

Analysis

2 **Forming a Hypothesis**   How does your hypothesis explain or answer your question?

3 **Analyzing Ideas**   List the possible variables in this experiment. Choose one variable.

4 **Analyzing Methods**   What equipment and tools will you need to test this variable?

5 **Predicting Consequences**   What might happen if you select inappropriate tools?

Chapter Summary

The Big Idea
The human body has organ systems that respond to its internal and external environments.

Section

Vocabulary

1 The Nervous System

Key Concept Your nervous system is an organ system that gathers, interprets, and responds to sensory information.

- The central nervous system processes and responds to all messages coming from the peripheral nervous system.

- The somatic nervous system controls voluntary movements. The autonomic nervous system controls functions that are involuntary.

- The brain is made up of many parts that function together as the control center of the nervous system.

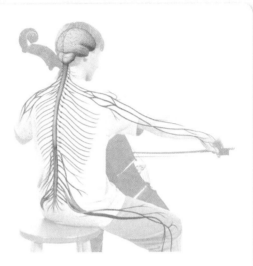

The nervous system is an important human organ system.

central nervous **system** p. 526
peripheral nervous **system** p. 526
neuron p. 527
nerve p. 528
brain p. 530

2 Sensing the Environment

Key Concept Your organ systems have specialized structures and functions to sense and gather information.

- Pressure, temperature, pain, and vibration are four sensations detected by receptors in the skin.

- A feedback mechanism is a cycle of events in which information from one step controls or affects another step.

- You see an object when it reflects visible light toward your eyes.

- Hearing is the sense that allows you to experience sound energy.

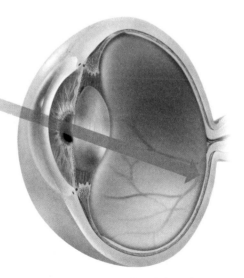

The eye gathers information about the body's external environment.

integumentary system p. 534
reflex p. 535
feedback mechanism p. 535
pupil p. 536
retina p. 536
iris p. 537
cochlea p. 538

Chapter Review

7.5.a, 7.5.b, 7.5.g, 7.6.b

Organize

Double Door   Review the FoldNote that you created at the beginning of the chapter. Add to or correct the FoldNote based on what you have learned.

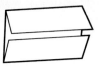

Using Vocabulary

1 **Academic Vocabulary**   Explain how the terms *structure* and *function* differ.

Complete each of the following sentences by choosing the correct term from the word bank.

cochlea	axon
reflex	nerve
retina	central nervous
neuron	system

2 The two parts of your ___ are your brain and spinal cord.

3 Sensory receptors in the ___ detect light.

4 A(n) ___ is an involuntary and almost immediate movement in response to a stimulus.

5 The ___ is a part of the ear that responds to vibrations by creating electric impulses.

6 A(n) ___ is a specialized cell that receives and conducts electric impulses.

Understanding Concepts

Multiple Choice

7 Which of the following has receptors for smelling?
a. cochlea cell
b. thermoreceptors
c. olfactory cell
d. optic nerve

8 Which of the following allows you to see the world in color?
a. cones
b. rods
c. lenses
d. retinas

9 What must first happen in order for you to see?
a. An object must reflect light.
b. Light must strike the cochlea.
c. The tympanic membrane must be open.
d. Motor neurons must send impulses.

10 The peripheral nervous system does NOT include
a. the spinal cord.
b. axons.
c. sensory receptors.
d. motor neurons.

11 Which part of the brain regulates blood pressure?
a. right cerebral hemisphere
b. left cerebral hemisphere
c. cerebellum
d. medulla

12 Which part of the ear gathers and directs sound waves into the ear canal?
a. stirrup
b. external ear
c. inner ear
d. eardrum

Short Answer

13 **Concluding**   What is the difference between the somatic nervous system and the autonomic nervous system? Why are both systems important to the body?

14 **Comparing**   What is the relationship between the CNS and the PNS?

15 **Describing**   What is the function of the bones in the middle ear?

16 Communicating Concepts Sensory organs, such as your eyes and ears, have special structures. Write a brief essay describing the relationship between the structures and functions of your eyes or ears.

17 Concept Mapping Use the following terms to create a concept map: *nervous system, spinal cord, medulla, peripheral nervous system, brain, cerebrum, central nervous system,* and *cerebellum.*

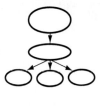

18 Making Comparisons Compare a feedback mechanism with a reflex.

19 Analyzing Ideas Why is it important for the eye to have a lens that can change shape?

20 Applying Concepts Why must your reflexes happen without your thinking about them?

21 Predicting Consequences What would happen if your autonomic nervous system stopped working?

22 Making Comparisons How are the peripheral nervous system and the central nervous system similar? How are they different?

23 Making Inferences Sensory organs are concentrated in the human head. You cannot see, hear, taste, or smell with any other part of your body. Why are the eyes, ears, tongue, and nose located so close to one another?

24 Expressing Opinions Most mammals, such as cats and dogs, walk on four legs. When they walk into a room, their head is the first part of their body to enter. Why is it important for their head to enter first?

25 Applying Concepts Draw an eye. Label all of the parts that you have learned about, and describe the function of each part.

26 Analyzing Processes Describe the steps involved in converting a sound wave into a nerve impulse in the human ear. Be sure to include the name of each structure involved in each step.

27 Making Comparisons How do the structure and function of the external ear of a human relate to the structure and function of the external ear of a rabbit?

INTERPRETING GRAPHICS Use the diagram below to answer the next question.

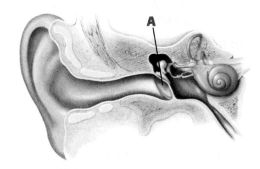

28 Making Inferences In the diagram above, how would the function of the ear be affected if A were not present?

29 Solving Problems Sound travels about 347 m/s. If your ear canal is 15 mm long, how long does a sound take to travel from the entrance of your ear canal to your eardrum?

30 Analyzing Relationships Describe how your nervous system responds to and regulates its internal environment.

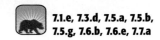
REVIEWING ACADEMIC VOCABULARY

1 Which of the following words means "the way in which something is put together"?

A built

B gathered

C symbolize

D structure

2 In the sentence "Cells, tissues, and organs contribute to the health of the human body," what does the word *contribute* mean?

A to help bring about a result

B to give money with others

C to submit writing for publication

D to pay a fee or tax

3 In the following sentence "A neuron's function is to pass along electric impulses," what does the word *function* mean?

A variable

B role

C relationship

D action

4 Which of the following words is closest in meaning to the word *detected*?

A retracted

B discovered

C interrupted

D investigated

5 Which of the following is the noun form of the word select?

A selective

B selected

C selection

D selectable

REVIEWING CONCEPTS

6 What two organs make up the central nervous system?

A the neurons and the receptors

B the brain and the spinal cord

C the cerebrum and the eyes

D the skin and the vertebrae

7 What role does the peripheral nervous system play in the body?

A It connects all parts of the body to the central nervous system.

B It sends messages along the spinal cord to muscles and glands.

C It controls activities such as speaking, reading, and writing.

D It interprets electric impulses from the nerves as sensations.

8 When you are startled, your heart rate increases, your pupils dilate, and your digestion slows. Which part of the nervous system controls this response?

A the sympathetic nervous system

B the parasympathetic nervous system

C the somatic nervous system

D the central nervous system

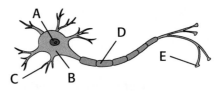

9 What part of the neuron is found at point E in the diagram above?

A dendrite

B axon

C axon terminal

D motor neuron

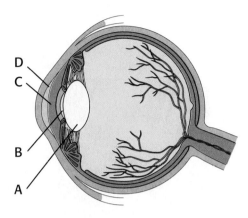

D
C
B
A

10 **At which point in the diagram above do you find the muscle that controls how much light enters the eye?**

A point A

B point B

C point C

D point D

11 **What role does the cochlea play in hearing?**

A It catches and funnels sound into the middle ear.

B It causes the stirrup, a bone in the ear, to vibrate.

C It makes the tympanic membrane, or eardrum, vibrate.

D It changes sound waves into electric impulses.

12 **Why do your eyes see a banana as yellow?**

A because the banana absorbs yellow light

B because the banana reflects white light

C because the banana reflects yellow light

D because the banana contains cone cells

REVIEWING PRIOR LEARNING

13 **Which of the following would you most likely need to conduct an experiment testing the function of rods and cones?**

A slides of eye cells

B a light with a dimmer switch

C hot and cold packs

D a diagram of the middle ear

14 **Which of the following explains why humans see various colors?**

A Different wavelengths produce different temperatures.

B Ultraviolet markings on objects determine what colors we see.

C Cone cells respond differently to light of various wavelengths.

D Chemical reactions convert visible light into various colors.

15 **What characteristic do all animals in the phylum Chordata have in common?**

A They have retractable claws.

B They nurse their young.

C They have a backbone.

D They have a hollow nerve cord.

16 **Through what process do neurons increase their numbers?**

A interphase

B mitosis

C respiration

D meiosis

Science in Action

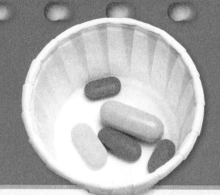

Scientific Discoveries

The Placebo Effect

A placebo (pluh SEE boh) is an inactive substance, such as a sugar pill, used in experimental drug trials. Some of the people who are test subjects are given a placebo as if it were the drug being tested. Usually, neither the doctor conducting the trial nor the test subjects know whether a person is taking a placebo or the test drug. In theory, any change in a subject's condition should be the result of the test drug. But for many years, scientists have known about the *placebo effect,* the effect of feeling better after taking the placebo pill. What makes someone who takes the placebo feel better? By studying brain activity, scientists are beginning to understand the placebo effect.

Social Studies ACTIVITY

Research the differences and similarities between ancient Chinese medical practices and traditional Western medical treatment. Both types of treatment depend in part on a patient's mental and emotional response to treatment. How might the placebo effect be part of both medical traditions? Create a poster showing the results of your research.

Science, Technology, and Society

Making Technology Accessible

When you think of a computer, you may think of a keyboard, a monitor, and a mouse. But computers can take many forms. Thanks to the Archimedes Project founded at Stanford University, now computers are accessible to people who have limited physical abilities. The goal of the Archimedes Project is to create technology that enables people who have a condition such as cerebral palsy or who are quadriplegic to use computers for many tasks.

Language Arts ACTIVITY

At the library or on the Internet, find examples of accessible technology. Research how the technology has been modified for people with disabilities. Write a report in your **Science Journal** about this technology. How does the life of a person with disabilities change when he or she has access to technology?

Bertha Madras

Studying Brain Activity The brain is an amazing organ. Sometimes, though, drugs or disease keep the brain from working properly. Bertha Madras is a biochemist who studies drug addiction. Dr. Madras studies brain activity to see how substances, such as cocaine, target cells or areas of the brain. Using a variety of brain-scanning techniques, Dr. Madras can observe a brain on drugs. She can see how a drug affects the normal activity of the brain. During her research, Dr. Madras realized that some of her results could be applied to Parkinson's disease and to attention deficit hyperactivity disorder (ADHD) in adults. Her research has led to new treatments for both problems.

 Math **ACTIVITY**

Using a search engine on a computer connected to the Internet, search the Internet for "reaction time experiment." Go to one of the Web sites and take the response-time experiment. Record the time that it took you to respond. Repeat the test nine more times, and record your response time for each trial. Then, make a line graph or a bar graph of your response times. Did your response times change? In what way did they change?

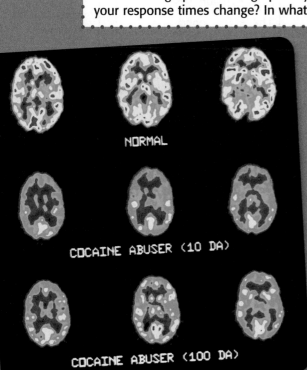

NORMAL

COCAINE ABUSER (10 DA)

COCAINE ABUSER (100 DA)

Internet Resources

- To learn more about careers in science, visit **www.scilinks.org** and enter the SciLinks code HY70225.
- To learn more about these Science in Action topics, visit **go.hrw.com** and type in the keyword HY7BD4F.
- Check out articles related to this chapter by visiting **go.hrw.com**. Just type in the keyword HY7BD4C.

Improving Comprehension

Graphic Organizers are important visual tools that can help you organize information and improve your reading comprehension. The Graphic Organizer below is called *combination notes*. Instructions for creating other types of Graphic Organizers are located in the **Study Skills** section of the Appendix.

How to Make Combination Notes

1 Draw a table like the one shown below. Draw the columns to be as long as you want them to be.

2 Write the topic of your notes in the section at the top of the table.

3 In the left column, write important phrases or sentences about the topic. In the right column, draw diagrams or pictures that illustrate the information in the left column.

When to Use Combination Notes

Combination notes let you express scientific information in words and pictures at the same time. Use combination notes to express information that a picture could help explain. The picture could be a diagram, a sketch, or another useful visual representation of the written information in your notes.

Human Development

- The process of human development usually begins when a man deposits millions of sperm into a woman's vagina and one sperm fertilizes an egg.

- Eleven to twelve days after fertilization, the fertilized egg is called an *embryo*.

- A normal pregnancy lasts about 40 weeks from the first day of a woman's last menstrual period.

Human Development Timeline	
Week #	**What happens?**
2	Fertilization takes place.
5	The spinal cord and brain begin to form.
11	The *embryo* is now called a *fetus*.
17	A layer of fat forms under the skin.
25	The lungs are almost ready to breathe air.
29	The eyes are open.
36	The skull has hardened.
40	The baby is born.

You Try It!

This Reading Strategy can also be used within the chapter that you are about to read. Practice making your own *combination notes* as directed in the Reading Strategy for Section **1**. Record your work in your **Science Journal.**

Unpacking the Standards

The information below "unpacks" the standards by breaking them down into basic parts. The higher-level, academic vocabulary is highlighted and defined to help you understand the language of the standards. "What It Means" restates the standards as simply as possible.

California Standard	Academic Vocabulary	What It Means
7.1.f Students know that as multicellular organisms develop, their cells **differentiate.**	**differentiate** (DIF uhr EN shee AYT) to become specialized in structure and function	As a living thing that is made of more than one cell grows, the structure of its cells change so that the cells perform specific jobs.
7.2.b Students know **sexual** reproduction produces offspring that inherit half their genes from each parent.	**sexual** (SEK shoo uhl) having to do with sex	Offspring that are produced through sexual reproduction get half of their genetic material from one parent and half of their genetic material from the other parent.
7.5.a Students know plants and animals have levels of organization for **structure** and **function,** including cells, tissues, organs, organ systems, and the whole organism.	**structure** (STRUHK chuhr) the arrangement of the parts of a whole **function** (FUHNGK shuhn) use or purpose	Plants and animals are made of smaller parts which are organized by shape and purpose. These layers of organization include cells, tissues, organs, organ systems, and the whole organism.
7.5.d Students know how the reproductive organs of the human female and male **generate** eggs and sperm and how **sexual** activity may lead to fertilization and pregnancy.	**generate** (JEN uhr AYT) to bring about, to produce	The reproductive organs of women make eggs, and the reproductive organs of men make sperm. When human sperm is present in the woman during ovulation, fertilization and pregnancy may happen.
7.5.e Students know the **function** of the umbilicus and placenta during pregnancy.		You must know the purpose of the umbilical cord and the placenta during pregnancy.

Reproduction and Development

The Big Idea

The human body has organ systems that function in reproduction and growth.

California Standards

Focus on Life Sciences

7.1 All living organisms are composed of cells, from just one to many trillions, whose details usually are visible only through a microscope. (Section 2)

7.2 A typical cell of any organism contains genetic instructions that specify its traits. Those traits may be modified by environmental influences. (Section 1)

7.5 The anatomy and physiology of plants and animals illustrate the complementary nature of structure and function. (Sections 1 and 2)

Investigation and Experimentation

7.7 Scientific progress is made by asking meaningful questions and conducting careful investigations. (Science Skills Activity)

Math

7.1.2, 7.1.3 Number Sense

English–Language Arts

7.1.3 Reading
7.2.5 Writing

About the Photo

When your mother was about 13 weeks pregnant with you, you probably looked much like this person. You started out as a single cell, and you became a complete person. And you are still growing and changing!

Organize

Pyramid

Before you read this chapter, create the FoldNote entitled "Pyramid." Label the sides of the pyramid with "The male reproductive system," "The female reproductive system," and "Growth and development." As you read the chapter, define each topic, and write characteristics of each topic on the appropriate side of the pyramid.

Instructions for creating FoldNotes are located in the Study Skills section on p. 579 of the Appendix.

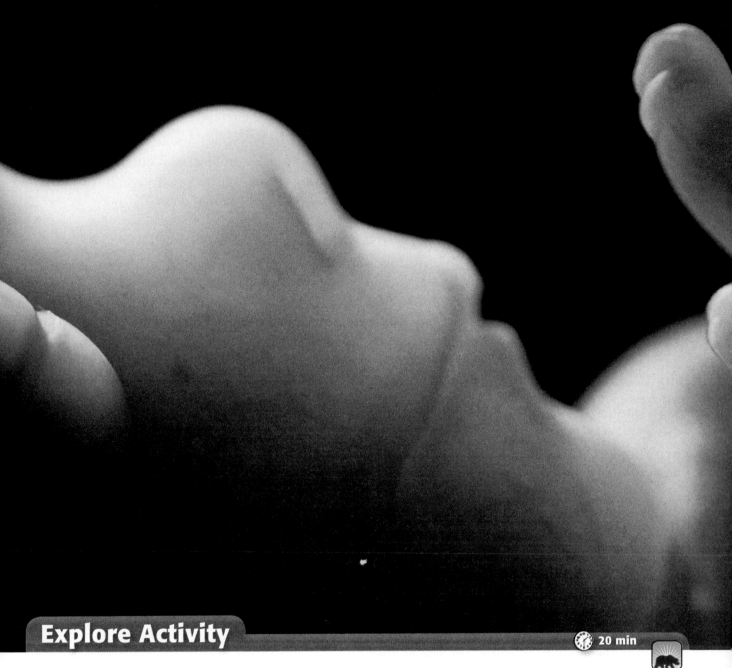

Explore Activity

⏱ 20 min

Dance of the Chromosomes

During meiosis, cells that have two copies of each chromosome divide to form sex cells that have one copy of each chromosome. This is an important process in human reproduction. Females produce sex cells called eggs. Males produce sex cells called sperm. Create a dance that illustrates the steps involved in the formation of egg and sperm cells.

Procedure

1. Review the process of meiosis as presented in Chapter 6, Heredity.

2. Work in a group with three other students.

3. Begin with a diploid cell that contains one pair of chromosomes. A diploid cell has two copies of each chromosome. To each group member assign the role of one chromosome or other cell part.

4. Create a dance that illustrates the behavior **7.2.b** of these chromosomes during the formation of haploid sex cells. Haploid cells have one copy of each chromosome.

5. Perform your dance for your classmates.

Analysis

6. Why is it important that sperm and eggs have only one copy of each chromosome?

7. When a sperm fertilizes an egg, how many copies of each chromosome does the new cell have?

Human Reproduction

Key Concept Humans reproduce sexually. They have specialized organs that are responsible for reproduction.

What You Will Learn

- The testes and penis are two structures of the male reproductive system.
- The ovaries, uterus, and vagina are three structures of the female reproductive system.
- Sperm are produced in the testes. Eggs are produced in the ovaries.
- During fertilization, each parent contributes one chromosome from each of his or her chromosome pairs to an offspring.

Why It Matters

Sexual reproduction results in offspring that resemble their parents but that are unique individuals.

Vocabulary

- testes
- penis
- ovary
- uterus
- vagina

READING STRATEGY

Graphic Organizer In your **Science Journal,** create Combination Notes that express how a child inherits genes from his or her grandparents. Use words and pictures or diagrams.

7.2.b Students know sexual reproduction produces offspring that inherit half their genes from each parent.

7.5.a Students know plants and animals have levels of organization for structure and function, including cells, tissues, organs, organ systems, and the whole organism.

7.5.d Students know how the reproductive organs of the human female and male generate eggs and sperm and how sexual activity may lead to fertilization and pregnancy.

▶ About nine months after a human sperm and egg combine and start to grow inside a woman's uterus, she gives birth to her baby. How do humans produce sperm and eggs?

The Male Reproductive System

The function of the male reproductive system is to make and deliver sperm to the female reproductive system. To perform this function, organs of the male reproductive system, shown in **Figure 1,** make sperm, hormones, and fluids. The **testes** (singular, *testis*) are a pair of organs that hang outside the body in the *scrotum,* a skin sac. Testes make sperm and testosterone (tes TAHS tuhr OHN), the main male sex hormone. Testosterone regulates sperm production and the development of male characteristics.

As sperm leave a testis, they are stored in the *epididymis* (EP uh DID i mis), a tube in which sperm mature. Another tube, a *vas deferens* (VAS DEF uh RENZ), passes from the epididymis into the body and through the *prostate gland.* As sperm move through the vas deferens, they mix with fluids from several glands, including the prostate gland. This mixture is *semen.*

Semen passes through the vas deferens into the *urethra* (yoo REE thruh), the tube that runs from the bladder through the penis. The **penis** is the external organ through which semen exits a male's body and can enter a female's body.

Standards Check Where are sperm produced? **7.5.d**

Figure 1 The Male Reproductive System

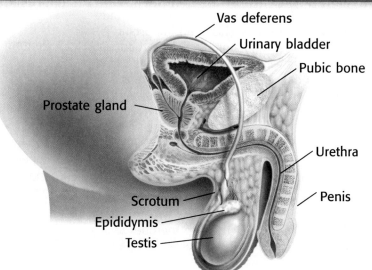

Vas deferens
Urinary bladder
Pubic bone
Prostate gland
Urethra
Scrotum
Epididymis
Penis
Testis

Delivery of Sperm

Of the sperm that leave the body, most sperm exit the penis during *ejaculation*. But, some sperm may exit the penis before ejaculation without the male's knowledge. Sexual activity that includes the release of any sperm—even a few—may lead to *fertilization* and pregnancy. Fertilization occurs when a sperm penetrates, or enters, an egg.

The Female Reproductive System

The female reproductive system, shown in **Figure 2,** produces eggs, nurtures fertilized eggs (zygotes), and gives birth. The two **ovaries** are the organs that make eggs. Ovaries also release estrogen (ES truh juhn) and progesterone (proh JES tuhr OHN), the main female sex hormones. These hormones regulate the release of eggs and development of female characteristics.

Standards Check Where are eggs produced in the female reproductive system? 7.5.d

The Egg's Journey

During *ovulation* (AHV yoo LAY shuhn), an egg is released from an ovary and passes into a *fallopian tube* (fuh LOH pee uhn TOOB). From each ovary, one of two fallopian tubes, also called *oviducts*, leads to the uterus. The egg passes through the fallopian tube into the uterus. Fertilization usually happens in the fallopian tube. If the egg is fertilized, the resulting zygote enters the uterus. The zygote may become embedded in the thickened lining of the uterus. The **uterus** is the organ in which a zygote develops into a baby.

When a baby is born, he or she passes from the uterus through the vagina and emerges outside the body. The **vagina** is the canal between the outside of the body and the uterus.

testes (TES TEEZ) the primary male reproductive organs, which produce sperm and testosterone (singular, *testis*)

penis (PEE nis) the male organ that transfers sperm to a female and that carries urine out of the body

ovary (OH vuh ree) in the female reproductive system of animals, an organ that produces eggs

uterus (YOO tuhr uhs) in female placental mammals, the hollow, muscular organ in which an embryo embeds itself and develops into a fetus

vagina (vuh JIEN uh) the female reproductive organ that connects the outside of the body to the uterus

Counting Eggs

1. The average woman ovulates one egg each month from about age 12 to about age 50. How many mature eggs could she produce from age 18 to age 50? Assume that she does not have any pregnancies.
2. A female's ovaries typically contain about 2 million immature eggs. If she ovulates regularly from age 12 to age 50, what percentage of her eggs will mature? Record your work in your **Science Journal.**

Figure 2 The Female Reproductive System

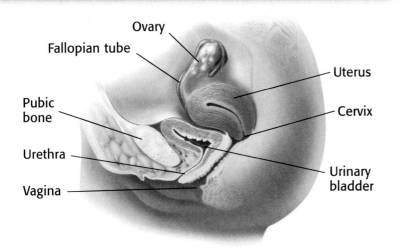

Ovary
Fallopian tube
Pubic bone
Urethra
Vagina
Uterus
Cervix
Urinary bladder

Twins and More

With an adult family member or guardian, discuss some challenges that are created by the birth of twins, triplets, quadruplets, or other multiples. Include financial, mental, emotional, and physical challenges.

Create a poster that shows these challenges. Include ways to meet each challenge.

If twins or other multiples are in your family, discuss how the individuals differ and how they are alike.

ACTIVITY

Menstrual Cycle

From puberty through her late 40s or early 50s, a woman's reproductive system goes through the *menstrual cycle* (MEN struhl SIE kuhl), a monthly cycle of changes. This cycle of about 28 days prepares the body for pregnancy. The first day of *menstruation* (MEN STRAY shuhn), the monthly discharge of blood and tissue from the uterus, is counted as the first day of the cycle. Menstruation lasts about 5 days. When menstruation ends, the lining of the uterus thickens.

Ovulation occurs on about the 14th day of the cycle. Before ovulation, an egg develops within a *follicle*. Follicles are structures in the ovaries. Ovulation occurs when the egg is released from the ovary into one of the fallopian tubes. The fallopian tubes lead from the ovaries into the uterus. If the egg is not fertilized, menstruation begins and flushes the egg away.

Standards Check What is the purpose of the menstrual cycle?

 7.5.a, 7.5.d

Fertilization

If sperm are present in the female reproductive system within a few days of ovulation, fertilization may occur. During fertilization, a single sperm penetrates an egg. A mature egg or sperm has only one copy of each chromosome. After fertilization, the fertilized egg has two copies of each chromosome. Remember, chromosomes and the genes that they contain are the genetic information in each of your cells. As **Figure 3** shows, the sperm and egg each contribute one chromosome to each chromosome pair in the fertilized egg, which is called a *zygote*.

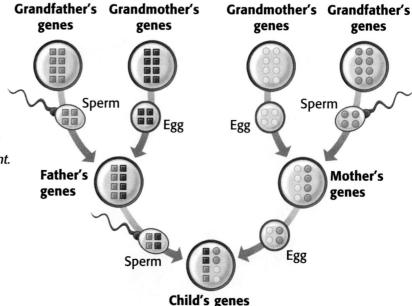

Figure 3 *Eggs and sperm contain chromosomes. You inherited half of your chromosomes from each parent.*

Quick Lab

Modeling Inheritance

During sexual reproduction, parents contribute genetic information to offspring. In this activity, you will model inheritance, the passing on of genetic information from parent to offspring.

1. Copy the table shown to the right. A trait is a form of a genetic characteristic. For example, blue fur is a form of fur color. For most characteristics, there is more than one trait that a parent may pass along to its offspring during sexual reproduction. The gene for each trait is called an *allele.* Alleles are represented by letters: capital letters for dominant alleles and lowercase letters for recessive alleles. For each characteristic, each parent gives one allele to each offspring. By knowing an offspring's two alleles for a characteristic, you can determine what the offspring looks like for that characteristic.

2. For each characteristic, flip a **coin** to pick which allele each parent will pass to the offspring. Heads represents a dominant allele (capital letter). Tails represents a recessive allele (lower case letter).

Parent Alleles				
Characteristic	Mother		Father	
Fur color	F	f	F	f
Number of eyes	E	e	E	e
Number of antennae	A	a	A	a

3. Record your results in your data table by circling the allele that each parent contributed.

4. Below your table, write the alleles that the offspring receives, such as FF, Ee, and aa.

5. Use the chart that your teacher drew to decide what the offspring in your model looks like. Sketch the offspring.

6. What did each parent contribute to the offspring?

7. Each parent has blue fur, five eyes, and four antennae. Does the offspring look like the parent? Why or why not?

20 min

Multiple Births

In a multiple birth, a mother gives birth to two or more babies at a time. The birth of twins is the most common multiple birth. Identical twins develop from a single egg that splits into two. Identical twins can be so similar that their parents cannot tell them apart. The boys in **Figure 4** are identical twins. Fraternal twins develop from two eggs and are more common than identical twins are. Fraternal twins can look very different from each other and can be of opposite sexes.

In every 1,000 births, about 30 sets of twins are born. About one-third of twin births are of identical twins. Some multiple births are of triplets (three babies). In the United States, there are about two sets of triplets in every 1,000 births. Rarer types of multiple births are births of quadruplets (four babies) and quintuplets (five babies). Births of five or more babies happen only once in about 53,000 births.

Figure 4 *Identical twins have genes that are exactly the same. Many identical twins who are raised apart have similar personalities and interests.*

Table 1	The Spread of STDs in the United States	
STD	Approximate number of new cases each year
Chlamydia	3 to 10 million
Genital HPV (human papillomavirus)	5.5 million
Genital herpes	1 million
Gonorrhea	650,000
Syphilis	70,000
HIV/AIDS	40,000 to 50,000

Choose Your Parents

Introduce the animal contestants of a new game show called "Choose Your Parents!" Go to **go.hrw.com,** and type in the keyword HY7BD5W.

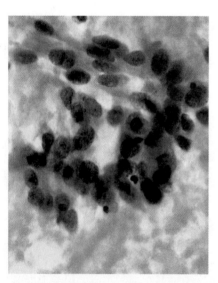

Figure 5 *Cancer of the cervix is one of the most common forms of reproductive system cancers in women.*

Reproductive System Problems

Most of the time, the reproductive system functions well. But problems such as disease and infertility can cause it to fail.

Sexually Transmitted Diseases (STDs)

Chlamydia and herpes are common sexually transmitted diseases. A *sexually transmitted disease* (STD) is a disease that can pass from one person to another person during sexual contact. STDs are also called *sexually transmitted infections* (STIs). These diseases affect many people each year, as shown in **Table 1.** The STD *acquired immune deficiency syndrome* (AIDS) is caused by the *human immunodeficiency virus* (HIV). AIDS is a fatal disease. HIV destroys the immune system by attacking white blood cells. Because of their weakened immune system, people who have AIDS generally die from infections other than HIV infection. These people are said to have died of AIDS-related causes.

The *hepatitis B virus* (HBV) causes an STD that is a liver disease. HBV can be spread by sexual contact. In the United States, about 140,000 new hepatitis B cases occur each year.

Cancer

Sometimes, cancer happens in reproductive organs. *Cancer is a disease in which cells grow at an uncontrolled rate. Cancer cells start out as normal cells. Then, something triggers, or causes, uncontrolled cell growth. These triggers vary for different types of cancer.

In men, the two most common reproductive system cancers are cancer of the testes and cancer of the prostate gland. In women, the two most common reproductive system cancers are breast cancer and cancer of the cervix. The *cervix* is the lower part, or neck, of the uterus. The cervix opens to the vagina. **Figure 5** shows cancerous cells from the cervix.

Infertility

In the United States, about 15% of married couples have difficulty producing offspring. Many of these couples are *infertile,* or unable to have children. Men who do not produce enough healthy sperm may be infertile. Women who do not ovulate normally may be infertile. Assisted reproductive technology (ART), one type of which is shown in **Figure 6,** helps some infertile couples conceive. Sexually transmitted diseases, such as gonorrhea and chlamydia, can cause infertility in women. STD-related infertility occurs in men, but not as commonly as in women.

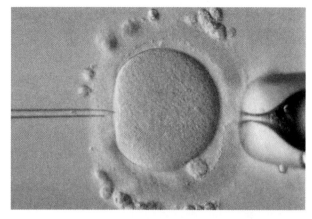

Figure 6 *In one type of assisted reproductive technology (ART), a single sperm is injected into a single egg.*

SECTION Review

7.2.b, 7.5.a, 7.5.d

Summary

- The male reproductive system produces sperm and can deliver sperm to the female reproductive system.

- The female reproductive system produces eggs, nurtures zygotes, and gives birth.

- If sperm are present in the female reproductive system within a few days of ovulation, fertilization may occur.

- A fertilized egg has one chromosome from each chromosome pair of the parents.

- Humans usually have one child per birth, but some people have multiple births.

- Human reproduction can be affected by infertility and by diseases such as cancer.

Using Vocabulary

1. Use *uterus* and *vagina* in the same sentence.

Understanding Concepts

2. **Identifying** What are the structures and functions of the male and female reproductive systems?

3. **Comparing** How is the production of sperm in the male reproductive system similar to the production of eggs in the female reproductive system?

4. **Describing** What are two reproductive system problems?

Critical Thinking

5. **Predicting Consequences** In females, an egg travels to the uterus through a fallopian tube approximately once a month. However, untreated STDs in women can block the fallopian tubes. How is fertilization affected in this situation?

6. **Applying Concepts** Twins can happen when a zygote splits in two or when two eggs are fertilized at the same time. Describe the difference between these situations in terms of how the offspring inherit genetic material from their father.

Math Skills

7. **Making Calculations** In one country, 7 out of 1,000 infants die before their first birthday. Convert this statistic into a percentage.

Challenge

8. **Identifying Relationships** How do the male and female reproductive systems rely on other organ systems?

Internet Resources

For a variety of links related to this chapter, go to www.scilinks.org

Topic: Reproduction System Irregularities or Disorders; Medicine in California

SciLinks code: HY71298; HY7C09

Growth and Development

Key Concept Between fertilization and birth, many changes occur. Humans continue to grow and develop until death.

What You Will Learn

- Fertilization is the beginning of an embryo's development during pregnancy.
- Organs and tissues develop as an embryo becomes a fetus.
- A developing human relies on the placenta and umbilical cord.
- There are many stages of human development from birth to death.

Why It Matters

The processes of growth and development shape human lives.

Vocabulary

- embryo
- placenta
- pregnancy
- umbilical cord
- fetus

READING STRATEGY

Outlining In your **Science Journal**, create an outline of the section. Use the headings from the section in your outline.

embryo (EM bree OH) in humans, a developing individual, from fertilization through the 10th week of pregnancy

7.1.f Students know that as multicellular organisms develop, their cells differentiate.
7.5.d Students know how the reproductive organs of the human female and male generate eggs and sperm and how sexual activity may lead to fertilization and pregnancy.
7.5.e Students know the function of the umbilicus and placenta during pregnancy.

▶ To develop into a baby, a single cell must divide many times. But the development of a baby from a single cell is only the first stage of human development.

From Fertilization to Embryo

Ordinarily, the process of human development starts as a result of sexual activity in which a man ejaculates millions of sperm into a woman's vagina. A few hundred sperm move from the vagina, through the uterus, and into a fallopian tube, or oviduct. If an egg is there, these sperm cover the egg's protective outer coating. Usually, only one sperm pierces, or *penetrates*, the coating. Penetration by a sperm causes a change in the coating that prevents penetration by other sperm. The sperm's nucleus and the egg's nucleus join, and the egg is fertilized.

Over five or six days, the fertilized egg, or zygote, travels down the fallopian tube to the uterus. The fertilized egg is also known as an **embryo.** During the trip, the embryo undergoes many cell divisions. By seven to eight days after fertilization, the embryo has become a tiny ball of cells. Then, implantation occurs. *Implantation* is the embedding of the embryo in the thick, nutrient-rich lining of the uterus. **Figure 1** shows fertilization and implantation.

Standards Check Where do the processes of fertilization and implantation occur? 🐻 **7.5.d**

Figure 1 Fertilization and Implantation

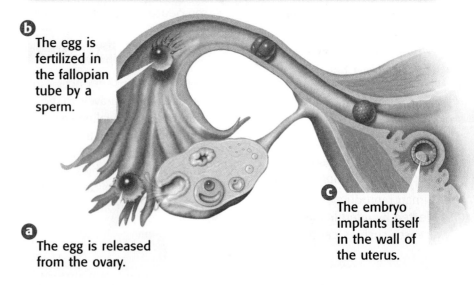

b The egg is fertilized in the fallopian tube by a sperm.

c The embryo implants itself in the wall of the uterus.

a The egg is released from the ovary.

From Embryo to Fetus

After implantation, the placenta forms. The **placenta** is a special two-way exchange organ. The placenta's network of blood vessels provides the embryo with oxygen and nutrients from the mother's blood. The embryo's wastes move into the mother's blood through the placenta. The mother's body then excretes the wastes. In the placenta, the embryo's blood and the mother's blood flow near each other but usually do not mix.

Weeks 1 and 2

Doctors commonly measure a woman's **pregnancy** as starting from the first day of her last menstrual period. On that day, fertilization has not yet taken place, but that day is an easy-to-recognize date from which to count. A normal pregnancy lasts about 40 weeks from that day.

Weeks 3 and 4

Fertilization occurs at about the end of week 2. In week 3, the zygote moves to the uterus. The zygote is an early stage of embryo. The embryo is called a *zygote* only from the time that the sperm and egg nuclei join until the time of the first cell division. As it moves, the embryo divides many times. It becomes a ball of cells that implants itself in the wall of the uterus. In this stage, some cells begin to specialize, or become *differentiated*. For example, some cells become blood cells.

Weeks 5 to 8

Weeks 5 to 8 of pregnancy are weeks 3 to 6 of embryonic development. From this stage until birth, the embryo is surrounded by a thin membrane called the *amnion* (AM nee AHN). Amniotic fluid fills the amnion, which cushions and protects the growing embryo. In week 5, the umbilical cord forms. The **umbilical cord** connects the embryo to the placenta. **Figure 2** shows the umbilical cord, amnion, and placenta. The umbilical cord is attached to the fetus at the *umbilicus,* or navel.

In this stage, the heart, brain, other organs, and blood vessels start to form and grow quickly. In weeks 5 and 6, eyes and ears form and the spinal cord begins to develop. In week 6, tiny limb buds that will become arms and legs appear. In week 8, muscles start to develop. Nerves in the shoulders and upper arms grow. Fingers and toes start to form. The embryo, now about 16 mm long, can swallow and blink.

Standards Check Why is the umbilical cord important? **7.5.e**

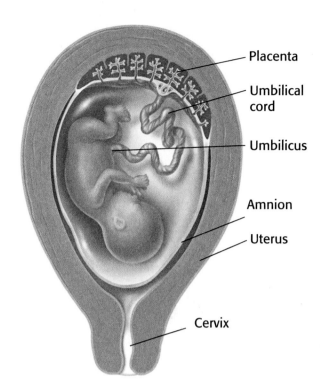

Figure 2 *The placenta, amnion, and umbilical cord are the life support system for the fetus. This fetus is about 20 to 22 weeks old.* **What is the function of the placenta?**

placenta (pluh SEN tuh) the partly fetal and partly maternal organ by which materials are exchanged between a fetus and the mother

pregnancy (PREG nuhn see) in medical practice, the period of time between the first day of a woman's last menstrual period and the delivery of her baby (about 280 days, or 40 weeks)

Wordwise **differentiated**
The prefix *dif-* means "apart" or "in different directions." The root *fer-* means "to bring" or "to bear."

umbilical cord (uhm BIL i kuhl KAWRD) the ropelike structure through which blood vessels pass and by which a developing mammal is connected to the placenta

fetus (FEET uhs) a developing human from the end of the 10th week of pregnancy until birth

Weeks 9 to 16

In this stage, the embryo changes as cells continue to form tissues and organs. At week 9, the embryo may make tiny movements. After week 10, the embryo is called a **fetus** (FEET uhs). At week 13, the fetus's face begins to look more human. Fetal muscle tissue grows stronger. As a result, the fetus can make a fist, and move. The fetus grows rapidly during this stage. Within a month, the size of the fetus doubles and then triples. For example, in week 10, the fetus is about 36 mm long. At week 16, the fetus is about 108 to 116 mm long. **Figure 3** shows changes that occur in the fetus as the fetus develops.

Standards Check Describe two things that a fetus can do in weeks 9 to 16 as a result of stronger fetal muscle tissue. **7.1.f**

Weeks 17 to 24

By week 17, the fetus can make faces. Usually, in week 18, the fetus starts to make movements that the mother can feel. By week 18, the fetus can hear sounds through the mother's body and may even jump at loud noises. By week 23, fetal movements may be vigorous. A fetus that is born at week 24 might survive if given intensive medical care. In weeks 17 to 24, the fetus grows to a length of 25 to 30 cm.

Weeks 25 to 36

At about 25 or 26 weeks, the fetus's lungs are well developed but not fully mature. The fetus still gets oxygen from its mother through the placenta. The fetus will not take its first breath of air until it is born. By the 32nd week, the fetus's eyes can open and close. Studies of fetal heart rate and brain activity show that fetuses respond to light. Some scientists have observed brain activity and eye movements in sleeping fetuses that resemble the brain activity and eye movements of sleeping children or adults. These scientists think that a sleeping fetus may dream. After 36 weeks, the fetus is almost ready to be born.

Birth

At 37 to 38 weeks, the fetus is fully developed. A full-term pregnancy usually lasts about 40 weeks. Typically, as birth begins, the mother's uterus begins a series of muscular contractions called *labor*. Usually, these contractions push the fetus through the mother's vagina, and the baby is born. The newborn is still connected to the placenta by its umbilical cord, which is tied and cut. All that will remain of the point where the umbilical cord was attached is the baby's navel. Soon, the mother expels the placenta, and labor is complete.

Figure 3 Pregnancy Timeline

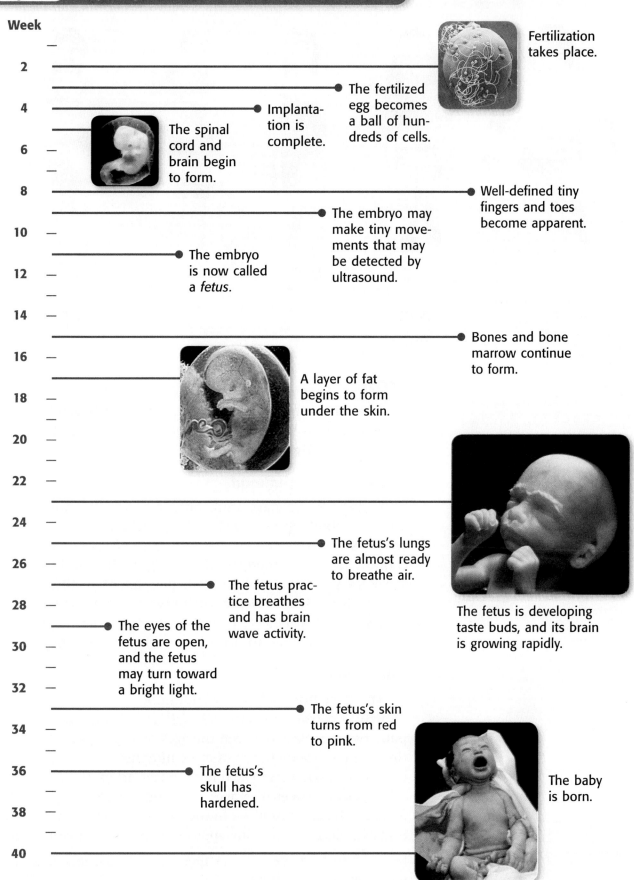

Week

2

4

6

8

10

12

14

16

18

20

22

24

26

28

30

32

34

36

38

40

Fertilization takes place.

The fertilized egg becomes a ball of hundreds of cells.

Implantation is complete.

The spinal cord and brain begin to form.

Well-defined tiny fingers and toes become apparent.

The embryo may make tiny movements that may be detected by ultrasound.

The embryo is now called a *fetus*.

Bones and bone marrow continue to form.

A layer of fat begins to form under the skin.

The fetus's lungs are almost ready to breathe air.

The fetus practice breathes and has brain wave activity.

The eyes of the fetus are open, and the fetus may turn toward a bright light.

The fetus is developing taste buds, and its brain is growing rapidly.

The fetus's skin turns from red to pink.

The fetus's skull has hardened.

The baby is born.

Figure 4 **Body Proportions During Stages of Human Development**

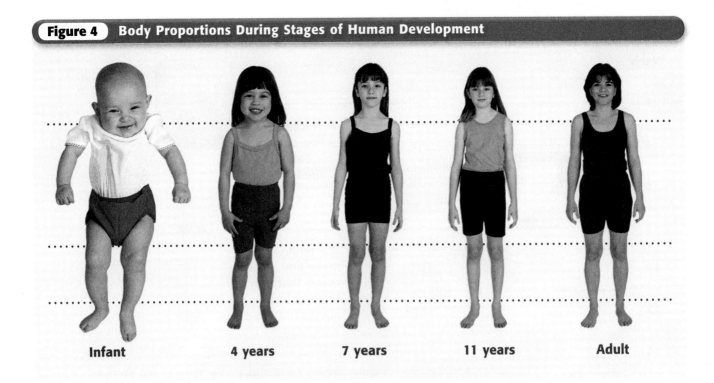

| Infant | 4 years | 7 years | 11 years | Adult |

From Birth to Death

After birth, the human body goes through several stages of development. A human's body proportions during those stages are shown in **Figure 4.**

Infancy and Childhood

Infancy is the stage from birth to age 2. During infancy, a person's body grows quickly. Baby teeth appear. As the nervous system and muscles develop, the person becomes more coordinated. Childhood, another fast-growth period, lasts from age 2 to puberty. In childhood, permanent teeth grow and replace baby teeth. Nerve pathways mature, which allows a person to learn new skills. Muscle coordination increases, which allows people to do things such as ride a bicycle.

Adolescence

The stage from puberty to adulthood is adolescence. During puberty, a person's reproductive system matures. In most boys, puberty takes place between the ages of 11 and 16. During this time, a male's body becomes more muscular, his voice becomes deeper, and body and facial hair appear. In most girls, puberty takes place between the ages of 9 and 14. During puberty in females, the amount of fat in the hips and thighs increases, the breasts enlarge, body hair appears, and menstruation begins.

Standards Check Describe an important change that takes place during adolescence. 7.5.d

Adulthood

From about age 20 to age 40 is the stage of young adulthood. Physical development is at its peak. Beginning around age 30, changes associated with aging begin. These changes are gradual and vary from person to person. Some early signs of aging include loss of muscle flexibility, deterioration of eyesight, increase in body fat, and some loss of hair.

The aging process continues in middle age, which occurs from age 40 to age 65. During this time, hair may turn gray, athletic abilities usually decline, and skin may wrinkle. A person who is more than 65 years old is considered an older adult. Although the aging process continues through the end of life, many older adults lead very active lives, as **Figure 5** shows.

Figure 5 *Many older adults can still enjoy activities that they enjoyed when they were younger.*

SECTION Review

7.1.f, 7.5.d, 7.5.e

Summary

- Fertilization occurs when a sperm from the male joins with an egg from the female.

- First as an embryo and then as a fetus, a developing human undergoes many changes between implantation and birth.

- During the development of a human, cells differentiate.

- The umbilical cord and placenta support the developing human during pregnancy by providing oxygen and nutrients and by removing waste materials.

- The first stage of human development lasts from fertilization to birth.

- After birth, a human goes through four more stages of growth and development.

Using Vocabulary

1. Write an original definition for *umbilical cord*.

2. Use *embryo* and *fetus* in the same sentence.

Understanding Concepts

3. **Describing** Outline the order of the development of tissues and organs in an embryo and fetus.

4. **Summarizing** Describe the processes of fertilization and implantation.

5. **Listing** What are five stages of human development?

INTERPRETING GRAPHICS Use the image below to answer the next question.

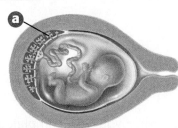

6. **Evaluating** What is the role of the structure indicated by **a**?

Critical Thinking

7. **Applying Concepts** Why does the egg's covering change after a sperm has entered the egg?

8. **Analyzing Ideas** Do you think that one stage of a human's life is more important than other stages are? Explain your answer.

Math Skills

9. **Making Calculations** Alice is 80 years old, and she entered puberty when she was 12 years old. Calculate the percentage of her life that she has spent in each of the four stages of development after birth.

Skills Practice Lab

OBJECTIVES

Construct a model of a human uterus protecting a fetus.

Compare the protection that a bird's egg gives a developing baby bird with the protection that a human uterus gives a fetus.

MATERIALS

- computer (optional)
- cotton, soft fabric, or other soft materials
- eggs, soft-boiled and in the shell (2 to 4)
- eggs, soft-boiled and peeled (3 or 4)
- gloves, protective
- mineral oil, cooking oil, syrup, or other thick liquid
- plastic bags, sealable
- water

SAFETY

7.5.e Students know the function of the umbilicus and placenta during pregnancy.

Investigation and Experimentation

7.7.c Communicate the logical connection among hypotheses, science concepts, tests conducted, data collected, and conclusions drawn from the scientific evidence.

7.7.d Construct scale models, maps, and appropriately labeled diagrams to communicate scientific knowledge (e.g., motion of Earth's plates and cell structure).

It's a Comfy, Safe World!

Before hatching, baby birds live inside a hard, protective shell until the baby has used up all of the food supply. Before birth, most mammal babies develop within their mother's uterus, in which they are surrounded by fluid and connected to a placenta. Before human babies are born, they lead a comfy life. By the seventh month of development, they suck their thumb, blink their eyes, and perhaps even dream.

Ask a Question

1 Inside which structure is a developing organism better protected from bumps and blows: the uterus of a placental mammal or the egg of a bird?

Form a Hypothesis

2 A placental mammal's uterus protects a developing organism from bumps and blows better than a bird's egg does.

Test the Hypothesis

3 Brainstorm ways to construct and test your model of a mammalian uterus. Then, use the materials provided by your teacher to build your model. A peeled, soft-boiled egg will represent the fetus inside your model uterus.

4 Make a data table similar to **Table 1** below. Test your model, examine the egg for damage, and record your results.

Table 1	First Test of Model Uterus
Original model	**Modified model**

5 Modify your model as necessary; test this modified model by using another peeled, soft-boiled egg; and record your results.

6 When you have completed the model's design, obtain another peeled, soft-boiled egg and a soft-boiled egg in the shell. The egg in the shell represents the baby bird inside the egg.

7 Make a data table similar to **Table 2** below. Test only the peeled egg inside the model. Then, test the egg in the shell as is. Examine the eggs for damage. Record the results in your data table.

Table 2	Final Test of Model Uterus
	Test results
Model	DO NOT WRITE IN BOOK
Egg in shell	

Analyze the Results

8 **Explaining Events**   Explain how the test results for the model differ from the test results for the egg in a shell.

9 **Analyzing Results**   What modification to your model protected the "fetus" most effectively?

Draw Conclusions

10 **Evaluating Data**   Review your hypothesis. Did your data support your hypothesis? Why or why not?

11 **Evaluating Models**   What modifications to your model might make it more like a uterus?

Big Idea Question

12 **Analyzing Relationships**   How is a human placenta and umbilical cord specialized to protect and provide for a developing human before he or she is born?

Applying Your Data

Use the Internet or the library to find information about the development of monotremes, such as the echidna or the platypus, and the development of marsupials, such as the koala or the kangaroo. Then, using what you have learned in this lab, compare the development of placental mammals with the development of marsupials and monotremes.

Science Skills Activity

Investigation and Experimentation

7.7.b Use a variety of print and electronic resources (including the World Wide Web) to collect information and evidence as part of a research project.

Using Print Resources for Research

▶ Tutorial

Print resources that you might use in a research project include newspapers, magazines, journals, encyclopedias, and other books. Reading is one way to get information from a print resource. But there are several other ways to quickly get information from a print resource. The following tips are ways to help you quickly find what you are looking for.

Procedure

1 List Your Keywords After you have gathered your print resources, make a list of keywords that are important to your research project.

2 Find the Main Idea Often, the main idea of the paragraph is stated in the first sentence. And the last sentence restates that idea.

3 Important Headings and Illustrations When you find a page that appears to have useful information, read the headings on that page to see if they relate to your topic. Then, look at any pictures, diagrams, charts, or maps on the page to see if they relate to your topic. Be sure to read the captions.

4 Scan the Resource Read only a few words here and there. Scan a passage in order to find keywords. By scanning, you can decide which parts of the text you should concentrate on.

5 Skim the Resource Read only a sentence or two. Look for sentences that look especially important. Skim a passage to get a general idea of what it is about or to determine if you want to read some parts more carefully.

▶ You Try It!

Some scientists study the reproduction and development of animals to understand human reproduction and development. Use chapter 14 in this textbook and the procedure above to research how and why animals reproduce.

Procedure

1 Before you begin, what keywords will be helpful to search for?

2 Follow each of the steps outlined above and make notes in a chart similar to the one below.

Research Topic:
Key Words:
Print Source:
Important Information:

Analysis

3 Describing Why is choosing your key words before you begin your research important?

4 Evaluating Did this print resource include useful information for your research topic?

5 Designing What other print resources would be useful for researching this topic? Newspapers, journals, and magazines often have information about new discoveries. Books usually have explanations of processes and facts that have been accepted by many scientists.

6 Concluding Describe the additional steps that you would need to follow to continue your research on this topic. Where might you find print resources that are useful for your research?

Chapter Summary

The Big Idea The human body has organ systems that function in reproduction and growth.

Section	Vocabulary

1 Human Reproduction

Key Concept Human beings reproduce sexually. They have specialized organs that are responsible for reproduction.

- The testes and penis are two structures of the male reproductive system.
- The ovaries, uterus, and vagina are three structures of the female reproductive system.
- Sperm and eggs are produced in specialized reproductive organs.
- During fertilization, each parent contributes one chromosome from each of his or her chromosome pairs to an offspring.

Male reproductive system

Female reproductive system

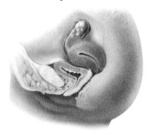

Male and female reproductive systems have specialized organs for reproduction.

testes p.556
penis p. 556
ovary p. 557
uterus p. 557
vagina p. 557

2 Growth and Development

Key Concept Between fertilization and birth, many changes occur. Humans continue to grow and develop until death.

- Fertilization is the beginning of an embryo's development during pregnancy.
- Organs and tissues develop as an embryo becomes a fetus.
- The embryo relies on the placenta and umbilical cord.
- There are many stages of human development from birth to death.

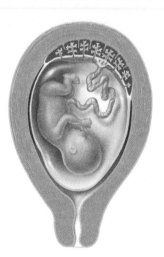

A developing fetus relies on the umbilical cord and placenta.

embryo p. 562
placenta p. 563
pregnancy p. 563
umbilical cord p. 563
fetus p. 564

Chapter Review

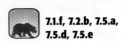

Organize

Pyramid Review the FoldNote that you created at the beginning of the chapter. Add to or correct the FoldNote based on what you have learned.

Using Vocabulary

1 **Academic Vocabulary** In the sentence "Human reproductive organs in the female and male generate eggs and sperm," what does the word *generate* mean?
a. make
b. cause
c. touch off
d. spawn

For each pair of terms, explain how the meanings of the terms differ.

2 *embryo* and *fetus*

3 *testes* and *ovaries*

4 *uterus* and *vagina*

5 *fertilization* and *implantation*

6 *umbilical* cord and *placenta*

Understanding Concepts

Multiple Choice

7 Tissues and organs develop as an embryo becomes a fetus. Humans grow in size as they become adults. How are cells responsible for the growth that humans experience as they become adults?
a. through cell division
b. through cell expansion
c. through cell death
d. through cell contraction

8 All of the following are sexually transmitted diseases EXCEPT
a. chlamydia.
b. AIDS.
c. infertility.
d. genital herpes.

9 The formation of identical twins occurs when
a. a fertilized egg splits in two.
b. two separate eggs are fertilized.
c. implantation occurs.
d. menstruation occurs.

10 Which of the following is a function of the reproductive system?
a. to produce all of the body's hormones
b. to regulate body temperature
c. to make hormones that fight disease
d. to regulate the development of male and female characteristics

Short Answer

11 **Identifying** Which human reproductive organs produce sperm? Which produce eggs?

12 **Describing** Explain how the fetus gets oxygen and nutrients and how the fetus gets rid of wastes.

13 **Summarizing** What are four stages of human life after birth? Describe each stage.

14 **Listing** Name and describe three problems that can affect the human reproductive system.

15 **Modeling** Draw a diagram showing the structures of the male and female reproductive systems. Label each structure, and explain how each structure contributes to fertilization and implantation.

16 **Describing** When do cells begin to differentiate in a developing human?

Writing Skills

17 **Writing from Research** You have been asked to research the effects of vitamins on the growth and development of a human fetus. Develop a thesis for your research project. Then, briefly describe your project.

Critical Thinking

18 Concept Mapping Use the following terms to create a concept map: *testes, penis, ovary, uterus, vagina, embryo, placenta, reproductive organs,* and *umbilical cord.*

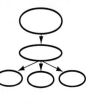

19 Applying Concepts How do parents contribute genetic material to their offspring?

20 Making Inferences The birth of twins is the most common type of multiple birth—30 sets of twins are born for every 1,000 births. But the birth of quintuplets is very rare—1 set of quintuplets is born in about 53,000 births. Why might multiple births in which a large number of babies are born be less common than multiple births in which a small number of babies are born?

21 Drawing Conclusions Menstruation is affected by a hormone called *estrogen.* A woman who produces little estrogen may not have a menstrual cycle. In turn, the production of estrogen is affected by body fat. A woman who has little body fat usually produces less estrogen. What might happen to the menstrual cycle of a female athlete who exercises a lot?

INTERPRETING GRAPHICS Use the image below to answer the next question.

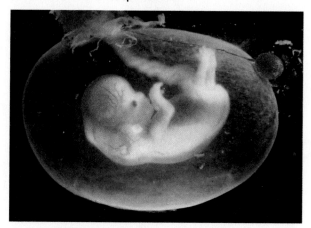

22 Identifying Relationships What is the name and function of the cord that connects the fetus to its mother?

INTERPRETING GRAPHICS The following graph shows the cycles of the female hormone estrogen and the male hormone testosterone. The blue line shows the estrogen level in a female over the 28 days of her menstrual cycle. The red line shows the testosterone level in a male over the same time period. Use the graph below to answer the next four questions.

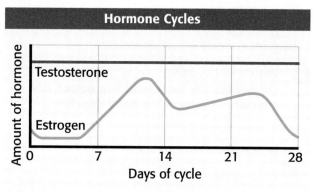

23 Evaluating Data Over the 28 days, how do the day-to-day levels of testosterone differ from the day-to-day levels of estrogen?

24 Applying Concepts Compare the estrogen cycle to a woman's menstrual cycle. How are they related?

25 Making Inferences Why might the level of testosterone stay the same?

26 Making Inferences Do you think that the above estrogen cycle would change in a pregnant woman? Explain your answer.

Math Skills

27 Making Calculations Identical twin births happen once in 100 births. How many sets of identical twins might you expect at a school that has 2,700 students?

Challenge

28 Identifying Relationships How is the placenta specialized for its function?

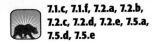
REVIEWING ACADEMIC VOCABULARY

1 In the sentence "The placenta performs an important function for the fetus," what does the word *function* mean?

  A position

  B organ

  C purpose

  D result

2 Which of the following words best completes the sentence: The uterus is a special ___ in which a baby develops.

  A structure

  B system

  C organism

  D method

3 Which of the following words is the closest in meaning to the word *generate*?

  A explain

  B produce

  C identify

  D accomplish

4 Which of the following sets of words best completes the following sentence:
In ___ , offspring receive traits from both of their parents.

  A asexual reproduction

  B sexual function

  C sexual selection

  D sexual reproduction

5 What is the noun used to describe "the process in which cells change to carry out specialized functions"?

  A production

  B fabrication

  C distinction

  D differentiation

REVIEWING CONCEPTS

6 Which of the following best describes the function of the placenta?

  A The placenta provides oxygen and nutrients to the fetus.

  B The placenta is the organ that holds the fetus as it grows and develops.

  C The placenta is a thin membrane that fills with fluid to protect the fetus.

  D The placenta sends nutrients to the mother's body.

7 Which of the following can cause a woman to become pregnant?

  A A man ejaculates sperm in or near the woman's vagina.

  B The woman experiences a menstrual cycle.

  C A man ejaculates his sperm during puberty.

  D The woman ovulates until middle age.

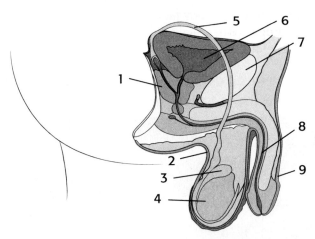

8 In the diagram above, which number labels the structure that produces sperm?

  A 2

  B 4

  C 5

  D 9

9 In humans, what has to occur for an egg to be considered fertilized?

A A sperm has to penetrate the outer coating of the egg.

B An egg has to be present when sperm enter the woman.

C A few hundred sperm have to cover the outer coating of the egg.

D The sperm nucleus and the egg nucleus must join.

10 Why does a child usually have physical characteristics from both parents?

A The child inherited genes from each parent.

B The child's genes are mixed while the child is in the uterus.

C The child's cells differentiate during development.

D The environment of the child is the same as that of the parents.

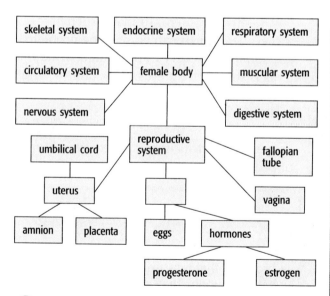

11 Which of the following best fits into the blank space in the concept map above?

A ovary

B scrotum

C zygote

D menstruation

REVIEWING PRIOR LEARNING

12 In a human cell, where are chromosomes located?

A nucleus

B vacuole

C chloroplasts

D mitochondria

13 Which of the following is the genetic material of all organisms?

A deoxyribonucleic acid

B endoplasmic reticulum

C adenosine triphosphate

D restriction endonuclease

14 What determines an inherited trait?

A Traits are inherited as a child grows older.

B Cell differentiation determines inherited traits.

C Inherited traits are determined by one or more genes.

D A child's parents decide what traits will be inherited.

15 Which of these describes a reproduction method of a sexual organism?

A forming a tuber

B fusing of sex cells from two parents

C producing runners

D division through binary fission

Science in Action

Doctors operated on a fetus, whose hand is visible in this photo, to correct spina bifida.

Science Discoveries

Embryonic Stem Cell Research

In the future, you may be able to buy new tissue for diseased or injured organs. Embryonic stem cells are undifferentiated cells from human embryos. In the right conditions, these cells are able to differentiate into any kind of human cell. Researchers at the University of California in San Francisco are working to develop regenerative medicine using embryonic stem cells. Regenerative medicine involves getting undifferentiated stem cells to differentiate into the type of cells that make the diseased tissues or organs in a patient. If USC researchers succeed, doctors will in the future be able to treat patients who have conditions such as Parkinson's disease and heart disease.

Language Arts ACTiViTY

Embryonic stem cell research is controversial. Research the advantages and disadvantages of this kind of research. On a poster, compare the benefits and drawbacks of embryonic stem cell research.

Science, Technology, and Society

Fetal Surgery

Sometimes, a developing fetus has a serious medical problem. In many such cases, surgery after birth can correct the problem. But some problems can be treated while the fetus is still in the uterus. For example, fetal surgery may be used to correct spina bifida (a disease in which part of the spinal cord is exposed because the backbone doesn't form properly). Doctors now can fix several types of problems before a baby is born.

Social Studies ACTiViTY

Research the causes of spina bifida. Write a brochure that tells expectant mothers what precautions they can take to prevent spina bifida.

Reva Curry

Diagnostic Medical Sonographer Sounds are everywhere in our world. But only some of those sounds—such as your favorite music playing on the stereo or the dog barking next door—are sounds that we can hear. There are sound waves whose frequency is too high for us to hear. These high-pitched sounds are called *ultrasound*. Some animals, such as bats, use ultrasound to hunt and to avoid midair collisions.

Humans use ultrasound, too. Ultrasound machines can peer inside the human body to look at hearts, blood vessels, and fetuses. Diagnostic medical sonographers are people who use sonography equipment to diagnose medical problems. Diagnostic medical sonographers also use sonography to follow the growth and development of a fetus while the fetus is still in the uterus. One of the leading professionals in the field of diagnostic medical sonography is Dr. Reva Curry. Dr. Curry spent many years as a sonographer. Her primary job was to use high-tech ultrasound instruments to create images of parts of the body and interpret the images for other professionals. Today, Dr. Curry works with students as the dean of a community college.

Math ACTiViTY

At 20°C, the speed of sound in water is 1,482 m/s, and the speed of sound in steel is 5,200 m/s. How long would it take a sound to travel 815.1 m in water? In the same amount of time, how far would a sound travel in a steel beam? Record your work in your **Science Journal**.

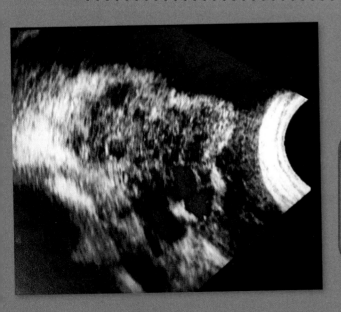

Internet Resources

- To learn more about careers in science, visit **www.scilinks.org** and enter the SciLinks code HY70225.

- To learn more about these Science in Action topics, visit **go.hrw.com** and type in the keyword HY7BD5F.

- Check out articles related to this chapter by visiting **go.hrw.com**. Just type in the keyword HY7BD5C.

Appendix

Ask a Question

Contents

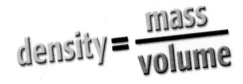

$$density = \frac{mass}{volume}$$

Study Skills: Making and Using FoldNotes

Have you ever tried to study for a test or quiz but didn't know where to start? Or have you read a chapter and found that you can remember only a few ideas? Well, FoldNotes are a fun and exciting way to help you learn and remember the ideas you encounter as you learn science!

FoldNotes are tools that you can use to organize concepts. One FoldNote focuses on a few main concepts. FoldNotes help you learn and remember how the concepts fit together. FoldNotes can help you see the "big picture." Below, you will find instructions for building 10 different FoldNotes.

Pyramid

A pyramid provides a unique way for taking notes. The three sides of the pyramid can summarize information into three categories. Use the pyramid as a tool for studying information in a chapter.

1. Place a **sheet of paper** in front of you. Fold the lower left-hand corner of the paper diagonally to the opposite edge of the paper.

2. Cut off the tab of paper created by the fold (at the top).

3. Open the paper so that it is a square. Fold the lower right-hand corner of the paper diagonally to the opposite corner to form a triangle.

4. Open the paper. The creases of the two folds will have created an X.

5. Using **scissors,** cut along one of the creases. Start from any corner, and stop at the center point to create two flaps. Use **tape** or **glue** to attach one of the flaps on top of the other flap.

Double-Door Fold

A double-door fold is useful when you want to compare the characteristics of two topics. The double-door fold can organize characteristics of the two topics side by side under the flaps. Similarities and differences between the two topics can then be easily identified.

1. Fold a **sheet of paper** in half from the top to the bottom. Then, unfold the paper.

2. Fold the top and bottom edges of the paper to the center crease.

Booklet

A booklet is a useful tool for taking notes as you read a chapter. Each page of the booklet can contain a main topic from the chapter. Write details of each main topic on the appropriate page to create an outline of the chapter.

1. Fold a **sheet of paper** in half from left to right. Then, unfold the paper.

2. Fold the sheet of paper in half again from the top to the bottom. Then, unfold the paper.

3. Refold the sheet of paper in half from left to right.

4. Fold the top and bottom edges to the center crease.

5. Completely unfold the paper.

6. Refold the paper from top to bottom.

7. Using **scissors,** cut a slit along the center crease of the sheet from the folded edge to the creases made in step 4. Do not cut the entire sheet in half.

8. Fold the sheet of paper in half from left to right. While holding the bottom and top edges of the paper, push the bottom and top edges together so that the center collapses at the center slit. Fold the four flaps to form a four-page book.

Layered Book

A layered book is a useful tool for taking notes as you read a chapter. The four flaps of the layered book can summarize information into four categories. Write details of each category on the appropriate flap to create a summary of the chapter.

1. Lay one **sheet of paper** on top of **another sheet.** Slide the top sheet up so that 2 cm of the bottom sheet is showing.

2. Holding the two sheets together, fold down the top of the two sheets so that you see four 2 cm tabs along the bottom.

3. Using a stapler, staple the top of the FoldNote.

Key-Term Fold

A key-term fold is useful for studying definitions of key terms in a chapter. Each tab can contain a key term on one side and its definition on the other. Use the key-term fold to quiz yourself on the definitions of the key terms in a chapter.

1. Fold a **sheet of lined notebook paper** in half from left to right.

2. Using **scissors,** cut along every third line from the right edge of the paper to the center fold to make tabs.

Four-Corner Fold

A four-corner fold is useful when you want to compare the characteristics of four topics. The four-corner fold can organize the characteristics of the four topics side by side under the flaps. Similarities and differences between the four topics can then be easily identified.

1. Fold a **sheet of paper** in half from left to right. Then, unfold the paper.

2. Fold each side of the paper to the crease in the center of the paper.

3. Fold the paper in half from the top to the bottom. Then, unfold the paper.

4. Using **scissors,** cut the top flap creases made in step 3 to form four flaps.

Three-Panel Flip Chart

A three-panel flip chart is useful when you want to compare the characteristics of three topics. The three-panel flip chart can organize the characteristics of the three topics side by side under the flaps. Similarities and differences between the three topics can then be easily identified.

1. Fold a **piece of paper** in half from the top to the bottom.

2. Fold the paper in thirds from side to side. Then, unfold the paper so that you can see the three sections.

3. From the top of the paper, cut along each of the vertical fold lines to the fold in the middle of the paper. You will now have three flaps.

Table Fold

A table fold is a useful tool for comparing the characteristics of two or three topics. In a table fold, all topics are described in terms of the same characteristics so that you can easily make a thorough comparison.

1. Fold a **piece of paper** in half from the top to the bottom. Then, fold the paper in half again.

2. Fold the paper in thirds from side to side.

3. Unfold the paper completely. Carefully trace the fold lines by using a pen or pencil.

Two-Panel Flip Chart

A two-panel flip chart is useful when you want to compare the characteristics of two topics. The two-panel flip chart can organize the characteristics of the two topics side by side under the flaps. Similarities and differences between the two topics can then be easily identified.

1. Fold a **piece of paper** in half from the top to the bottom.

2. Fold the paper in half from side to side. Then, unfold the paper so that you can see the two sections.

3. From the top of the paper, cut along the vertical fold line to the fold in the middle of the paper. You will now have two flaps.

Tri-Fold

A tri-fold is a useful tool that helps you track your progress. By organizing the chapter topic into what you know, what you want to know, and what you learn, you can see how much you have learned after reading a chapter.

1. Fold a piece a paper in thirds from the top to the bottom.

2. Unfold the paper so that you can see the three sections. Then, turn the paper sideways so that the three sections form vertical columns.

3. Trace the fold lines by using a **pen** or **pencil**. Label the columns "Know," "Want," and "Learn."

Study Skills: Making and Using Graphic Organizers

Have you ever wished that you could "draw out" the many concepts you learn in your science class? Sometimes, being able to see how concepts are related really helps you remember what you've learned. Graphic Organizers do just that! They give you a way to draw or map out concepts.

All you need to make a Graphic Organizer is a piece of paper and a pencil. Below you will find instructions for nine different Graphic Organizers designed to help you organize the concepts you'll learn in this book.

Concept Map

How to Make a Concept Map

1. Identify main ideas from the text, and write the ideas as short phrases or single words.

2. Select a main concept. Place this concept at the top or center of a piece of paper.

3. Place other ideas under or around the main concept based on their relationship to the main concept. Draw a circle around each idea.

4. Draw lines between the concepts, and add linking words to connect the ideas.

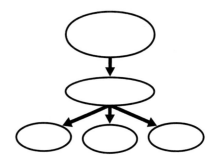

When to Use a Concept Map

Concept maps are useful when you are trying to identify how several ideas are connected to a main concept. Concept maps may be based on vocabulary terms or on main topics from the text. As you read about science, look for terms that can be organized in a concept map.

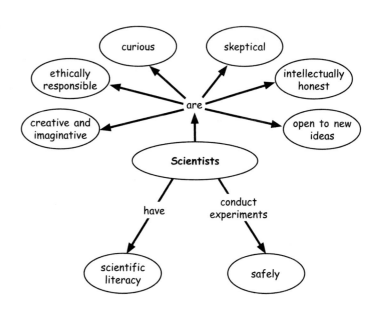

Cause-and-Effect Map

How to Make a Cause-and-Effect Map

1. Draw a box, and write a cause in the box. You can have as many cause boxes as you want. The diagram shown here is one example of a cause-and-effect map.

2. Draw another box to the right of the cause box to represent an effect. You can have as many effect boxes as you want. Draw arrows from each cause box to the appropriate effect boxes.

3. In the cause boxes, explain the process that makes up the cause. In the effect boxes, write a description of the effect or details about the effect.

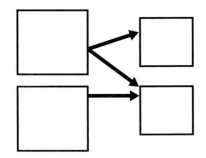

When to Use a Cause-and-Effect Map

A cause-and-effect map is a useful tool for illustrating a specific type of scientific process. Use a cause-and-effect map when you want to describe how, when, or why one event causes another event. As you read, look for events that are either causes or results of other events, and draw a cause-and-effect map that shows the relationships between the events.

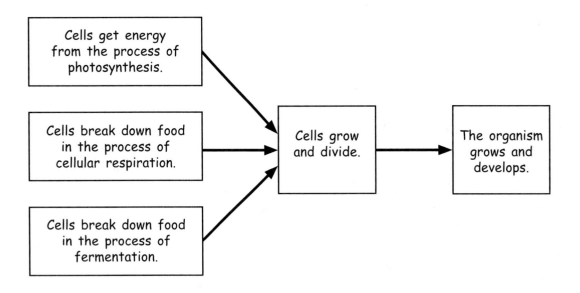

Appendix

Spider Map

How to Make a Spider Map

1. Draw a diagram like the one shown here. In the circle, write the main topic.

2. From the circle, draw legs to represent the main ideas or characteristics of the topic. Draw as many legs as you want to draw. Write an idea or characteristic along each leg.

3. From each leg, draw horizontal lines. As you read the chapter, write details about each idea on the idea's horizontal lines. To add more details, make the legs longer and add more horizontal lines.

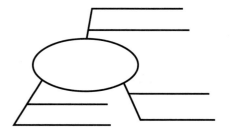

When to Use a Spider Map

A spider map is an effective tool for classifying the details of a specific topic in science. A spider map divides a topic into ideas and details. As you read about a topic, look for the main ideas or characteristics of the topic. Within each idea, look for details. Use a spider map to organize the ideas and details of each topic.

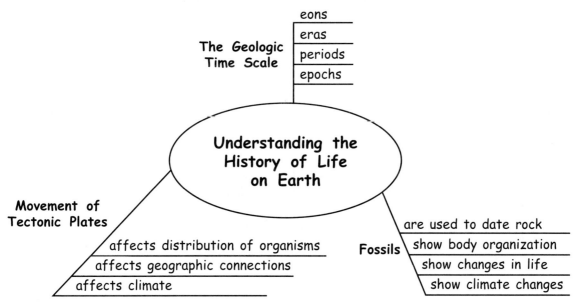

Comparison Table

How to Make a Comparison Table

1. Draw a table like the one shown here. Draw as many columns and rows as you want to draw.

2. In the top row, write the topics that you want to compare.

3. In the left column, write the general characteristics that you want to compare. As you read the chapter, fill in the characteristics for each topic in the appropriate boxes.

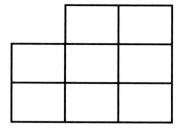

When to Use a Comparison Table

A comparison table is useful when you want to compare the characteristics of two or more topics in science. Organizing information in a table helps you compare several topics at one time. In a table, all topics are described in terms of the same list of characteristics, which helps you make a thorough comparison. As you read, look for topics whose characteristics you may want to compare in a table.

	Skeletal System	**Muscular System**
Parts	• bones, cartilage, connective tissue	• muscles
Structure	• Bone is made of connective tissue and minerals. • Compact bone is rigid and dense bone tissue. • Spongy bone is bone tissue that has open spaces.	• Smooth muscle is in the digestive tract and in the walls of blood vessels. • Cardiac muscle is in the heart. • Skeletal muscle is attached to bones.
Function	• Some bones protect organs. • Bones store minerals that help nerves and muscles function. • Bones provide the body with structure. • Some bones make blood cells.	• Muscles let a person move. • Voluntary action is action that can be controlled. (skeletal) • Involuntary action is action that cannot be controlled. (smooth, cardiac, or skeletal) • Muscles often work in pairs.

Venn Diagram

How to Make a Venn Diagram

1. Draw a diagram like the one shown here. Draw one circle for each topic. Make sure that each circle partially overlaps the other circles.

2. In each circle, write a topic that you want to compare with the topics in the other circles.

3. In the areas of the diagram where circles overlap, write the characteristics that the topics in the overlapping circles share.

4. In the areas of the diagram where circles do not overlap, write the characteristics that are unique to the topic of the particular circle.

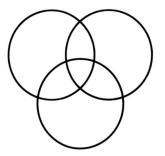

When to Use a Venn Diagram

A Venn diagram is a useful tool for comparing two or three topics in science. A Venn diagram shows which characteristics the topics share and which characteristics are unique to each topic. Venn diagrams are ideal when you want to illustrate relationships in a pair or small group of topics. As you read, look for topics that have both shared and unique characteristics, and draw a Venn diagram that shows how the topics are related.

Seed Plants
- produce seeds
- gametophytes are dependent on sporophyte
- do not need water to reproduce sexually
- grouped into gymnosperms and angiosperms

- carry out photosynthesis
- reproduce sexually and asexually
- have a two-stage lifecycle
- have qualities that are useful for humans

Seedless Plants
- need water to reproduce sexually
- gametophytes live independently of sporophyte
- divided into two groups: vascular and nonvascular

Process Chart

How to Make a Process Chart

1. Draw a box. In the box, write the first step of a process, chain of events, or cycle.

2. Under the box, draw another box, and draw an arrow to connect the two boxes. In the second box, write the next step of the process or the next event in the timeline.

3. Continue adding boxes until each step of the process, chain of events, or cycle is written in a box. For cycles only, draw an arrow to connect the last box and the first box.

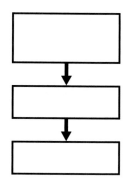

When to Use a Process Chart

Science is full of processes. A process chart shows the steps that a process takes to get from one point to another point. Timelines, chains of events, and cycles are examples of the kinds of information that can be organized well in a process chart. As you read, look for information that is described in steps or in a sequence, and draw a process chart that shows the progression of the steps or sequence.

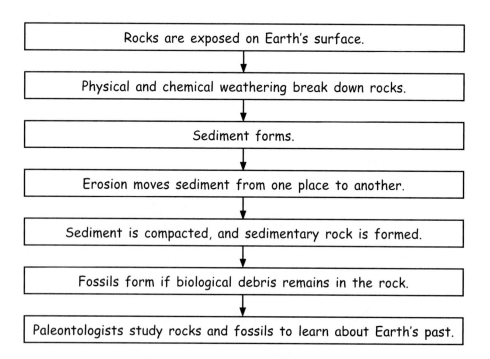

Idea Wheel

How to Make an Idea Wheel

1. Draw a circle. Draw a larger circle around the first circle. Divide the ring between the circles into sections by drawing lines from one circle to the other across the ring. Divide the ring into as many sections as you want.

2. Write a main idea or topic in the smaller circle. Label each section in the ring with a category or characteristic of the main idea.

3. In each section of the ring, include details that are unique to the topic.

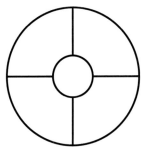

When to Use an Idea Wheel

An idea wheel is an effective type of visual organization in which ideas in science can be divided into categories or parts. It is also a useful way to illustrate characteristics of a main idea or topic. As you read, look for topics that are divided into ideas or categories that can be organized around an idea wheel.

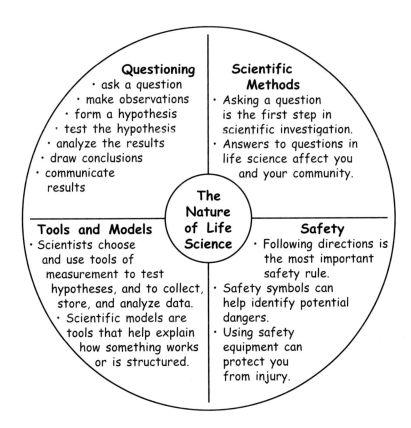

Combination Notes

How to Make Combination Notes

1. Draw a table like the one shown here. Draw the columns to be as long as you want them to be.

2. Write the topic of your notes in the section at the top of the table.

3. In the left column, write important phrases or sentences about the topic. In the right column, draw diagrams or pictures that illustrate the information in the left column.

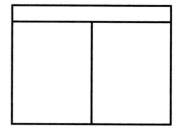

When to Use Combination Notes

Combination notes let you express scientific information in words and pictures at the same time. Use combination notes to express information that a picture could help explain. The picture could be a diagram, a sketch, or another useful visual representation of the written information in your notes.

Heredity	
• Gregor Mendel helped establish the basics of modern genetics. • Mendel discovered that an offspring inherits two **alleles** for each gene, one allele from each parent. • Through **meiosis** and sexual reproduction, genetic material combines. • **Punnett squares** are used to predict the possible **genotypes** for a particular combination of genes.	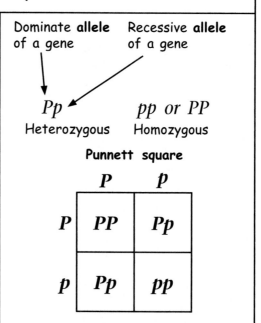

Pyramid Chart

How to Make a Pyramid Chart

1. Draw a triangle that is divided into sections like the one shown here. Draw as many sections as you need to draw.

2. Draw a box to the left of the triangle, as shown in the example. Write the topic of your pyramid chart in the box.

3. In each section of your triangle, write information about the topic in the appropriate level of the pyramid.

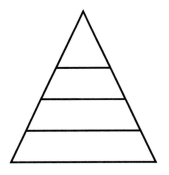

When to Use a Pyramid Chart

A pyramid chart is used to organize information in a hierarchy of importance, detail, or magnitude. As the shape of the pyramid suggests, the pyramid's bottom level contains information that is largest in terms of magnitude and broadest, or least specific, in terms of detail. As you read about science, look for information that you can organize into a hierarchy.

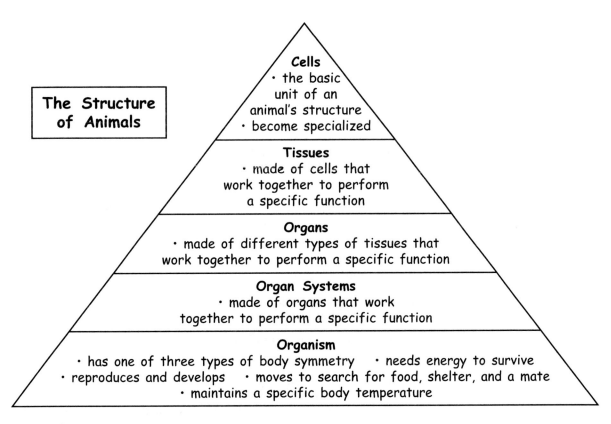

The Structure of Animals

Cells
- the basic unit of an animal's structure
- become specialized

Tissues
- made of cells that work together to perform a specific function

Organs
- made of different types of tissues that work together to perform a specific function

Organ Systems
- made of organs that work together to perform a specific function

Organism
- has one of three types of body symmetry • needs energy to survive
- reproduces and develops   • moves to search for food, shelter, and a mate
- maintains a specific body temperature

Understanding Word Parts

Many scientific words are made up of parts based on Greek and Latin languages. Understanding the meaning of the parts will help you understand the meaning of the scientific words. The table below provides a definition and an example of prefixes, roots, and suffixes that you will see in this textbook.

Prefix	Definition	Example
a-	not	asexual reproduction: reproduction that does not involve the union of sex cells
aero-	air	aerobic: describes a process that requires oxygen, usually from air
amphi-	both	amphibian: an animal that lives both in water and on land
bio-	life	biology: the science of life
di-	apart	divergent boundary: the type of tectonic plate boundary in which tectonic plates move apart
dif-	apart; in different directions	differentiation: the process in which the structure and function of the parts of an organism change, or develop in different directions, or pathways, to enable specialization of those parts
ecto-	outside	ectotherm: an organism that needs sources of heat outside itself
endo-	within	endoskeleton: a skeleton that forms within the body and is made of bone and cartilage
ev-	space of time	evolution: the process in which inherited characteristics within a population change over time (measured in generations) such that new species sometimes arise
exo-	outside; external	exoskeleton: a hard, external, supporting structure
meta-	changed	metamorphosis: a process in the life cycle of many animals during which a rapid change from the immature organism to the adult takes place
non-	not	nonvascular plant: a plant that does not have vascular tissue, or specialized conducting tissues, true roots, stems, and leaves
peri-	around; near	peripheral nervous system: all of the parts of the nervous system except for the brain and the spinal cord; the parts of the nervous system around the brain and spinal cord
super-	above; over	superposition: a principle that states that younger rocks lie above older rocks if the layers have not been disturbed
sym-	together	symbiosis: a relationship in which two different organisms live together
un-	not; the lack of	unconformity: a break in the geologic record created when rock layers are eroded or when sediment is not deposited for a long period of time; a gap in the rock record that does not show a continuous record of geologic time
trans-	across; through	transmission: the passing of light or another form of energy through matter

Appendix

Word root	Definition	Example
chlor	green	chloroplast: an organelle found in plant and algae cells where photosynthesis occurs; contains green pigment
dipl	twice, double	diploid: a cell that contains two haploid sets of chromosomes
funct	to perform	function: the special, normal, or proper performance of an organ
gymn	naked	gymnosperm: a woody, vascular seed plant whose seeds are "naked," or not enclosed by an ovary or fruit
lip	fat	lipid: a fat molecule or a molecule that has similar properties; examples include oils, waxes, and steroids
micro	small	microscope: an instrument that produces an enlarged image of a small object
mut	to change	mutation: a change in the nucleotide-base sequence of a gene or DNA molecule
paleo	old	paleontology: the scientific study of fossils
phot	light	photosynthesis: the process by which plants, algae, and some bacteria use sunlight, carbon dioxide, and water to make food
press	to press	blood pressure: the force of blood pressing on the walls of arteries
sed	to sit; to settle	sediment: fragments of organic or inorganic material that are transported and deposited by wind, water, or ice and that settle, or accumulate, in layers on Earth's surface
sperm	seed	angiosperm: a flowering plant that produces seeds within a fruit
struct	to build; to arrange	structure: the arrangement of parts in an organism
tax	to arrange	taxonomy: the science of describing, naming, and classifying organisms; a logical arrangement of different kinds of organisms
thesis	proposition	hypothesis: a testable idea or explanation that leads to scientific investigation
zo	pertaining to animals	Cenozoic: the current geologic era; also called the *Age of Mammals*

Suffix	Definition	Example
-emia	condition of the blood	leukemia: a progressive cancer of the blood-forming organs
-ism	a belief in	catastrophism: a principle that states that geologic change occurs suddenly; the belief that geologic change happens suddenly
-logy	the science of	biology: the scientific study of life
-nomy	the science of	taxonomy: the science of describing, naming, and classifying organisms
-ole	little	bronchiole: one of the small branches of the bronchi
-scope	an instrument for seeing or observing	microscope: an instrument that produces an enlarged image of a small object

Common Words with Multiple Meanings

Scientific words may have common meanings that you already know. Understanding the difference between common meanings and scientific meanings will help you develop a scientific vocabulary. The table below provides common and scientific meanings for words that you will see in this textbook.

Word	Common meaning	Scientific meaning
area	a region (for example, a rural area)	a measure of the size of a surface or a region
cell	a small, confining room	the smallest structural and functional unit of all living organisms
class	a group of students who are taught together at regular meetings	a taxonomic category below the phylum and above the order
condensation	the droplets of liquid on the outside of a glass or window	the change of state from a gas to a liquid
consumer	someone who purchases goods or services	an organism that eats other organisms or organic matter
date	an engagement to go out socially	to measure the age of an event or object
daughter	one's female child	the offspring of cell division; not dependent on gender
egg	a thin-shelled product from a bird used in cooking	a sex cell produced by a female
family	all of the members of a household	the taxonomic category below the order and above the genus
fault	responsibility for a mistake	a break in a body of rock along which one block slides relative to another
gas	short for *gasoline*; a liquid fuel used by vehicles, such as cars and buses	a form of matter that does not have a definite volume or shape
host	to serve as the entertainer or receiver of guests	an organism from which a parasite takes food or shelter
instrument	a device used for making music (for example, a trumpet)	a piece of equipment used during experimentation (for example, a scalpel)
kingdom	a region ruled by a king or queen	the taxonomic category below the domain and above the phylum
labor	to work	the process by which the fetus and the placenta come out of the uterus
law	a rule of conduct established by the government	a descriptive statement or equation that reliably predicts events under certain conditions

Word	Common meaning	Scientific meaning
legend	a romanticized story or myth	a list of map symbols and their meanings
mass	a quantity of material that has an unspecified shape	a measure of the amount of matter in an object
matter	a subject of concern or topic of discussion	anything that has mass and takes up space
medium	an intermediate measurement between small and large	a physical environment in which phenomena occur
model	a person who poses (for example, a fashion model)	a pattern, plan, representation, or description designed to show the structure or workings of an object, system, or concept
order	a command	the taxonomic category below the class and above the family
organ	a musical instrument similar to a piano	a collection of tissues that carry out a specialized function of the body
organic	describes an organism or object that is produced without the use of synthetic drugs, fertilizers, or hormones	describes a material that is derived from living organisms and that contains carbon
product	something available for sale (for example, a computer product)	a substance that forms in a chemical reaction
reaction	a response to a stimulus	the process by which one or more substances change to produce one or more different substances
resolution	an expression of intent (for example, a New Year's resolution)	in microscopes, the ability to form images in fine detail
scale	a machine used to measure weight	the relationship between the measurements on a model, map, or diagram and the actual measurement or distance
slide	a piece of playground equipment	a thin piece of glass on which a specimen is placed for viewing with a microscope
stereo	a machine that plays music	three-dimensional
table	a piece of furniture that has a flat, horizontal surface	an orderly arrangement of data
theory	an assumption based on limited knowledge	a system of ideas that explains many related observations and is supported by a large body of evidence acquired through scientific investigation
tissue	a soft, absorbent piece of paper	a group of similar cells that perform a common function
volume	a measure of how loud a sound is	a measure of the size of a body or region in three-dimensional space

Math Refresher

Science requires an understanding of many math concepts. The following pages will help you review some important math skills.

Averages

An **average,** or **mean,** simplifies a set of numbers into a single number that *approximates* the value of the set.

> **Example:** Find the average of the following set of numbers: 5, 4, 7, and 8.

Step 1: Find the sum.
$$5 + 4 + 7 + 8 = 24$$

Step 2: Divide the sum by the number of numbers in your set. Because there are four numbers in this example, divide the sum by 4.
$$\frac{24}{4} = 6$$

The average, or mean, is **6.**

Ratios

A **ratio** is a comparison between numbers, and it is usually written as a fraction.

> **Example:** Find the ratio of thermometers to students if you have 36 thermometers and 48 students in your class.

Step 1: Make the ratio.
$$\frac{36 \text{ thermometers}}{48 \text{ students}}$$

Step 2: Reduce the fraction to its simplest form.
$$\frac{36}{48} = \frac{36 \div 12}{48 \div 12} = \frac{3}{4}$$

The ratio of thermometers to students is **3 to 4,** or $\frac{3}{4}$. The ratio may also be written in the form 3:4.

Proportions

A **proportion** is an equation that states that two ratios are equal.
$$\frac{3}{1} = \frac{12}{4}$$

To solve a proportion, first multiply across the equal sign. This is called *cross-multiplication*. If you know three of the quantities in a proportion, you can use cross-multiplication to find the fourth.

> **Example:** Imagine that you are making a scale model of the solar system for your science project. The diameter of Jupiter is 11.2 times the diameter of Earth. If you are using a plastic-foam ball that has a diameter of 2 cm to represent Earth, what must the diameter of the ball representing Jupiter be? $\frac{11.2}{1} = \frac{x}{2 \text{ cm}}$

Step 1: Cross-multiply.
$$\frac{11.2}{1} \diagup\!\!\!\!\diagdown \frac{x}{2}$$
$$11.2 \times 2 = x \times 1$$

Step 2: Multiply.
$$22.4 = x \times 1$$

Step 3: Isolate the variable by dividing both sides by 1.
$$x = \frac{22.4}{1}$$
$$x = 22.4 \text{ cm}$$

You will need to use a ball that has a diameter of **22.4** cm to represent Jupiter.

Percentages

A **percentage** is a ratio of a given number to 100.

> **Example:** What is 85% of 40?

Step 1: Rewrite the percentage by moving the decimal point two places to the left.

$$0.\overset{\frown}{85}$$

Step 2: Multiply the decimal by the number that you are calculating the percentage of.

$$0.85 \times 40 = 34$$

85% of 40 is **34.**

Decimals

To **add** or **subtract decimals,** line up the digits vertically so that the decimal points line up. Then, add or subtract the columns from right to left. Carry or borrow numbers as necessary.

> **Example:** Add the following numbers: 3.1415 and 2.96.

Step 1: Line up the digits vertically so that the decimal points line up.

$$\begin{array}{r} 3.1415 \\ + 2.96 \\ \hline \end{array}$$

Step 2: Add the columns from right to left, and carry when necessary.

$$\begin{array}{r} \overset{1\ \ 1}{3.1415} \\ + 2.96 \\ \hline 6.1015 \end{array}$$

The sum is **6.1015.**

Fractions

Numbers tell you how many; **fractions** tell you *how much of a whole.*

> **Example:** Your class has 24 plants. Your teacher instructs you to put 5 plants in a shady spot. What fraction of the plants in your class will you put in a shady spot?

Step 1: In the denominator, write the total number of parts in the whole.

$$\frac{?}{24}$$

Step 2: In the numerator, write the number of parts of the whole that are being considered.

$$\frac{5}{24}$$

So, $\frac{5}{24}$ of the plants will be in the shade.

Reducing Fractions

It is usually best to express a fraction in its simplest form. Expressing a fraction in its simplest form is called *reducing* a fraction.

> **Example:** Reduce the fraction $\frac{30}{45}$ to its simplest form.

Step 1: Find the largest whole number that will divide evenly into both the numerator and denominator. This number is called the *greatest common factor* (GCF).

Factors of the numerator 30:

$$1, 2, 3, 5, 6, 10, \mathbf{15,} 30$$

Factors of the denominator 45:

$$1, 3, 5, 9, \mathbf{15,} 45$$

Step 2: Divide both the numerator and the denominator by the GCF, which in this case is 15.

$$\frac{30}{45} = \frac{30 \div 15}{45 \div 15} = \frac{2}{3}$$

Thus, $\frac{30}{45}$ reduced to its simplest form is $\frac{2}{3}$.

Adding and Subtracting Fractions

To **add** or **subtract fractions** that have the **same denominator,** simply add or subtract the numerators.

> **Examples:**
>
> $$\frac{3}{5} + \frac{1}{5} = ? \quad \text{and} \quad \frac{3}{4} - \frac{1}{4} = ?$$

Step 1: Add or subtract the numerators.

$$\frac{3}{5} + \frac{1}{5} = \frac{4}{} \quad \text{and} \quad \frac{3}{4} - \frac{1}{4} = \frac{2}{}$$

Step 2: Write the sum or difference over the denominator.

$$\frac{3}{5} + \frac{1}{5} = \frac{4}{5} \quad \text{and} \quad \frac{3}{4} - \frac{1}{4} = \frac{2}{4}$$

Step 3: If necessary, reduce the fraction to its simplest form.

$$\frac{4}{5} \text{ cannot be reduced, and } \frac{2}{4} = \frac{1}{2}.$$

To **add** or **subtract fractions** that have **different denominators,** first find the least common denominator (LCD).

> **Examples:**
>
> $$\frac{1}{2} + \frac{1}{6} = ? \quad \text{and} \quad \frac{3}{4} - \frac{2}{3} = ?$$

Step 1: Write the equivalent fractions that have a common denominator.

$$\frac{3}{6} + \frac{1}{6} = ? \quad \text{and} \quad \frac{9}{12} - \frac{8}{12} = ?$$

Step 2: Add or subtract the fractions.

$$\frac{3}{6} + \frac{1}{6} = \frac{4}{6} \quad \text{and} \quad \frac{9}{12} - \frac{8}{12} = \frac{1}{12}$$

Step 3: If necessary, reduce the fraction to its simplest form.

The fraction $\frac{4}{6} = \frac{2}{3}$, and $\frac{1}{12}$ cannot be reduced.

Multiplying Fractions

To **multiply fractions,** multiply the numerators and the denominators together, and then reduce the fraction to its simplest form.

> **Example:**
>
> $$\frac{5}{9} \times \frac{7}{10} = ?$$

Step 1: Multiply the numerators and denominators.

$$\frac{5}{9} \times \frac{7}{10} = \frac{5 \times 7}{9 \times 10} = \frac{35}{90}$$

Step 2: Reduce the fraction.

$$\frac{35}{90} = \frac{35 \div 5}{90 \div 5} = \frac{7}{18}$$

Dividing Fractions

To **divide fractions,** first rewrite the divisor (the number you divide by) upside down. This number is called the *reciprocal* of the divisor. Then multiply and reduce if necessary.

> **Example:**
>
> $$\frac{5}{8} \div \frac{3}{2} = ?$$

Step 1: Rewrite the divisor as its reciprocal.

$$\frac{3}{2} \rightarrow \frac{2}{3}$$

Step 2: Multiply the fractions.

$$\frac{5}{8} \times \frac{2}{3} = \frac{5 \times 2}{8 \times 3} = \frac{10}{24}$$

Step 3: Reduce the fraction.

$$\frac{10}{24} = \frac{10 \div 2}{24 \div 2} = \frac{5}{12}$$

Scientific Notation

Scientific notation is a short way of representing very large and very small numbers without writing all of the place-holding zeros.

Example: Write 653,000,000 in scientific notation.

Step 1: Write the number without the place-holding zeros.
653

Step 2: Place the decimal point after the first digit.
6.53

Step 3: Find the exponent by counting the number of places that you moved the decimal point.
6.53000000
The decimal point was moved eight places to the left. Therefore, the exponent of 10 is positive 8. If you had moved the decimal point to the right, the exponent would be negative.

Step 4: Write the number in scientific notation.
$$6.53 \times 10^8$$

Finding Area

Area is the number of square units needed to cover the surface of an object.

Formulas:
area of a square = side × side
area of a rectangle = length × width
area of a triangle = $\frac{1}{2}$ × base × height

Examples: Find the areas.

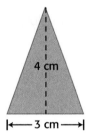

Triangle
area = $\frac{1}{2}$ × base × height
area = $\frac{1}{2}$ × 3 cm × 4 cm
*area = **6 cm²***

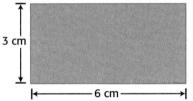

Rectangle
area = length × width
area = 6 cm × 3 cm
*area = **18 cm²***

Square
area = side × side
area = 3 cm × 3 cm
*area = **9 cm²***

Finding Volume

Volume is the amount of space that something occupies.

Formulas:
volume of a cube =
side × side × side

volume of a prism =
area of base × height

Examples:
Find the volume of the solids.

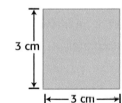

Cube
volume = side × side × side
volume = 4 cm × 4 cm × 4 cm
*volume = **64 cm³***

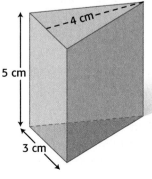

Prism
volume = area of base × height
volume = (area of triangle) × height
volume = ($\frac{1}{2}$ × 3 cm × 4 cm) × 5 cm
volume = 6 cm² × 5 cm
*volume = **30 cm³***

Making Graphs

Line Graphs

Line graphs are most often used to demonstrate continuous change. For example, Mr. Smith's students analyzed the population records for their hometown, Appleton, between 1900 and 2000. Examine the data at right.

Because the year and the population change, they are the *variables*. The population is determined by, or dependent on, the year. Therefore, the population is called the **dependent variable**, and the year is called the **independent variable.** Each set of data is called a **data pair.** To prepare a line graph, you must first organize data pairs into a table like the one at right.

Population of Appleton, 1900–2000	
Year	**Population**
1900	1,800
1920	2,500
1940	3,200
1960	3,900
1980	4,600
2000	5,300

How to Make a Line Graph

① Place the independent variable along the horizontal (*x*) axis. Place the dependent variable along the vertical (*y*) axis.

② Label the *x*-axis "Year" and the *y*-axis "Population." Look at your largest and smallest values for the population. For the *y*-axis, determine a scale that will provide enough space to show these values. You must use the same scale for the entire length of the axis. Next, find an appropriate scale for the *x*-axis.

③ Choose reasonable starting points for each axis.

④ Plot the data pairs as accurately as possible.

⑤ Choose a title that accurately represents the data.

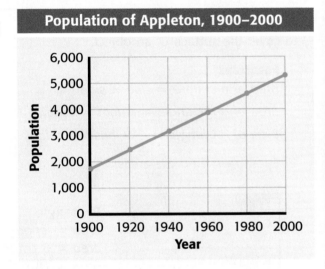

How to Determine Slope

Slope is the ratio of the change in the *y*-value to the change in the *x*-value, or "rise over run."

① Choose two points on the line graph. For example, the population of Appleton in 2000 was 5,300 people. Therefore, you can define point *a* as (2000, 5,300). In 1900, the population was 1,800 people. You can define point *b* as (1900, 1,800).

② Find the change in the *y*-value.
(*y* at point *a*) − (*y* at point *b*) =
5,300 people − 1,800 people =
3,500 people

③ Find the change in the *x*-value.
(*x* at point *a*) − (*x* at point *b*) =
2000 − 1900 = 100 years

④ Calculate the slope of the graph by dividing the change in *y* by the change in *x*.

$$slope = \frac{change\ in\ y}{change\ in\ x}$$

$$slope = \frac{3{,}500\ people}{100\ years}$$

$$slope = 35\ people\ per\ year$$

In this example, the population in Appleton increased by a fixed amount each year. The graph of these data is a straight line. Therefore, the relationship is **linear.** When the graph of a set of data is not a straight line, the relationship is **nonlinear.**

Appendix

Using Algebra to Determine Slope

The equation in step ④ may also be arranged to be

$$y = kx$$

where y represents the change in the y-value, k represents the slope, and x represents the change in the x-value.

$$slope = \frac{change\ in\ y}{change\ in\ x}$$

$$k = \frac{y}{x}$$

$$k \times x = \frac{y \times x}{x}$$

$$kx = y$$

Bar Graphs

Bar graphs are useful for comparing data values. For example, if you want to compare the amounts of several types of municipal solid waste, you might use a bar graph. The table at right contains the data used to make the bar graph below.

How to Make a Bar Graph

❶ Use an appropriate scale and a reasonable starting point for each axis.

❷ Label the axes, and plot the data.

❸ Choose a title that accurately represents the data.

| United States Municipal Solid Waste ||
Material	Percentage of total waste
Paper	38.1
Yard waste	12.1
Food waste	10.9
Plastics	10.5
Metals	7.8
Rubber, leather, and textiles	6.6
Glass	5.5
Wood	5.3
Other	3.2

Pie Graph

A pie graph shows how each group of data relates to all of the data. Each part of the circle forming the graph represents a category of the data. The entire circle represents all of the data. For example, a biologist studying a hardwood forest found that there were five types of trees. The data table at right summarizes the biologist's findings.

Hardwood Trees	
Type of tree	Number found
Oak	600
Maple	750
Beech	300
Birch	1,200
Hickory	150
Total	3,000

How to Make a Pie Graph

1 To make a pie graph of these data, first find what percentage all of the trees of each type of tree represents. Divide the number of trees of each type by the total number of trees, and multiply by 100.

$$\frac{600 \text{ oak}}{3,000 \text{ trees}} \times 100 = 20\%$$

$$\frac{750 \text{ maple}}{3,000 \text{ trees}} \times 100 = 25\%$$

$$\frac{300 \text{ beech}}{3,000 \text{ trees}} \times 100 = 10\%$$

$$\frac{1,200 \text{ birch}}{3,000 \text{ trees}} \times 100 = 40\%$$

$$\frac{150 \text{ hickory}}{3,000 \text{ trees}} \times 100 = 5\%$$

2 Now, determine the size of the wedges that make up the pie graph. Multiply each percentage by 360°. Remember that a circle contains 360°.

20% × 360° = 72°   25% × 360° = 90°

10% × 360° = 36°   40% × 360° = 144°

5% × 360° = 18°

3 Check that the sum of the percentages is 100 and that the sum of the degrees is 360.

20% + 25% + 10% + 40% + 5% = 100%

72° + 90° + 36° + 144° + 18° = 360°

4 Use a compass to draw a circle and mark the center of the circle.

5 Then, use a protractor to draw angles of 72°, 90°, 36°, 144°, and 18° in the circle.

6 Finally, label each part of the graph, and choose an appropriate title.

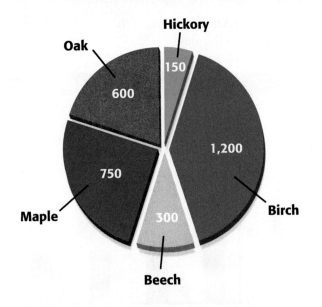

A Community of Hardwood Trees

Physical Science Refresher

Atoms and Elements

Every object in the universe is made up of particles of some kind of matter. **Matter** is anything that takes up space and has mass. All matter is made up of elements. An **element** is a substance that cannot be separated into simpler components by ordinary chemical means. The reason is that each element consists of only one kind of atom. An **atom** is the smallest unit of an element that maintains the properties of that element.

Atomic Structure

Atoms are made up of small particles called **subatomic particles.** The three major types of subatomic particles are **electrons, protons, and neutrons.** Electrons have a negative electric charge, protons have a positive electric charge, and neutrons have no electric charge. The protons and neutrons are packed close to one another to form the **nucleus.** The protons give the nucleus a positive charge. Electrons are most likely to be found in regions around the nucleus called **electron clouds.** The negatively charged electrons are attracted to the positively charged nucleus. An atom may have several energy levels in which electrons are located.

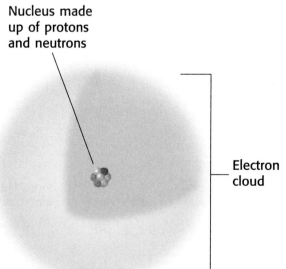

Nucleus made up of protons and neutrons

Electron cloud

Atomic Number

To help in the identification of elements, scientists have assigned an **atomic number** to each kind of atom. The atomic number is the number of protons in the atom. Atoms that have the same number of protons are the same kind of element. In an uncharged, or electrically neutral, atom, the numbers of protons and electrons are equal. Therefore, the atomic number equals the number of electrons in an uncharged atom. The number of neutrons, however, can vary for a given element. Atoms of the same element that have different numbers of neutrons are called **isotopes.**

Periodic Table of the Elements

In the periodic table, the elements are arranged from left to right in order of increasing atomic number. Each element in the table is in a separate box. An uncharged atom of each element has one more electron and one more proton than does an uncharged atom of the element to its left. Each horizontal row of the table is called a **period.** Changes in chemical properties of elements across a period correspond to changes in the electron arrangements of the atoms of the elements. Each vertical column of the table, known as a **group,** lists elements that have similar properties. The elements in a group have similar chemical properties because their atoms have the same number of electrons in their outer energy level. For example, the elements helium, neon, argon, krypton, xenon, and radon have similar properties and are known as the *noble gases.*

Molecules and Compounds

When two or more elements are joined chemically, the resulting substance is called a **compound.** A compound is a new substance whose properties differ from the properties of the elements that compose the compound. For example, water, H_2O, is a compound formed when hydrogen, H, and oxygen, O, combine. The smallest complete unit of a compound that has the properties of that compound is called a **molecule.** A chemical formula indicates the elements in a compound. It also indicates the relative number of atoms of each element present. The chemical formula for water is H_2O, which indicates that each water molecule consists of two atoms of hydrogen and one atom of oxygen. The subscript number after the symbol for an element indicates how many atoms of that element are in a single molecule of the compound.

Acids, Bases, and pH

An **ion** is an atom or group of atoms that has an electric charge because it has lost or gained one or more electrons. When an acid, such as hydrochloric acid, HCl, is mixed with water, it separates into ions. An **acid** is a compound that produces hydrogen ions, H^+, in water. The hydrogen ions then combine with water molecules to form hydronium ions, H_3O^+. A **base,** on the other hand, is a substance that produces hydroxide ions, OH^-, in water.

To determine whether a solution is acidic or basic, scientists use pH. The **pH** is a measure of the hydronium ion concentration in a solution. The pH scale ranges from 0 to 14. The middle point, pH = 7, is neutral—neither acidic nor basic. Acids have a pH less than 7; bases have a pH greater than 7. The lower the number is, the more acidic the solution. The higher the number is, the more basic the solution.

Chemical Equations

A chemical reaction occurs when a chemical change takes place. (In a chemical change, new substances that have new properties form.) A chemical equation is a useful way of describing a chemical reaction by means of chemical formulas. The equation indicates what substances react and what the products are. For example, when carbon and oxygen combine, they can form carbon dioxide. The equation for the reaction is as follows: $C + O_2 \rightarrow CO_2$.

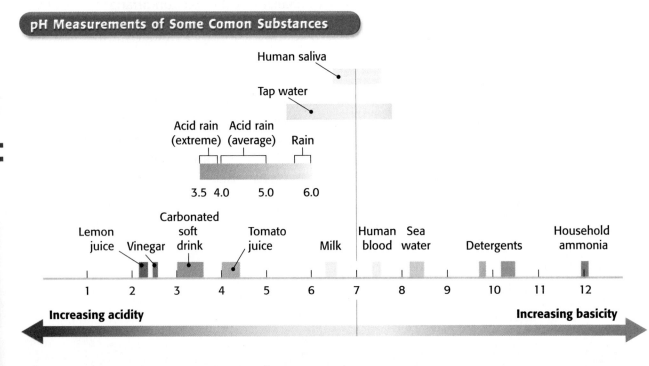

pH Measurements of Some Comon Substances

Human saliva

Tap water

Acid rain (extreme)   Acid rain (average)   Rain

3.5 4.0   5.0   6.0

Lemon juice   Vinegar   Carbonated soft drink   Tomato juice   Milk   Human blood   Sea water   Detergents   Household ammonia

1   2   3   4   5   6   7   8   9   10   11   12

Increasing acidity   Increasing basicity

Appendix

Physical Science Laws and Principles

Newton's Laws of Motion

Newton's first law of motion states that an object at rest remains at rest and an object in motion remains in motion at constant speed and in a straight line unless acted on by an unbalanced force.

The first part of the law explains why a football will remain on a tee until it is kicked off or until a gust of wind blows it off.

The second part of the law explains why a bike rider will continue moving forward after the bike comes to an abrupt stop. Gravity and the friction of the sidewalk will eventually stop the rider.

Newton's second law of motion states that the acceleration of an object depends on the mass of the object and the amount of force applied.

The first part of the law explains why the acceleration of a 4 kg bowling ball will be greater than the acceleration of a 6 kg bowling ball if the same force is applied to both balls.

The second part of the law explains why the acceleration of a bowling ball will be larger if a larger force is applied to the bowling ball.

The relationship of acceleration (a) to mass (m) and force (F) can be expressed mathematically by the following equation:

$$acceleration = \frac{force}{mass}, \text{ or } a = \frac{F}{m}$$

This equation is often rearranged to the form

$$force = mass \times acceleration, \text{ or } F = m \times a$$

Newton's third law of motion states that whenever one object exerts a force on a second object, the second object exerts an equal and opposite force on the first.

This law explains that a runner is able to move forward because of the equal and opposite force that the ground exerts on the runner's foot after each step.

Law of Conservation of Mass

Mass cannot be created or destroyed during ordinary chemical or physical changes.

The total mass in a closed system is always the same no matter how many physical changes or chemical reactions occur.

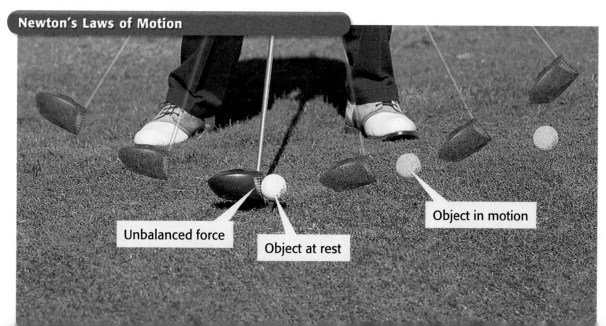

Newton's Laws of Motion

Unbalanced force

Object at rest

Object in motion

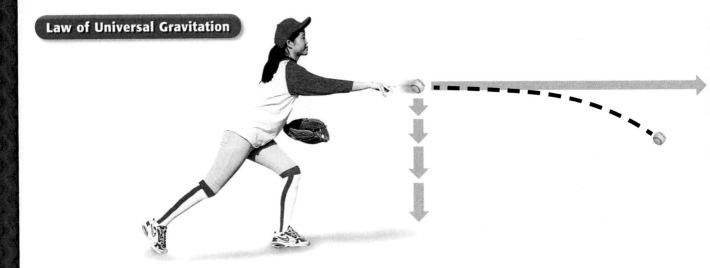

Law of Universal Gravitation

All objects in the universe attract each other by a force called *gravity*. The size of the force depends on the masses of the objects and the distance between the objects.

The first part of the law explains why lifting a bowling ball is much harder than lifting a marble. Because the bowling ball has a much larger mass than the marble does, the amount of gravity between Earth and the bowling ball is greater than the amount of gravity between Earth and the marble.

The second part of the law explains why a satellite can remain in orbit around Earth. The satellite is carefully placed at a distance great enough to prevent Earth's gravity from immediately pulling the satellite down but small enough to prevent the satellite from completely escaping Earth's gravity and wandering off into space.

Law of Conservation of Energy

Energy can be neither created nor destroyed.

The total amount of energy in a closed system is always the same. Energy can be changed from one form to another, but all of the different forms of energy in a system always add up to the same total amount of energy no matter how many energy conversions occur.

Charles's Law

Charles's law states that for a fixed amount of gas at a constant pressure, the volume of the gas increases as the temperature of the gas increases. Likewise, the volume of the gas decreases as the temperature of the gas decreases.

If a basketball that was inflated indoors is left outside on a cold winter day, the air particles inside the ball will move more slowly. They will hit the sides of the basketball less often and with less force. The ball will get smaller as the volume of the air decreases.

Boyle's Law

Boyle's law states that for a fixed amount of gas at a constant temperature, the volume of a gas increases as the pressure of the gas decreases. Likewise, the volume of a gas decreases as its pressure increases.

If an inflated balloon is pulled down to the bottom of a swimming pool, the pressure of the water on the balloon increases. The pressure of the air particles inside the balloon must increase to match that of the water outside, so the volume of the air inside the balloon decreases.

Pascal's Principle

Pascal's principle states that a change in pressure at any point in an enclosed fluid will be transmitted equally to all parts of that fluid.

When a mechanic uses a hydraulic jack to raise an automobile off the ground, he or she increases the pressure on the fluid in the jack by pushing on the jack handle. The pressure is transmitted equally to all parts of the fluid-filled jacking system. As fluid presses the jack plate against the frame of the car, the car is lifted off the ground.

Archimedes' Principle

Archimedes' principle states that the buoyant force on an object in a fluid is equal to the weight of the volume of fluid that the object displaces.

A person floating in a swimming pool displaces 20 L of water. The weight of that volume of water is about 200 N. Therefore, the buoyant force on the person is 200 N.

Bernoulli's Principle

Bernoulli's principle states that as the speed of a moving fluid increases, the fluid's pressure decreases.

The lift on an airplane wing can be explained in part by using Bernoulli's principle. Because of the shape of the wing, the air moving over the top of the wing is moving faster than the air below the wing. This faster-moving air above the wing exerts less pressure than the slower-moving air below it does. The resulting increased pressure below exerts an upward force and pushes the wing up.

Law of Reflection

The **law of reflection** states that the angle of incidence is equal to the angle of reflection. This law explains why light reflects off a surface at the same angle that the light strikes the surface.

Law of Reflection

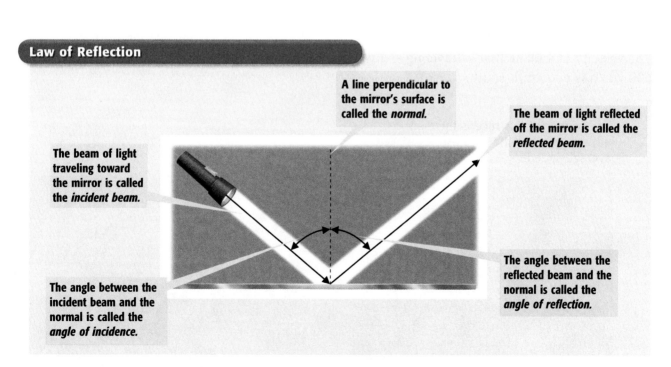

The beam of light traveling toward the mirror is called the *incident beam.*

A line perpendicular to the mirror's surface is called the *normal.*

The beam of light reflected off the mirror is called the *reflected beam.*

The angle between the incident beam and the normal is called the *angle of incidence.*

The angle between the reflected beam and the normal is called the *angle of reflection.*

Useful Equations

Average Speed

The rate at which an object moves is its *speed.* Speed depends on the distance traveled and the time taken to travel that distance. **Average speed** is calculated using the following equation:

$$\text{average speed} = \frac{\text{total distance}}{\text{total time}}$$

Example: A bicycle messenger traveled a distance of 136 km in 8 h. What was the messenger's average speed?

$$\frac{136\ \text{km}}{8\ \text{h}} = 17\ \text{km/h}$$

The messenger's average speed was **17 km/h.**

Velocity

The speed of an object in a particular direction is **velocity.** Speed and velocity are not the same even though they are calculated by using the same equation. Velocity must include a direction, so velocity is described as speed in a certain direction. For example, the speed of a plane that is traveling south at 600 km/h is 600 km/h. The velocity of a plane that is traveling south at 600 km/h is 600 km/h south.

Velocity can also be thought of as the rate of change of an object's position. An object's velocity remains constant only if its speed and direction don't change. Therefore, constant velocity occurs only along a straight line.

Average Acceleration

The rate at which velocity changes is called *acceleration.* **Average acceleration** can be calculated by using the following equation:

$$\frac{\text{average}}{\text{acceleration}} = \frac{\text{final velocity} - \text{starting velocity}}{\text{time it takes to change velocity}}$$

Example: Calculate the average acceleration of an Olympic sprinter who reached a velocity of 20 m/s south at the finish line of a 100 m dash. The race was in a straight line and lasted 10 s.

$$\frac{20\ \text{m/s} - 0\ \text{m/s}}{10\ \text{s}} = 2\ \text{m/s/s}$$

The sprinter's average acceleration was **2 m/s/s south.**

The winner of this race is the athlete who has the greatest average speed.

Net Force

Forces in the Same Direction

When forces are in the same direction, add the forces together to determine the net force.

Example: Calculate the net force on a stalled car that is being pushed by two people. One person is pushing with a force of 13 N northwest, and the other person is pushing with a force of 8 N in the same direction.

$$13\ N + 8\ N = 21\ N$$

The net force is **21 N northwest.**

Forces in Opposite Directions

When forces are in opposite directions, subtract the smaller force from the larger force to determine the net force. The net force will be in the direction of the larger force.

Example: Calculate the net force on a rope that is being pulled on each end. One person is pulling on one end of the rope with a force of 12 N south. Another person is pulling on the opposite end of the rope with a force of 7 N north.

$$12\ N - 7\ N = 5\ N$$

The net force is **5 N south.**

The forces exerted by the dogs on the rope are in opposite directions. The net force is found by subtracting the smaller force from the larger force.

Pressure

Pressure is the force exerted over a given area. The SI unit for pressure is the pascal (Pa).

$$pressure = \frac{force}{area}$$

Example: Calculate the pressure of the air in a soccer ball if the air exerts a force of 25,000 N over an area of 0.15 m².

$$pressure = \frac{25{,}000\ N}{1\ m^2} = \frac{167{,}000\ N}{m^2} = 167{,}000\ Pa$$

The pressure of the air inside the soccer ball is **167,000 Pa.**

Density

The mass per unit volume of a substance is **density.** Thus, a material's density is the amount of matter it contains in a given space. To find density, you must measure both mass and volume. Density is calculated by using the following equation:

$$density = \frac{mass}{volume}$$

Example: Calculate the density of a sponge that has a mass of 10 g and a volume of 40 cm³.

$$\frac{10\ g}{40\ cm^3} = \frac{0.25\ g}{cm^3}$$

The density of the sponge is $\frac{0.25\ g}{cm^3}$.

Concentration

A measure of the amount of one substance that is dissolved in another substance is **concentration.** The substance that is dissolved is the solute. The substance that dissolves another substance is the solvent. Concentration is calculated by using the following equation:

$$concentration = \frac{mass\ of\ solute}{volume\ of\ solvent}$$

Example: Calculate the concentration of a solution in which 10 g of sugar is dissolved in 125 mL of water.

$$\frac{10\ g\ of\ sugar}{125\ mL\ of\ water} = \frac{0.08\ g}{mL}$$

The concentration of this solution is $\frac{0.08\ g}{mL}$.

These solutions were made by using the same volume of water. But less solute was dissolved in the beaker on the left. So, the concentration of the solution on the left is lower than the concentration of the solution on the right.

Work

Work is done by exerting a force through a distance. Work is expressed in joules (J), which are equivalent to newton-meters (N•m).

$$work = force \times distance$$

Example: Calculate the amount of work done by a man who lifts a 100 N toddler 1.5 m off the floor.

$$work = 100\ N \times 1.5\ m = 150\ N•m = 150\ J$$

The man did **150 J** of work.

Power

Power is the rate at which work is done. Power is expressed in watts (W), which are equivalent to joules per second (J/s).

$$power = \frac{work}{time}$$

Example: Calculate the power of a weight-lifter who raises a 300 N barbell 2.1 m off the floor in 1.25 s.

$$work = 300\ N \times 2.1\ m = 630\ N•m = 630\ J$$

$$power = \frac{30\ J}{1.25\ s} = \frac{504\ J}{s} = 504\ W$$

The weightlifter's power is **504 W.**

Heat

Heat is the energy transferred between objects that are at different temperatures. Heat is expressed in joules (J). In general, if you know an object's mass, change in temperature, and specific heat, you can calculate heat. Specific heat is the amount of energy needed to change the temperature of 1 kg of a substance by 1°C. Specific heat is expressed in joules per kilogram-degree Celsius (J/kg•°C).

heat = specific heat × mass × **change in temperature**

Example: Calculate the heat transferred to a mass of 0.2 kg of water to change the temperature of the water from 25°C to 80°C. The specific heat of water is 4,184 J/kg•°C.

$$heat = 4{,}184 \text{ J/kg•°C} \times 0.2 \text{ kg} \times (80°C - 25°C) = 46{,}024 \text{ J}$$

The heat transferred is **46,024 J.**

Work and Heat

James Joule, an English scientist, performed experiments to explore the relationship between **work** and **heat.** He found that a given amount of work always generated the same amount of heat. By applying the law of conservation of energy, we know that the amount of heat generated can never be larger than the work done.

Example: What is the maximum amount of heat that can be generated from the work done if a force of 75 N is exerted over a distance of 5 m?

$$work = 75 \text{ N} \times 5 \text{ m} = 375 \text{ N•m} = 375 \text{ J}$$

The maximum amount of heat that can be generated is **375 J.**

Example: A force of 299 N is exerted through a distance of 210 m. The resulting work is converted into heat and absorbed by 2.0 kg of water. What is the maximum change in temperature if the specific heat of water is 4,184 J/kg•°C?

$$work = 299 \text{ N} \times 210 \text{ m} = 62{,}790 \text{ N•m} = 62{,}790 \text{ J}$$

$$\frac{\text{change in}}{\text{temperature}} = \frac{heat}{\text{mass} \times \text{specific heat}}$$

$$\frac{\text{change in}}{\text{temperature}} = \frac{62{,}790 \text{ J}}{2.0 \text{ kg} \times 4{,}184 \text{ J/kg•°C}} = 7.5°C$$

The maximum change in temperature is **7.5°C.**

As the air in this balloon absorbs heat, the temperature of the air rises.

Scientific Methods

The ways in which scientists answer questions and solve problems are called **scientific methods.** The same steps are often used by scientists as they look for answers. However, there is more than one way to use these steps. Scientists may use all of the steps or just some of the steps during an investigation. They may even repeat some of the steps. The goal of using scientific methods is to come up with reliable answers and solutions.

Six Steps of Scientific Methods

 **1 Ask a Question**

Good questions come from careful **observations.** You make observations by using your senses to gather information. Sometimes, you may use instruments, such as microscopes and telescopes, to extend the range of your senses. As you observe the natural world, you will discover that you have many more questions than answers. These questions drive investigations.

Questions beginning with *what, why, how,* and *when* are important in focusing an investigation. Here is an example of a question that could lead to an investigation.

> **Question:** How does acid rain affect plant growth?

 **2 Form a Hypothesis**

After you ask a question, you need to form a **hypothesis.** A hypothesis is a clear statement of what you expect the answer to your question to be. Your hypothesis will represent your best "educated guess" based on what you have observed and what you already know. A good hypothesis is testable. Otherwise, the investigation can go no further. Here is a hypothesis based on the question "How does acid rain affect plant growth?"

> **Hypothesis:** Acid rain slows plant growth.

The hypothesis can lead to predictions. A prediction is what you think the outcome of your experiment or data collection will be. Predictions are usually stated in an if-then format. Here is a sample prediction for the hypothesis that acid rain slows plant growth.

> **Prediction:** If a plant is watered with only acid rain (which has a pH of 4), then the plant will grow at half its normal rate.

3 Test the Hypothesis

After you have formed a hypothesis and made a prediction, your hypothesis should be tested. One way to test a hypothesis is with a controlled experiment. A **controlled experiment** tests only one factor at a time. In an experiment to test the effect of acid rain on plant growth, the **control group** would be watered with normal rainwater. The **experimental group** would be watered with acid rain. All of the plants should receive the same amount of sunlight and water each day. The air temperature should be the same for all groups. However, the acidity of the water will be a variable. In fact, any factor that differs from one group to another is a **variable.** If your hypothesis is correct, then the acidity of the water and plant growth are *dependant variables.* The amount that a plant grows is dependent on the acidity of the water. However, the amount of water and the amount of sunlight received by each plant are *independent variables.* Either of these factors could change without affecting the other factor.

Sometimes, the nature of an investigation makes a controlled experiment impossible. For example, Earth's core is surrounded by thousands of meters of rock. Under such circumstances, a hypothesis may be tested by making detailed observations.

 **4 Analyze the Results**

After you have completed your experiments, made your observations, and collected your data, you must analyze all of the information that you have gathered. Tables and graphs are often used in this step to organize the data.

 **5 Draw Conclusions**

After analyzing your data, you can determine if your results support your hypothesis. If your hypothesis is supported, you (or others) might want to repeat the observations or experiments to verify your results. If your hypothesis is not supported by the data, you may have to check your procedure for errors. You may even have to reject your hypothesis and make a new one. If you cannot draw a conclusion from your results, you may have to try the investigation again or carry out further observations or experiments.

 **6 Communicate Results**

After any scientific investigation, you should report your results. By preparing a written or oral report, you let others know what you have learned. They may repeat your investigation to see if they get the same results. Your report may even lead to another question and then to another investigation.

Scientific Methods in Action

Scientific methods contain loops in which several steps may be repeated over and over again. In some cases, certain steps are unnecessary. Thus, there is not a "straight line" of steps. For example, sometimes scientists find that testing one hypothesis raises new questions and new hypotheses to be tested. And sometimes, testing the hypothesis leads directly to a conclusion. Furthermore, the steps in scientific methods are not always used in the same order. Follow the steps in the diagram, and see how many different directions scientific methods can take you.

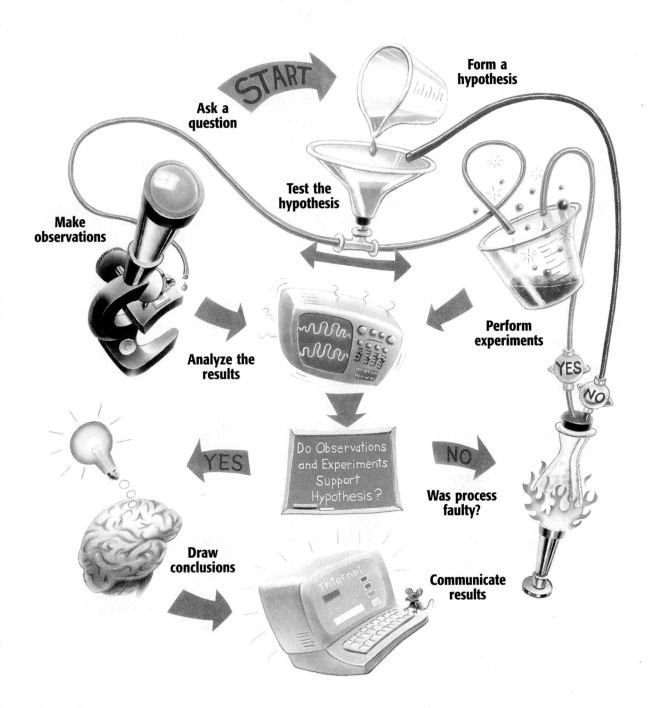

Appendix

SI Measurement

The International System of Units, or SI, is the standard system of measurement used by many scientists. Using the same standards of measurement makes it easier for scientists to communicate with one another.

SI works by combining prefixes and base units. Each base unit can be used with different prefixes to define smaller and larger quantities. The table below lists common SI prefixes.

SI Prefixes			
Prefix	**Symbol**	**Factor**	**Example**
kilo-	k	1,000	kilogram, 1 kg = 1,000 g
hecto-	h	100	hectoliter, 1 hL = 100 L
deka-	da	10	dekameter, 1 dam = 10 m
		1	meter, liter, gram
deci-	d	0.1	decigram, 1 dg = 0.1 g
centi-	c	0.01	centimeter, 1 cm = 0.01 m
milli-	m	0.001	milliliter, 1 mL = 0.001 L
micro-	μ	0.000 001	micrometer, 1 μm = 0.000 001 m

SI Conversion Table		
SI units	**From SI to English**	**From English to SI**
Length		
kilometer (km) = 1,000 m	1 km = 0.621 mi	1 mi = 1.609 km
meter (m) = 100 cm	1 m = 3.281 ft	1 ft = 0.305 m
centimeter (cm) = 0.01 m	1 cm = 0.394 in.	1 in. = 2.540 cm
millimeter (mm) = 0.001 m	1 mm = 0.039 in.	
micrometer (μm) = 0.000 001 m		
nanometer (nm) = 0.000 000 001 m		
Area		
square kilometer (km^2) = 100 hectares	1 km^2 = 0.386 mi^2	1 mi^2 = 2.590 km^2
hectare (ha) = 10,000 m^2	1 ha = 2.471 acres	1 acre = 0.405 ha
square meter (m^2) = 10,000 cm^2	1 m^2 = 10.764 ft^2	1 ft^2 = 0.093 m^2
square centimeter (cm^2) = 100 mm^2	1 cm^2 = 0.155 in.^{2}	1 in.^{2} = 6.452 cm^2
Volume		
liter (L) = 1,000 mL = 1 dm^3	1 L = 1.057 fl qt	1 fl qt = 0.946 L
milliliter (mL) = 0.001 L = 1 cm^3	1 mL = 0.034 fl oz	1 fl oz = 29.574 mL
microliter (μL) = 0.000 001 L		
Mass	*Equivalent weight at Earth's surface	
kilogram (kg) = 1,000 g	1 kg = 2.205 lb*	1 lb* = 0.454 kg
gram (g) = 1,000 mg	1 g = 0.035 oz*	1 oz* = 28.350 g
milligram (mg) = 0.001 g		
microgram (μg) = 0.000 001 g		

Measuring Skills

Using a Graduated Cylinder

When using a graduated cylinder to measure volume, keep the following procedures in mind:

1 Place the cylinder on a flat, level surface before measuring liquid.

2 Move your head so that your eye is level with the surface of the liquid.

3 Read the mark closest to the liquid level. On glass graduated cylinders, read the mark closest to the center of the curve in the liquid's surface.

Using a Meterstick or Metric Ruler

When using a meterstick or metric ruler to measure length, keep the following procedures in mind:

1 Place the ruler firmly against the object that you are measuring.

2 Align one edge of the object exactly with the 0 end of the ruler.

3 Look at the other edge of the object to see which of the marks on the ruler is closest to that edge. (Note: Each small slash between the centimeters represents a millimeter, which is one-tenth of a centimeter.)

Using a Triple-Beam Balance

When using a triple-beam balance to measure mass, keep the following procedures in mind:

1 Make sure the balance is on a level surface.

2 Place all of the countermasses at 0. Adjust the balancing knob until the pointer rests at 0.

3 Place the object to be measured on the pan. **Caution:** Do not place hot objects or chemicals directly on the balance pan.

4 Move the largest countermass along the beam to the right until it is at the last notch that does not tip the balance. Follow the same procedure with the next-largest countermass. Then, move the smallest countermass until the pointer rests at 0.

5 Add the readings from the three beams together to determine the mass of the object.

6 When determining the mass of crystals or powders, first find the mass of a piece of filter paper. Then, add the crystals or powder to the paper, and remeasure. The actual mass of the crystals or powder is the total mass minus the mass of the paper. When finding the mass of liquids, first find the mass of the empty container. Then, find the combined mass of the liquid and container. The mass of the liquid is the total mass minus the mass of the container.

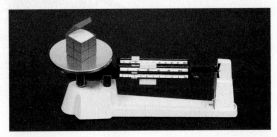

Using the Microscope

Parts of the Compound Light Microscope

- The **ocular lens** magnifies the image 10×.
- The **low-power objective** magnifies the image 10×.
- The **high-power objective** magnifies the image either 40× or 43×.
- The **revolving nosepiece** holds the objectives and can be turned to change from one magnification to the other.
- The **body tube** maintains the correct distance between the ocular lens and objectives.
- The **coarse-adjustment knob** moves the body tube up and down to allow focusing of the image.

- The **fine-adjustment knob** moves the body tube slightly to bring the image into sharper focus. It is usually located in the center of the coarse-adjustment knob.
- The **stage** supports a slide.
- **Stage clips** hold the slide in place for viewing.
- The **diaphragm** controls the amount of light coming through the stage.
- The light source provides a **light** for viewing the slide.
- The **arm** supports the body tube.
- The **base** supports the microscope.

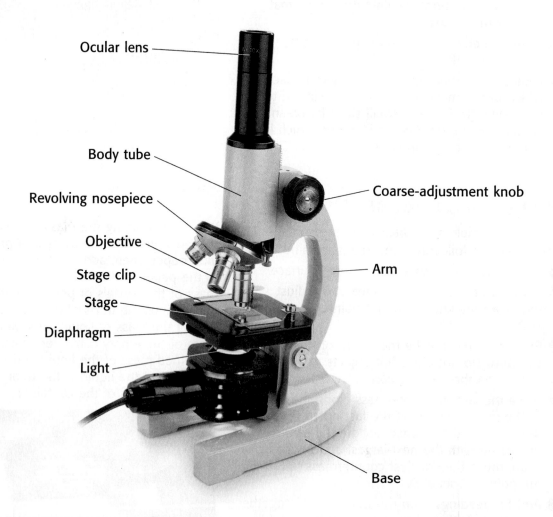

Ocular lens

Body tube

Revolving nosepiece

Objective

Stage clip

Stage

Diaphragm

Light

Coarse-adjustment knob

Arm

Base

Proper Use of the Compound Light Microscope

1. Use both hands to carry the microscope to your lab table. Place one hand beneath the base, and use the other hand to hold the arm of the microscope. Hold the microscope close to your body while carrying it to your lab table.

2. Place the microscope on the lab table at least 5 cm from the edge of the table.

3. Check to see what type of light source is used by your microscope. If the microscope has a lamp, plug it in and make sure that the cord is out of the way. If the microscope has a mirror, adjust the mirror to reflect light through the hole in the stage.
   Caution: If your microscope has a mirror, do not use direct sunlight as a light source. Direct sunlight can damage your eyes.

4. Always begin work with the low-power objective in line with the body tube. Adjust the revolving nosepiece.

5. Place a prepared slide over the hole in the stage. Secure the slide with the stage clips.

6. Look through the ocular lens. Move the diaphragm to adjust the amount of light coming through the stage.

7. Look at the stage from eye level. Slowly turn the coarse adjustment to lower the objective until the objective almost touches the slide. Do not allow the objective to touch the slide.

8. Look through the ocular lens. Turn the coarse adjustment to raise the low-power objective until the image is in focus. Always focus by raising the objective away from the slide. Never focus the objective downward. Use the fine adjustment to sharpen the focus. Keep both eyes open while viewing a slide.

9. Make sure that the image is exactly in the center of your field of vision. Then, switch to the high-power objective. Focus the image by using only the fine adjustment. Never use the coarse adjustment at high power.

10. When you are finished using the microscope, remove the slide. Clean the ocular lens and objectives with lens paper. Return the microscope to its storage area. Remember to use both hands when carrying the microscope.

Making a Wet Mount

1. Use lens paper to clean a glass slide and a coverslip.

2. Place the specimen that you wish to observe in the center of the slide.

3. Using a medicine dropper, place one drop of water on the specimen.

4. Hold the coverslip at the edge of the water and at a 45° angle to the slide. Make sure that the water runs along the edge of the coverslip.

5. Lower the coverslip slowly to avoid trapping air bubbles.

6. Water might evaporate from the slide as you work. Add more water to keep the specimen fresh. Place the tip of the medicine dropper next to the edge of the coverslip. Add a drop of water. (You can also use this method to add stain or solutions to a wet mount.) Remove excess water from the slide by using the corner of a paper towel as a blotter. Do not lift the coverslip to add or remove water.

Periodic Table of the Elements

Each square on the table includes an element's name, chemical symbol, atomic number, and atomic mass.

The color of the chemical symbol indicates the physical state at room temperature. Carbon is a solid.

6
C
Carbon
12.0

— Atomic number
— Chemical symbol
— Element name
— Atomic mass

The background color indicates the type of element. Carbon is a nonmetal.

Background
- Metals
- Metalloids
- Nonmetals

Chemical symbol
- Solid
- Liquid
- Gas

Period 1

1
H
Hydrogen
1.0

Group 1	Group 2							
Period 2 3 **Li** Lithium 6.9	4 **Be** Beryllium 9.0							
Period 3 11 **Na** Sodium 23.0	12 **Mg** Magnesium 24.3	Group 3	Group 4	Group 5	Group 6	Group 7	Group 8	Group 9
Period 4 19 **K** Potassium 39.1	20 **Ca** Calcium 40.1	21 **Sc** Scandium 45.0	22 **Ti** Titanium 47.9	23 **V** Vanadium 50.9	24 **Cr** Chromium 52.0	25 **Mn** Manganese 54.9	26 **Fe** Iron 55.8	27 **Co** Cobalt 58.9
Period 5 37 **Rb** Rubidium 85.5	38 **Sr** Strontium 87.6	39 **Y** Yttrium 88.9	40 **Zr** Zirconium 91.2	41 **Nb** Niobium 92.9	42 **Mo** Molybdenum 95.9	43 **Tc** Technetium (98)	44 **Ru** Ruthenium 101.1	45 **Rh** Rhodium 102.9
Period 6 55 **Cs** Cesium 132.9	56 **Ba** Barium 137.3	57 **La** Lanthanum 138.9	72 **Hf** Hafnium 178.5	73 **Ta** Tantalum 180.9	74 **W** Tungsten 183.8	75 **Re** Rhenium 186.2	76 **Os** Osmium 190.2	77 **Ir** Iridium 192.2
Period 7 87 **Fr** Francium (223)	88 **Ra** Radium (226)	89 **Ac** Actinium (227)	104 **Rf** Rutherfordium (261)	105 **Db** Dubnium (262)	106 **Sg** Seaborgium (266)	107 **Bh** Bohrium (264)	108 **Hs** Hassium (277)	109 **Mt** Meitnerium (268)

A row of elements is called a *period*.

A column of elements is called a *group* or *family*.

Values in parentheses are the mass numbers of those radioactive elements' most stable or most common isotopes.

Lanthanides

58 **Ce** Cerium 140.1	59 **Pr** Praseodymium 140.9	60 **Nd** Neodymium 144.2	61 **Pm** Promethium (145)	62 **Sm** Samarium 150.4

These elements are placed below the table to allow the table to be narrower.

Actinides

90 **Th** Thorium 232.0	91 **Pa** Protactinium 231.0	92 **U** Uranium 238.0	93 **Np** Neptunium (237)	94 **Pu** Plutonium (244)

Topic: **Periodic Table**
Go To: go.hrw.com
Keyword: **HN0 PERIODIC**
Visit the HRW Web site for
updates on the periodic table.

Group 18

2
He
Helium
4.0

	Group 13	**Group 14**	**Group 15**	**Group 16**	**Group 17**	

> This zigzag line reminds you where the metals, nonmetals, and metalloids are.

Group 13	**Group 14**	**Group 15**	**Group 16**	**Group 17**
5 **B** Boron 10.8	6 **C** Carbon 12.0	7 **N** Nitrogen 14.0	8 **O** Oxygen 16.0	9 **F** Fluorine 19.0

10
Ne
Neon
20.2

13 **Al** Aluminum 27.0	14 **Si** Silicon 28.1	15 **P** Phosphorus 31.0	16 **S** Sulfur 32.1	17 **Cl** Chlorine 35.5	18 **Ar** Argon 39.9

Group 10	**Group 11**	**Group 12**					
28 **Ni** Nickel 58.7	29 **Cu** Copper 63.5	30 **Zn** Zinc 65.4	31 **Ga** Gallium 69.7	32 **Ge** Germanium 72.6	33 **As** Arsenic 74.9	34 **Se** Selenium 79.0	35 **Br** Bromine 79.9	36 **Kr** Krypton 83.8
46 **Pd** Palladium 106.4	47 **Ag** Silver 107.9	48 **Cd** Cadmium 112.4	49 **In** Indium 114.8	50 **Sn** Tin 118.7	51 **Sb** Antimony 121.8	52 **Te** Tellurium 127.6	53 **I** Iodine 126.9	54 **Xe** Xenon 131.3
78 **Pt** Platinum 195.1	79 **Au** Gold 197.0	80 **Hg** Mercury 200.6	81 **Tl** Thallium 204.4	82 **Pb** Lead 207.2	83 **Bi** Bismuth 209.0	84 **Po** Polonium (209)	85 **At** Astatine (210)	86 **Rn** Radon (222)
110 **Ds** Darmstadtium (281)	111 **Uuu** Unununium (272)	112 **Uub** Ununbium (285)	113 **Uut** Ununtrium (284)	114 **Uuq** Ununquadium (289)	115 **Uup** Ununpentium (288)			

The discovery of elements 113, 114, and 115 has been reported but not confirmed.

> The names and three-letter symbols of elements are temporary. They are based on the atomic numbers of the elements. Official names and symbols will be approved by an international committee of scientists.

63 **Eu** Europium 152.0	64 **Gd** Gadolinium 157.2	65 **Tb** Terbium 158.9	66 **Dy** Dysprosium 162.5	67 **Ho** Holmium 164.9	68 **Er** Erbium 167.3	69 **Tm** Thulium 168.9	70 **Yb** Ytterbium 173.0	71 **Lu** Lutetium 175.0
95 **Am** Americium (243)	96 **Cm** Curium (247)	97 **Bk** Berkelium (247)	98 **Cf** Californium (251)	99 **Es** Einsteinium (252)	100 **Fm** Fermium (257)	101 **Md** Mendelevium (258)	102 **No** Nobelium (259)	103 **Lr** Lawrencium (262)

Appendix

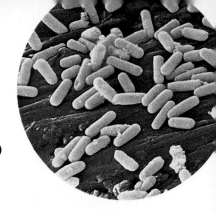

Domains and Kingdoms

All organisms are divided into one of three domains: Domain Archaea, Domain Bacteria, or Domain Eukarya. Some of the groups within these domains are shown below. (Remember that genus names are italicized.)

Domain Archaea

The organisms in this domain are single-celled prokaryotes, many of which live in extreme environments.

Archaea		
Group	**Example**	**Characteristics**
Methanogens	*Methanococcus*	produce methane gas; can't live in oxygen
Thermophiles	*Sulpholobus*	require sulphur; can't live in oxygen
Halophiles	*Halococcus*	live in very salty environments; most can live in oxygen

Domain Bacteria

Organisms in this domain are single-celled prokaryotes and are found in moderate environments.

Bacteria		
Group	**Example**	**Characteristics**
Bacilli	*Escherichia*	rod shaped; some fix nitrogen; some cause disease
Cocci	*Streptococcus*	spherical shaped; cause diseases; can form spores
Spirilla	*Treponema*	spiral shaped; cause diseases, such as syphilis

Domain Eukarya

Organisms in this domain are single-celled or multicellular eukaryotes.

Kingdom Protista

There are single-celled and multicellular organisms in this kingdom.

Protists		
Group	**Example**	**Characteristics**
Sarcodines	*Amoeba*	radiolarians; single-celled consumers
Ciliates	*Paramecium*	single-celled consumers
Flagellates	*Trypanosoma*	single-celled parasites
Sporozoans	*Plasmodium*	single-celled parasites
Euglenas	*Euglena*	single celled; photosynthesize
Diatoms	*Pinnularia*	most are single celled; photosynthesize
Dinoflagellates	*Gymnodinium*	single celled; some photosynthesize
Algae	*Volvox*	single celled or multicellular; photosynthesize
Slime molds	*Physarum*	single celled or multicellular; consumers or decomposers
Water molds	powdery mildew	single celled or multicellular; parasites or decomposers

Kingdom Fungi

There are single-celled and multicellular eukaryotes in this kingdom. There are four major groups of fungi.

Fungi		
Group	**Examples**	**Characteristics**
Threadlike fungi	bread mold	spherical; decomposers
Sac fungi	yeast; morels	saclike; parasites and decomposers
Club fungi	mushrooms; rusts; smuts	club shaped; parasites and decomposers
Lichens	British soldier	symbiotic with algae

Kingdom Plantae

The organisms in this kingdom are multicellular eukaryotes. They have specialized organ systems for different life processes. They are classified in divisions instead of phyla.

Plants		
Group	**Examples**	**Characteristics**
Threadlike fungi	mosses; liverworts	reproduce by spores
Club mosses	*Lycopodium;* ground pine	reproduce by spores
Horsetails	rushes	reproduce by spores
Ferns	spleenworts; sensitive fern	reproduce by spores
Conifers	pines; spruces; firs	reproduce by seeds; cones
Cycads	*Zamia*	reproduce by seeds
Gnetophytes	*Welwitschia*	reproduce by seeds
Ginkgoes	*Ginkgo*	reproduce by seeds
Angiosperms	all flowering plants	reproduce by seeds; flowers

Kingdom Animalia

This kingdom contains multicellular eukaryotes. Most of the organisms in this kingdom have specialized tissues and complex organ systems.

Animals		
Group	**Examples**	**Characteristics**
Sponges	glass sponges	no symmetry or segmentation; aquatic
Cnidarians	jellyfish; coral	radial symmetry; aquatic
Flatworms	planaria; tapeworms; flukes	bilateral symmetry; organ systems
Roundworms	*Trichina;* hookworms	bilateral symmetry; organ systems
Annelids	earthworms; leeches	bilateral symmetry; organ systems
Mollusks	snails; octopuses	bilateral symmetry; organ systems
Echinoderms	sea stars; sand dollars	radial symmetry; organ systems
Arthropods	insects; spiders; lobsters	bilateral symmetry; organ systems
Chordates	fish; amphibians; reptiles; birds; mammals	bilateral symmetry; complex organ systems

Temperature Scales

Temperature can be expressed by using three scales: the Fahrenheit, Celsius, and Kelvin scales. The SI unit for temperature is the kelvin (K). Although 0 K is much colder than 0°C, a change of 1 K is equal to a change of 1°C.

Three Temperature Scales

	Fahrenheit	Celsius	Kelvin
Water boils	212°	100°	373
Body temperature	98.6°	37°	310
Room temperature	68°	20°	293
Water freezes	32°	0°	273

Temperature Conversion Table

Conversion	Equation	Example
degrees Celsius to degrees Fahrenheit °C → °F	$°F = \left(\dfrac{9}{5} \times °C\right) + 32$	Convert 45°C to °F. $°F = \left(\dfrac{9}{5} \times 45°C\right) + 32 = 113°F$
degrees Fahrenheit to degrees Celsius °F → °C	$°C = \dfrac{5}{9} \times (°F - 32)$	Convert 68°F to °C. $°C = \dfrac{5}{9} \times (68°F - 32) = 20°C$
degrees Celsius to kelvins °C → K	$K = °C + 273$	Convert 45°C to K. $K = 45°C + 273 = 318\ K$
kelvins to degrees Celsius K → °C	$°C = K - 273$	Convert 32 K to °C. $°C = 32K - 273 = -241°C$

English and Spanish Glossary

with Academic Vocabulary

A

absolute dating (AB suh LOOT DAYT ing) any method of measuring the age of an event or object in years (246)

datación absoluta cualquier método que sirve para determinar la edad de un suceso u objeto en años (246)

absorption (ab SAWRP shuhn) in optics, the transfer of light energy to particles of matter (84)

absorción en la óptica, la transferencia de energía luminosa a las partículas de materia (84)

adaptation (AD uhp TAY shuhn) a characteristic that improves an individual's ability to survive and reproduce in a particular environment (298)

adaptación una característica que mejora la capacidad de un individuo para sobrevivir y reproducirse en un determinado ambiente (298)

* **adaptive** (uh DAP tiv) able to adjust to changes (295)

adaptativo capaz de adecuarse a los cambios (295)

* **affect** (uh FEKT) to change; to have an effect on; to influence (261, 421, 463, 493, 523)

afectar cambiar algo; tener un efecto; influir (261, 421, 463, 493, 523)

allele (uh LEEL) one of the alternative forms of a gene that governs a characteristic, such as hair color (180)

alelo una de las formas alternativas de un gene que rige un carácter, como por ejemplo, el color del cabello (180)

alveolus (al VEE uh luhs) any of the tiny air sacs of the lungs where oxygen and carbon dioxide are exchanged (509)

alveolo cualquiera de las diminutas bolsas de aire de los pulmones, en donde ocurre el intercambio de oxígeno y dióxido de carbono (509)

angiosperm (AN jee oh SPUHRM) a flowering plant that produces seeds within a fruit (362)

angiosperma una planta que da flores y que produce semillas dentro de la fruta (362)

Animalia (AN i MAY lee uh) a kingdom made up of complex, multicellular organisms that lack cell walls, can usually move around, and quickly respond to their environment (342)

Animalia un reino formado por organismos pluricelulares complejos que no tienen pared celular, normalmente son capaces de moverse y reaccionan rápidamente a su ambiente (342)

* **appropriate** (uh PROH pree it) correct for the use; proper (5)

apropiado correcto para un determinado uso; adecuado (5)

* **appropriately** (uh PROH pree it lee) in a correct or proper way (5)

apropiadamente de forma correcta o apropiada (5)

* **approximately** (uh PRAHK suh mit lee) almost; about (261)

aproximadamente casi; alrededor de (261)

Archaea (ahr KEE uh) in a modern taxonomic system, a domain made up of prokaryotes that differ from other prokaryotes in the makeup of their cell walls and in their genetics; this domain aligns with the traditional kingdom Archaebacteria (339)

Archaea en un sistema taxonómico moderno, un dominio compuesto por procariotes que se diferencian de otros procariotes por la composición de su pared celular y su composición genética; este dominio coincide con el reino tradicional Archaebacteria (339)

*Academic Vocabulary

Glossary

area (ER ee uh) a measure of the size of a surface or a region (23)

área una medida del tamaño de una superficie o región (23)

artery (ART uhr ee) a blood vessel that carries blood away from the heart to the body's organs (498)

arteria un vaso sanguíneo que transporta sangre del corazón a los órganos del cuerpo (498)

asexual reproduction (ay SEK shoo uhl REE pruh DUHK shuhn) reproduction that does not involve the union of sex cells and in which one parent produces offspring that are genetically identical to the parent (54)

reproducción asexual reproducción que no involucra la unión de células sexuales, en la que un solo progenitor produce descendencia que es genéticamente igual al progenitor (54)

ATP (AY TEE PEE) adenosine triphosphate, a molecule that acts as the main energy source for cell processes (60)

ATP adenosín trifosfato, una molécula orgánica que funciona como la fuente principal de energía para los procesos celulares (60)

B

Bacteria (bak TIR ee uh) in a modern taxonomic system, a domain made up of prokaryotes that differ from other prokaryotes in the makeup of their cell walls and in their genetics; this domain aligns with the traditional kingdom Eubacteria (339)

Bacteria en un sistema taxonómico moderno, un dominio compuesto por procariotes que se diferencian de otros procariotes por la composición de su pared celular y su composición genética; este dominio coincide con el reino tradicional Eubacteria (339)

blood (BLUHD) the fluid that carries gases, nutrients, and wastes through the body and that is made up of platelets, white blood cells, red blood cells, and plasma (502)

sangre el líquido que lleva gases, nutrientes y desechos por el cuerpo y que está formado por plaquetas, glóbulos blancos, glóbulos rojos y plasma (502)

blood pressure (BLUHD PRESH uhr) the force that blood exerts on the walls of the arteries (504)

presión sanguínea la fuerza que la sangre ejerce en las paredes de las arterias (504)

brain (BRAYN) the mass of nerve tissue that is the main control center of the nervous system (530)

encéfalo el órgano que es el centro principal de control del sistema nervioso (530)

bronchus (BRAHNG kuhs) one of the two tubes that connect the lungs with the trachea (509)

bronquio uno de los dos tubos que conectan los pulmones con la tráquea (509)

C

cancer (KAN suhr) a tumor in which the cells begin dividing at an uncontrolled rate and can become invasive (157)

cáncer un tumor en el cual las células comienzan a dividirse a una tasa incontrolable y pueden volverse invasivas (157)

capillary (CAP uh LER ee) a tiny blood vessel that allows an exchange between blood and cells in tissue (498)

capilar diminuto vaso sanguíneo que permite el intercambio entre la sangre y las células de los tejidos (498)

carbohydrate (CAHR boh HIE drayt) a class of molecules that includes sugars, starches, and fiber; contains carbon, hydrogen, and oxygen (59)

carbohidrato una clase de moléculas entre las que se incluyen azúcares, almidones y fibra; contiene carbono, hidrógeno y oxígeno (59)

cardiovascular system (KAHR dee OH VAS kyoo luhr SIS tuhm) a collection of organs that transport blood throughout the body; the organs in this system include the heart, the arteries, and the veins (496)

aparato cardiovascular un conjunto de órganos que transportan la sangre a través del cuerpo; los órganos de este sistema incluyen al corazón, las arterias y las venas (496)

*Academic Vocabulary

cartilage (KAHRT uhl ij) a flexible and strong connective tissue (444)

cartílago un tejido conectivo flexible y fuerte (444)

catastrophism (kuh TAS truh FIZ uhm) a principle that states that geologic change occurs suddenly (235)

catastrofismo un principio que establece que los cambios geológicos ocurren súbitamente (235)

cell (SEL) the smallest functional and structural unit of all living organisms; usually consists of a nucleus, cytoplasm, and a membrane (52, 114)

célula la unidad funcional y estructural más pequeña de todos los seres vivos; generalmente está compuesta por un núcleo, un citoplasma y una membrana (52, 114)

cell cycle (SEL SIE kuhl) the life cycle of a cell (152)

ciclo celular el ciclo de vida de una célula (152)

cell membrane (SEL MEM BRAYN) a phospholipid layer that covers a cell's surface and acts as a barrier between the inside of a cell and the cell's environment (117)

membrana celular una capa de fosfolípidos que cubre la superficie de la célula y funciona como una barrera entre el interior de la célula y el ambiente de la célula (117)

cellular respiration (SEL yoo luhr RES puh RAY shuhn) the process by which cells use oxygen to produce energy from food (149, 397)

respiración celular el proceso por medio del cual las células utilizan oxígeno para producir energía a partir de los alimentos (149, 397)

cell wall (SEL WAWL) a rigid structure that surrounds the cell membrane and provides support to the cell (120)

pared celular una estructura rígida que rodea la membrana celular y le brinda soporte a la célula (120)

central nervous system (SEN truhl NUHR vuhs SIS tuhm) the brain and the spinal cord; its main function is to control the flow of information in the body (526)

sistema nervioso central el cerebro y la médula espinal; su principal función es controlar el flujo de información en el cuerpo (526)

chlorophyll (KLAWR uh FIL) a green pigment that captures light energy for photosynthesis (396)

clorofila un pigmento verde que capta la energía luminosa para la fotosíntesis (396)

chloroplast (KLAWR uh PLAST) an organelle found in plant and algae cells where photosynthesis occurs (124)

cloroplasto un organelo que se encuentra en las células vegetales y en las células de las algas, en el cual se lleva a cabo la fotosíntesis (124)

chromosome (KROH muh SOHM) in a eukaryotic cell, one of the structures in the nucleus that are made up of DNA and protein; in a prokaryotic cell, the main ring of DNA (152)

cromosoma en una célula eucariótica, una de las estructuras del núcleo que está hecha de ADN y proteína; en una célula procariótica, el anillo principal de ADN (152)

classification (KLAS uh fi KAY shuhn) the division of organisms into groups, or classes, based on specific characteristics (332)

clasificación la división de organismos en grupos, o clases, en función de características específicas (332)

closed circulatory system (KLOHZD SUHR kyuh luh TAWR ee SIS tuhm) circulatory system in which the heart circulates blood through a network of vessels that form a closed loop (440)

aparato circulatorio cerrado un aparato circulatorio en el que el corazón hace que la sangre circule a través de una red de vasos que forman un circuito cerrado; la sangre no sale de los vasos sanguíneos y los materiales pasan a través de las paredes de los vasos por difusión (440)

English and Spanish Glossary   **627**

cochlea (KAHK lee uh) a coiled tube that is found in the inner ear and that is essential to hearing (538)

cóclea un tubo enrollado que se encuentra en el oído interno y es esencial para poder oír (538)

coelom (SEE luhm) a body cavity that contains the internal organs (426)

celoma una cavidad del cuerpo que contiene los órganos internos (426)

* **communicate** (kuh MYOO ni KAYT) to make known; to tell (5)

comunicar hacer saber; decir (5)

compound light microscope (kahm POWND LIET MIE kruh SKOHP) an instrument that magnifies small objects so that they can be seen easily by using two or more lenses (21)

microcopio óptico compuesto un instrumento que magnifica objetos pequeños de modo que se puedan ver fácilmente usando dos o más lentes (21)

* **computer** (kuhm PYOOT uhr) an electronic device that stores, retrieves, and calculates data (5)

computadora un dispositivo electrónico que almacena, recupera y calcula datos (5)

concave lens (kahn KAYV LENZ) a lens that is thinner in the middle than at the edges (94)

lente cóncava una lente que es más delgada en la parte media que en los bordes (94)

* **concept** (KAHN SEPT) an idea or thought (5)

concepto una idea o un pensamiento (5)

* **conclusion** (kuhn KLOO zhuhn) an idea developed from reasoning and investigating (295)

conclusión una idea que se desarrolla a partir del razonamiento y la investigación (295)

* **conduct** (kuhn DUHKT) to carry out; to do (5)

realizar llevar a cabo; hacer (5)

* **confer** (kuhn FUHR) to give (463)

conceder dar (463)

* **construct** (kuhn STRUHKT) to build; to make from parts (5, 295, 329)

construir armar; hacer con partes (5, 295, 329)

consumer (kuhn SOOM uhr) an organism that eats other organisms or organic matter (57, 426)

consumidor un organismo que se alimenta de otros organismos o de materia orgánica (57, 426)

continental drift (KAHN tuh NENT'l DRIFT) the hypothesis that a single large landmass broke up into smaller landmasses to form the continents, which then drifted to their present locations; the movement of continents (272)

deriva continental la hipótesis de que una sola masa de tierra se dividió en masas de tierra más pequeñas para formar los continentes, los cuales se fueron a la deriva hasta terminar en sus ubicaciones actuales; el movimiento de los continentes (272)

* **contribution** (KAHN truh BYOO shuhn) a part given toward a whole (421, 463, 493, 523)

contribución parte que se da a un todo (421, 463, 493, 523)

controlled experiment (kuhn TROHLD ek SPER uh muhnt) an experiment that tests only one factor at a time by using a comparison of a control group with an experimental group (16)

experimento controlado un experimento que prueba sólo un factor a la vez, comparando un grupo de control con un grupo experimental (16)

convex lens (kahn VEKS LENZ) a lens that is thicker in the middle than at the edges (93)

lente convexa una lente que es más gruesa en la parte media que en los bordes (93)

* **cycle** (SIE kuhl) a repeating series of changes (49, 231, 261, 357, 393, 421)

ciclo una serie de cambios que se repiten (49, 231, 261, 357, 393, 421)

cytokinesis (SIET oh ki NEE sis) the division of the cytoplasm of a cell (153)

citoquinesis la división del citoplasma de una célula (153)

*Academic Vocabulary

Glossary

cytoskeleton (SIET oh SKEL uh tuhn) the cytoplasmic network of protein filaments that plays an essential role in cell movement, shape, and division (122)

citoesqueleto la red citoplásmica de filamentos de proteínas que juega un papel esencial en el movimiento, forma y división de la célula (122)

D

decomposer (dee kuhm POHZ uhr) an organism that gets energy by breaking down the remains of dead organisms or animal wastes and consuming or absorbing the nutrients (57)

descomponedor un organismo que, para obtener energía, desintegra los restos de organismos muertos o los desechos de animales y consume o absorbe los nutrientes (57)

* **derived** (di RIEVD) gotten from something else (295, 329)

derivado que se obtiene de otra cosa (295, 329)

* **detect** (dee TEKT) to notice (73, 523)

detectar notar (73, 523)

* **device** (di VIES) a piece of equipment made for a specific use (463)

dispositivo un equipo hecho para un uso específico (463)

* **differentiate** (DIF uhr EN shee AYT) to become specialized in structure and function (111, 393, 553)

diferenciarse especializarse en estructura y función (111, 393, 553)

differentiation (DIF uhr EN shee AY shuhn) the process in which the structure and function of the parts of an organism change to enable specialization of those parts (427)

diferenciación el proceso por medio del cual la estructura y función de las partes de un organismo cambian para permitir la especialización de esas partes (427)

diploid (DIP LOYD) a cell that contains two haploid sets of chromosomes (189)

diploide una célula que contiene dos juegos de cromosomas haploides (189)

* **display** (di SPLAY) to show (5)

presentar mostrar (5)

* **distribution** (DIS tri BYOO shuhn) the relative arrangement of objects or organisms in time or space (261)

distribución disposición relativa de objetos u organismos en el tiempo o el espacio (261)

* **diversity** (duh VUHR suh tee) variety (295)

diversidad variedad (295)

DNA (DEE EN AY) **d**eoxyribo**n**ucleic **a**cid, a molecule that is present in all living cells and that contains the information that determines the traits that a living thing inherits and needs to live (208)

ADN **á**cido **d**esoxirribo**n**ucleico, una molécula que está presente en todas las células vivas y que contiene la información que determina los caracteres que un ser vivo hereda y necesita para vivir (208)

dominant trait (DAHM uh nuhnt TRAYT) the trait observed in the first generation when parents that have different traits are bred (177)

carácter dominante el carácter que se observa en la primera generación cuando se cruzan progenitores que tienen caracteres diferentes (177)

dormant (DAWR muhnt) describes the inactive state of a seed or other plant part when conditions are unfavorable to growth (402)

aletargado término que describe el estado inactivo de una semilla u otra parte de las plantas cuando las condiciones son desfavorables para el crecimiento (402)

E

electromagnetic spectrum (ee LEK troh mag NET ik SPEK truhm) all of the frequencies or wavelengths of electromagnetic radiation (77)

espectro electromagnético todas las frecuencias o longitudes de onda de la radiación electromagnética (77)

electromagnetic wave (ee LEK troh mag NET ik WAYV) a wave that consists of electric and magnetic fields that vibrate at right angles to each other (76)

onda electromagnética una onda que está formada por campos eléctricos y magnéticos que vibran formando un ángulo recto unos con otros (76)

electron microscope (ee LEK TRAHN MIE kruh SKOHP) a microscope that focuses a beam of electrons to magnify objects (21)

microscopio electrónico microscopio que enfoca un haz de electrones para aumentar la imagen de los objetos (21)

embryo (EM bree OH) in humans, a developing individual from fertilization through the 10th week of pregnancy (562)

embrión en los seres humanos, un individuo en desarrollo desde la fecundación hasta el final de la décima semana del embarazo (562)

endoplasmic reticulum (en doh PLAZ mik ri TIK yuh luhm) a system of membranes that is found in a cell's cytoplasm and that assists in the production, processing, and transport of proteins and in the production of lipids (123)

retículo endoplásmico un sistema de membranas que se encuentra en el citoplasma de la célula y que tiene una función en la producción, procesamiento y transporte de proteínas y en la producción de lípidos (123)

endoskeleton (EN doh SKEL uh tuhn) an internal skeleton made of bone and cartilage (434)

endoesqueleto un esqueleto interno hecho de hueso y cartílago (434)

* energy (EN uhr jee) the capacity to do work (111, 145, 357, 393)

energía la capacidad de realizar un trabajo (111, 145, 357, 393)

* environment (en VIE ruhn muhnt) the surrounding natural conditions that affect an organism (231, 261)

ambiente las condiciones naturales circundantes que afectan a un organismo (231, 261)

Eukarya (yoo KAR ee uh) in a modern taxonomic system, a domain made up of all eukaryotes; this domain aligns with the traditional kingdoms Protista, Fungi, Plantae, and Animalia (340)

Eukarya en un sistema taxonómico moderno, un dominio compuesto por todos los eucariotes; este dominio coincide con los reinos tradicionales Protista, Fungi, Plantae y Animalia (340)

eukaryote (yoo KAR ee OHT) an organism made up of cells that have a nucleus enclosed by a membrane; eukaryotes include protists, animals, plants, and fungi but not archaea or bacteria (119)

eucariote un organismo cuyas células tienen un núcleo contenido en una membrana; entre los eucariotes se encuentran protistas, animales, plantas y hongos, pero no arqueas ni bacterias (119)

* evidence (EV uh duhns) information showing whether an idea or belief is true or valid (231, 261, 295)

prueba información que demuestra si una idea o creencia es verdadera o válida (231, 261, 295)

evolution (EV uh LOO shuhn) the process in which inherited characteristics within a population change over generations such that new species sometimes arise (299)

evolución el proceso por medio del cual las características heredadas dentro de una población cambian con el transcurso de las generaciones de manera tal que a veces surgen nuevas especies (299)

*Academic Vocabulary

exoskeleton (EKS oh SKEL uh tuhn) a hard, external, supporting structure (433)

exoesqueleto una estructura de soporte, dura y externa (433)

*expand (ek SPAND) to make more detailed; to enlarge (295, 329)

expandir hacer más detallado; agrandar (295, 329)

extinct (ek STINGKT) describes a species that has died out completely (316)

extinto término que describe a una especie que ha desaparecido por completo (316)

extinction (ek STINGK shuhn) the death of every member of a species (278)

extinción la muerte de todos los miembros de una especie (278)

F

*factor (FAK tuhr) a condition or event that brings about or contributes to a result (295)

factor una condición o un suceso que produce un resultado o contribuye a él (295)

feedback mechanism (FEED BAK MEK uh NIZ uhm) a cycle of events in which information from one step controls or affects a previous step (535)

mecanismo de retroalimentación un ciclo de sucesos en el que la información de una etapa controla o afecta a una etapa anterior (535)

fermentation (FUHR muhn TAY shuhn) the breakdown of food without the use of oxygen (149)

fermentación la descomposición de los alimentos sin utilizar oxígeno (149)

fetus (FEET uhs) a developing human from the end of the 10th week of pregnancy until birth (564)

feto un ser humano en desarrollo desde el final de la décima semana del embarazo hasta el nacimiento (564)

first aid (FUHRST AYD) emergency medical care for someone who has been hurt or who is sick (37)

primeros auxilios atención médica de emergencia para una persona que se lastimó o está enferma (37)

fossil (FAHS uhl) the trace or remains of an organism that lived long ago, most commonly preserved in sedimentary rock (264, 300)

fósil los indicios o los restos de un organismo que vivió hace mucho tiempo, comúnmente preservados en las rocas sedimentarias (264, 300)

fossil record (FAHS uhl REK uhrd) the history of life in the geologic past as indicated by the traces or remains of living things (300)

registro fósil la historia de la vida en el pasado geológico según la indican los rastros o restos de seres vivos (300)

*framework (FRAYM WUHRK) a basic structure that supports something (421, 463)

armazón estructura básica que sostiene algo (421, 463)

function (FUHNGK shuhn) the special, normal, or proper activity of an organ or part (130)

función la actividad especial, normal o adecuada de un órgano o parte (130)

*function (FUHNGK shuhn) (n.) use or purpose (111, 357, 393, 421, 463, 493, 523, 553)

función uso o propósito (111, 357, 393, 421, 463, 493, 523, 553)

*function (FUHNGK shuhn) (v.) to work (49, 111, 205, 329, 421, 463, 493, 523)

funcionar trabajar (49, 111, 205, 329, 421, 463, 493, 523)

Fungi (FUHN JIE) a kingdom made up of non-green, eukaryotic organisms that have no means of movement, reproduce by using spores, and get food by breaking down substances in their surroundings and absorbing the nutrients (340)

Fungi un reino formado por organismos eucarióticos no verdes que no tienen capacidad de movimiento, se reproducen por esporas y obtienen alimento al descomponer sustancias de su entorno y absorber los nutrientes (340)

G

gene (JEEN) one set of instructions for an inherited trait (180)

gene un conjunto de instrucciones para un carácter heredado (180)

*generate (JEN uhr AYT) to bring about; to produce (357, 393, 493, 553)

generar provocar; producir (357, 393, 493, 553)

genotype (JEE nuh TIEP) the entire genetic makeup of an organism; also the combination of genes for one or more specific traits (181)

genotipo la constitución genética completa de un organismo; *también,* la combinación de genes para uno o más caracteres específicos (181)

geologic time scale (JEE uh LAHJ ik TIEM SKAYL) the standard method used to divide Earth's long natural history into manageable parts (276)

escala de tiempo geológico el método estándar que se usa para dividir la larga historia natural de la Tierra en partes razonables (276)

Golgi complex (GOHL jee KAHM PLEKS) a cell organelle that helps make and package materials to be transported out of the cell (125)

aparato de Golgi un organelo celular que ayuda a hacer y a empacar los materiales que serán transportados al exterior de la célula (125)

gymnosperm (JIM noh SPUHRM) a woody, vascular seed plant whose seeds are not enclosed by an ovary or fruit (362)

gimnosperma una planta leñosa vascular que produce semillas que no están contenidas en un ovario o fruto (362)

H

half-life (HAF LIEF) the time required for half of a sample of a radioactive isotope to break down by radioactive decay to form a daughter isotope (247)

vida media el tiempo que se requiere para que la mitad de una muestra de un isótopo radiactivo se descomponga por desintegración radiactiva y forme un isótopo hijo (247)

haploid (HAP LOYD) describes a cell, nucleus, or organism that has only one set of unpaired chromosomes (189)

haploide término que describe a una célula, núcleo u organismo que tiene sólo un juego de cromosomas que no están asociados en pares (189)

heredity (hee RED i tee) the passing of genetic traits from parent to offspring (174)

herencia la transmisión de caracteres genéticos de padres a hijos (174)

homeostasis (HOH mee OH STAY sis) the maintenance of a constant internal state in a changing environment (53)

homeostasis la capacidad de mantener un estado interno constante en un ambiente en cambio (53)

homologous chromosomes (hoh MAHL uh guhs KROH muh SOHMZ) chromosomes that have the same sequence of genes and the same structure (189)

cromosomas homólogos cromosomas con la misma secuencia de genes y la misma estructura (189)

hypothesis (hie PAHTH uh sis) a testable idea or explanation that leads to scientific investigation (14)

hipótesis una idea o explicación que conlleva a la investigación científica y que se puede probar (14)

*Academic Vocabulary

Glossary

I

*identical (ie DEN ti kuhl) being exactly the same (145, 171)

idéntico exactamente igual (145, 171)

*impact (IM PAKT) a striking together; collision (231)

impacto choque; colisión (231)

*incidence (IN suh duhns) the point at which a line or something moving in a straight line, such as a ray of light, meets a surface (73)

incidencia el punto en el que una línea o algo que se mueve en línea recta, como un rayo de luz, se encuentra con una superficie (73)

index fossil (IN DEKS FAHS uhl) a fossil that is used to establish the age of a rock layer because the fossil is distinct, abundant, and widespread and the species that formed that fossil existed for only a short span of geologic time (268)

fósil guía un fósil que se usa para establecer la edad de una capa de roca debido a que puede diferenciarse bien de otros, es abundante y está extendido; la especie que formó ese fósil existió sólo por un corto período de tiempo geológico (268)

*indicate (IN di KAYT) to be or give a sign of; to show (261)

indicar ser o dar una señal de algo; mostrar (261)

*individual (IN duh VIJ oo uhl) being a single, separate entity; particular (421, 463, 493, 523)

individual se dice de una entidad única e independiente; particular (421, 463, 493, 523)

*insufficient (IN suh FISH uhnt) not enough (295)

insuficiente que no basta (295)

integumentary system (in TEG yoo MEN tuhr ee SIS tuhm) the organ system that forms a protective covering on the outside of the body (534)

sistema integumentario el sistema de órganos que forma una cubierta de protección en la parte exterior del cuerpo (534)

invertebrate (in VUHR tuh brit) an animal that does not have a backbone (431)

invertebrado un animal que no tiene columna vertebral (431)

*investigation (in VES tuh GAY shuhn) a detailed search for answers (5)

investigación búsqueda cuidadosa de respuestas (5)

iris (IE ris) the colored, circular part of the eye (537)

iris la parte coloreada y circular del ojo (537)

J

joint (JOYNT) a place where two or more bones meet (474)

articulación un lugar donde se unen dos o más huesos (474)

L

*labeled (LAY buhld) marked with a name or description (5)

rotulado identificado con un nombre o una descripción (5)

large intestine (LAHRJ in TES tuhn) the wider and shorter portion of the intestine that removes water from mostly digested food and that turns the waste into semisolid feces, or stool (447)

intestino grueso la porción más ancha y más corta del intestino, que elimina el agua de los alimentos casi totalmente digeridos y convierte los desechos en heces semisólidas o excremento (447)

larynx (LAR ingks) the area of the throat that contains the vocal cords and produces vocal sounds (509)

laringe el área de la garganta que contiene las cuerdas vocales y que produce sonidos vocales (509)

Glossary

law (LAW) a descriptive statement or equation that reliably predicts events under certain conditions (29)

ley una ecuación o afirmación descriptiva que predice sucesos de manera confiable en determinadas condiciones (29)

law of crosscutting relationships (LAW UHV KRAWS KUHT ing ri LAY shuhn SHIPS) the principle that a fault or body of rock is younger than any other body of rock that it cuts through (243)

ley de las relaciones entrecortadas el principio que establece que una falla o cuerpo rocoso siempre es más joven que cualquier otro cuerpo rocoso que atraviese (243)

* **layer** (LAY uhr) a separate or distinct portion of matter that has thickness (231, 261)

capa una parte separada o diferenciada de materia que tiene espesor (231, 261)

lens (LENZ) a transparent object that refracts light waves such that they converge or diverge to create an image (92)

lente un objeto transparente que refracta las ondas de luz de modo que converjan o diverjan para crear una imagen (92)

lever (LEV uhr) a simple machine that consists of a bar that pivots at a fixed point called a *fulcrum* (478)

palanca una máquina simple formada por una barra que gira en un punto fijo llamado *fulcro* (478)

* **liberate** (LIB uhr AYT) to release; to set free (111, 145, 357, 393)

liberar soltar; poner en libertad (111, 145, 357, 393)

life science (LIEF SIE uhns) the study of living things (8)

ciencias biológicas el estudio de los seres vivos (8)

lipid (LIP id) a fat molecule or a molecule that has similar properties; examples include oils, waxes, and steroids (60)

lípido una molécula de grasa o una molécula que tiene propiedades similares; algunos ejemplos son los aceites, las ceras y los esteroides (60)

* **located** (LOH KAYT id) to be in a certain place (145, 171, 205)

ubicarse estar en determinado lugar (145, 171, 205)

* **logical** (LAHJ i kuhl) reasoned, well thought out (5)

lógico razonado, bien pensado (5)

lysosome (LIE suh SOHM) a cell organelle that contains digestive enzymes (126)

lisosoma un organelo celular que contiene enzimas digestivas (126)

M

* **major** (MAY juhr) of great importance or large scale (231)

principal de gran importancia o gran escala (231)

mass (MAS) a measure of the amount of matter in an object (24)

masa una medida de la cantidad de materia que tiene un objeto (24)

mechanical advantage (muh KAN i kuhl ad VANT ij) a number that tells you how many times a machine multiplies force (478)

ventaja mecánica un número que dice cuántas veces una máquina multiplica una fuerza (478)

* **mechanism** (MEK uh NIZ uhm) any system or means by which something gets done (295)

mecanismo cualquier sistema o medio que sirve para hacer algo (295)

*Academic Vocabulary

Glossary

*medium (MEE dee uhm) a substance through which something else is sent or carried (73)

medio una sustancia a través de la cual se envía o transporta algo (73)

meiosis (mie OH sis) a process in cell division during which the number of chromosomes decreases to half the original number by two divisions of the nucleus, which results in the production of sex cells (gametes or spores) (190)

meiosis un proceso de división celular durante el cual el número de cromosomas disminuye a la mitad del número original por medio de dos divisiones del núcleo, lo cual resulta en la producción de células sexuales (gametos o esporas) (190)

metabolism (muh TAB uh LIZ uhm) the sum of all chemical processes that occur in an organism (54)

metabolismo la suma de todos los procesos químicos que ocurren en un organismo (54)

metamorphosis (MET uh MAWR fuh sis) a process in the life cycle of many animals during which a rapid change from the immature organism to the adult takes place; an example is the change from larva to adult in insects (442)

metamorfosis un proceso del ciclo de vida de muchos animales durante el cual ocurre un cambio rápido de la forma inmadura del organismo a la adulta; un ejemplo es el cambio de larva a adulto en los insectos (442)

*method (METH uhd) a way of doing something (357, 393, 421)

método una forma de hacer algo (357, 393, 421)

mitochondrion (MIET oh KAHN dree uhn) in eukaryotic cells, the cell organelle that is surrounded by two membranes and that is the site of cellular respiration (124)

mitocondria en las células eucarióticas, el organelo celular rodeado por dos membranas que es el lugar donde se lleva a cabo la respiración celular (124)

mitosis (mie TOH sis) in eukaryotic cells, a process of cell division that forms two new nuclei, each of which has the same number of chromosomes (153)

mitosis en las células eucarióticas, un proceso de división celular que forma dos núcleos nuevos, cada uno de los cuales posee el mismo número de cromosomas (153)

model (MAHD'l) a pattern, plan, representation, or description designed to show the structure or workings of an object, system, or concept (26)

modelo un diseño, plan, representación o descripción cuyo objetivo es mostrar la estructura o funcionamiento de un objeto, sistema o concepto (26)

muscular system (MUHS kyoo luhr SIS tuhm) the organ system whose primary function is movement and flexibility (477)

sistema muscular el sistema de órganos cuya función principal es permitir el movimiento y la flexibilidad (477)

mutation (myoo TAY shuhn) a change in the nucleotide-base sequence of a gene or DNA molecule (216)

mutación un cambio en la secuencia de la base de nucleótidos de un gen o de una molécula de ADN (216)

N

natural selection (NACH uhr uhl suh LEK shuhn) the process by which individuals that are better adapted to their environment survive and reproduce more successfully than less well adapted individuals do; a theory to explain the mechanism of evolution (310)

selección natural el proceso por medio del cual los individuos que están mejor adaptados a su ambiente sobreviven y se reproducen con más éxito que los individuos menos adaptados; una teoría que explica el mecanismo de la evolución (310)

nerve (NUHRV) a collection of nerve fibers through which impulses travel between the central nervous system and other parts of the body (528)

nervio un conjunto de fibras nerviosas a través de las cuales se desplazan los impulsos entre el sistema nervioso central y otras partes del cuerpo (528)

neuron (NOO RAHN) a nerve cell that is specialized to receive and conduct electrical impulses (527)

neurona una célula nerviosa que está especializada en recibir y transmitir impulsos eléctricos (527)

nonvascular plant (nahn VAHS kyuh luhr PLANT) a plant that lacks specialized conducting tissues and true roots, stems, and leaves (362)

planta no vascular una planta que carece de tejidos transportadores y de raíces, tallos y hojas verdaderos (362)

nucleic acid (noo KLEE ik AS id) a molecule made up of subunits called *nucleotides* (61)

ácido nucleico una molécula formada por subunidades llamadas *nucleótidos* (61)

nucleotide (NOO klee oh TIED) in a nucleic-acid chain, a subunit that consists of a sugar, a phosphate, and a nitrogenous base (208)

nucleótido en una cadena de ácidos nucleicos, una subunidad formada por un azúcar, un fosfato y una base nitrogenada (208)

nucleus (NOO klee uhs) in a eukaryotic cell, a membrane-bound organelle that contains the cell's DNA and that has a role in processes such as growth, metabolism, and reproduction (117)

núcleo en una célula eucariótica, un organelo cubierto por una membrana, el cual contiene el ADN de la célula y participa en procesos tales como el crecimiento, metabolismo y reproducción (117)

O

*occur (uh KUHR) to happen (231, 295)

ocurrir pasar (231, 295)

open circulatory system (OH puhn SUHR kyuh luh TAWR ee SIS tuhm) a circulatory system in which the circulatory fluid is not contained entirely within vessels (440)

aparato circulatorio abierto un aparato circulatorio en el que el fluido circulatorio no está totalmente contenido en los vasos sanguíneos; un corazón bombea fluido por los vasos sanguíneos, los cuales se vacían en espacios llamados senos (440)

organ (AWR guhn) a collection of tissues that carry out a specialized function of the body (131, 468)

órgano un conjunto de tejidos que desempeñan una función especializada en el cuerpo (131, 468)

organelle (AWR guh NEL) one of the small bodies in a cell's cytoplasm that are specialized to perform a specific function (117)

organelo uno de los cuerpos pequeños del citoplasma de una célula que están especializados para llevar a cabo una función específica (117)

organism (AWR guh NIZ uhm) a living thing; anything that can carry out life processes independently (128)

organismo un ser vivo; cualquier cosa que pueda llevar a cabo procesos vitales independientemente (128)

organ system (AWR guhn SIS tuhm) a group of organs that work together to perform body functions (132)

aparato (o sistema) de órganos un grupo de órganos que trabajan en conjunto para desempeñar funciones corporales (132)

ovary (OH vuh ree) in flowering plants, the lower part of a pistil that produces eggs in ovules (380); in the female reproductive system of animals, an organ that produces eggs (557)

ovario en las plantas con flores, la parte inferior del pistilo que produce óvulos (380); en el aparato reproductor femenino de los animales, un órgano que produce óvulos (557)

*Academic Vocabulary

Glossary

ovule (AHV YOOL) a structure in the ovary of a seed plant that contains an embryo sac and that develops into a seed after fertilization (380)

óvulo una estructura del ovario de una planta con semillas que contiene un saco embrionario y se desarrolla para convertirse en una semilla después de la fecundación (380)

P

paleontology (PAY lee uhn TAHL uh jee) the scientific study of fossils (237)

paleontología el estudio científico de los fósiles (237)

penis (PEE nis) the male organ that transfers sperm to a female and that carries urine out of the body (556)

pene el órgano masculino que transfiere espermatozoides a una hembra y que lleva la orina hacia el exterior del cuerpo (556)

*period (PIR ee uhd) an interval or unit (231)

período intervalo o unidad (231)

peripheral nervous system (puh RIF uhr uhl NUHR vuhs SIS tuhm) all of the parts of the nervous system except for the brain and the spinal cord (526)

sistema nervioso periférico todas las partes del sistema nervioso, excepto el encéfalo y la médula espinal (526)

petal (PET uhl) one of the usually brightly colored, leaf-shaped parts that make up one of the rings of a flower (379)

pétalo una de las partes de una flor que normalmente tienen colores brillantes y forma de hoja, las cuales forman uno de los anillos de una flor (379)

pharynx (FAR ingks) the passage from the mouth to the larynx and esophagus (509)

faringe en los gusanos planos, el tubo muscular que va de la boca a la cavidad gastrovascular; en los animales que tienen tracto digestivo, el conducto que va de la boca a la laringe y al esófago (509)

phenotype (FEE noh TIEP) an organism's appearance or other detectable characteristic (180)

fenotipo la apariencia de un organismo u otra característica perceptible (180)

phloem (FLOH EM) the tissue that conducts food in vascular plants (374)

floema el tejido que transporta alimento en las plantas vasculares (374)

phospholipid (FAHS foh LIP id) a lipid that contains phosphorus and that is a structural component in cell membranes (60)

fosfolípido un lípido que contiene fósforo y que es un componente estructural de la membrana celular (60)

photosynthesis (FOHT oh SIN thuh sis) the process by which plants, algae, and some bacteria use sunlight, carbon dioxide, and water to make food (148, 396)

fotosíntesis el proceso por medio del cual las plantas, las algas y algunas bacterias utilizan la luz solar, el dióxido de carbono y el agua para producir alimento (148, 396)

pistil (PIS til) the female reproductive part of a flower that produces seeds and consists of an ovary, style, and stigma (380)

pistilo la parte reproductora femenina de una flor, la cual produce semillas y está formada por el ovario, estilo y estigma (380)

placenta (pluh SEN tuh) the partly fetal and partly maternal organ by which materials are exchanged between a fetus and the mother (563)

placenta el órgano parcialmente fetal y parcialmente materno por medio del cual se intercambian materiales entre el feto y la madre (563)

Plantae (PLAN tee) a kingdom made up of complex, multicellular organisms that are usually green, have cell walls made of cellulose, cannot move around, and use the sun's energy to make sugar by photosynthesis (341)

Plantae un reino formado por organismos pluricelulares complejos que normalmente son verdes, tienen una pared celular de celulosa, no tienen capacidad de movimiento y utilizan la energía del Sol para producir azúcar mediante la fotosíntesis (341)

plate tectonics (PLAYT tek TAHN iks) the theory that explains how large pieces of Earth's outermost layer, called *tectonic plates,* move and change shape (270)

tectónica de placas la teoría que explica cómo se mueven y cambian de forma las placas tectónicas, que son grandes porciones de la capa más externa de la Tierra (270)

pollen (PAHL uhn) the tiny granules that contain the male gametophyte of seed plants (368)

polen los gránulos diminutos que contienen el gametofito masculino en las plantas con semilla (368)

pollination (PAWL uh NAY shuhn) the transfer of pollen from the male reproductive structures to the female structures of seed plants (371)

polinización la transferencia de polen de las estructuras reproductoras masculinas a las estructuras femeninas de las plantas con semillas (371)

pregnancy (PREG nuhn see) in medical practice, the period of time between the first day of a woman's last menstrual period and the delivery of her baby (about 280 days, or 40 weeks); in developmental biology, the period of time in which a woman carries a developing human from fertilization until the birth of the baby (about 266 days, or 38 weeks) (563)

embarazo en medicina, el período de tiempo que transcurre entre el primer día del último período menstrual de una mujer y el nacimiento de su bebé (aproximadamente 280 días, o 40 semanas); en biología del desarrollo, el período de tiempo durante el cual una mujer lleva en su interior a un ser humano en desarrollo desde la fecundación hasta el nacimiento del bebé (aproximadamente 266 días, o 38 semanas) (563)

*principle (PRIN suh puhl) basic law, rule, or belief (463)

principio ley, regla o creencia básica (463)

probability (PRAHB uh BIL uh tee) the likelihood that a possible future event will occur in any given instance of the event (182)

probabilidad la probabilidad de que ocurra un posible suceso futuro en cualquier caso dado del suceso (182)

*process (PRAH ses) a set of steps, events, or changes (145, 231, 357, 393)

proceso una serie de pasos, sucesos o cambios (145, 231, 357, 393)

producer (proh DOOS uhr) an organism that can make its own food by using energy from its surroundings (57)

productor un organismo que puede elaborar sus propios alimentos utilizando la energía de su entorno (57)

*project (PRAH jekt) a special task done to use, explain, or add information to classroom lessons (5)

proyecto tarea especial que se realiza para aplicar o explicar las lecciones o para agregar información (5)

prokaryote (proh KAR ee oht) a single-celled organism that does not have a nucleus or membrane-bound organelles; examples are archaea and bacteria (118)

procariote un organismo unicelular que no tiene núcleo ni organelos cubiertos por una membrana, por ejemplo, las arqueas y las bacterias (118)

protein (PROH teen) a molecule that is made up of amino acids and that is needed to build and repair body structures and to regulate processes in the body (58)

proteína una molécula formada por aminoácidos que es necesaria para construir y reparar estructuras corporales y para regular procesos del cuerpo (58)

*Academic Vocabulary

Protista (proh TIST uh) a kingdom of mostly one-celled eukaryotic organisms that are different from plants, animals, archaea, bacteria, and fungi (340)

Protista un reino compuesto principalmente por organismos eucarióticos unicelulares que son diferentes de las plantas, animales, arqueas, bacterias y hongos (340)

pulmonary circulation (PUL muh NER ee SUHR kyoo LAY shuhn) the flow of blood from the heart to the lungs and back to the heart through the pulmonary arteries, capillaries, and veins (499)

circulación pulmonar el flujo de sangre del corazón a los pulmones y de vuelta al corazón a través de las arterias, los capilares y las venas pulmonares (499)

pupil (PYOO puhl) the opening that is located in the center of the iris of the eye and that controls the amount of light that enters the eye (536)

pupila la abertura que se ubica al centro del iris del ojo y que controla la cantidad de luz que entra en el ojo (536)

R

radioactive decay (RAY dee oh AK tiv dee KAY) the process in which a radioactive isotope tends to break down into a stable isotope of the same element or another element (246)

desintegración radiactiva el proceso por medio del cual un isótopo radiactivo tiende a desintegrarse y formar un isótopo estable del mismo elemento o de otro elemento (246)

radiometric dating (RAY dee oh MET rik DAYT ing) a method of determining the absolute age of an object by comparing the relative percentages of a radioactive (parent) isotope and a stable (daughter) isotope (247)

datación radiométrica un método para determinar la edad absoluta de un objeto comparando los porcentajes relativos de un isótopo radiactivo (precursor) y un isótopo estable (hijo) (247)

*react (ree AKT) to act in return; to respond (73)

reaccionar actuar en respuesta a otra cosa; responder (73)

recessive trait (ri SES iv TRAYT) a trait that reappears in the second generation after disappearing in the first generation when parents with different traits are bred (177)

carácter recesivo un carácter que vuelve a aparecer en la segunda generación después de desaparecer en la primera generación, cuando se cruzan progenitores con caracteres diferentes (177)

reflection (ri FLEK shuhn) the bouncing back of a ray of light, sound, or heat when the ray hits a surface that it does not go through (82)

reflexión el rebote de un rayo de luz, sonido o calor cuando el rayo golpea una superficie pero no la atraviesa (82)

reflex (REE FLEKS) an involuntary and almost immediate movement in response to a stimulus (535)

reflejo un movimiento involuntario y prácticamente inmediato en respuesta a un estímulo (535)

refraction (ri FRAK shuhn) the bending of a wavefront as the wavefront passes between two substances in which the speed of the wave differs (90)

refracción el curvamiento de un frente de ondas a medida que el frente pasa entre dos sustancias en las que la velocidad de las ondas difiere (90)

relative dating (REL uh tiv DAYT ing) any method of determining whether an event or object is older or younger than other events or objects (238)

datación relativa cualquier método que se utiliza para determinar si un acontecimiento u objeto es más viejo o más joven que otros acontecimientos u objetos (238)

*research (REE SUHRCH) a careful search for and study of information (5)

investigación búsqueda y análisis cuidadosos de información (5)

* resource (REE SAWRS) anything that can be used to take care of a need (5)

recurso cualquier cosa que se puede usar para satisfacer una necesidad (5)

respiration (RES puh RAY shuhn) in biology, the exchange of oxygen and carbon dioxide between living cells and their environment; includes breathing and cellular respiration (508)

respiración en biología, el intercambio de oxígeno y dióxido de carbono entre células vivas y su ambiente; incluye la respiración y la respiración celular (508)

respiratory system (RES puhr uh TAWR ee SIS tuhm) a collection of organs whose primary function is to take in oxygen and expel carbon dioxide; the organs of this system include the lungs, the throat, and the passageways that lead to the lungs (508)

aparato respiratorio un conjunto de órganos cuya función principal es tomar oxígeno y expulsar dióxido de carbono; los órganos de este aparato incluyen a los pulmones, la garganta y las vías que llevan a los pulmones (508)

retina (RET 'n uh) the light-sensitive inner layer of the eye, which receives images formed by the lens and transmits them through the optic nerve to the brain (536)

retina la capa interna del ojo, sensible a la luz, que recibe imágenes formadas por el lente ocular y las transmite al cerebro por medio del nervio óptico (536)

rhizoid (RIE ZOYD) a rootlike structure in nonvascular plants that holds the plants in place and helps plants get water and nutrients (364)

rizoide una estructura parecida a una raíz que se encuentra en las plantas no vasculares; mantiene a las plantas en su lugar y las ayuda a obtener agua y nutrientes (364)

rhizome (RIE ZOHM) a horizontal, underground stem that produces new leaves, shoots, and roots (366)

rizoma un tallo horizontal subterráneo que produce nuevas hojas, brotes y raíces (366)

ribosome (RIE buh SOHM) a cell organelle composed of RNA and protein; the site of protein synthesis (123, 215)

ribosoma un organelo celular compuesto de ARN y proteína; el sitio donde ocurre la síntesis de proteínas (123, 215)

RNA (AHR EN AY) **r**ibo**n**ucleic **a**cid, a molecule that is present in all living cells and that plays a role in protein production (214)

ARN **á**cido **r**ibo**n**ucleico, una molécula que está presente en todas las células vivas y que juega un papel en la producción de proteínas (214)

S

scale (SKAYL) the relationship between the measurements on a model, map, or diagram and the actual measurement or distance (28)

escala la relación entre las medidas de un modelo, mapa o diagrama y la medida o distancia real (28)

scattering (SKAT uhr ing) an interaction of light with matter that causes light to change its energy, direction of motion, or both (85)

dispersión una interacción de la luz con la materia que hace que la luz cambie su energía, la dirección del movimiento o ambas (85)

scientific methods (SIE uhn TIF ik METH uhds) a series of steps followed to solve problems (12)

métodos científicos una serie de pasos que se siguen para solucionar problemas (12)

sedimentary rock (SED uh MEN tuhr ee RAHK) a rock that forms from compressed or cemented layers of sediment (238)

roca sedimentaria una roca que se forma a partir de capas comprimidas o cementadas de sedimento (238)

segment (SEG muhnt) any part of a larger structure, such as the body of an organism, that is set off by natural or arbitrary boundaries (439)

segmento cualquier parte de una estructura más grande, como el cuerpo de un organismo, que se determina por límites naturales o arbitrarios (439)

*Academic Vocabulary

*select (suh LEKT) to choose; to pick out (5)

seleccionar elegir; escoger (5)

*selection (suh LEK shuhn) the process of choosing (295)

selección proceso de elegir (295)

selective breeding (suh LEK tiv BREED ing) the human practice of breeding animals or plants that have certain desired traits (308)

reproducción selectiva la práctica humana de cruzar animales o plantas que tienen ciertos caracteres deseados (308)

sepal (SEE puhl) in a flower, one of the outermost rings of modified leaves that protect the flower bud (379)

sépalo en una flor, uno de los anillos más externos de hojas modificadas que protegen el capullo de la flor (379)

*sexual (SEK shoo uhl) having to do with sex (171, 357, 393, 421, 553)

sexual relacionado con el sexo (171, 357, 393, 421, 553)

sexual reproduction (SEK shoo uhl REE pruh DUHK shuhn) reproduction in which the sex cells from two parents unite to produce offspring that share traits from both parents (54)

reproducción sexual reproducción en la que se unen las células sexuales de los dos progenitores para producir descendencia que comparte caracteres de ambos progenitores (54)

*significant (sig NIF uh kuhnt) important (261)

significativo importante (261)

*similar (SIM uh luhr) almost the same (231)

similar casi igual (231)

*similarly (SIM uh luhr lee) in almost the same way (49, 111, 205, 329)

de modo similar casi del mismo modo (49, 111, 205, 329)

skeletal system (SKEL i tuhl SIS tuhm) the organ system whose primary function is to support and protect the body and to allow the body to move (473)

sistema esquelético el sistema de órganos cuya función principal es sostener y proteger el cuerpo y permitir que se mueva (473)

small intestine (SMAWL in TES tuhn) the organ between the stomach and the large intestine where most of the breakdown of food happens and most of the nutrients from food are absorbed (447)

intestino delgado el órgano que se encuentra entre el estómago y el intestino grueso en el cual se produce la mayor parte de la descomposición de los alimentos y se absorben la mayoría de los nutrientes (447)

speciation (SPEE shee AY shuhn) the formation of new species as a result of evolution (314)

especiación la formación de especies nuevas como resultado de la evolución (314)

species (SPEE seez) a group of organisms that are closely related and can mate to produce fertile offspring (298)

especie un grupo de organismos que tienen un parentesco cercano y que pueden aparearse para producir descendencia fértil (298)

stamen (STAY muhn) the male reproductive structure of a flower that produces pollen and consists of an anther at the tip of a filament (380)

estambre la estructura reproductora masculina de una flor, que produce polen y está formada por una antera ubicada en la punta del filamento (380)

stimulus (STIM yoo luhs) anything that causes a reaction or change in an organism or any part of an organism (404)

estímulo cualquier cosa que causa una reacción o cambio en un organismo o cualquier parte de un organismo (404)

stoma (STOH muh) one of many openings in a leaf or a stem of a plant that enable gas exchange to occur (plural, *stomata*) (398)

estoma una de las muchas aberturas de una hoja o de un tallo de una planta, la cual permite que se lleve a cabo el intercambio de gases (398)

* **structural** (STRUHK chuhr uhl) having to do with the arrangement of the parts of a whole (421, 463)

estructural relacionado con la distribución de las partes de un todo (421, 463)

structure (STRUHK shuhr) the arrangement of parts in an organism (130)

estructura el orden y distribución de las partes de un organismo (130)

* **structure** (STRUHK chuhr) the arrangement of the parts of a whole (111, 357, 393, 421, 463, 493, 523)

estructura la forma en que se distribuyen las partes de un todo (111, 357, 393, 421, 463, 493, 523)

superposition (SOO puhr puh ZISH uhn) a principle that states that younger rocks lie above older rocks if the layers have not been disturbed (240)

superposición un principio que establece que las rocas más jóvenes se encontrarán sobre las rocas más viejas si las capas no han sido alteradas (240)

* **survival** (suhr VIE vuhl) the continuing to live or exist (295)

supervivencia acción de continuar viviendo o existiendo (295)

systemic circulation (sis TEM ik SUHR kyoo LAY shuhn) the flow of blood from the heart to all parts of the body and back to the heart (499)

circulación sistémica el flujo de sangre del corazón a todas las partes del cuerpo y de vuelta al corazón (499)

T

taxonomy (taks AHN uh mee) the science of describing, naming, and classifying organisms (333)

taxonomía la ciencia de describir, nombrar y clasificar organismos (333)

technology (tek NAHL uh jee) the application of science for practical purposes; the use of tools, machines, materials, and processes to meet human needs (20)

tecnología la aplicación de la ciencia con fines prácticos; el uso de herramientas, máquinas, materiales y procesos para satisfacer las necesidades de los seres humanos (20)

* **technology** (tek NAHL uh jee) tools, including electronic products (5)

tecnología herramientas; incluye los productos electrónicos (5)

temperature (TEM puhr uh chuhr) a measure of how hot (or cold) something is; specifically, a measure of the average kinetic energy of the particles in an object (25)

temperatura una medida de qué tan caliente (o frío) está algo; específicamente, una medida de la energía cinética promedio de las partículas de un objeto (25)

testes (TES TEEZ) the primary male reproductive organs, which produce sperm and testosterone (singular, *testis*) (556)

testículos los principales órganos reproductores masculinos, los cuales producen espermatozoides y testosterona (556)

theory (THEE uh ree) a system of ideas that explains many related observations and is supported by a large body of evidence acquired through scientific investigation (29)

teoría un sistema de ideas que explica muchas observaciones relacionadas y que está respaldado por una gran cantidad de pruebas obtenidas mediante la investigación científica (29)

* Academic Vocabulary

tissue (TISH oo) a group of similar cells that perform a common function (131, 467)

tejido un grupo de células similares que llevan a cabo una función común (131, 467)

trace fossil (TRAYS FAHS uhl) a fossilized structure, such as a footprint or coprolite, that formed in sedimentary rock by animal activity on or within soft sediment (266)

fósil traza una estructura fosilizada, como una huella o un coprolito, que se formó en una roca sedimentaria por la actividad de un animal sobre sedimento blando o dentro de éste (266)

trachea (TRAY kee uh) the tube that connects the larynx to the lungs (509)

tráquea en los insectos, miriápodos y arañas, uno de los conductos de una red de conductos de aire; en los vertebrados, el conducto que une la laringe con los pulmones (509)

trait (TRAYT) a genetically determined characteristic (308)

carácter una característica determinada genéticamente (308)

transmission (trans MISH uhn) the passing of light or other form of energy through matter (85)

transmisión el paso de la luz u otra forma de energía a través de la materia (85)

*transmit (trans MIT) to send or cause to go from one thing to another (73)

transmitir enviar o hacer que algo se mueva de un lugar a otro (73)

transpiration (TRAN spuh RAY shuhn) the process by which plants release water vapor into the air through stomata (398)

transpiración el proceso por medio del cual las plantas liberan vapor de agua al aire por medio de los estomas; *también,* la liberación de vapor de agua al aire por otros organismos (398)

tropism (TROH PIZ uhm) growth of all or part of an organism in response to an external stimulus, such as light (406)

tropismo el crecimiento de un organismo o de una parte de él en respuesta a un estímulo externo, como por ejemplo, la luz (406)

U

umbilical cord (uhm BIL i kuhl KAWRD) the ropelike structure through which blood vessels pass and by which a developing mammal is connected to the placenta (563)

cordón umbilical la estructura con forma de cuerda a través de la cual pasan vasos sanguíneos y por medio de la cual un mamífero en desarrollo está unido a la placenta (563)

unconformity (uhn kuhn FAWRM uh tee) a break in the geologic record created when rock layers are eroded or when sediment is not deposited for a long period of time (242)

disconformidad una ruptura en el registro geológico, creada cuando las capas de roca se erosionan o cuando el sedimento no se deposita durante un largo período de tiempo (242)

uniformitarianism (YOON uh FAWRM uh TER ee uhn IZ uhm) a principle that geologic processes that occurred in the past can be explained by current geologic processes (234)

uniformitarianismo un principio que establece que es posible explicar los procesos geológicos que ocurrieron en el pasado en función de los procesos geológicos actuales (234)

uterus (YOO tuhr uhs) in female placental mammals, the hollow, muscular organ in which an embryo embeds itself and develops into a fetus (557)

útero en los mamíferos placentarios hembras, el órgano hueco y muscular en el que el embrión se incrusta y se desarrolla hasta convertirse en feto (557)

Glossary

V

vagina (vuh JIEN uh) the female reproductive organ that connects the outside of the body to the uterus (557)

vagina el órgano reproductivo femenino que conecta la parte exterior del cuerpo con el útero (557)

variable (VER ee uh buhl) a factor that changes in an experiment in order to test a hypothesis (16)

variable un factor que se modifica en un experimento con el fin de probar una hipótesis (16)

*****variation** (VER ee AY shuhn) a difference in the usual form or function (295)

variación diferencia en la forma o función habitual (295)

vascular plant (VAHS kyuh luhr PLANT) a plant that has specialized tissues that conduct materials from one part of the plant to another (362)

planta vascular una planta que tiene tejidos especializados que transportan materiales de una parte de la planta a otra (362)

vein (VAYN) in biology, a vessel that carries blood to the heart (498)

vena en biología, un vaso que lleva sangre al corazón (498)

vertebrate (VUHR tuh brit) an animal that has a backbone (434)

vertebrado un animal que tiene columna vertebral (434)

vesicle (VES i kuhl) a small cavity or sac that contains materials in a eukaryotic cell; forms when part of the cell membrane surrounds the materials to be taken into the cell or transported within the cell (125)

vesícula una cavidad o bolsa pequeña que contiene materiales en una célula eucariótica; se forma cuando parte de la membrana celular rodea los materiales que van a ser llevados al interior la célula o transportados dentro de ella (125)

*****visible** (VIZ uh buhl) that can be seen (73)

visible que se puede ver (73)

volume (VAHL yoom) a measure of the size of a body or region in three-dimensional space (23)

volumen una medida del tamaño de un cuerpo o región en un espacio de tres dimensiones (23)

W

weight (WAYT) a measure of the gravitational force exerted on an object; its value can change with the location of the object in the universe (24)

peso una medida de la fuerza gravitacional ejercida sobre un objeto; su valor puede cambiar en función de la ubicación del objeto en el universo (24)

X

xylem (ZIE luhm) the type of tissue in vascular plants that provides support and conducts water and nutrients from the roots (374)

xilema el tipo de tejido que se encuentra en las plantas vasculares, el cual provee soporte y transporta el agua y los nutrientes desde las raíces (374)

*Academic Vocabulary

Glossary

Index

Boldface page numbers refer to illustrative material, such as figures, tables, margin elements, photographs, and illustrations.

A

Index

Index

Index

D

Index

Index

G

Galápagos Islands, Darwin's studies on, 307, **307**, 315, **315**
gametophytes
  of gymnosperms, 371, **371**
  of nonvascular plants, **364,** 365
  in plant reproduction, 361
  of seedless vascular plants, 366, **366**
  of seed plants, 368
Garibaldi fish, 435, **435**
gelatin, pineapple enzymes and, 59
genera (singular, *genus*), 334, **335**
generations, in genetics studies, 177, **177**, 182, **182**
genes. *See also* chromosomes
  alleles of, 180–182, **181, 182,** 189, 192
  in blending inheritance, 174
  definition of, 180
  dominant, 177–178, **178**, 192, **192**
  genetic variation, 186, **186**, 312, **312**
  location of, 208
  multiple genes acting together, 185, **185**
  mutations in, 216–217, **216**
  one gene affecting many traits, 184, **184**
  recessive, 177–178, **178**, 192, **192**
  structure of, 212
genetically modified organisms, 179, **179**, 226
genetic code, 206–217. *See also* DNA
  analysis by PCR, 226, **226**
  as characteristic of life, 54
  in chromosomes, 152
  discovery of, 209, **209**
  in evolution, 304
  in nucleus of cells, 117, **117,** 122, **122**
  protein formation and, 61, 214–215, **214–215**
genetic counselors, 203, **203**
genetic disorders, 184, 196, 202
genetic engineering, 179, **179**, 226
genetic information. *See also* DNA
  on appearance, **172–173**
  in DNA, 54, 61, 117
  in fertilization, 558–559, **558**
  mutations and, 216–217, **216**
  in nucleus of cells, 117, **117,** 122, **122**
  in prokaryotes, 118, **118**

genetic instruction. *See also* genetics; traits
  environment and, 185, **185**
  gene mutations and, 216–217, **216**
  genotypes and, 181–182, **181, 182**
  phenotypes and, 180, **180**
  for protein formation, 123, 214–215, **214–215**
genetic material. *See also* DNA
  as characteristic of life, 54
  in chromosomes, 152
  discovery of, 209, **209**
  in nucleus of cells, 117, **117,** 122, **122**
genetic researchers, 227
genetics. *See also* DNA; genetic code; genetic information; genetic instruction; genetic material
  blending inheritance, 174
  as characteristic of life, 54
  characteristics in, 176
  dominant vs. recessive traits, 177–178, **178**
  environment and, 185, **185**
  evolution and, 311
  exceptions to Mendel's principles, 184–185
  in fertilization, 189, 192, **192,** 558–559, **558**
  genetic variation, 186, **186, 310,** 312, **312**
  genotype, 181–182, **181, 182,** 192, **192**
  homologous chromosomes, 153, **153,** 189, **189, 190–191**
  labs on, 177, 181, 182, 191, 194–195
  meiosis and, 192–193, **192**
  Mendel's experiments on, 175–178, **175, 176, 177, 178**
  numbers of chromosomes, 153, **153,** 188, **188, 189**
  phenotypes, 180, **180,** 186, **186, 192**
  probability and, 182–183
  protein formation and, 123, 214–215, **214–215**
genetic variation, 186, **186, 310,** 312, **312**
genital herpes, **560**
genomes, 202
genotype, 181–182, **181, 182,** 192, **192**
genus (plural, *genera*), 334, **335**
geographic connections and species distribution
  continental drift and, 272, **272**

in Darwin's finches, 307–308, **307**, 315, **315**
Panama Land Bridge and, 274, **274**
geologic layers
  disturbed rock layers, 241–242, **241, 242**
  law of crosscutting relationships, 243
  principle of superposition in, 240, **240**
  puzzles in, 243–244, **243, 244**
  rock cycle and, 238–239, **238**
geologic processes
  deposition, **238,** 239
  disturbed rock layers, 241–242, **241, 242**
  erosion, 238–239, **238, 242,** 242–243, **243**
  law of crosscutting relationships, 243
  rate of, 309
  rock cycle, 238–239, **238**
  unconformities, 242–243, **242, 243**
  uniformitarianism vs. catastrophism in, 234–236, **234, 235, 236**
geologic record, 239
geologic time scale, 276–277, **276, 277**
geology
  absolute dating methods, 246–249, **246, 247, 248,** 250–251
  age of Earth, 239, 249, **249,** 299, 309
  continental drift, 272–274, **272, 273, 274**
  disturbed rock layers, 241–242, **241, 242**
  early study of, 234–235, **234, 235**
  geologic record and, 239
  geologic time scale, 276–277, **276, 277**
  index fossils, 268–269, **268, 269**
  lab on, 236
  paleontology, 237, 293, **293**
  Panama Land Bridge, 270–275, **270, 271, 272, 273**
  plate tectonics, 270–275, **270, 271, 272, 273**
  principle of superposition, 240, **240**
  relative dating methods, 240–244, **240, 241, 242, 243**
  rock cycle, 238–239, **238**
  uniformitarianism vs. catastrophism in, 234–236, **234, 235, 236**

Index

implantation, 562, **562**
infertility, 561, **561**
male reproductive system, 556–557, **556**
multiple births, 559, **559**
pregnancy timeline, 564, **565**
problems in, 560–561, **560,** 576, **576**
Hutton, James, *Theory of the Earth,* 234–235, **234**
hydras
  budding in, 54, **54,** 427, 442, **442**
  nervous system in, **441**
hydrophilic heads, 121, **121**
hydrophobic tails, 121, **121**
hydrozoans, 432
hypertension (high blood pressure), 500, **500,** 504, 531
Hypohippus, 337
hypotheses (singular, *hypothesis*)
  forming, 14–15, **14–15**
  modifying, 484
  testing, 16–17, **16, 17,** 320

ice, fossils in, 265, **265**
idea wheel instructions (Graphic Organizer), 4, 392, 589, **589**
identical twins, 559, **559**
identifying unknown objects, 7
igneous rocks, 238, **238,** 247, **248**
illuminated objects, 84
impacts of asteroids, **232–233,** 236, **236,** 281
implantation, 562, **562**
impulses, nervous, 527, **527**
incidence, 82, **82**
incident beams, **82**
incomplete metamorphosis, 443, **443**
index fossils, 268–269, **268, 269**
infancy, 566, **566**
infertility, 561, **561**
infrared waves, **77,** 78, **78**
inheritance
  blending, 174
  as characteristic of life, 54
  definition of heredity, 174
  dominant vs. recessive traits, 177–178, **178**
  environment and, 185, **185**
  evolution and, 311
  exceptions to Mendel's principles, 184–185

in fertilization, 189, 192, **192,** 558–559, **558**
genetic variation, 186, **186**
genotypes, 181–182, **181, 182**
homologous chromosomes, 153, **153,** 189, **189, 190–191**
labs on, 177, 181, 182, 191, 194–195
meiosis and, 192–193, **192**
Mendel's experiments, 175–178, **175, 176, 177, 178**
numbers of chromosomes, 153, **153,** 188, **188, 189**
phenotypes, 180, **180**
probability and, 182–183
inherited traits
  in blending inheritance, 174
  definition of, 176, 308
  DNA instructions for, 54
  dominant, 177–178, **178,** 192, **192**
  dominant vs. recessive, 177–178, **178**
  labs on, 173, 177, 181, 182, 194–195
  meiosis and, 192–193, **192**
  modeling, 173, 297, 559
  multiple genes acting together, 185, **185**
  mutations and, 217
  ratios of, 178, **178**
  recessive, 177–178, **178,** 192, **192**
  selective breeding for, 308, **308**
  single genes influencing multiple, 184, **184**
  of survivors, 309
  variations within populations, 312, **312**
inherited variation, natural selection and, **310**
injuries, 475, **475,** 481, 532
input force, on levers, 478–479
insects
  classification of, **330–331**
  compound eyes in, 441, **441**
  exoskeletons in, 433, **433**
  fossilized in amber, 264, **264**
  metamorphosis in, 442–443, **442, 443**
  segmentation in, 439, **439**
insulin production, 227
integumentary system, 534, **534**
International System of Units (SI), 22–25, **22, 23, 24, 25**
Internet resources for research, 9, 40
interphase, 153, **154**
intrusions, 241, **241,** 243, **243**

invertebrates, 438–443
  annelids, 433, **433**
  arthropods, 433, **433**
  body symmetry in, 438, **438**
  characteristics of, 431, 438
  circulatory systems in, 440
  cnidarians, 432, **432**
  digestive systems in, 440, **440**
  echinoderms, 434, **434**
  excretory systems in, 440, **440**
  flatworms, 432, **432**
  metamorphosis in, 442–443, **442, 443**
  mollusks, 433, **433**
  nervous systems in, 441, **441**
  reproduction in, 442–443, **442, 443**
  respiratory systems in, 440, **440**
  roundworms, 432
  segmentation of, 439, **439**
  sponges, 431
investigations
  analyzing results, 17, **17**
  asking questions, 8–11, **10, 11,** 13
  collecting data, 38–39, 64, 544
  communicating results, 18, **18,** 196, 286, 346
  data analysis, 136, **136,** 452, **452**
  data collection, 64, 100
  displaying data, 412
  distribution maps, 452, **452**
  drawing conclusions, 18, 160
  electronic resources for, 9, 40
  evaluating resources for research, 514
  forming hypotheses, 14–15, **14–15**
  labeled diagrams, 252, **252**
  microscope data, **13,** 100, **100**
  models, 286
  modifying hypotheses, 484
  oral reports, 196
  print resources for, 570
  safety in, 32–37, **33, 36**
  scale diagrams, 136, **136,** 384, **384**
  scientific methods in, 220
  testing hypotheses, 16–17, **16, 17,** 320
  tools for displaying data, 412
  tools for performing tests, 544
  written reports, 346
involuntary actions, 476, 530, 531
iris, in eyes, **536,** 537
isotopes, in radiometric dating, 246, **246**

Index

motor nerves, 447
motor neurons, 528
mouse embryos, 427, **427**
movement
    flying, 428, **428, 445**
    methods of, 428, **428**
    by mollusks, 433, **433**
    muscles and, 477, **477**
    role of muscle and bone in,
      450–451, 477, **477**
mRNA (messenger RNA), **214,** 215
mucus, 445
multicellular organisms
    characteristics of, 128–129, **128,**
      425
    division of labor in, 129
    evolution of, 279
    lab on, 129
    levels of organization in,
      130–132, **130, 131, 132**
multiple births, 559, **559**
muscle cells, **467**
muscle fatigue, 151
muscle tissue, 131, **131, 467, 468**
muscular system, 476–481
    exercise and, 480, **480**
    injuries to, 481
    labs on, 479, 482–483
    levers and, 478–479, **478,**
      482–483
    movement and, 477, **477**
    muscle types, 476, **476**
musculoskeletal system. *See also*
    muscular system; skeletal
    system
    levers in, 478–479, **478,**
      482–483
    movement and, 450–451, 477,
      477
mutagens, 216
mutations in genes, 216–217, **216**

N

nanometers, 78
NASA nutritionist, 71, **71**
National Park Service, forest fire
    policy of, 46
naturalists, 306
natural selection
    environmental factors in, 307,
      307, 313
    extinction, 316–317, **316, 317**
    genetics and, 311
    genetic variations in populations
      and, 312, **312**
    lab on, 318–319
    in new species formation,
      314–315, **314, 315**

population changes and,
    312–313, **312**
theory of, 310–311, **310**
of lizards in white sands, 326,
    326
nautilus, **428**
nearsightedness, 537, **537**
neatness in science activities,
    importance of, 34
nectar, 379
Neohipparion, **336,** 337
nerve cells, 527, **527**
nerves
    auditory, 538, **538**
    motor, 447
    optic, 536, **536**
    sensory, 447
    structure of, 528, **528**
nervous systems
    autonomic, 529, **529**
    axons in, 527, **527,** 528, **528**
    central, 530–532, **530, 531, 532**
    in invertebrates, 441, **441**
    lab on, 532
    major parts of, 526, **526**
    peripheral, 527–529, **527, 528,**
      529
    somatic, 529
    spinal cords, 532, **532**
    in vertebrates, 447, **447**
nervous tissue, 131, **466, 468**
net force, equation for, 609
neurons
    building, 532
    motor, 528
    sensory, 528
    structure of, **467,** 527, **527**
neuroscientist, 167, **167**
newtons (units), 24
Newton's laws of motion, 605
nicotine, brain effects from, 167
night vision, 536
nitrogen, excreted from the body,
    447
nonvascular plants, 362, **362,**
    364–365, **364**
normal, in law of reflection, **82**
nose, 509
notochords, 434, **434**
nuclear-powered bacteria, 258, **258**
nucleic acids, 61
nucleolus, 122, **122**
nucleotides
    in DNA structure, 61, 212, **213**
    models of, 210, 218–219
    in protein formation, 61, 214
    types of, 208, **208**
nucleus, cell
    function of, 117, **126**
    genetic information in, 117, 122,
      122

as repository, 117
    structure of, **121,** 122, **122**
numbats, 316, **316**
nutrients, 58–60
nutritionist, 71, **71**
nymphs, 443, **443**

O

observations, 9, 13, **13**
oceanic plates, 270–271, **270, 271**
oceanographer, 107, **107**
octopuses, 433
offspring
    blending inheritance in, 174
    genotypes in, 181–182, **181, 182**
    phenotypes in, 180, **180**
    probability of traits in, 182–183
    selective breeding for, 308, **308**
    of sexual reproduction, 427
oils, 60
older adults, 567, **567**
olfactory cells, 540, **540**
On the Origin of Species (Darwin),
    310
opaque objects, 86–87, **86, 87**
open circulatory systems, 440
opossums, 436
optical illusions, 91–92, **91**
optical instruments, 95–96, **95, 96**
optic nerve, 536, **536**
oral report preparation, 18, 196
orders, 334, **335**
organelles, 117, **117,** 126. *See also*
    names of specific organelles
organisms
    cell theory and, 115, **115**
    extinct, 336, **336**
    genetically modified, 179, **179,**
      226
    geographic connections and,
      274, **274,** 307–308, 315, **315**
    levels of organization in,
      130–132, **130, 131, 132**
    multicellular, 128–129, **128,** 425
    scientific names for, 334–335,
      334–335
    unicellular, 128, 133, **133**
organization levels, 128–133, **132.**
    See also body organization
    cell level, 130, **130**
    impact of failure in one, 425,
      468
    lab on, 129
    multicellular organisms,
      128–129, **128**
    organism level, 132
    organ level, 131
    organ systems, 132, **132,** 425,
      425

Index

Index

Index

spongy bone, 473, **473**
spores
    of gymnosperms, 371, **371**
    in mosses, **364**
    in the sporophyte stage, 361
    spread by wind, 369
sporophytes
    of ferns, **366**
    of gymnosperms, 371, **371**
    of mosses, **364**
    in plant life cycle, 361
    structure of, 369, **369**
sprains, 475
spring scales, 24, **24**
square meters, 23
squids, 433, **433**
squirrels, speciation in, 314, **314**
stamens, 380, **380**
starch, from photosynthesis, 397
STDs (sexually transmitted
    diseases), 560–561, **560**
stem cells, 142, **142**, 576, **576**
stems, **358–359**, 376–377, **376,**
    377
steroids, anabolic, 481
stigma, 380, **380**, 400, **400**
stimulus (plural, *stimuli*), 53, 404
stingrays, 435
stirrup, in the ear, 538, **538**
stomach, 131, 468, **468**
    lab on, 470
stomata (singular, *stoma*), 130,
    130, 378, **378**, 398, **398**
strains, muscle or tendon, 481
strawberry poison arrow frog, 298,
    298
strokes, 500
structural framework for movement,
    450–451, 477, **477**
structure, function and, 130, **130,**
    369, 374–380, 427, 448,
    466–467, 473–474
    labs on, 361, 369, 382–383,
    395, 441, 447, 450–451, 465,
    470, 474
sucrose, 397
sugar, from photosynthesis,
    396–397, **397**
sugar pills, 550
sunburns, 80, **80**
sundews, 378
sunlight
    plant growth toward, 406, **406**
    visible light from, 79
sunlight energy
    chemical energy from, 78, **78,**
    396, **396**
    chlorophyll and, 124, **124**, 360,
    360, 396
    leaves and, 377–378, **378**
    making sugar from, 397, **397**

in photosynthesis, 78, **78**, 148,
    396, **396**
    relationship between photosyn-
    thesis and respiration and,
    150, 151
sun protection factor (SPF), 80
sunscreens, 80
superposition, principle of, 240,
    240
surface area–to-volume ratio, 116
survival, 217, **310**
sweat glands, **534**, 535
symbols, safety, 33, **33**
symmetry in body plans
    description of, 426, **426**
    in invertebrates, 438, **438**
    in vertebrates, 444, **444**
sympathetic nervous system, 529,
    529
syphilis, **560**
systematics, 333
systemic circulation, 499, **499**
systolic pressure, 504

T

table fold instructions (FoldNote),
    582, **582**
tables of data, **38–39**, 39
tadpoles, 435
tapeworms, 432
taproot systems, 375
taste, sense of, 540
taste buds, **524–525**, 540
taste cells, 540
taxonomy, 333
technology in science, 20–21, **20,**
    21
tectonic plates, 270–271, **270, 271**
telescopes, 96, **96**
telophase, 153, **155, 158**
TEMs (transmission electron
    microscopes), 21, **21**
temperature
    body, 53, 429, 504, 535
    definition of, 25
    measuring, **22**, 25, **25**
    scales, 624
tendinitis, 481
tendons, 477, 481
tentacles, 432, **432**, 433, **433**
testes (singular, *testis*), 556, **556,**
    560
testing hypotheses, 16–17, **16, 17,**
    320
testosterone, 556
theories, scientific, 29–31
theory of evolution, 296–327
    canine, 327, **327**
    comparing organisms in, 304,
    304

Darwin's thinking on, 308–309,
    308, 309
Darwin's voyage on the HMS
    Beagle, 306–307, **306, 307**
definition of, 299
drawing connections between
    species, 301, **301**
environmental factors in, 307,
    307, 313
evolutionary relationships,
    336–337, **336**
extinction and, 316–317, **316,**
    317, 336
fossil record and, 300, **300**
humans in the Cenozoic Era,
    282, **282**
lab on, 318–319
natural selection in, 310–311,
    310
new species formation,
    314–315, **314, 315**
population changes and,
    312–313, **312**
of whales, 301–303, **301,**
    302–303
Theory of the Earth (Hutton),
    234–235, **234**
thermometers, 25, **25**
thermoreceptors, 534, **534**
thighs, 474
third-class levers, **478**, 479
three-panel flip chart instructions
    (FoldNote), 581, **581**
thymine, 208–209, **208**, 210
tilting, 241, **241**
time scale, geologic, 276–277, **276,**
    277
tissues, 131, **131, 466–467**, 467
toads, 435
tongue, **524–525,** 540
tools
    for collecting data, 64, 544
    computers in science, 9, 20, 40
    for displaying data, 412
    for measurement, 22–25, **22, 23,**
    24, 25
    for performing tests on data,
    544
touch, sense of, 534, **534**
trace fossils, 266, **266**
tracheae, 440, **508**, 509, **509**
traits. *See also* heredity
    in blending inheritance, 174
    definition of, 176, 308
    DNA instructions for, 54
    dominant, 177–178, **178**, 192,
    192

dominant vs. recessive, 177–178, **178**
environmental influences on, 185, **185**
labs on, 173, 177, 181, 182, 194–195
meiosis and, 192–193, **192**
modeling, 173, 297, 559
multiple genes acting together, 185, **185**
mutations and, 217
ratios of, 178, **178**
recessive, 177–178, **178,** 192, **192**
selective breeding for, 308, **308**
single genes influencing multiple, 184, **184**
of survivors, 309
variations within populations, 312, **312**
transfer RNA (tRNA), 215, **215**
transform boundaries, 271, **271**
transfusions, 506, **506**
translucent objects, 86–87, **86, 87**
transmission electron microscopes (TEMs), 21, **21**
transmitted light, 85–86, **85, 86**
transparent objects, 86–87, **86, 87**
transpiration, 398, **398**
transport tissue, 131
tree, oldest, 390, **390**
tree of life, 301
trees
conifers, 281, **281,** 370–371, **370**
deciduous, 408, **408**
eucalyptus, 416, **416**
evergreen, 409
oldest, 390, **390**
trunks of, 376–377, **376, 377**
triceps muscle, 477, **477**
tri-fold instructions (FoldNote), 582, **582**
trilobites, 268, **268, 300**
triplets, 559
tropisms, 406–407, **406, 407**
Tropites, 269, **269**
true-breeding plants, 175–176, **175**
trunks, 376–377, **376, 377**
tubers, 402, **403**
tumors, treatment for, 166. *See also* cancer
tunicates, 434
turtles, 435, **446**
twins, 559, **559**
two-panel flip chart instructions (FoldNote), 582, **582**
tympanic membrane, 538–539, **538**
Tyrannosaurus rex, 335, **335**

U

ultrasound procedures, 577
ultraviolet light (UV light)
bad effects of, 80, **80**
bees and, 76, **76**
frog deformities and, 16–18, **16, 17, 18**
good effects of, 81, **81**
mutations from, 216
umbilical cord, 563, **563**
umbilicus, 563, **563**
unconformities, 242–243, **242, 243**
unicellular organisms, 128, 133, **133**
uniformitarianism, 234–236
units, SI, 22–25, **22, 23, 24, 25**
universal gravitation, law of, 606
University of California, San Francisco, 576
uracil, 214, **214**
uranium, 248, 250, 258, **258,** 259
urea, 447
urethra, 556, **556**
uterus
compared with a bird's egg, 568–569
contractions during birth, **564**
implantation in, 557, **557**
location of, 562, **562**
modeling a fetus in, **564**
UV light (ultraviolet light)
bad effects of, 80, **80**
bees and, 76, **76**
good effects of, 81, **81**
mutations from, 216

V

vacuoles, **120,** 126, **126**
vagina, 557, **557**
valves, heart, 495, 497, **497**
variable, definition of, 16
vascular plants, 362, **362**
vascular tissues
definition of, 362
in leaves, 378, **378**
in monocots and dicots, **372**
in roots, 374, **375**
in seedless plants, 365
in stems, 376–377, **376, 377**
vas deferens, 556, **556**
veins, 446, 498–499, **498, 499**
venn diagram instructions (Graphic Organizer), 356, 492, 587, **587**

ventral side, 444
ventricles, 497, **497**
Venus' flytraps, **53, 394–395**
vertebrae, 434, 445, 532, **532**
vertebrates, 434–436
amphibians, 435, **435,** 445
birds, 436, **436,** 445, **445**
body coverings, 445, **445**
body symmetry in, 444, **444**
characteristics of, 434
digestive systems in, 132, 447
endoskeletons in, 445, **445,** 450–451
excretory systems in, 447
fishes, 435, **435,** 445–448, **446, 447**
mammal characteristics, 436, **436**
nervous systems in, 447, **447**
parental care in, 449, **449**
reptiles, 435, **435,** 448, **448**
respiratory systems in, 446, **446**
vesicles, 125, **125**
vessels, blood, 498, **498**
vestibular canals, **538,** 539
Virchow, Rudolf, 115
virtual images, 93–94, **93, 94**
visible light, 77–79, **77, 78, 79.** *See also* light
visible spectrum, 79, **79**
vision
bionic eyes, 106
colors of objects in, 86–87, **87**
compound eyes, 94
dissecting cow's eyes, 542–543
emitted light in, 536, **536**
eye color, 185, **185**
glasses for correction of, 537, **537**
in invertebrates, 441, **441**
lenses of eyes, 93–94, **93, 94,** 536–537, **537**
light colors and, 79, **79,** 86–87, **87**
night, 536
optical illusions, 91–92, **91**
sense of sight, 536, **536**
transmission, reflection, and absorption of light in, 85, **85**
vitamin K, 339
vocal cords, 509
volcanic eruptions, catastrophic effects of, 236
volume, units of, **22,** 23
voluntary actions, 530
voluntary muscle actions, 476

W

Wallace, Alfred Russel, 310
warbler finches, **307**
warblers, **57**
water, refraction of light in, 91–91, **91**
water transport
  in echinoderms, 434
  in leaves, 378, **378**
  in monocots and dicots, **372**
  as necessity of life, 56
  in photosynthesis, 396–397, **397**
  in roots, 374, **375**
  in seedless plants, 365
  in seed plants, 374–375, **375**
  in stems, 376–377, **376, 377**
  transpiration, 398, **398**
water vascular system, in echinoderms, 434
Watson, James, 209–210, **209**

wavelength
  definition of, 77, **77**
  of infrared light, **77,** 78
  refraction and, 91, **91**
  of visible light, **77,** 78–79, **79**
waves, electromagnetic, 76–77, **77**
weight, measurement of, 24, **24**
whales, evolution of, 301–303, **301, 302–303**
white blood cells (WBCs), **112–113, 494–495,** 503, **503**
white light, 79
white tigers, 184, **184**
woody stems, **376,** 377, **377**
woolly mammoths, **265**
word parts, understanding, **592–593**
work and heat, equation for, 611
World Wide Web resources, 9, 40
wrists, 474, **474**
written reports, 346

X

X rays, 77, **77,** 209, 216
xylem
  in leaves, 378, **378**
  in roots, 374, **375**
  in stems, 376–377, **376, 377**

Y

yeast experiments, 18
yellow-fever remedy, 391
Yellowstone National Park, 339
Yosemite Valley (California), 248, **248**

Z

zygotes, 557, 563

Index

Acknowledgments

continued from p. ii

Advisors

Kristin L. Baker
Science Teacher
Starr King Middle School
Carmichael, California

Laura L. Bauer
Department Chair
Toby Johnson Middle School
Elk Grove, California

Jack Bettencourt
Science Department Chair
Joseph Kerr Middle School
Elk Grove, California

Rebecca Buschang
Science Partner
University of California, Los Angeles;
   Los Angeles Unified School District
Los Angeles, California

Eddyce Pope Moore
Science Teacher
Daniel Webster Middle School
Los Angeles, California

Kim O'Donnell
Science Teacher
Earle E. Williams Middle School
Tracy, California

Theresa Pearse
Science Teacher
Fremont Middle School
Stockton, California

Manuel Sanchez
Science Department Chair
Greer Middle School
Galt, California

Chuck Schindler
*Secondary Math and
   Science Coordinator*
San Bernardino City Unified
   School District
San Bernardino, California

William W. Tarr Jr., Ed.D.
Coordinator, Secondary Periodic Assessments
Los Angeles Unified School District
Los Angeles, California

Hong Tran
Science Teacher
Westlake Middle School
Oakland, California

Academic Reviewers

Jennifer Armstrong, Ph.D.
Assistant Professor of Biology
Joint Science Department
The Claremont Colleges
Claremont, California

Lisa M. Baird, Ph.D.
Professor of Biology
Department of Biology
University of San Diego
San Diego, California

Leonard Brand, Ph.D.
Professor of Biology and Paleontology
Department of Earth and Biological Sciences
Loma Linda University
Loma Linda, California

Darleen A. DeMason, Ph.D.
Professor of Botany
Department of Botany and Plant Sciences
University of California, Riverside
Riverside, California

Douglas J. Eernisse, Ph.D.
Professor
Department of Biological Sciences
California State University, Fullerton
Fullerton, California

Daniel C. Garza, M.D.
Attending Physician
Stanford University
School of Medicine
Stanford, California

Rayudu Gopalakrishna, Ph.D.
Associate Professor
Department of Cell & Neurobiology
University of Southern California
Los Angeles, California

L. Lee Grismer, Ph.D.
Professor
Department of Biology
La Sierra University
Riverside, California

H. Craig Heller, M.D.
*Professor of Biological Sciences
   and Human Biology*
Stanford University
Palo Alto, California

Jeffrey Johnson, Ph.D.
Postdoctoral Scholar
Center for Neuroscience
University of California, Davis
Davis, California

Lee B. Kats, Ph.D.
Professor of Biology
Natural Science Division
Pepperdine University
Malibu, California

Elena Levine Keeling, Ph.D.
Associate Professor
Biological Sciences Department
California Polytechnic State University
San Luis Obispo, California

Susan L. Keen, Ph.D.
Lecturer
Section of Evolution and Ecology
University of California, Davis
Davis, California

Harold Koopowitz, Ph.D.
Professor Emeritus of Biology
Department of Ecology and
   Evolutionary Biology
University of California, Irvine
Irvine, California

L. Jeanne Perry, Ph.D.
Director
Protein Expression Technology Center
   Institute for Genomics and Proteomics
University of California, Los Angeles
Los Angeles, California

Susannah M. Porter, Ph.D.
Assistant Professor
Department of Earth Science
University of California, Santa Barbara
Santa Barbara, California

Martin G. Ramirez, Ph.D.
Associate Professor of Biology
Department of Biology
Loyola Marymount University
Los Angeles, California

John J. Stachowicz, Ph.D.
Associate Professor of Evolution and Ecology
Section of Evolution and Ecology
University of California, Davis
Davis, California

Elizabeth Wenk, Ph.D.
Visiting Scholar
University Herbarium
University of California, Berkeley
Berkeley, California

Lisa D. White, Ph.D.
Professor of Geology
Department of Geosciences
San Francisco State University
San Francisco, California

Adam D. Woods, Ph.D.
Assistant Professor of Geology
Department of Geological Sciences
California State University, Fullerton
Fullerton, California

Teacher Reviewers

Karen Benitez
Science Teacher
George V. LeyVa Middle School
San Jose, California

Joel S. Brener
Science Teacher
Daniel Webster Middle School
Los Angeles, California

Dana Carrigan
Vice Principal
Cordova High School
Rancho Cordova, California

Laskey Chatham
Science Teacher
Daniel Webster Middle School
Los Angeles, California

Ann Marie Cica
Science Teacher
Bret Harte Middle School
San Jose, California

Michelle B. Emelle
Science Teacher
Audubon Middle School
Los Angeles, California

Robin Joyce Franklin
Science Teacher
Gomper Continuation High School
Richmond, California

Catherine D. Haynes
Science Teacher
El Segundo Middle School
El Segundo, California

Treena Joi
Science Teacher
Corte Madera Middle School
Portola Valley, California

Sushma Kashyap, MSc
Science Teacher
Alvarado School
Diamond Bar, California

Carol Lindstrom
Science Teacher and Curriculum Specialist
Herman Intermediate School
San Jose, California

Peggy Lubchenco, MSc
Department Chair and Teacher
La Colina Junior High School
Santa Barbara, California

Heather O'Donnell
Science Teacher
Roosevelt Junior High School
San Diego, California

Anne Stephens, MA
Science Teacher
Marsh Junior High School
Co-Director, Hands-on Science Lab
College of Natural Sciences
California State University, Chico
Chico, California

Gayle Van Fossen
Science Teacher
George V. LeyVa Middle School
San Jose, California

Lab Development

Diana Scheidle Bartos
Research Associate
Colorado School of Mines
Golden, Colorado

Carl Benson
Science Teacher
Plains High School
Plains, Montana

Charlotte Blassingame
Technology Coordinator
White Station Middle School
Memphis, Tennessee

Marsha Carver
Department Chair and Science Teacher
McLean County High School
Calhoun, Kentucky

Kenneth E. Creese
Science Teacher
White Mountain Junior High School
Rock Springs, Wyoming

Linda A. Culp
Department Chair and Science Teacher
Thorndale High School
Thorndale, Texas

James Deaver
Department Chair and Science Teacher
West Point High School
West Point, Nebraska

Michael A. DiSpezio
Professional Development Specialist
JASON Project
Cape Cod, Massachusetts

Frank McKinney, Ph.D.
Professor of Geology
Appalachian State University
Boone, North Carolina

Alyson M. Mike
Department Chair
East Valley Middle School
East Helena, Montana

C. Ford Morishita
Biology Teacher
Clackamas High School
Milwaukee, Oregon

Patricia D. Morrell, Ph.D.
Associate Professor
School of Education
University of Portland
Portland, Oregon

Hilary C. Olson, Ph.D.
Research Associate
Institute for Geophysics
The University of Texas at Austin
Austin, Texas

James B. Pulley
Science Editor and Former Science Teacher
North Kansas City, Missouri

Denice Lee Sandefur
Science Chairperson
Nucla High School
Nucla, Colorado

Patti Soderberg
Science Writer
The BioQUEST Curriculum Consortium
Biology Department
Beloit College
Beloit, Wisconsin

Phillip Vavala
Department Chair and Science Teacher
Salesianum School
Wilmington, Delaware

Albert C. Wartski, M.A.T.
Biology Teacher
Chapel Hill High School
Chapel Hill, North Carolina

Lynn Marie Wartski
Science Writer and Science Teacher
Hillsborough, North Carolina

Ivora D. Washington
Department Chair and Science Teacher
Hyattsville Middle School
Washington, D.C.

Lab Testing

Karen Benitez
Science Teacher
George V. LeyVa Middle School
San Jose, California

Christine Erskine
Science Teacher
Brier School
Fremont, California

Rhonda DuPar
Science Teacher
La Colina Junior High School
Santa Barbara, California

Catherine D. Haynes
Science Teacher
El Segundo Middle School
El Segundo, California

Sushma Kashyap, MSc
Science Teacher
Alvarado School
Diamond Bar, California

Carol Lindstrom
Science Teacher and Curriculum Specialist
Herman Intermediate School
San Jose, California

Peggy Lubchenco, MSc
Department Chair and Teacher
La Colina Junior High School
Santa Barbara, California

Kelly Sullivan
Science Teacher
Marsh Junior High School
Chico, California

Gayle Van Fossen
Science Teacher
George V. LeyVa Middle School
San Jose, California

Feature Development

Hatim Belyamani
John A. Benner
David Bradford
Jennifer Childers
Mickey Coakley
Susan Feldkamp
Jane Gardner
Erik Hahn
Christopher Hess
Abby Jones
Deena Kalai
Charlotte W. Luongo, MSc
Michael May
Persis Mehta, Ph.D.
Eileen Nehme, MPH
Catherine Podeszwa
Dennis Rathnaw
Daniel B. Sharp
John M. Stokes
April Smith West
Molly F. Wetterschneider

Staff Credits

The people who contributed to **Holt California Life Science** are listed below. They represent editorial, design, production, emedia, and permissions.

Chris Allison, Wesley M. Bain, Juan Baquera, Angela Beckmann, Ed Blake, Marc Burgamy, Rebecca Calhoun, Kimberly Cammerata, Soojinn Choi, Julie Dervin, Michelle Dike, Lydia Doty, Jen Driscoll, Diana Goetting, Angela Hemmeter, Tim Hovde, Wilonda Ieans, Elizabeth Ihry, Jevara Jackson, Simon Key, Jane A. Kirschman, Cathy Kuhles, Denise Mahoney, Michael Mazza, Kristen McCardel, Richard Metzger, Christina Murray, Micah Newman, Janice Noske, Dustin Ognowski, Joeleen Ornt, Laura Prescott, Bill Rader, Jim Ratcliffe, Peter Reid, Michael Rinella, Kelly Rizk, Jeff Robinson, Audrey Rozsypal, Beth Sample, Kay Selke, Chris Smith, Dawn Marie Spinozza, Sherry Sprague, Jeff Streber, Roshan Strong, Jeannie Taylor, Bob Tucek, Tam Voynick, Clay Walton, Kira J. Watkins, Ken Whiteside, Holly Whittaker, David Wisnieski, Monica Yudron

Credits

Abbreviations used: (t) top, (c) center, (b) bottom, (l) left, (r) right, (bkgd) background

PHOTOGRAPHY

Front Cover Susumu Nishinaga/Photo Researchers, Inc.

Table of Contents iv, Peter Van Steen/HRW Photo; v (t), Visuals Unlimited/Stanley Flegler; v (b), Ted Kinsman/Photo Researchers, Inc.; vi (tl), Photodisc, Inc.; vi (b), Ed Reschke/Peter Arnold, Inc.; vii (bl), Ed Reschke/Peter Arnold, Inc.; vii (bc & br), Biology Media/Photo Researchers, Inc.; vii (t), Nancy Kedersha/Photo Researchers, Inc.; viii (b), David M. Phillips/Visuals Unlimited; viii (tl, tc & cl), Sam Dudgeon/HRW Photo; ix (tl), Sam Dudgeon/HRW Photo; ix (b),Edmond Van Hoorick/SuperStock; x (cl), James Beveridge/Visuals Unlimited; x (bl), © Gail Shumway/Getty Images/FPG International; x (t), Howard Grey/Getty Images/Stone; xi (t), SuperStock; xi (b). James L. Amos/CORBIS; xii (br), Ed Reschke/Peter Arnold, Inc.; xii (bl), Runk/Rannels/Grant Heilman Photography; xiii (tl), Courtesy of Valent BioSciences Corporation; xiii (bl), Norbert Wu; xiv (t), Bob Torrez/Getty Images/Stone; xv (b), Sam Dudgeon/HRW Photo; xvi (tl), Photo Lennart Nilsson/Albert Bonniers Forlag AB, A Child Is Born, Dell Publishing Company; xvi (cr), Digital Image copyright © 2005 PhotoDisc

Safety First! xxx, Sam Dudgeon/HRW; xxxi(t), John Langford/HRW; xxxi(bc), xxxii(br) & xxxiii(tl), Sam Dudgeon/HRW xxxii(bl), Stephanie Morris/HRW; xxxiii(tl), Sam Dudgeon/HRW xxxiii(tr), Jana Birchum/HRW; xxxiii(b), Sam Dudgeon/HRW

Unit One 2 (tl), O.S.F./Animals Animals; 2 (cl), Hulton Archive/Getty Images; 2 (bl), Digital Image copyright © 2005 PhotoDisc; 2-3 (br & bl), Peter Veit/DRK Photo; 3 (cl), University of Pennsylvania/Hulton Getty; 3 (t), National Portrait Gallery, Smithsonian Institution/Art Resources; 3 (br), National Geographic Image Collection/ O. Louis Mazzatenta; 3 (cr), Digital Image copyright © 2005 PhotoDisc

Chapter One 6-7 Craig Line/AP/Wide World Photos; 7 (br), John Morrison/Morrison Photography; 8 & 9 (tr), Peter Van Steen/HRW Photo; 9 (inset), International Colored Gemstone Association (ICA); 9 (b), Victoria Smith/HRW Photo; 10 (l), Hank Morgan/ Photo Researchers, Inc.; 10 (b), Matt Meadows/Peter Arnold, Inc.; 11 (t), Annie Griffiths Belt/CORBIS; 11 (b), Wayne Lynch/DRK Photo; 13& 14, Sam Dudgeon/HRW Photo; 16, John Mitchell/Photo Researchers, Inc.; 18, Sam Dudgeon/HRW Photo; 20, PhotoDisc/Getty Images; 21 (tr), Pascal Goetgheluck/Photo Researchers, Inc.; 21(tl), CENCO; 21 (cl), Robert Brons/Biological Photo Service; 21 (tc), Sinclair Stammers/Science Photo Library/Photo Researchers, Inc.; 21 (c), Microworks/ Phototake; 21 (cr), Visuals Unlimited/Karl Aufderheide; 22 (tl, bc & b), Victoria Smith/ HRW Photo; 22 (c), Sam Dudgeon/HRW Photo; 23, Peter Van Steen/HRW Photo; 24, Victoria Smith/HRW Photo; 25 (cr), Dr. Jeremy Burgess/Science Photo Library/ Photo Reseachers, Inc.; 26, Royalty-Free/CORBIS; 28 (b), John Morrison/Morrison Photography; 29, Art by Christopher Sloan/Photograph by Mark Thiessen/both National Geographic Image Collection/ © National Geographic Image Collection; 32, 33, 34 & 35, Sam Dudgeon/HRW; 36, Victoria Smith/HRW; 38, John Morrison/ Morrison Photography; 41 (t), Peter Van Steen/HRW; 41 (c), Victoria Smith/HRW; 41 (bc), Art by Christopher Sloan/Photograph by Mark Thiessen/both National Geographic Image Collection/ © National Geographic Image Collection; 46, Craig Fugii/©1988 The Seattle Times; 47 (r & l), NASA

Chapter Two 50-51, Rick Friedman/Blackstar Publishing/Picture Quest; 51 (br), John Morrison/Morrison Photography; 52 (br), Visuals Unlimited/Science Visuals Unlimited; 52 (bl), William H.Mullins/Photo Researchers, Inc.; 53, David M. Dennis/Tom Stack and Associates; 54 (l), Visuals Unlimited/Stanley Flegler; 54 (tr), James M. McCann/ Photo Researchers, Inc.; 56 (b), Wolfgang Bayer; 57 (t), Visuals Unlimited/Rob Simpson; 57 (b), Alex Kerstitch/Visuals Unlimited, Inc.; 58 (bl), William J. Hebert/ Stone; 58 (bc), SuperStock; 58 (br), Kevin Schafer/Peter Arnold, Inc.; 59 (b), Peter Dean/Grant Heilman Photography; 59 (t), John Morrison/Morrison Photography; 63 (b), Victoria Smith/HRW; 63 (t), The Garden Picture Library/Alamy; 67, Victoria Smith/HRW; 70 (l), Sean O'Neill/Spectrum Photofile; 71 (t), Courtesy Janis Davis-Street/NASA; 71 (b), NASA

Chapter Three 74-5, Richard Herrmann/OSF/Animals Animals; 75 (br), John Morrison/Morrison Photography; 76 (c), Michael Fogden and Patricia Fogden/Corbis; 76 (bl & br), Leonard Lessin/Photo Researchers, Inc.; 78, Ted Kinsman/Photo Researchers, Inc.; 79, Cameron Davidson; 80 (t), John Morrison/Morrison Photography; 80 (b), SINCLAIR STAMMERS/SPL/Photo Researchers, Inc.; 81, Patrik Giardino/CORBIS; 83 (t), John Morrison/Morrison Photography; 84, Darwin Dale/ Photo Researchers, Inc.; 85 (b), Stephanie Morris/HRW; 85 (t), Sovfoto/Eastfoto; 86, John Langford/HRW; 87 (br), ART on FILE/CORBIS; 87 (tl), Image copyright ©1998 PhotoDisc, Inc.; 87 (tr), Renee Lynn/Davis/Lynn Images; 88 (b), Index Stock Photography, Inc.; 89 (t), Rob Matheson/The Stock Market; 89 (cr), Peter Van Steen/ HRW; 90, Richard Megna/Fundamental Photographs; 92 (b & c), Fundamental Photographs, New York; 92 (t), John Morrison/Morrison Photography; 93 (cl), Russell Holley; 93 (tl), Peter Van Steen/HRW; 94 (tl), Juniors Bildarchiv/Alamy; 94 (bc), Jerome Wexler/Photo Researchers, Inc.; 99 (br), Sam Dudgeon/HRW; 100 (b), Robert Brons/Biological Photo Service; 101 (t), SINCLAIRSTAMMERS/SPL/Photo Researchers, Inc.; 102 (cr), Ken Kay/Fundamental Photographs; 103 (t), Charles D. Winters/Photo Researchers, Inc.; 103 (c), Mark E. Gibson; 103 (b), Richard Megna/Fundamental Photographs; 106 (r), M. Spencer Green/AP/Wide World Photos; 106 (tl), Dr. E. R. Degginger; 107 (b), E. Widder/HBOI/Visuals Unlimited;107 (t), Tom Smoyer/HBO!

Unit Two 108 (c), The National Archives/Corbis; 108 (b), Cold Spring Harbor Laboratory; 108 (t), Burstein Collection/CORBIS; 109 (t & bcl), Ed Reschke/Peter Arnold, Inc; 109 (tcr), Keith Porter/Photo Researchers, Inc.; 109 (br), Dr. Ian Wilmut/ Liaison/Getty News Images; 109 (bl), Dan McCoy/Rainbow; 109 (bcr), Glen Allison/ Getty Images/Stone; 109 (tcl), Bettmann/CORBIS

Chapter Four 112-113, Dennis Kunkel/Phototake; 113 (br), John Morrison/Morrison Photography; 114 (bl), Visuals Unlimited/Kevin Collins; 114 (br), Leonard Lessin/ Peter Arnold, Inc.; 115 (tl), Eric Grave/Phototake; 115 (tr), Biodisc/Visuals Unlimited; 115 (tcr), Michael Abbey/Visuals Unlimited; 115 (tcl), Steve Allen/Photo Researchers, Inc.; 115 (br), CENCO; 117 (t), William Dentler/Biological Photo Service; 117 (b), Dr. Gopal Murti/Science Photo Library/Photo Researchers, Inc.; 122 (br), Don Fawcett/ Visuals Unlimited; 123 (br), R. Bolender-D. Fawcett/Visuals Unlimited; 124 (cl), Don Fawcett/Visuals Unlimited; 124 (br), Newcomb & Wergin/Biological Photo Service; 125 (tr), Garry T Cole/Biological Photo Service; 126 (cl), Dr. Jeremy Burgess/Science PhotoLibrary/Science Source/Photo Researchers, Inc.; 126 (tl), DR GOPAL MURTI/ SCIENCE PHOTO LIBRARY; 128 (l, bl & br), Dr. Yorgos Nikas/Science Photo Library/ Photo Researchers, Inc.; 128 (br), Lennart Nilsson/Albert Bonniers Forlag AB, A C HILD IS BORN; 129, John Morrison/Morrison Photography; 130 (t), Quest/Science Photo Library/Photo Researchers, Inc.; 130 (b), Ed Reschke/Peter Arnold, Inc.; 131, Manfred Kage/Peter Arnold, Inc.; 133 (t), David M. Dennis/Tom Stack & Associates; 134 (c & cl), Runk/Schoenberger/Grant Heilman; 134 (cr), Michael Abbey/ Photo Researchers, Inc.; 134 (b), Sam Dudgeon/HRW Photo; 135, Runk/ Schoenberger/Grant Heilman; 136 (br), Eric Grave/Phototake; 136 (b), Steve Allen/ Photo Researchers, Inc.; 136 (l), Michael Abbey/Visuals Unlimited; 142 (r), Photo Researchers, Inc.; 142 (l), Science Photo Library/Photo Researchers, Inc.; 143 (l), Digital Image copyright © 2005 Artville; 143 (r), Courtesy Caroline Schooley

Chapter Five 146-7, Grant Heilman Photography; 147 (br), John Morrison/Morrison Photography; 148 (bl), Runk/Schoenberger/Grant Heilman Photography; 149 (br), John Langford/HRW; 152, CNRI/Science Photo Library/Photo Researchers, Inc.; 153 (b), L. Willatt, East Anglian Regional Genetics Service/Science Photo Library/ Photo Researchers, Inc.; 153 (t), Biophoto Associates/Photo Researchers, Inc.; 154 (b), Visuals Unlimited/R. Calentine; 154 (t) & 155 (tl), Ed Reschke/Peter Arnold, Inc.; 155 (tc & tr) Biology Media/Photo Researchers, Inc.; 155 (br), John Morrison/ Morrison Photography; 157, Nancy Kedersha/Photo Researchers, Inc.; 158 (l), Authors Image/Alamy; 158, Peter Arnold, Inc./Alamy; 159, Sam Dudgeon/HRW; 161 (bc), Biology Media/Photo Researchers, Inc.; 166, SIU BioMed/Custom Medical Stock Photo; 167 (tr), Courtesy Dr. Jarrel Yakel; 167 (c), David McCarthy/SPL/Photo Researchers, Inc

Unit Three 168 (bc), Ted Thai/Time Magazine; 168 (t), David L. Brown/Tom Stack; 169 (cl), MBL/WHOI Library; 169 (cr), Ken Eward/Bio Grafx/Photo Researchers, Inc.; 169 tr), John Conrad/CORBIS; 169 (bl), Dr. Tony Brain/Science Photo Library/Photo Researchers, Inc.

Periodic Table of the Elements

Each square on the table includes an element's name, chemical symbol, atomic number, and atomic mass.

The color of the chemical symbol indicates the physical state at room temperature. Carbon is a solid.

6	— Atomic number
C	— Chemical symbol
Carbon	— Element name
12.0	— Atomic mass

The background color indicates the type of element. Carbon is a nonmetal.

Background
- Metals
- Metalloids
- Nonmetals

Chemical symbol
- Solid
- Liquid
- Gas

Period 1

| 1 |
| **H** |
| Hydrogen |
| 1.0 |

A row of elements is called a *period*.

A column of elements is called a *group* or *family*.

Values in parentheses are the mass numbers of those radioactive elements' most stable or most common isotopes.

These elements are placed below the table to allow the table to be narrower.

	Group 1	Group 2	Group 3	Group 4	Group 5	Group 6	Group 7	Group 8	Group 9
Period 2	3 **Li** Lithium 6.9	4 **Be** Beryllium 9.0							
Period 3	11 **Na** Sodium 23.0	12 **Mg** Magnesium 24.3							
Period 4	19 **K** Potassium 39.1	20 **Ca** Calcium 40.1	21 **Sc** Scandium 45.0	22 **Ti** Titanium 47.9	23 **V** Vanadium 50.9	24 **Cr** Chromium 52.0	25 **Mn** Manganese 54.9	26 **Fe** Iron 55.8	27 **Co** Cobalt 58.9
Period 5	37 **Rb** Rubidium 85.5	38 **Sr** Strontium 87.6	39 **Y** Yttrium 88.9	40 **Zr** Zirconium 91.2	41 **Nb** Niobium 92.9	42 **Mo** Molybdenum 95.9	43 **Tc** Technetium (98)	44 **Ru** Ruthenium 101.1	45 **Rh** Rhodium 102.9
Period 6	55 **Cs** Cesium 132.9	56 **Ba** Barium 137.3	57 **La** Lanthanum 138.9	72 **Hf** Hafnium 178.5	73 **Ta** Tantalum 180.9	74 **W** Tungsten 183.8	75 **Re** Rhenium 186.2	76 **Os** Osmium 190.2	77 **Ir** Iridium 192.2
Period 7	87 **Fr** Francium (223)	88 **Ra** Radium (226)	89 **Ac** Actinium (227)	104 **Rf** Rutherfordium (261)	105 **Db** Dubnium (262)	106 **Sg** Seaborgium (266)	107 **Bh** Bohrium (264)	108 **Hs** Hassium (277)	109 **Mt** Meitnerium (268)

Lanthanides	58 **Ce** Cerium 140.1	59 **Pr** Praseodymium 140.9	60 **Nd** Neodymium 144.2	61 **Pm** Promethium (145)	62 **Sm** Samarium 150.4
Actinides	90 **Th** Thorium 232.0	91 **Pa** Protactinium 231.0	92 **U** Uranium 238.0	93 **Np** Neptunium (237)	94 **Pu** Plutonium (244)